2005 IEEE International Symposium
on Electromagnetic Compatibility

EMC 2005

Workshop Notes

8–12 August 2005

Chicago, Illinois, USA

◆ **IEEE**

SOCIETY

Handwritten annotations:

SC = Sub Committee
MRA - Mutual Recognition Agreement

CLASS A   LOOSE Limits
CLASS B   TIGHTER Limits
CLASS C   MOST TIGHT Limits

Unexplained Failures / Quanity
- Foresite
- DE CAP IC

Joel Schindler TWV
Indy SDD

Shogun/Aurora better
Equivalent n of
where's the proof
Do side by side testing

John MAAS
IBM
List of std websites
will e-mail 1 slide
8/12/05

AST - Lessons Learned
www.NIST.gov NVLAV
Standards PASSWORD
S. Reimeim Standards
AURORA - Relibility Plan
EMC PLS PCB
info for Aurora

Table of Contents

Nanotechnology and Advanced Materials (MO-AM-WS-5)

Basic Antenna & Probe Use in EMC Workshop (MO-PM-WS-7)

Intentional EMI (MO-PM-WS-8)

BPL: The Issues (MO-PM-WS-9)

Fundamentals of Signal Integrity (MO-PM-WS-10)

EMC Directive in Europe (MO-PM-WS-11)

Basic EMC Measurements Tutorial (FR-AM-WS-13)

The Shielding Effectiveness Of Enclosures: Theory And Measurement Techniques (FR-AM-WS-14)

Product Safety Workshop (FR-AM-WS-15)

Product EMC Design Strategies and Practices (FR-PM-WS-17)

Guide to Accreditation of EMC Laboratories in the US (FR-PM-WS-18)

ISO 17025

EMC Issues Affecting Audio Systems for Professional, Broadcast, and Consumer Use (FR-PM-WS-19)

WORKSHOP: FUNDAMENTALS OF EMC DESIGN (MO-AM-WS-1)
Dr. Maqsood Mohd

The Education and Student Activities Committee (ESAC) of the IEEE EMC-Society sponsors this *two-part and all-day long tutorial* on Fundamentals of EMC Design. In this 12th year of its offering, the emphasis of this year's Tutorial on Fundamentals of EMC is on understanding and applying good EMC design principles in a variety of situations that a design engineer encounters. This tutorial introduces the basic concepts of EMC engineering and addresses the needs of those that are new to the EMC field. The tutorial focuses on how to design circuits and systems with built-in EMC. Experienced leaders in the field will present topics relating to EMI and EMC design. Starting with the introduction of EMI and EMC, the session continues with basic understanding of cross talk in cables and then guidelines for lightning protection are presented. The session topics also include how to diagnose design problems and find their fixes, along with an in-depth discussion of RFID technology and its influence on EMI and EMC. The Tutorial will conclude with a panel discussion where the audience may ask EMI/EMC questions to the presenters. Ample time for questions and answers is also planned immediately after each presentation. The tutorial presenters are Clayton Paul, Todd Hubing, Daryl Gerke, and Robert Nelson.

This landmark tutorial was initiated 12 years ago in Chicago. To commemorate the Chicago beginning, this year's tutorial will include a presentation about newer technology that is intricately related to the EMI and EMC discipline. We at ESAC hope and trust that this tutorial continues to address the educational needs of our membership. Plan to attend and enjoy the 2005 Fundamentals Tutorial and the Chicago Symposium.

Presentations not available for publication.

NOTES

WORKSHOP: LEAN AND SIX SIGMA (MO-AM-WS-2)
George Alukal

The goal of this workshop is to provide the EMC professional an introduction to the two important topics of Six Sigma and Lean. Everyone who is impacted by design, development, processing, quality, operations issues should attend.

This workshop will explain Process Improvement, Six Sigma and Lean, currently very popular topics. We will present a case study using Six Sigma and Lean. Hands-on exercise(s) will be used to tie the theory to application. We will discuss how to make processes (including design) more efficient, accurate, value-added and timely. We will introduce the DMAIC methodology, the Eight Wastes of Lean and the Six Sigma and Lean tools and techniques. We will touch upon Risk Analysis and Reliability issues. The presenters are Rama Shankar and George Alukal.

Presentation not available for publication.

NOTES

Using Lean and Six Sigma as Improvement Tools

ISO 9000, Lean and Six Sigma

- ISO 9001:2000 provides assurance that an organization has effectively implemented a standardized and harmonized Quality Management System, and improves it continually
- Lean addresses both incremental and breakthrough improvements: cost, cycle time, "waste" reduction & quality improvement
- Six Sigma attacks the variation within a process using mostly statistical methods, thus improving it which results in less defects and nonconformities

---

Lean and Six Sigma

George Alukal

Why the Emphasis on Six Sigma and Lean Now?

- Global economy
- Fast-paced technological changes
- Continued focus on quality, cost, delivery
- Higher and higher expectations of customers
- Quality standards such as TS 16949 or ISO 9000:2000
- Holding on to "Core Competencies", outsourcing the rest
- Market-driven pricing: Customers expect better performance at lower prices year after year

ISO 9001:2000

- The new revision of ISO 9001 has an increased focus on customer requirements, including monitoring of customer satisfaction, communication with customers regarding products, inquiries, contracts, order handling, amendments, complaints and feedback
- The new revision is getting closer to a TQM model as compared to the 1994 revision which was still more of a comprehensive Quality Assurance System rather than a QMS
- Continual improvement is also emphasized

---

8 Wastes of Lean

- Overproduction
- Motion
- Inventory
- Transportation
- Waiting
- Underutilized People
- Defects *Six Sigma techniques are most appropriate to attack the waste of "defects"
- Over-processing

Lean Manufacturing

Continuous Improvement & Kaizen Blitz

	Cellular & Flow	Pull System & Kanban	
TPM	JIT	Autonomation	V° S° M
Poka-yoke	Self Inspection	Quick Changeover	
POUS	Batch Size Reduction	Visual	5S
Layout	Standard Work		
Change Management	Teams		

Improvements Tools using Lean and Six Sigma

	Lean	Six Sigma
Quality	Quality at the Source, Autonomation, Poka-yoke, Standard Work	Attack Variation
Cost	8 Wastes of Lean and Building Blocks	Emphasis on ROI
Delivery	J.I.T., Cycle Time Reduction	Voice of the Customer
Customer Service	Quality at the Source, Teamwork, Standard Work	Business Support Processes
Willingness to Partner	Kanban-Pull Systems, Batch Size Reduction, Quality at the Source	Customer focused improvements

Six Sigma

Various Steps in using the Six Sigma method:

- Define customer expectations
- Map the process
- Identify critical, major and minor characteristics
- Collect relevant data
- Calculate the total defects per unit (TDPU)
- Convert this into defects-per-opportunity (DPMO)
- Translate this into a sigma value
- Benchmark against best-in-class
- Implement improvement

Six Sigma and Lean

Six Sigma

- Define, Measure, Analyze, Improve, Control methodology
- Focus on Reducing Variation
- Use of Statistical Techniques
- Six Sigma for Stability
- Six Sigma focus is on Quality

Lean

- Plan, Do, Check, Act methodology
- Focus on Time or Speed
- Reducing or Eliminating Non-value Added Activities
- Lean for Velocity
- Lean focus is on waste reduction and speed

Six Sigma

- Allows us to draw comparisons to other similar or dissimilar products, services and processes.
- Six Sigma level will only yield about three instances of non-conformance out of every million opportunities for non-conformance, (whereas four sigma translates to about 6,200 instances)
- Normally, DMAIC (or Define, Measure, Analyze, Improve & Control) methodology is used

Six Sigma

- Select projects that support the firms overall strategic/ business plan
- Use cost-benefit analysis
- Develop a problem statement (or desired outcome)
- In the process map, use the input – output model
- Use statistical and other improvement tools, as necessary
- Train employees in Pareto charts, Fishbone diagrams, Regression, Hypothesis testing, DOE, EVOP, ANOVA, Process capability analysis, Control charting, etc.

Lean and Six Sigma

- Both use a process model
- S-I-P-O-C

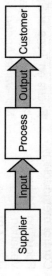

Supplier → Input → Process → Output → Customer

- Variations in the inputs will cause variations in the outputs
- The goal is standardized, consistent inputs so outputs are of acceptable quality

Lean and Six Sigma

- Project Selection
  - Lean: use Value Stream Mapping
  - Six Sigma: use "Voice of the Customer"
- Both Lean and Six Sigma are results oriented
  - Lean: metrics might include inventory turns, through-put, productivity, quality, etc.
  - Six Sigma: financial benefits (ROI, NPV, Payback, etc.), error rate (PPM) are emphasized

Lean and Six Sigma

Plan — Do — Check — Act (Lean)

Define — Measure — Analyze — Improve — Control (Six Sigma)

Lean and Six Sigma

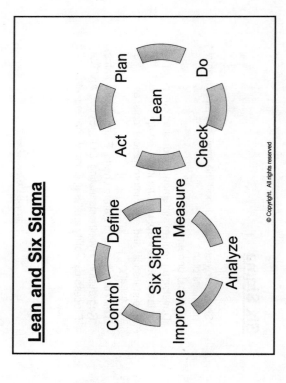

- Control the input variations
  - Man
  - Machine
  - Material
  - Methods
  - Measurement
  - Information
  - Environment
- Resulting in controlled output variation

Lean and Six Sigma

- Six Sigma emphasizes a "Charter" with objectives, scope, resource requirements, time-line, cost benefit analysis, etc.
- Lean uses the "Future State" vision for aggressive goal setting and utilizes tools such as benchmarking, team brainstorming, "roll up your sleeves" immediate implementation.
  - Creativity before capital translates into low cost/no cost solutions first.

Lean and Six Sigma

- Lean axiom is: an improvement done immediately is better than a perfect solution that is late
- Six Sigma: uses statistical techniques with emphasis on data analysis, experimentation, etc.

Lean and Six Sigma

- Both Lean and Six Sigma are Team based
- Both require good Change Management to sustain improvements for the long-term
- At the end of each project both emphasize Standardization to prevent Juran's "Saw tooth" effect

Lean and Six Sigma

Both require discipline, top management commitment, customer focus, "cultural" change and control/ standardization.

Further, Six Sigma focuses on minimizing variation and rigorous data driven improvement.

Understanding Variation

- All processes have variability
  - Manufacturing as well as administrative
- Variation due to:
  - Common causes
  - Special causes
- Control the important causes of variability
  - First all special causes
  - Then reduce the common causes

Understanding Variation

The averages of a series of samples:
- Have a standard deviation smaller than for the distribution of the individual samples
- Have a normal distribution even if the curve for the individuals is not bell-shaped

Understanding Variation

- Normal curve – "bell-shaped"
- Normal distribution is the most common pattern of variation in nature
- Normal curve can be described through its center-line (the mean) and by its spread (standard deviation or "sigma")

Capability vs. "In Control"

- Capable means that the process is able to consistently have output within specification
- "In Control" means that the process is stable or predictable (but not necessarily acceptable). Only common causes are present

Relationship between Sigma and DPMO

± Sigma	DPMO (or %)
1	68.26%
2	95.46%
3	99.73%
3	66,807
4	6,210
5	233
6	3.4

Six Sigma Examples

Average company is operating at about 4 Sigma level:

At Six Sigma Level:
- 1 unsafe minute of drinking water approx. every seven months
- 1 hour without electric power approx. every 34 years

Domestic airline flight fatality rate is approx. 0.43ppm

Six Sigma History

Brief History:
- Continuous Improvement tools made popular by Deming, Juran, Shewhart, Ishikawa & Taguchi in the sixties, seventies and eighties
- Motorola introduces the concept of "Six Sigma" quality (3.4 ppm philosophy)
- Firms like GE, Allied Signal (now Honeywell) publicized benefits of Six Sigma

More Six Sigma History

- ASQ and others start Six Sigma training & certifications
- Many firms call their continuous improvement programs as Six Sigma (or roll their existing programs into "Six Sigma"), but not necessarily using strictly statistical tools

Six Sigma

- Is rigorous, data-driven: both collection and analysis
- Linking improvements to stake-holders (internally & externally):
  - To the organization's strategic goals
  - To the "Voice of the customer", and critical to Quality in the customers' eyes
  - Internal "Process Owners"
  - Tight linkage to quality tools
  - Project Charter & Plan, Project Team, ROI calculation
  - The five stage process (DMAIC)

Six Sigma - Measure

MEASURE phase

- Understand the "Current State" through baseline performance assessment
- Validate that the current measurement system is accurate
- Verify the current Cost of Poor Quality (COPQ)
- Use tools such as Process Capability studies, Gage R & R, Cost-Benefit analysis, etc.

Six Sigma - Define

DEFINE phase

- Project Charter:
  - Define the defect/problem, the scope of the Six Sigma project, the customer and the business impact
  - CTQ (Critical to Quality) for the customer
  - Assign target dates, resources
  - Set improvement goals
  - Confirm strategic business linkage
  - Process Mapping can be used as a tool to understand the "Current State"

Six Sigma - Analyze

ANALYZE phase

- Uncover the root cause(s) of the defect
- Once potential factors are isolated, use statistical or quality tools to see the cause & effect relationship
- Use graphical analysis tools (e.g. scatter diagrams, run charts, etc.), statistical testing (e.g. hypothesis testing, regression, ANOVA, etc.), risk analysis (e.g. FMEA, contingency plans, etc.)

Six Sigma - Improve

IMPROVE phase

- Predict our improved performance when the problem is fixed. If the projected savings are not worth the effort, abort the project at this stage before more resources are spent
- Use DOE, EVOP, and other statistical tools in this phase of the DMAIC cycle.

Six Sigma - Roles

Roles:

- Blackbelt
- Master Blackbelt
- Greenbelt
- Executive Sponsor
- Deployment Champion
- Process Owner

Six Sigma - Improve

IMPROVE phase

- Now that the identification of root cause(s) is done:
  - Make side by side comparison of the proposed solutions
  - Benchmark against competition's performance, if possible

Six Sigma - Control

CONTROL phase

- Integrate the solution into the operational environment
- Standardize, so as not to slip back
- Migrate "lessons learnt" across the organization
- Use SPC techniques, updated process capability, Lean tools, error-proofing, etc.

Six Sigma – Blackbelt

Blackbelt

- The technical process expert
- Familiar with the DMAIC phases and quality & statistical tools
- Often act as the project manager, facilitator
- Normally, trained for four weeks in Six Sigma

Six Sigma – Master Blackbelt

Master Blackbelt

- Responsible for training other roles in Six Sigma
- Provide on-going support wherever needed
- Partner with process owners and deployment champions to develop and prioritize the business transformation plan, aligning projects, etc.
- Coach Blackbelts on tools & techniques
- Training: After Blackbelt training, additional 2 to 3 weeks more, typically with a time gap of 12 to 18 months

Six Sigma – Greenbelt

Greenbelt

- Typically, work on projects in their subject areas only (as subject matter experts)
- Support the Blackbelts
- Responsible for the "Control" phase
- Training can be from 2 days to 4 weeks

Six Sigma - Sponsor

Executive Sponsor

- Responsible for:
  - Securing funding
  - Providing resources
  - Removing roadblocks
  - Co-ordinating between all impacted parties
  - Rewarding the project team
  - Training normally runs from one-half to 2 days

Six Sigma - Champion

Deployment Champion

- Responsible for:
  - Helping with Six sigma team formation.
  - "Owning" the Define phase with input from the Master Blackbelt
  - Preventing conflicts between functions, different improvement efforts, etc.
  - Typically, the training is for 2 to 3 days

Six Sigma - Plan

Master Plan for Six Sigma:

- Communication & Change Management
- HR issues
  - Pay, recognition, incentives, retention
  - Six Sigma training & certification
  - Avoid another layer of bureaucracy
  - Conflict resolution

Six Sigma - Champion

Deployment Champion

- High ranking person in the firm
- Responsible for:
  - Setting the long term vision
  - Planning and supporting change management
  - Co-ordinating the Six Sigma management system
  - Ensuring the linkages between the projects and the business goals and tied to the "voice of the customer".
  - Creating the project portfolio & prioritization.

Six Sigma – Process Owner

Process Owner

- Works in the individual business units
- Responsible for:
  - Project reviews
  - Providing any additional resources
  - Approving the solutions
  - Maintaining ownership once the project is complete
  - Training normally runs 1 to 2 days

Six Sigma - Plan

Master Plan for Six Sigma:

– Initial deployment considerations: Centralized support from "Center of Excellence", Consulting Team, Training Staff, Infrastructure for Customer Satisfaction, Benchmarking and Measurement

Six Sigma - DFSS

Design for Six Sigma (DFSS):

- For designing new products or services, or for re-designing existing processes and products
- Design new process to deliver at a defect-free rate from the start
- For re-designs, take the process apart and then put it back in the improved way

An Example of Combining Six Sigma and Lean

Define

- Strategic link to Business Plan
- Defined Business Impact
- Structured Brainstorming
- Cause and Effect Diagrams to identify critical factors
- Metrics defined and charted
- Develop a focused Problem Statement and Objective(s)

An Example of Combining Six Sigma and Lean

Measure

- Develop a Process Map and/or FMEA
- Develop a *Current State Map*
- Identify the variables and how to measure them
- Analyze measurement system capability
- Assess the specification (Is one in place? Is it the right one?)

An Example of Combining Six Sigma and Lean

Improve

- 5S & Visual Controls
- *Setup Time Reduction (SMED)*
- *Pull System, Kanban*
- *Cell Design, Level Loading, Line Balancing*
- Use of Design of Experiments (DOE)
- Move the distribution if necessary, Shrink the spread, Confirm the results

Six Sigma, Lean and TOC

- Lean, Six Sigma and Theory of Constraints are complimentary, not mutually exclusive

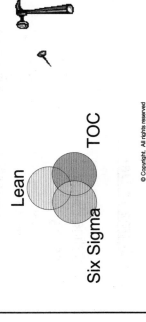

An Example of Combining Six Sigma and Lean

Analyze

- Look at the raw data and Characterize the response
- Abnormal? Other clues? Mean or Variance problem?
- *Spaghetti Diagram*
- *Takt Time*
- *Future State Map*
- *Standard Work Combination (as part of Standard Work)*
- Use Graphical Analysis, ANOVA, and other statistical tools

An Example of Combining Six Sigma and Lean

Control

- Mistake proof the process - *Poka-yoke, Autonomation*
- Measure the final capability
- Deploy the appropriate process controls
- On the critical characteristics:
  - Document the efforts and results
  - *Standard Work*
  - *TPM*

Benefits of Lean and Six Sigma

- Eliminate waste and variation
- Improved quality
- Reduced costs for suppliers ⇨ reduced price for the customer
- Better delivery and customer satisfaction
- Smoother, seamless, supply chain
- Less overproduction, inventory costs, obsolescence
- More predictability and consistency

Six Sigma in Detail

(A) Define Phase

Identify

- Customer needs and strategic business needs
- Processes/Products to be improved
- The scope of the Six Sigma project
- Project goals
- Stake-holders

Six Sigma in Detail

(A) Define Phase

- Create problem statement and project charter
- Financial analysis
- Business impact ($ savings, bottom line improvements, etc.)
- Project plans & timeline
- Project team members

Six Sigma in Detail

(A) Define Phase

- High-level process map
- Gap analysis
- Define the performance measures/standards
- Define supplier-customer relationships (hand-off)

Six Sigma in Detail

(B) <u>Measure Phase</u>

- Understand the current state
- Set improvement goals
- Agree on the improved future state
- Define inputs – outputs of the process
- Causes of variation
- Validate the measurement system

Six Sigma in Detail

(B) <u>Measure Phase</u>

- Detailed process map
- Data collection
- Measurement system analysis (Gage R & R)
- Process capability determination
- Graphical techniques

Six Sigma in Detail

(B) <u>Measure Phase</u>

- Create Failure Mode & Effects Analysis (FMEA) (risk analysis)
- Cause and effect relationships
- DPMO
- Z value

Six Sigma in Detail

(C) <u>Analyze Phase</u>

- Rigorous analysis of data collected
- Sources of variation identified
- Potential causes of variation prioritized

Six Sigma in Detail

(C) Analyze Phase

- Team brainstorming
- Fishbone diagram
- RPN (Risk Priority Number) reviews & contingency plans (FMEA)
- Hypothesis testing
- Correlation & regression analysis

Six Sigma in Detail

(C) Analyze Phase

- Update the detailed process map
- Update the project goals and financial analysis
- Verify assumptions made
- Validate the cost-benefit equation or make decision to abort the project

Six Sigma in Detail

(D) Improve Phase

- Identify the improvements
- Establish implementation plan
- Do simulation or pilot run
- Improve process capability

Six Sigma in Detail

(D) Improve Phase

- Designed experiments (DOE)
- ANOVA (Analysis of Variance)
- Improved state process map
- Corrective actions

Six Sigma in Detail

(D) Improve Phase

- Confirm results
- Validate improvements
- Optimize inputs
- Specify new output tolerances and acceptance criteria

Six Sigma in Detail

(E) Control Phase

- Document and monitor
- Assign responsibilities
- Permanently capture the gains
- Revise S.O.Ps, logs, checklists (for CTQs, especially)
- Operator definitions
- FMEAs (for control)
- Train immediately

Six Sigma in Detail

(E) Control Phase

- Preventive actions
- Implement process controls
- S.P.C; where needed
- Mistake proofing
- Periodic audits
- Financial validation

Six Sigma in Detail

(E) Control Phase

- Preventive maintenance (and TPM)
- Control plans
- Gage calibration plans
- Supplier management
- Finalize transition to process owner
- Customer feedback

Six Sigma: Definitions

Project Charter: Consists of the customer needs, the project's scope, objectives, project success criteria, project team, their roles and responsibilities, resource allocation, deadlines, etc.

Six Sigma: Definitions

Project plan & timeline:

- All the work to be done
- Who will do what
- By when will the tasks be done
- Allocate resources
- Develop a project schedule with milestones & review points

Gantt chart, critical path method, activity network diagram

Six Sigma: Definitions

Problem statement: Document the issue that the Six Sigma team is going to improve. State the problem concisely but in enough detail so that everyone can comprehend. This describes the project.

Six Sigma: Definitions

Financial Impact: With the use of "best" assumptions, calculate the Return on Investment (ROI), Internal Rate of Return (IRR), Net Present Value (NPV), or Payback Period in doing the Six Sigma project.

Six Sigma: Definitions

Project Team:

Team leader (Black Belt)

Team members (Green Belts, Process Owner, Technical Expert, etc.)

Six Sigma: Definitions

Process Map: Identifies the flow of materials and information in a series of processes, along with the inputs and outputs in each step of the way.

Six Sigma: Definitions

Supplier – Customer (SIPOC): Identifies the internal provider (supplier) and user (customer) along with the inputs, transformation (process) and outputs.

Six Sigma: Definitions

Current State: The as-is situation at present in the process, where the Six Sigma project is selected to be implemented.

Six Sigma: Definitions

Causes of Variation: The 5Ms, Environment, Information

5Ms are Manpower, Materials, Machines, Methods and Measurement.

Training, Supplier Control, Maintenance, Documentation & Mistake Proofing and Calibration are ways to control the variation due to 5Ms.

Six Sigma: Definitions

Gage R & R (Repeatability & Reproducibility)

Repeatability: One operator, same gage, measure one part multiple times

Reproducibility: Multiple operators, same gage, measure one part multiple times

Six Sigma: Definitions

Future State: The improved state of the process after the Six Sigma project is completed.

Six Sigma: Definitions

Measurement System Analysis:

- Bias (Accuracy)
- Linearity
- Stability
- Discrimination
- Precision (Repeatability and Reproducibility)

Six Sigma: Definitions

Graphical techniques:

- Histograms
- Scatter Diagrams
- Run Charts
- Pareto Chart

(Flow-charts, Fishbone Diagrams, Control Charts, etc. are also graphical)

Six Sigma: Definitions

DPMO or Defects Per Million Opportunities, helps to determine the capability of a process. How the DPMO is calculated will depend on whether the data is variable or attribute, and if there is one or more than one opportunity for a defect.

Six Sigma: Definitions

Process Capability (Cpk): Ratio of the distance between the process average and the closest specification limit divided by three standard deviations of the short term process variation.

$Cp = (USL - LSL) / Six Sigma$

Generally, process capability of 2 is considered to be "world class" quality and equals Six Sigma

Six Sigma: Definitions

Failure Mode and Effects Analysis (FMEA) is a risk assessment tool if a failure were to occur; it also helps to decide what are the counter-measures to minimize this risk.

Risk Priority Number (RPN) =
   Severity x Occurrence x Detection

Six Sigma: Definitions

Brainstorming: A technique for a team to efficiently and very creatively generate a large number of ideas on a topic without criticism or judgment, and then quickly reach consensus.

Six Sigma: Definitions

Hypothesis testing: To determine if a change to an input will alter the output significantly; and also to determine if there are differences between two or more process outputs.

Six Sigma: Definitions

Z value = The distance between a data point and the mean divided by the standard deviation ("x" minus mu divided by sigma).

Six Sigma: Definitions

Fishbone or Cause & Effect Diagram:

A team-based tool to identify, analyze and display in detail the potential causes which might result in a problem ("Effect") so as to discover root cause(s).

Six Sigma: Definitions

Correlation Analysis: To determine the strength of linear relationships between two process variables. It helps to compare an input to an output, or two inputs or outputs against each other.

Six Sigma: Definitions

Regression: To determine the strength of association between independent factor(s), called regressors and a dependent variable, called a response variable. Normally computer programs are used to perform regression analysis.

Six Sigma: Definitions

· Designed Experiments (DOE): How output(s) are affected by changes in inputs and their interactions. A series of tests to build understanding and predictability of a process. There are a variety of Design of Experiments.

Six Sigma: Definitions

ANOVA or Analysis of Variance: When there are multiple inputs, ANOVA methods help us to identify which factors (or input variables) affect the output significantly.

Six Sigma: Definitions

Statistical Process Control (S.P.C.): Controlling a process at source using statistical techniques, rather than inspecting the output of the process. Control charts are used to monitor, control and improve process performance over time by focusing on variation. X-bar, R charts are commonly used for variable data.

Six Sigma: Definitions

Total Productive Maintenance (TPM):
A "Lean" technique to maximize Overall Equipment Effectiveness (OEE).

OEE = Uptime x Performance x First-pass-yield

Six Sigma: Definitions

Corrective & Preventive Actions:

– Action take to eliminate the cause of non-conformities to prevent recurrence

– Action taken to eliminate the cause of potential non-conformities to prevent occurrence

Six Sigma: Definitions

Mistake proofing: Methods that help humans to avoid mistakes; the devices used are usually low-cost, highly reliable mechanisms that will not permit an error to be made, or shut down the equipment immediately if it is trending to make a defect.

Six Sigma: Definitions

Gage calibration: Comparison to a higher standard so as to analyze and control the gage's accuracy.

Six Sigma Case Study (continued)

The Team
- Supervisor
- Maintenance
- Four operators (all three shifts represented)
- Quality
- Office
- External facilitator

Six Sigma: Definitions

Control Plan: A "frozen" process so that the outputs are predictable and acceptable. It also documents the control activities required of a Six Sigma project in the "Control" phase.

Six Sigma Case Study

- Artificial sweetener operation
- Too much "rework" and too little First-Pass-Yield
- Ten step process, three shift operation
- Management called us in for improving the line
- See handout for further information & layout

Example - Sweetener Process

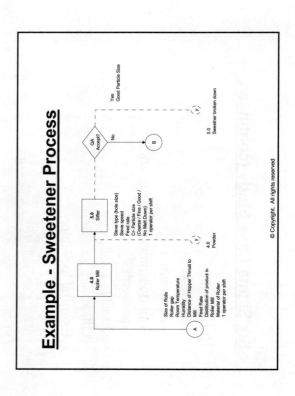

Size of Rolls
Roller gap
Room Temperature
Humidity
Distance of Hopper Throat to Mill
Feed Rate
Distribution of product in Mill
Roller Mill
Material of Roller
1 operator per shift

Sieve type (hole size)
Sieve speed
Feed rate
C - Particle size
(Coarse / Fine / Good / No Melt Down)
1 operator per shift

4.0 Roller Mill
5.0 Sifter

QA Accept?

Yes
Good Particle Size

No

4.0 Powder
5.0 Sweetener broken down

Example - Sweetener Process

SWEETENER PROCESS

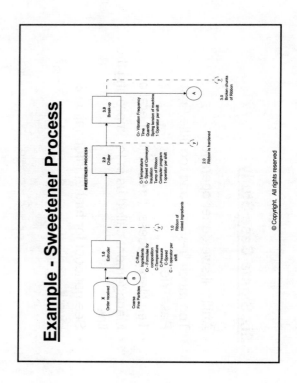

X Order received

Coarse
Fine Particles

C-Raw Ingredients
C - Formulas for composition
C-Temperature
C-Pressure
C-Speed
C - 1 operator per shift

C-Temperature
C- Speed of Conveyor
Insulation
Temp of Ribbon
Computer program
1 operator per shift

C- Vibration Frequency
Time
Quantity
Spring tension of machine
1 Operator per shift

1.0 Extruder
2.0 Chiller
3.0 Break-up

1.0 Ribbon of mixed ingredients
2.0 Ribbon is hardened
3.0 Broken chunks of Ribbon

28

WORKSHOP: COMPREHENSIVE REVIEW OF VCCI AND CISPR/I EMC ACTIVITIES, AND CURRENT EMC CONTROL ACTIVITIES IN TAIWAN AND KOREA (MO-AM-WS-3)

Bob Hofmann *(chair)*
Hofmann EMC Engineering
Akihisa Sakurai *(co-chair)*
IBM Japan

This workshop will provide a comprehensive review of the Voluntary Control Council for Interference by Information Technology Equipment (VCCI) on its 20 years of voluntary control activities in Japan. It will also review measurement technology developments contributing to international standardization, and the latest development of a new quality qualification program which is expected to give related industries a powerful electromagnetic characteristic qualification system for kit modules of information technology equipment.

Furthermore, current hot issues in CISPR/I will be discussed by the CISPR/I chairman, and EMC regulatory authorities from Taiwan and Korea will update the current EMC status in those countries.

This is a great opportunity for all EMC-related people to refresh and learn the latest information on Asian EMC movements as well as working highlights of CISPR/I that may have a strong influence on individual country EMC regulations.

Presentations:

(1) 20 Years Review of VCCI
Haruyoshi Nagasawa

(2) VCCI Technical Development and Contribution to Worldwide Standard Issues
Kunihiro Osabe

(3) Introduction of VCCI, NEW System "Kit Module Program" and Technical Background
Hirokazu Toya

(4) Progress in CISPR/I, EMC of Multimedia Equipment and Requirements for Wireline Systems
Martin Wright

(5) EMC Requirements Now and in the Future in Taiwan
Yung-Chi Tang

(6) Today and Tomorrow of Korea's Certification Scheme
Jungsuk Seo

NOTES

This wAS A Course in Reading Slides

CISPR 16 ; 22 (pg 30)

BSMI (pg 50) -

29

Slide 1

20 years review of VCCI

August 8, 2005

Haruyoshi NAGASAWA

Executive Board Director/ VCCI

Contents
1. History of VCCI – Why Self Industry Regulation?
2. Current status and activity
3. Ground work for MRA
4. Awareness development
5. Findings
6. The Advantages of Industry Self-Regulation as a regulatory practice
7. "Industry Self-Regulations" fulfill all the conditions for regulation

1

Slide 2

1.History of VCCI

VCCI Events	WW EMC Events
	(1979) FCC Enforced
	(1985) CISPR 22 released
(1985/12) VCCI established — Steering Comm. / Marketing SC / Technical SC / Communication SC	
(1986/06) VCCI enforced (DoC)	
(1989) International Relations SC	(1991) Korea
(1993/04) Test site registration system — Measurement Registration Comm. / Education & Training SC	(1996) EMC Directive (DoC) / (1996) FCC DoC / (1997) Australia (DoC) / (1998) Taiwan
(1998/04) VLAC established / Test lab accreditation system	
(2004/04) Kit Module EMI Program	

2

Slide 3

2.Current status and activity
1. VCCI coverage in EMC-related Regulation of Japan

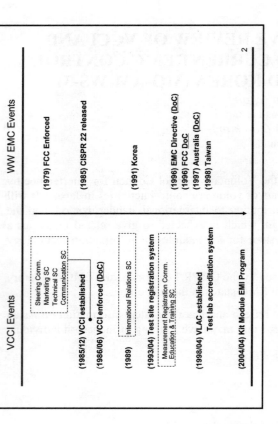

Product Group	Emission		Immunity
ITE	VCCI Computer, PDA, Peripheral		
TTE	Facsimile, Modem, Radio, Mobile Phone	Radio Law	
Electrical Appliance	Copier, TV, VCR, Refrigerator, Transformer, Electric Wire, Fluorescent Light, Others	DEN-AN Law / Microwave Oven (PS E) (PS E)	Each Industrial Association's Standard
Medical Electrical Equipment	MRI, CT, X-ray Generator, Others / JIS T0601-1-2 (IEC 60601-1-2)	Pharmaceutical Affairs Law	

3

Slide 4

2. Current Status of VCCI

VCCI Voluntary Control Council
for Interference by Information Technology Equipment

Inauguration
1985 (when CISPR 22 released)

1985 By Related Industry Associations
- JEIDA (IT)
- EIAJ (Electronic Devices, Home)   > JEITA (Oct, 2000)
- JBMIA (Business machines)
- CIAJ (Telecom)

Membership Operation
No Restriction with Nationality
1,205 membership (as of Mar, 31, 2005)

Exclusiveness
No other bodies controlling EMI of ITE in Japan

Technical specification
Well harmonized with CISPR 22 and CISPR 16

Self Declaration Approach
Filing a declaration with VCCI office (No approval process)
More than 6,000 in 2004
e-filing* started since 2002

Regular Market Sampling test practice
More than 650 samples tested cumulatively
Increasing annual sampling
*e-filing: Product registration through VCCI WEB page

4

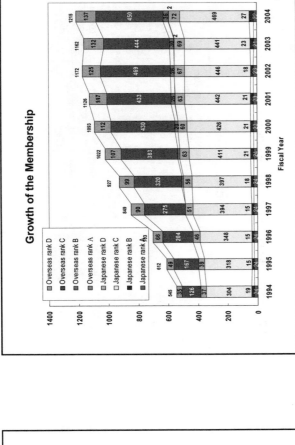

Growth of the Membership

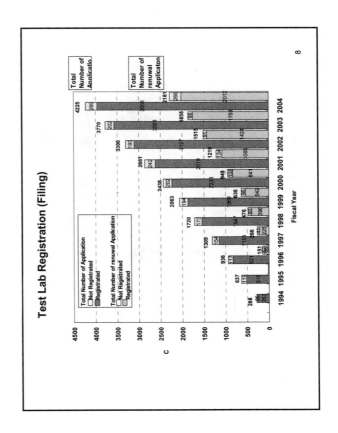

Test Lab Registration (Filing)

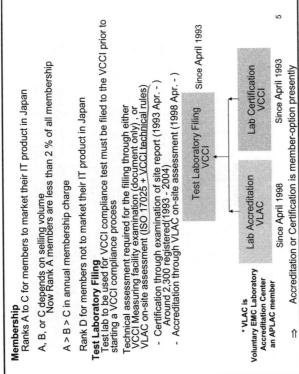

Membership

Ranks A to C for members to market their IT product in Japan

A, B, or C depends on selling volume
Now Rank A members are less than 2 % of all membership

A > B > C in annual membership charge

Rank D for members not to market their IT product in Japan

Test Laboratory Filing

Test lab to be used for VCCI compliance test must be filed to the VCCI prior to starting a VCCI compliance process

Technical assessment required for the filing through either
VCCI Measuring facility examination (document only) , or
VLAC on-site assessment (ISO 17025 + VCCI technical rules)

- Certification through examination of site report (1993 Apr. -)
  Around 2,300 registered(1993 - 2004)
- Accreditation through VLAC on-site assessment (1998 Apr. -)

Lab Accreditation VLAC	Test Laboratory Filing VCCI	Lab Certification VCCI
Since April 1998		Since April 1993

Since April 1993

* VLAC is
Voluntary EMC Laboratory Accreditation Center
an APLAC member

⇨ Accreditation or Certification is member-option presently

5

Membership Details

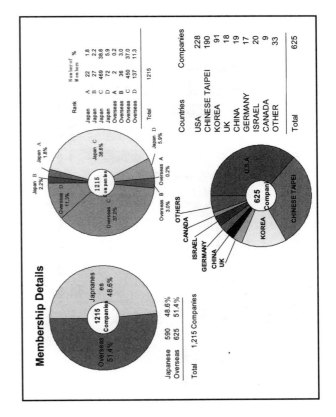

Rank		Number of Members	%
Japan	A	22	1.8
Japan	B	27	2.2
Japan	C	469	38.6
Japan	D	72	5.9
Overseas	A	2	0.2
Overseas	B	36	3.0
Overseas	C	450	37.0
Overseas	D	137	11.3
Total		1215	

Countries	Companies
USA	228
CHINESE TAIPEI	190
KOREA	91
UK	18
CHINA	19
GERMANY	17
ISRAEL	20
CANADA	9
OTHER	33
Total	625

Japanese	590	48.6%
Overseas	625	51.4%
Total	1,215 Companies	

Overview of VCCI controlling scheme

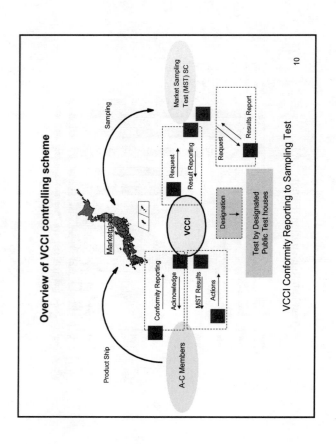

VCCI Conformity Reporting to Sampling Test

Details of Test Labs Registered (Filed)

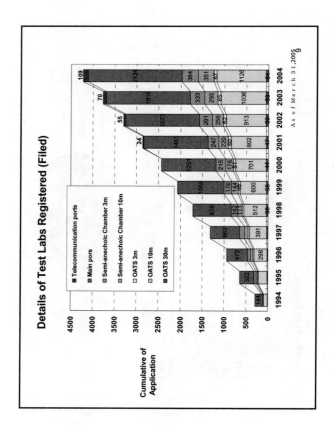

As of March 31, 2005

VCCI Self-Declaration Process Flow example

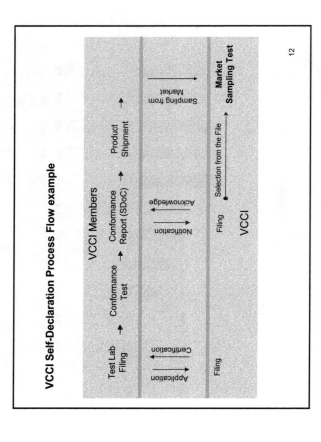

Where VCCI Scheme located in the WW Regulations?

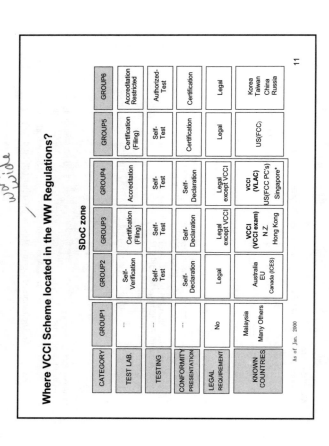

As of Jan. 2000

FILED VCCI CONFORMANCE REPORTS / YEAR

Product Categories renewed

Legend: Others, LAN Equipment, Communications Equipment, Modem, Facsimile, Terminal, I/O Device, Display, Printer

Fiscal Year: 1994, 1995, 1996, 1997, 1998, 1999, 2000, 2001, 2002, 2003, 2004

Totals: 4601, 4938, 5471, 5536, 6168, 5795, 6061, 6047, 6029, 6114, 6110

A s o f M a r c h 31, 2005
14

---

3. Ground work for MRA

Establishment of VLAC

- Voluntary Laboratory Accreditation Center (VLAC) established by VCCI in April 1998
- An legally Identifiable organization as an Incorporated company
- The accreditation body recognized by VCCI
- Independent of VCCI operation
- Observes ISO/IEC Guide 58/ ISO/IEC 17011
- Accredits laboratories with VCCI Technical Requirement/ CISPR 22 / CISPR 24/ FCC Part15/18 with ISO/IEC 17025
- VLAC's service is open to any laboratories
- Accepted by APLAC as a Full Membership in October, 2001
- Became a signatory of APLAC MRA on November 13, 2003
- Standing by to serve as Designated Evaluation Organization under the Japan-EU MRA put into effect in March 2002

MRA between Japan and USA
- Under negotiation between the both Governments as of April 2005
- To realize mutual acceptance of test results for EMI of ITE from EMC laboratories accredited in each country

4. Awareness development
Actions · Reached out to Industry Associations (in Japan and Overseas)
· Invited a number of competent people into the VCCI committee activities
· Took every opportunity to participate in various Computer and
Business Exhibitions
16

ORGANIZATION

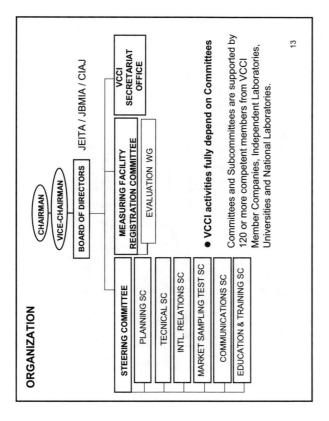

CHAIRMAN
VICE-CHAIRMAN
BOARD OF DIRECTORS — JEITA / JBMIA / CIAJ

MEASURING FACILITY REGISTRATION COMMITTEE
EVALUATION WG

VCCI SECRETARIAT OFFICE

STEERING COMMITTEE
- PLANNING SC
- TECNICAL SC
- INTL. RELATIONS SC
- MARKET SAMPLING TEST SC
- COMMUNICATIONS SC
- EDUCATION & TRAINING SC

● VCCI activities fully depend on Committees

Committees and Subcommittees are supported by 120 or more competent members from VCCI Member Companies, Independent Laboratories, Universities and National Laboratories.

13

VCCI Sampling Test Record (-2004)

Fiscal Year	-2002	2003						2004						Total	
Testing No.	Sub total	No.					Sub total	No.					Sub total		
		1	2	3	4	5		1	2	3	4	5			
Samples tested	796	8	23	12	21	7	71	21	11	19	25	9	85	952	
Result compiled	544	3	11	8	10	4	36	10	1	8	18		37	617	
Warning	236	5	12	4	9	2	32	8	9	10	6		33	301	
Not-compiled	16	0	0	0	2	1	3	3	1	1	1		6	25	

Under Testing

VCCI has been achieving very low "average Not-complied Rare" as 2.6%

Number of testing samples a year will reach 100 in 2005

15

Slide 18

5. Findings

- High Participation Rate (more that 95 % in the market)
- Membership steadily growing from around the world
- Market sampling tests seldom come across non-compliance products
- Reliable activity and achievement are leading to MRA between foreign Government
- Grown to a Well-known Major EMI Controlling Scheme

Example

VCCI mark is adopted one of conditions to PC and Printers to get the ECO mark

The Eco Mark Program
is administrated by the Japan Environment Association (JEA) under the auspices of the Ministry of Environment

The Japanese word means
" This product is ecologically sound"

http://www.jeas.or.jp/ecomark/english/

18

Slide 20

7. "Industry Self-Regulations" fulfill all the conditions for regulation

Key Elements	COST to Market	TIME to Market	Compliance Reliability
Implementing International Standards timely-basis	v	v	-
Extending Uniform interpretation of rules	v	v	v
Producing Mind-set as "Our Rule"	v	v	v

20

Slide 17

- Held annual Technical Workshops / Seminars
- Ran advertisement in Magazines and Newspapers / Ad. Posters

Results · VCCI standards incorporated into member companies' standards as essential as their quality standards
· VCCI compliance has become a de Facto requisite for trades in Japan
· VCCI mark won the recognition of the Eco Mark Program for PCs and Printers
· VCCI mark steadily gaining public recognition

Ad. Poster   in the Japan Railway Station "Shinjuku"

in the car of Tokyo Metro

Exhibition
EMC Japan 2004
COMPUTEX Taipei 2004

17

Slide 19

6. The Advantages of Industry Self-Regulation as a regulatory Practice

1. From an Economic Aspect
The policy of Government of Japan to honor industry's voluntarism in controlling EMC was very successful as consumers and manufacturers have enjoyed saving amounting to as much as:
- US$ 200M since the establishment of VCCI (1985) – direct benefit only

2. From an Industry Development Aspect
Has greatly fostered IT industry with :
- Less legal burden
- Flexible operation
- Adoption of Up-to-date International Standards

3. From an International Trade Aspect
Has greatly contributed to ITE trade facilitation with:
- No red tape
- Faster market access

19

VCCI Technical Development and Contribution to Worldwide Standard Issues

August, 2005

Kunihiro Osabe
osabe@vlac.co.jp
VCCI Technical Sub-Committee

Contents

- Outline of VCCI Technical Requirement

- Contribution to International Standard Issues

  Test Arrangement for Emission Measurement
  Experimental Study on
  * Radiated Emission Measurement
  * Conducted Emission Measurement
  * Test Site Validation Method using Broadband Antenna

Outline of VCCI Technical Requirement

- **Main Reference Standard: CISPR22**

- **National Standardization:**

  The National Standardization Report of CISPR22 is prepared by the Japanese National Committee and reported to the Ministry from the Information and Communications Council in MIC.
  (MIC* : Ministry of Internal Affairs and Communications, Former: MPHPT)

- **VCCI Technical Requirement (V-3):**

  VCCI Technical Requirement (V3) based on the Report is prepared by VCCI Technical Sub-committee.

Procedure for Harmonization between National Standards and CISPR Standards

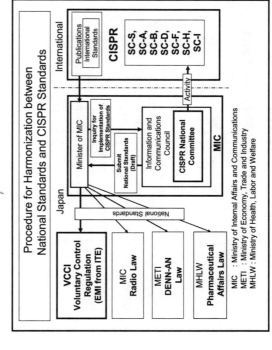

MIC : Ministry of Internal Affairs and Communications
METI : Ministry of Economy, Trade and Industry
MHLW : Ministry of Health, Labor and Welfare

Current Movement of Technical Requirement

- **CISPR/SC-I**
  CISPR22 5th Ed. was published on 2005-04 including the improvement of Test Setup, Annex C and Measurement Uncertainty.

- **the Japanese National Committee**
  The NC will prepare the National Standardization Report of CISPR22 5th Ed. for the Information and Communications Council of MIC. (End of 2005 ??)

- **VCCI Technical Requirement**
  When the National Standardization report is published, VCCI Technical Sub Committee will amend the Technical Requirement based on the National Standardization Report of CISPR22 5th Edition. (Next Revision: 2006-04)

Contribution to International Standard Issues

- **Test Arrangement for Emission Measurement**

- **Radiated Emission Measurement**

- **Conducted Emission Measurement**

- **Test Site Validation Method using Broadband Antenna**

The Deviations of VCCI Technical Requirement from current CISPR22

1) Construction of the technical requirement
   The clause of the measurement instrumentation/equipment and the clause of measuring method have been completely divided, although the current CISPR22 is constructed one clause for both.
2) 3 meters separation measurement for radiated emission.
   There is 20 years experience with this requirement.
3) Test site validation method for the radiated emission measurement
   The validation method based on CISPR16-1-4 has been introduced as an alternative method since 2001-04.
4) Telecommunication port conducted emission measurement
   It will be reflected in the next revision of VCCI Technical Requirement
5) Ferrite clamp on AC power cord
   Deviation was cancelled in CISPR22 5th Edition

Organization of Technical Sub-Committee

Technical Sub-Committee
Chair: Mr. S. Satake/Hitachi, Vice-chair: Mr. K. Osabe
Secretary : Jiro Kawano/VCCI Secretariat
34 members from 25 Manufacturers & Test laboratories
5 Working Groups

CISPR-WG	: Contribution and study on proposal document to the CISPR Japanese NC and CISPR/SC-I
Radiated Emission Measurement-WG	: Experimental study on Radiated Emission Limit and Measurement Method
Conducted Emission Measurement-WG	: Experimental study on Conducted Emission Limit and Measurement Method
Kit/Modules-WG	: Experimental study on Kit/Modules Measurement Method
Revision-WG	: Preparation of the revision of VCCI Technical Requirement and VCCI Voluntary Control Program

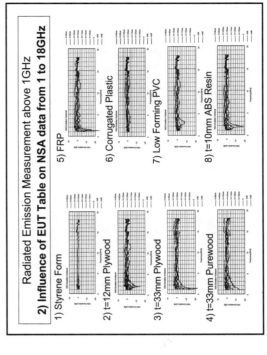

Radiated Emission Measurement

1) Influences of EUT Size and Receiving Antenna Beamwidth

When EUT size is large, the proportional conversion into 3m distance is difficult and when you search for the worst value, a receiving antenna should be continuously moved vertically and horizontally.

2) Influence of EUT Table on NSA data from 1 to 18GHz

A relative permittivity ε_r of less than 1.5 is an appropriate specification for the EUT table material for above 1GHz measurement.

3) Influence of EUT Tables on the Transmission Data in the frequency range from 30MHz to 1GHz

EUT Table should select a material not to increase the measurement uncertainty in the frequency above 300MHz.

Radiated Emission Measurement above 1GHz
2) Influence of EUT Table on NSA data from 1 to 18GHz

1) Styrene Form

2) t=12mm Plywood

3) t=33mm Plywood

4) t=33mm Purewood

5) FRP

6) Corrugated Plastic

7) Low Forming PVC

8) t=10mm ABS Resin

Test Arrangement for Emission Measurement

CISPR22 5th Edition :2005-04

Non-conductive table

Figure 7 – Example test arrangement for tabletop equipment (conducted emission measurement – alternative 2)

Figure 10 – Example test arrangement for tabletop equipment (radiated emission measurement)

Ferrite clamps or tube was deleted

This figure has been proposed from Technical Sub-Committee and adopted in CISPR22 5th Ed.

Radiated Emission Measurement above 1GHz
1) Influences of EUT Size and Receiving Antenna Beamwidth

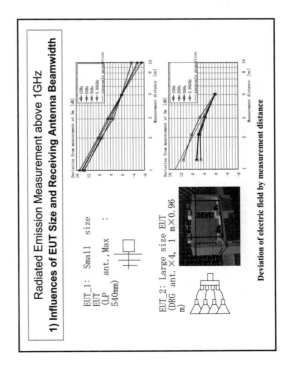

EUT_1: Small size
EUT (LP 540mm) ant., Max :

EUT_2: Large size EUT
(DRG ant. ×4, 1 m×0.96 m)

Deviation of electric field by measurement distance

More studies needed, but still Suggesting 3m

37

Conducted Emission Measurement

1) Evaluation of New ISN available on the market according to CISPR 22 4th Edition

LCL Characteristics of new ISN satisfies the specification of CISPR22 4th Edition.

Nearly same data within 4dB can be measured with different ISNs available on the market.

2) Correlation experiments between ISN and Non Invasive measurement (CISPR/I/93/CD)

Measurement data of ISN and CVP has almost same result, when the common mode impedance of AE side is set to constant by connecting the ISN.

However, if it is not constant, the measurement repeatability and correlation could not be achieved, even if the power limit is introduced to the Non-Invasive Test Method.

---

2) Correlation Experiments between ISN and Non Invasive measurement (CISPR/I/93/CD)

(CISPR22 Annex C1.3)
AE side: Non-constant Impedance

EUT: Note PC

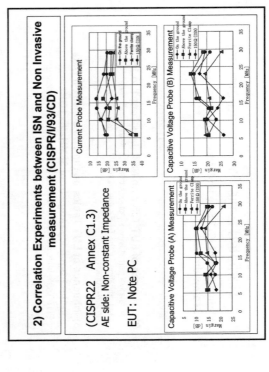

---

3) Influence of EUT Tables on the Transmission Data in the frequency range from 30MHz to 1GHz

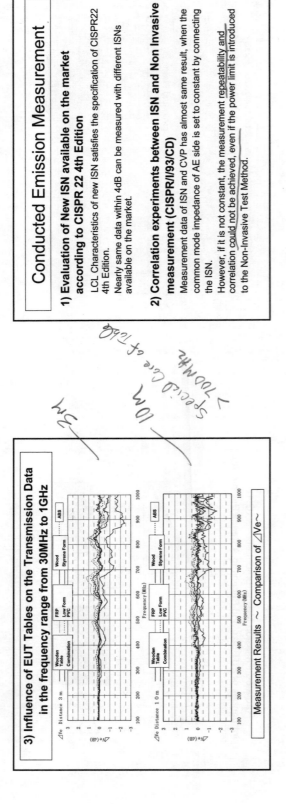

Measurement Results ~ Comparison of △Ve~

---

1) Evaluation of New ISN available on the market according to CISPR 22 4th Edition

Measurement Results of LCL of New ISN (75dB)

Test Site Validation Method using Broadband Antenna

1) Test site validation measurement using a pair of biconical antenna below 300MHz
The NSA calculation should be consider the correction factor.

2) Test site validation measurement using a pair of log-periodic antenna above 300MHz
It is possible to calculate the NSA without any correction factor.

3) Test site validation measurement using a pair of full-range hybrid broadband antenna
It is actually not appropriate, specially in the frequency range from 80 MHz to 200MHz.

---

1) Test site validation measurement using a pair of biconical antenna below 300MHz

NSA(Biconical:CISPR16-1-4)-NSA(Dipole)

Measurement Distance 3m

Measurement Distance 10m

NSA(Biconical:ANSI C63.5)-NSA(Dipole)

Measurement Distance 3m

Measurement Distance 10m

---

2) Test site validation measurement using a pair of Log-Periodic antenna above 300MHz

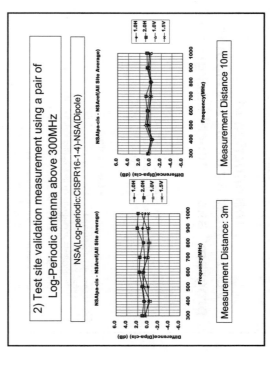

NSA(Log-periodic:CISPR16-1-4)-NSA(Dipole)

Measurement Distance: 3m

Measurement Distance 10m

---

3) Test site validation measurement using a pair of Full-range hybrid broadband antenna

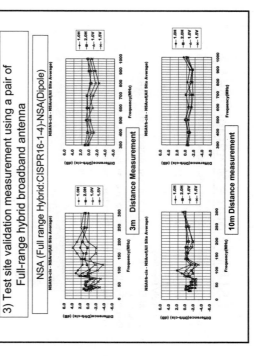

NSA (Full range Hybrid:CISPR16-1-4)-NSA(Dipole)

3m Distance Measurement

10m Distance measurement

LSI EMI Source Mechanisms

- Inverter generates electromagnetic solitary wave (EM Soliton) in each switching period
  - Inverter in the LSI is major ITE EMI Source
- Generated Signal EM Soliton will transmit in the exclusive and relatively fine line
- Signal EM Soliton will be consumed in each transmission cycle
- Over 10 million inverters are in a microprocessor
- 1% or less of inverters form the clock circuit

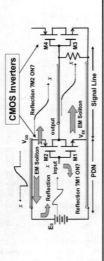

CMOS Inverters

Development of Magnetic Field Probing Technology

- Most effective EMI probing method on the PCB will be detecting the magnetic field in the PDN
  - Large amount of electromagnetic wave exist in the PDN
  - Impedance of PDN is relatively low
  - Transformation of measured magnetic field value to current value is necessary for digital engineer
- International Standardization of our developed magnetic probe (MP) method is necessary
  - Our developed magnetic probes have been shipped to the market for technical evaluation before submitting the proposal to IEC
  - Semiconductor engineers in national committee of IEC/SC47 WG9 supported MP method and submitted to IEC as proposer

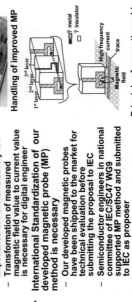

Handling of improved MP

? metal   ? insulator

Principle of magnetic probing

Introduction of
VCCI', NEW System "Kit Module program" and technical background

August 2005

Hirokazu Toya （Ph. D．）
Chairman of Steering Committee, VCCI
Chief of Kit Module WG, VCCI

- Contents -

- Technical background
  - Study of EMI source mechanism
  - Development of magnetic probe focusing high frequency power line current and IEC standardization
  - Development of EMI suppressing technology focusing power line decoupling
- Motives and developing progress of the Kit Module program in VCCI
  - Evaluation result by typical 3 methods
  - Outline of Kit module program and standards

PDN EMI Source Mechanisms

- Secondary generated EM Soliton will leak to the power distribution network (PDN)
  - PDN in the LSI Chip is formed Mesh and PDN in the Printed Circuit Board (PCB) is formed plane
  - EM Soliton will not be consumed in each signal transmission cycle
- Large amount of asynchronous disturbance wave and small amount of synchronous disturbance wave exist in the PDN continuously
- Clock originated synchronous disturbance wave in the PDN will occurs ITE EMI problem mainly
  - A part of the synchronous disturbance wave in the PDN will leak as the common mode radiated or conducted disturbance wave from the I/O cable or the power line cable
  - Logic originated asynchronous disturbance wave in the PDN will reduce the signal integrity by power noise
  - A part of the asynchronous disturbance wave in the common PDN will go round the unidentifiable signal lines

Mesh forming of PDN in LSI Chip

Typical cross section of 10-layer PCB

Leakage wave flow image in PDN of ITE

What is Magnetic Probe Method?

MP Method is for EMI evaluation by only measuring the power line current

Compare with other methods

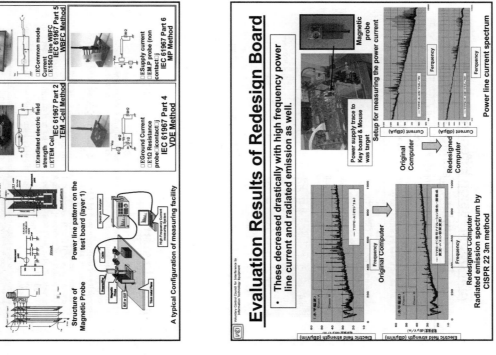

Structure of Magnetic Probe

Power line pattern on the test board (layer 1)

A typical Configuration of measuring facility

- E:Common mode Current
- E:150Ω line WBFC
  IEC 61967 Part 5
  WBFC Method
- E:Radiated electric field strength
- K:TEM Cell IEC 61967 Part 2
  TEM -Cell Method
- E:Supply current
- E:M.P probe (non contact:j
  IEC 61967 Part 6
  MP Method
- E:Ground Current
- E:1Ω Resistance probe: j:contact:j
  IEC 61967 Part 4
  VDE Method

Evaluation Results of Redesign Board

- These decreased drastically with high frequency power line current and radiated emission as well.

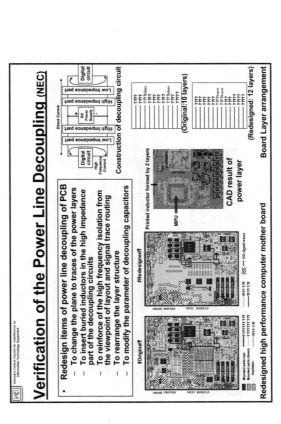

Setup for measuring the power current

Power supply trace to Key board & Mouse was target

Magnetic probe

Original Computer

Redesigned Computer

Power line current spectrum

Electric field strength (dBμV/m)

Original Computer

Redesigned Computer
Radiated emission spectrum by CISPR 22 3m method

Progress in IEC Standardization of Measurement Method for IC EMI

- IEC 61967 "Integrated circuits - Measurement of electromagnetic emissions, 150 kHz to 1 GHz" @Part1, 2, 4, 5, 6 had been listed as IS

Submitted measurement method

No.	Standard	IEC61967 Part 2	IEC61967 Part 4 (2002-06)	IEC61967 Part 5	IEC61967 Part 6 (2002-06)	TC
	Method	TEM Cell	IC Test Board (VDE)	Workbench Faraday Cage	Magnetic Probe (MP)	Loop Antenna
1	Proposal Ref No.	47A/429/ NP	47A/429/ NP	47A/ netherlands/ NP	47A/ WG9	47A/ 429/ NP
2	Proposer	France	France	Netherlands	Japan	France
3	Date of Proposal	Feb. 1996	Feb. 1996	Sep. 1997	Apr. 1998	Feb. 1996
4	Developer	Bell Northen	VDE	Phillips	NEC	Bell Northen
5	EMI	?	?	?	?	-
6	Immunity	(?)	-	?	?	-
7	Instrument	TEM Cell	test board	cable	magnetic field probe	loop probe
8	Emission Type	radiative	conductive	conductive	conductive	radiative
9	Measuring quantity	magnetic field	voltage (current)	voltage	magnetic field (current)	magnetic field

---

Verification of the Power Line Decoupling (NEC)

- Redesign items of power line decoupling of PCB
  - To change the plane to traces of the power layers
  - To insert buried inductors in the high impedance part of the decoupling circuits
  - To reinforce of the high frequency isolation from the viewpoint of layout and signal trace routing
  - To rearrange the layer structure
  - To modify the parameter of decoupling capacitors

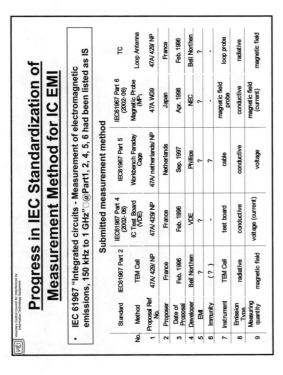

Construction of decoupling circuit

Printed inductor formed by 2 layers

CAD result of power layer

(Original:10 layers)

(Redesigned: 12 layers)

Board Layer arrangement

Redesigned high performance computer mother board

EMI Suppression Effect of Advanced Decoupling Technology (NEC)

- High frequency power line current of FPGA is well suppressed
- 24mm Chip length Mini-bus type LILCs were mounted around the FPGA
  - LILC has low impedance and moderate insertion loss
  - 12 K bits resisters in the FPGA are synchronizing to the internal 35 MHz clock.
  - I/O signal traces are nothing on the board.

Mounted Mini-bus type LILCs

Power line current spectrum on PCB

LILC* application for power line decoupling
* low impedance line structure component

$$S_{21} = \sqrt{1 - S_{11}^2} \cdot e^{-j\Theta}$$

Mini-bus type LILC and typical characteristics

Motives to start studying of Kit Module program

- To cope with ever increasing number of Store-Brand PC released unchecked
  - 30 million Store-Brand PCs are estimated to ship in 2004 Japanese Market
  - No standard and regulation are available in the industry for Module based EMI control
- Necessity of improvement of EMC Quality Control System for compliance to EMI regulation at the IT manufactures
  - To introduce the effective module evaluation method before confirmation of compliance of ITE or IT system in the EMC Quality Control System
  - To simplify EMI testing of options A and B in current VCCI regulation
- "Magnetic Probe (MP) Method" was developed and published as part 6 of IEC 61697 in June 2002
  - MP method can improve the design efficiency from the viewpoint of compliance to EMI regulation
  - MP method suggests to be able to apply the high frequency power current specification to conventional interface specification as an EMC interface item
  - MP method is far easier than CISPR 22 method of ITE or IT system
  - Any digital design engineers can understand MP method and the meaning of described EMC interface specification based on MP method easily.
- To activate the EMC academic activity by presenting the future problems
  - Correlation between MP method and CISPR 22 method by adding any parameters
  - Broadband high performance microscopic magnetic probing technology
  - EMI Source Mechanisms in digital integrated circuit

EMI Suppression Effect of Redesign ASIC (NEC)

- Quantity of decrease of a spectrum value of radiated emission is approximately the same as Power line current

- Conventional EMI suppression techniques ware applied to ASIC
  - To minimize the primitive cell size
  - To increase the on-chip decoupling capacitors
- Measurement of High frequency power current
  - ASIC was mounted on the test board
  - Current was measured at the power terminal of ASIC
- Measurement of radiated emission
  - Electric field strength was measured at 3m distance from the bare test board

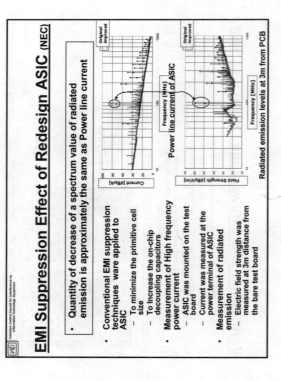

Power line current of ASIC

Radiated emission levels at 3m from PCB

EMI Suppression Effect of LILC

- Current Note PC was used as platform of redesign
- Most of ceramic capacitors and tantalum capacitors in the PDN are replaced to 146 pieces of LILC
- Radiated emission level from Note-PC remarkably suppressed especially in less than 200MHz
  - Limitation of redesign and board mounting type LILC

Note PC applied Mini-bus type LILC
(Under battery mode and displaying H pattern)

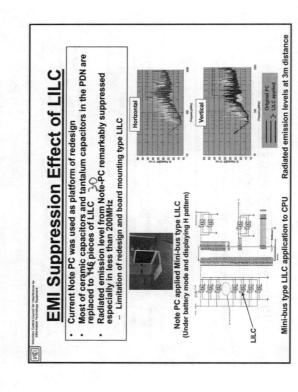

Mini-bus type LILC application to CPU

Radiated emission levels at 3m distance

42

Evaluation result by 3 measurement methods

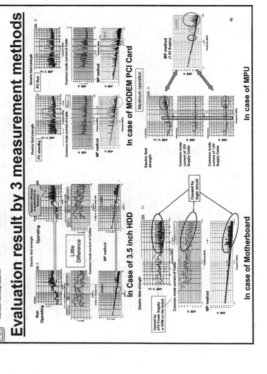

In Case of 3.5 inch HDD

In case of Motherboard

In case of MODEM PCI Card

In case of MPU

Basic flow of Kit Module Program

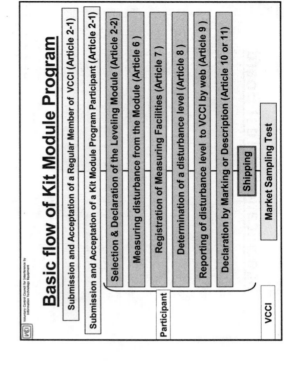

Participant

- Submission and Acceptance of a Regular Member of VCCI (Article 2-1)
- Submission and Acceptance of a Kit Module Program Participant (Article 2-1)
- Selection & Declaration of the Leveling Module (Article 2-2)
- Measuring disturbance from the Module (Article 6)
- Registration of Measuring Facilities (Article 7)
- Determination of a disturbance level (Article 8)
- Reporting of disturbance level to VCCI by web (Article 9)
- Declaration by Marking or Description (Article 10 or 11)

Shipping

VCCI

Market Sampling Test

Developing progress of the Kit Module Program in VCCI

- Preparing WG
  - From April 2002 to July 2002
  - Examination of the IEC61967 and EMI problem of semiconductors and PCBs
- 1st stage WG
  - From September 2002 to October 2003
  - WG consisted of IT Engineers, Semiconductor Engineers, Vehicle Engineers, Professor and Researchers
  - Several kit modules were evaluated by Current Probe Method, Electric Field Antenna Method and MP Method
    - Kit Module and cables were drawn from the Desk-Top PC at the evaluation by Current Probe Method and Electric Field Antenna Method
- 2nd stage WG
  - From December 2003 to December 2004
  - WG consisted of IT Engineers, Vehicle Engineers, Professor and Researchers
  - Discussed Items
    - Scope, Program, Targets, Setup condition, Operating condition, Test Method, Permissible disturbance levels and others
- Kit Module program started it on April 1, 2005

Definition of Kit Module

- A PCB or part of a equipment whose rated power voltage is less than 600V, typically with single or multiple port (s) for information communication, which mainly performs input, storing, display, search, transfer, processing, exchange and/or control of data and telecommunication messages.
- A Kit Module, installed externally to a system, does not include cables for connection with the system.
- Kit Modules typically include a built-in FDD, built-in Hard Disk, RAM, ROM board, IC card, font cartridge, DIMM board, PCI board, PCMICA card, mother board and MPU.
- The figure in the right illustrates examples of kit module. Option A with the cable detached and Option B are regarded as a kit module.

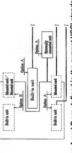

Option A and B are defined in the current VCCI standard

Specification of Test Board

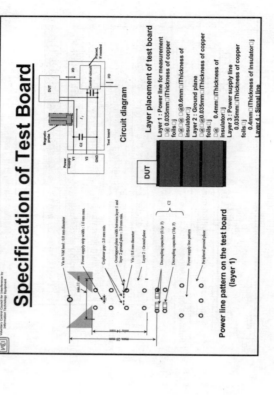

Circuit diagram

Power line pattern on the test board (layer 1)

Layer 1 : Power line for measurement
（0.035mm：Thickness of copper foils）
（@0.6mm：Thickness of insulator）

Layer 2 : Ground plane
（0.035mm：Thickness of copper foils）

Layer 3 : Power supply line
（0.035mm：Thickness of copper foils）
（0.4mm：Thickness of insulator）

Layer 4 : Signal line

Marking

In the case that a kit module also is a Option A for Class B ITE

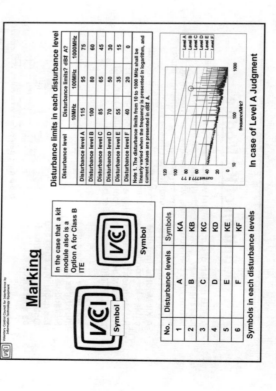

Symbol

Disturbance limits in each disturbance level

Disturbance level	Disturbance limits? dB? A?		
	10MHz	100MHz	1000MHz
Disturbance level A	115	95	75
Disturbance level B	100	80	60
Disturbance level C	85	65	45
Disturbance level D	70	50	30
Disturbance level E	55	35	15
Disturbance level F	40	20	0

Note 1. The disturbance limits from 10 to 1000 MHz shall be linearly varied when the frequency is presented in logarithm, and current values are presented in dBμ A.

In case of Level A Judgment

Symbols in each disturbance levels

No.	Disturbance levels	Symbols
1	A	KA
2	B	KB
3	C	KC
4	D	KD
5	E	KE
6	F	KF

References

- Study of magnetic probing technology
  - TAMAKI, N., MASUDA, N., Yamaguti, M., " Multilayer magnetic probe having high performance space resolution", Technical Report of IEICE, EMC J97-36, pp15（20 (1997.7).
  - WABUKA, H., MASUDA, N., TAMAKI, N., TOHYA, H., WATANABE, T. and ISHIZUKA, N., Evaluation of RF Current at LSI Structure Terminal Using Magnetic Proves with Multilayer Structure, Technical Report of IEICE EMCJ98-6, pp39（J43, (1998.4)
  - N. TAMAKI, H. MASUDA, N. TOHYA, H. ISHIZUKA, K. Yamaguti, M. Arai, " Characteristics and calibration of the Multilayer magnetic probe", Technical Report of IEICE, EMCJ98-103, pp55（J61 (1999.1).
  - MASUDA, N., TAMAKI, N., WABUKA, H., WATANABE, T. and OSHIZUKA, K., RF Current Estimation Method for ICs, 1999 International Symposium on EMC in Tokyo (EMC'99Tokyo), pp801-805, S14, May 1999.
- Study of EMI Source Mechanisms and EMI suppressing design technology
  - H. Tohya, "New Technologies Doing Much For Solving the EMC Problem in the High Performance Digital PCBs and Equipment" IEICE Transactions on Fundamentals of Electronics, Communications and Computer Sciences, Vol.E82- A, No.3, MARCH 1999.
  - S. Yoshida, H. Tohya "Novel Decoupling Circuit Comprising Magnetic Materials and Build-in Choking Coils" IEICE (IEEJ IEEE @International Symposium on Electromagnetic Compatibility (EMC '99 TOKYO) Record, pp615-619, MAY, 1999.
  - Hirokazu Tohya, Koichiro Masuda, Satoshi Arai, "Power De-coupling Technology for High Speed Digital Circuits", IEEJ, MAG-00-169, SEPTEMBER 2000, in Japanese.
  - Vittorio Ricchiuti, L'Aquila, "Power-Supply Decoupling on Fully Populated High-Speed Digital PCBs", IEEE TRANSACTIONS ON EMC, VOL. 43, NO. 4, pp671-676, NOVEMBER 2001.
  - Minjia Xu, Todd H. Hubing, Juan Chen, P. Van Doren, James L. Drewniak and Richard E. DuBroff, "Power-Bus Decoupling With Embedded Capacitance in Printed Circuit Board Design", IEEE TRANSACTIONS ON EMC, VOL. 45, NO. 1, pp671-676, FEBRUARY 2003
  - Hirokazu TOHYA, Koichiro MASUDA, Hideki Shimizu and Yoshiaki WATABAYASHI, "Low Impedance Lune Structure Component (LILC) for Power Distribution System in the High-Performance Digital Circuit" 2003 Southwest Symposium on Mixed-Signal Design in Las Vegas, Vol. 1, pp60-pp65, February 23-25,2003.
  - T. Okimura , B. Deutschmann, C. Bacharu, Schöb Premsta titen, "Influence of the power supply on the radiated electromagnetic emission of integrated circuits", Microelectronics Journal 35 (2004) pp525-535
  - H. Tohya, "Novel Power Distribution System that can contribute to improve the performance and to stabilize the operation of VLSI" 17th Workshop on Circuit and Systems in Karuizawa, IEICE, pp. 573-578, APRIL 2004, in Japanese.
  - Frank B. J. Leferink, Wim C. van etten, "Reduction of Radiated Electromagnetic Fields by Removing Power Planes", 2004 Int. sympo. On EMC, Silicon Valley, US, pp.226-230, Aug. 2004.
- IEC Standards
  - IEC61967-1 (2002)Integrated circuits – Measurement of electromagnetic emissions, 150kHz to 1 GHz part1: General conditions and definitions
  - IEC61967-4 (2002)Integrated circuits – Measurement of electromagnetic emissions, 150kHz to 1 GHz part6: Measurement of conducted emissions – Magnetic probe method
  - CISPR16-1-1 (2003) Specification for radio disturbance and immunity-measuring apparatus and methods
- VCCI Standards Up loaded at http://www.vcci.or.jp/vcci_e/member/kiyaku/kiyaku.html
  - Rules of Kit Module program
  - Normative Annex 1: Technical Requirements for measuring disturbance from kit modules
  - Normative Annex 1-1: Conditions for measuring disturbances from kit module under test
  - Normative Annex 2: for Registration of Kit Module Measuring Facilities
  - Normative Annex 2-2: Instructions in filling in the Form for Registration for Kit Module Measuring Facility

---

Conclusions

- Introduced the recent R&D result of IT Module EMI technology
  - LSI EMI Source Mechanisms
  - PDN EMI Source Mechanisms
  - Development of MP method for IC and IT module
  - IC EMI IEC Standards including MP method
- Developed the Kit Module Program of VCCI
  - Typical Kit Module evaluation by Current Probe Method, Electric Field Antenna Method and MP Method at 1st stage WG
  - Technical requirement depends on the part 1 (general) and part 6 (MP method) of IEC61967 "Integrated circuits - Measurement of electromagnetic emissions, 150 kHz to 1 GHz"
  - Voluntary Control Program by the Participant for the Participant and Equipment Manufacturer supporting by VCCI
  - Improvement of the EMI Quality Control System in IT Manufacturers including VCCI members
  - Up loaded the standards of Kit module in 1st April 2005 on VCCI Web Site
- To Spread the Kit module standards
  - To start corporation with ECMA and ITI in this year
  - To submit standard of Kit Module to IEC/CISPR in near future
- To spread the concept of EMC Interface
  - For development of IT Industry & Academy

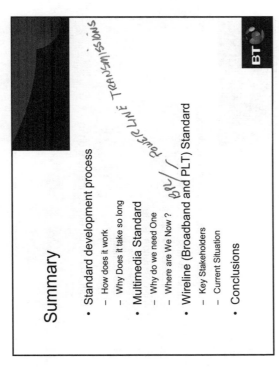

Summary

- Standard development process
  - How does it work
  - Why Does it take so long
- Multimedia Standard
  - Why do we need One
  - Where are We Now ?
- Wireline (Broadband and PLT) Standard
  - Key Stakeholders
  - Current Situation
- Conclusions

(handwritten: POWER LINE TRANSMISSIONS, BPL / PLT)

BT

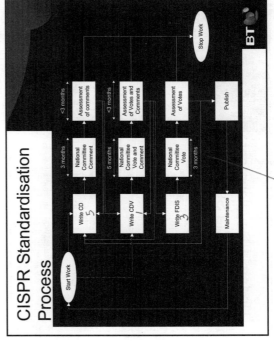

CISPR Standardisation Process

(handwritten notes at top: AGREEMENT/VOTE, 7⅔ positive (PASS), <25% neg (fail))

(handwritten: 2 months)

BT

Progress in CISPR/I, EMC of multimedia equipment and requirements for wireline systems

Martin Wright, Chairman CISPR I

BT

EMC Standardisation Principles

- The standard shall be …… *(handwritten: limits ; HOW U TEST)*
  - A Product Standard
  - Technology Independent
  - Based on equivalent probability of interference
  - Ease the use of new technology
  - End user friendly
  - Timely
  - Democratically agreed
  - Useable

BT

Update 1 Development of Multimedia Standard

- Technology Convergence Issue Raised in late 1990s
- Example
  - Internet Ready TV
    - EMC requirements- CISPR 13 and CISPR 20
  - PC with Broadcast Reception card
    - EMC requirements- CISPR 22 and CISPR 24
  - Requirements Fairly Similar, Test Methods quite diverse
  - Performance criteria quite diverse
- CISPR I set up in 2001 from CISPR E and CISPR G
  - Set up WG 2 - Multimedia (Convenor R Storrs, Secretary D Traver)
  - 2003 added WG4 - Multimedia Immunity (Convenor J Davies, Secretary C Verholt)

Emission/ Immunity

- Emission standard much more advanced – *oct new std*
- Immunity standard began this year
  - will be based on CISPR 24 structure
- Co-ordination issue
  - Same scope
  - Same definitions
- Concentrate on emissions here on in

Why does it take so long ?

Example- Conducted emissions from Telecommunications ports

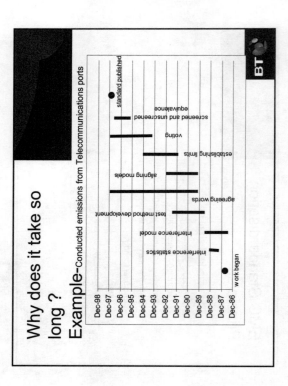

Scope of Multimedia Standards

- Replacement for existing standards
  - CISPR 13, CISPR 22
  - CISPR 20, CISPR 24
- Options
  - Combination of existing standards
  - New start, best practice across the board
  - Choices from a menu of methods
- Latest Thinking
  - New start, best practice across the board
  - 13, 20, 22, 24 may still exist for simple analogue kit

Requirements

- Emission requirements are not a big issue
- Based on CISPR 22
- but……
- Some old arguments are re surfacing in WG
  - extent of manufacturers freedom
  - conducted emission requirements
  - applicability of mains harmonics

Update 2- Emissions from Broadband Systems
Definition of Broadband System:

- This limit should apply to all systems which utilise data transmission and/or data processing techniques which utilise broad band techniques. In this context broadband means systems which produce emissions from wanted signals across parts of the frequency band which are wider than 10kHz (where the carrier frequencies are below 30MHz). This definition is intended to include systems which either use frequency hopping or dithered clocks and systems which use spread spectrum techniques.

- Examples: ADSL, ISDN, PLT, Ethernet etc.

Remaining Issues

- Class A/ Class B
  - Latest Thinking
    - Based on Professional/ Non professional equipment
    - Not based on environment
    - Proposed to be two standards
- Test Methods
  - Options
    - Continuation of existing (OATS, Stripline etc)
    - New best practice (FAR)
  - Combination
    - Choice of options
    - Correlation issue

Timeline

- Proposed (best case) timeline
  - DC (CIS I/ 146/DC) published end Feb 2005
  - CD by end June 2005
  - CDV after CIS I meeting in October 2005
  - FDIS mid 2006
  - Publication early 2007
- More likely, new standard published by end 2007

- Immunity requirements likely to be 1 year to 18 months later

DC: Doc. for Comment

CISPR Interference Model

- Key task- protection of radio services
- Process
  - Wanted field strength, Protection Ratio, Emission Limit
  - $E_d = E_w - R_{req}$ where
    - E_d is the wanted field strength in dB(μV/m)
    - E_w is the disturbance field strength in dB(μV/m)
    - R is the required protection Ratio
  - R_{actual} can be expressed as a sum of probability functions (in dB)
    - $R_{actual} = \Sigma (p_1, \ldots, p_n)$
    - $(p_1, \ldots, p_n)$ are Probability factors

Key Probability Functions for Broadband Systems

E field

frequency

- **P₄** Probability that the disturbance source frequency is the same as the susceptibility frequency
- **P₅** Radiation efficiency factor
  - 6dB for analogue systems
  - For broad band systems varies across the band (0-10dB)
  - correction is -6 to +4 dB for broad band systems
- **P₁₀** Attenuation Factor
  - Based on radiated field interference
  - 10dB protection for internal to building, 0dB for external

Main Stakeholders

- Regulators
  - DTI etc
- Wireline Operators
  - Broadband and powerline
  - BT, EDF etc
- Equipment Manufacturers
- Broadcasters
  - EBU, BBC etc.
- Standards Bodies

Probability Functions

	Description
P₁	Emitting Antenna Gain (0dB for isotropic antenna)
P₂	Receiving Antenna Gain (6dB default)
P₃	Mobility factor (0 for non mobile receivers)
P₄	Probability that the disturbance source frequency is the same as the susceptibility frequency
P₅	Radiation efficiency factor (6dB exc for broad band systems)
P₆	Factor allowing for Analogue: digital effect
P₇	Time factor (victim service usage)
P₈	Distance factor (based on 30m in domestic environment)
P₉	Service coverage factor (fringe effects)
P₁₀	Attenuation Factor (0dB for internal, 10dB for external)
P₁₁	Situation specific factor

PLT Documents issued by CISPR I

- CIS/I/7/DC issued 17 August 2001
  - 16 pages of comments covers all broadband- no support (impact on existing systems and evidence of interference cases questioned)
- CIS/I/26/DC issued 21 December 2001
  - 16 pages of comments mainly editorial and applicable limits
- CIS/I/44/CD issued 12 July 02
  - 28 pages of comments mainly on limits and test methods questions on applicability of LCL and LCL values (CIS/I/63/CC, 13th December 2003)
- CIS/I/89/CD issued 14 November 2003
  - 29 pages of comments mainly on limits and test methods, more questions on applicability of LCL and LCL values (CIS/I/102/CC, 23th April 2004)
- CIS/I/143/INF issued 21 January 2005
  - statement of position (intended as PAS but insufficient support)
- CIS/I/145/NP issued 28 January 2005
  - closed 29th April 2005

Thank You

Any Questions ?

Martin Wright, Chairman CISPR I

Initial Proposals to JWG (Aug 2003)

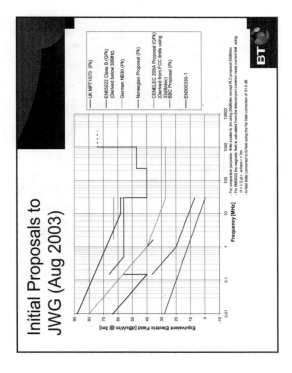

- UK MPT1570 (Pk)
- EN55022 Class B (QPk) (Derived below 30MHz)
- German NB30 (Pk)
- Norwegian Proposal (Pk)
- CENELEC 205A Proposal (QPk) (Derived from FCC limits using 33dBdec)
- BBC Proposal (Pk)
- EN300330-1

- For comparison purposes limits scaled to 3m using 20dB/dec except PLC proposal 33dB/dec
- For EN55022 the magnetic field is calculated from the telecom port common mode current limit using
  H = I / 2 π r where r = 3m
- H-field limits converted to E-field using the far field correction of 51.5 dB

Frequency [MHz]

Equivalent Electric Field [dBuV/m @ 3m]

Conclusions

- CISPR 22
  - has an established interference model
  - work is ongoing to clarify application to PLC
  - Coherence with CISPR 22 existing limit is a key question
- Ongoing Work
  - New NP
    - Validity of LCL measurement
    - Relationship with measured fields
    - Opinions on limitsstill X dB s apart
      » X up to about 17 dB with 30dB notches at specified frequencies

EMC Requirements Now and in the Future in Taiwan

Tang, Yung-Chi

Bureau of Standards, Metrology and Inspection (BSMI)

Agencies for product EMC (& Safety) certification

Executive Yuan

- MOTC — Ministry of Transportation & Communication
  - DGT — Directorate General of Telecommunications
  - Telecommunication Act
  - Telecom Device (Wire/Wireless)
- MOEA — Ministry of Economic Affair
  - BSMI — Bureau of Standards, Metrology and Inspection
  - Commodity Inspection Act
  - ITE/Household TV / Audio, etc.

1

Current DGT EMC Scheme

Scope	Wire devices: (terminal) telephone, modem card, ADSL...etc.	Mobile phone: PHS, GSM...etc	Wireless devices: Bluetooth, wireless LAN, wireless AP...etc
Related EMI Standard	PSTN01, ADSL01, IS6100	PLMN01, PLMN02, PLMN06	LP0002, RTTE01
Mark	XxxYYyyy-Z	XxxYYyyy-Z	XXXyyyLPDzzzz-x
Certification Body	DGT, ETC, CHTTL (Nonprofit Org.)	DGT	DGT, ETC, CHTTL / ADT,CCS (Private labs)
Designated Lab.	Local Labs: TAF Accreditation Foreign Labs: MRA		
Applicant	Foreign manufacturer direct apply or, Local manufacturer, or importer, or agent (registered company in Taiwan)		

2

Required Labeling Description

◆ Labeling for radio wave (Low Power) device: XXXyyyLPDzzzz-x
  - XXX - RCB ID, three alphabet letters
  - LPD - designating DGT standard LP0002
  - yyy - approval year
  - ZZZ - certificate serial number
  - x - family approval serial number (if applicable)

◆ Labeling for Telecommunications (Terminal): XxxYYyyy-Z
  - X - RCB ID, one alphabet letter
  - xx - approval year
  - YY - device code
  - yyy - certificate serial number
  - Z - family approval serial number (if applicable)

3

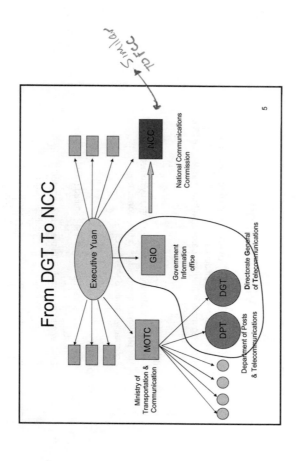

From DGT To NCC

Executive Yuan

Ministry of
Transportation &
Communication

MOTC

GIO

Government
Information
office

DPT

DGT

Department of Posts
& Telecommunications

Directorate General
of Telecommunications

NCC

National Communications
Commission

TO FCC Similar

5

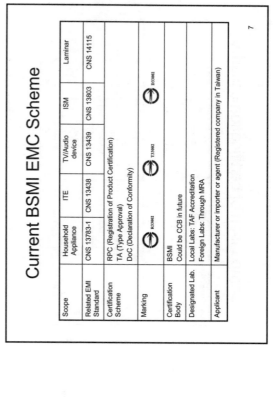

Current BSMI EMC Scheme

Scope	Household Appliance	ITE	TV/Audio device	ISM	Laminar
Related EMI Standard	CNS 13783-1	CNS 13438	CNS 13439	CNS 13803	CNS 14115
Certification Scheme	RPC (Registration of Product Certification) TA (Type Approval) DoC (Declaration of Conformity)				
Marking	R33902		T33902		D33902
Certification Body	BSMI Could be CCB in future				
Designated Lab.	Local Labs: TAF Accreditation Foreign Labs: Through MRA				
Applicant	Manufacturer or importer or agent (Registered company in Taiwan)				

7

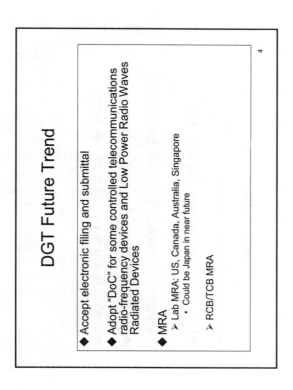

DGT Future Trend

◆ Accept electronic filing and submittal

◆ Adopt "DoC" for some controlled telecommunications radio-frequency devices and Low Power Radio Waves Radiated Devices

◆ MRA

➢ Lab MRA: US, Canada, Australia, Singapore
  • Could be Japan in near future

➢ RCB/TCB MRA

4

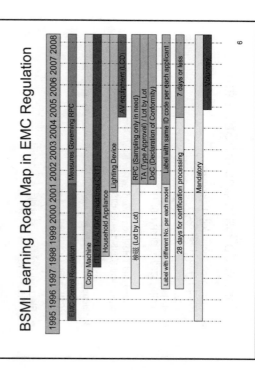

BSMI Learning Road Map in EMC Regulation

1995 1996 1997 1998 1999 2000 2001 2002 2003 2004 2005 2006 2007 2008

EMC Control Regulation

Measures Governing RPC

Copy Machine

ITE / TV Audio (traditional CRT)

Household Appliance

Lighting Device

AV equipment (LCD)

檢驗 (Lot by Lot)

RPC (Sampling only in need)

TA (Type Approval) / Lot by Lot

DoC (Declaration of Conformity)

Label with different No. per each model

Label with same ID code per each applicant

28 days for certification processing

7 days or less

Mandatory

Voluntary

6

Comparison of certification scheme

Certification Scheme	RPC *Registration of Product Certification*	TA *Type Approval*	DoC *Declaration of Conformity*
Technical folder requirement	Folder shall be submitted to BSMI for review	Folder shall be submitted to BSMI for review	Applicant keeps the folder and sign up DoC form
Inspection prior on the market	X	Lot by Lot (Check on Custom)	X
Fee	Application fee Annual fee	0.1% / Lot (custom inspection fee)	X
Labeling	R33002	T33002 if any	D33002
Certificate Valid	3 Years	3 Years	

9

Worldwide Harmonized Standards

◆ Information Technology Equipment (CNS 13438 , CISPR 22)

◆ Household appliances, electric tools and similar apparatus (CNS 13783-1, CISPR 14-1)

◆ Sound and Television Broadcast receivers and associated equipment (CNS 13439, CISPR 13)

◆ Industrial, Scientific and Medical Radio-Frequency equipment (only microwave oven & induction cooker) (CNS 13803, CISPR 11)

◆ Electrical Lighting and similar equipment (CNS 14415, CISPR 15)

8

VPC Initiation

◆ Mid of 2004, "Black TV" event (lack of conscience)
➢ Loses consumers' confidence
➢ Shopping malls refuse any product without compliance label put on their site.

◆ Mandatory
➢ It is difficult to identify responsible authority sometimes.
➢ The proclamation procedure is time-consuming.
➢ Acceptable standard shall be CNS.

◆ Voluntary
➢ More products can be verified and certified (manufactures request).
➢ Consumers can identify with the quality product.

11

BSMI Future Trend

◆ Reduce certification process and time

◆ Open Commodity Certification Body (CCB) for issuing certificate

◆ Implement Voluntary of Product Certification (*VPC*)

◆ Open MRA for more countries

◆ Continue consistency operation (monthly technical meeting)
➢ Free discussion
➢ No limitation for attendees

10

VPC marking

Fundamental drawing   Extended drawing

0005678 - BSMI

Voluntary Product Certification

13

Conclusion

- EMC control system is the first "type test" approach in BSMI (Lot by lot sampling inspection implemented previously)

- Implement EMC control step by step

- Improve EMC control process in each available period

- Introduce voluntary certification system, it could reduce mandatory items in future

- On a way to the better system

15

VPC Platform

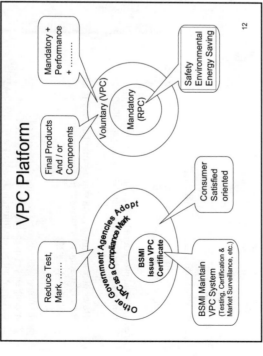

- Reduce Test, Mark, ...
- Other Government Agencies Adopt VPC as a Compliance Mark
- BSMI Issue VPC Certificate
- Consumer Satisfied oriented
- BSMI Maintain VPC System (Testing, Certification & Market Surveillance, etc.)
- Final Products And / or Components
- Voluntary (VPC)
- Mandatory (RPC)
- Mandatory + Performance + ...
- Safety Environmental Energy Saving

12

VPC EMC related items

◆ Vehicles and Car Components EMC Certification
  ➢ MOTC

◆ Digital TV EMS Certification

◆ Chip Set EMC Certification

◆ Others ....

14

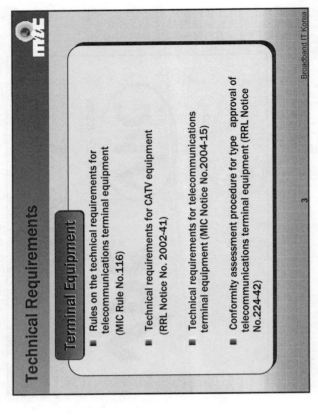

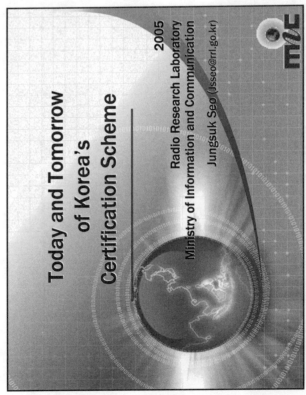

Contents

Contents

- Technical Regulations
- Certification Scheme
- Market Surveillance
- Designation of Testing Lab
- MRA
- Planned Changes

Broadband IT Korea

1

Technical Requirements

Terminal Equipment

- Rules on the technical requirements for telecommunications terminal equipment (MIC Rule No.116)
- Technical requirements for CATV equipment (RRL Notice No. 2002-41)
- Technical requirements for telecommunications terminal equipment (MIC Notice No.2004-15)
- Conformity assessment procedure for type approval of telecommunications terminal equipment (RRL Notice No.224-42)

Broadband IT Korea

3

Today and Tomorrow
of Korea's
Certification Scheme

2005

Radio Research Laboratory
Ministry of Information and Communication

Jungsuk Seo (Jsseo@rrl.go.kr)

Technical Regulations

Administrative provisions

- Rules on certification of information and communication equipment (MIC Rule No. 129)
- Detailed procedure for the certification and communication equipment (RRL Notice No.2002-41)
- Rules on designation and management of testing labs for information and communication equipment (MIC Rule No.123)
- Detailed procedure for the designation and management of testing labs for information and communication equipment (RRL Notice No 2002-419)

Broadband IT Korea

2

Technical Requirements

Radio Equipment

- Rules on radio equipments (MIC Rule No.135)
- Technical requirements for the radio equipment for telecommunications service (RRL Notice No.2005-24)
- Technical requirements for the radio equipment for maritime mobile service & maritime radio navigation service (RRL Notice No.2005-22)
- Technical requirements for the radio equipment for aeronautical radio navigation service (RRL Notice No.2005-23)
- Technical requirements for the radio equipment for other service than broadcasting, maritime, aeronautical and telecommunications service (RRL Notice No.2005-25)
- Technical requirements for the human protection against electromagnetic waves (MIC Notice No.2001-88)
- Technical requirements for measurement of specific absorption rate (RRL Notice No. 2004-67)
- Technical requirements for measurement of electromagnetic field strength and specific absorption rate (RRL Notice No.2004-66)
- Conformity assessment procedure for electromagnetic field strength and specific absorption rate (RRL Notice No.2004-68)
- Conformity assessment procedure for type official approval and type registration of radio equipment (RRL Notice No.2004-90)

4

Technical Requirements

EMC Registration

- Technical requirements for electromagnetic interference (RRL Notice No.2004-69)
- Technical requirements for electromagnetic susceptibility (RRL Notice No.2004-70)
- Conformity assessment procedure for electromagnetic interference (RRL Notice No.2004-30)
- Conformity assessment procedure for electromagnetic susceptibility (RRL No.2004-31)

5

Certification

Certification Players

- RA (Regulatory Authority) - Ministry of Information and Communication
  - ▶ The authority to make public notices of technical requirements is delegated to RRL
- DA (Designation Authority) - Radio Research Laboratory
- AB (Accreditation Body) - Radio Research Laboratory
- CB (Certification Body) - Radio Research Laboratory
- Designated Testing Labs

6

Classifications of Certification

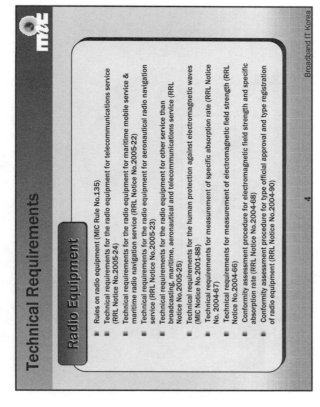

	Terminal Equipment	Radio Equipment	IT Equipment
Approval Type	Type Approval	Type Official Approval / Type Registration	EMC Registration
Law	Framework Act on Telecommunications	Radio Waves Act	Radio Waves Act
Test Report	Telecom Test / Safety Test / EMI Test, EMS Test	Radio Performance Test / SAR Test	EMI Test / EMS Test
Equipment	Terminal Equipment (Telephone, Analog Modem etc.) / Systems(PABX etc.) / Digital Equipment(E1, T3) / ISDN Equipment / ADSL Equipment / Cable Modem / CATV Equipment etc.	Radio Equipment for Personal safe and shipwreck etc. / Mobile Telephone / Wireless LAN / Remote Control etc./	Personal Computer and peripheral device / Internal Card of PC etc.

- ✦ SAR Test is only required for PCS and Cellular phone at the time of Dec. 2004.
- ✦ Type Official Approval is for radio equipment with human safety such as maritime and aeronautical mobile service equipment

7

Certification

Application for Certification

- Applicant for certification : Manufacturer, Importer, Seller
- Attached document for application
  - Description of the product
  - Comprehensive System diagram
  - Circuit diagram
  - Figure of External appearance, component lay-out view or photos
  - Parts lists of major components
  - Specification (for approval of radio equipment only)
  - Test report
  - Users manual (for EMC only)
- All documents in Korean language
  - English test report from MRA partners is acceptable
- Foreign applicant can use domestic agent

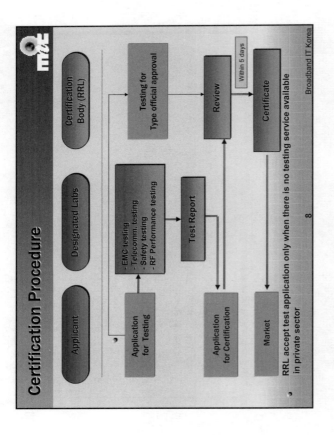

Certification Procedure

Certification Body (RRL)

Designated Labs

Applicant

- EMC testing
- Telecomm. testing
- Safety testing
- RF Performance testing

Testing for Type official approval

Test Report

Review

Within 5 days

Certificate

Application for Testing

Application for Certification

Market

RRL accept test application only when there is no testing service available in private sector

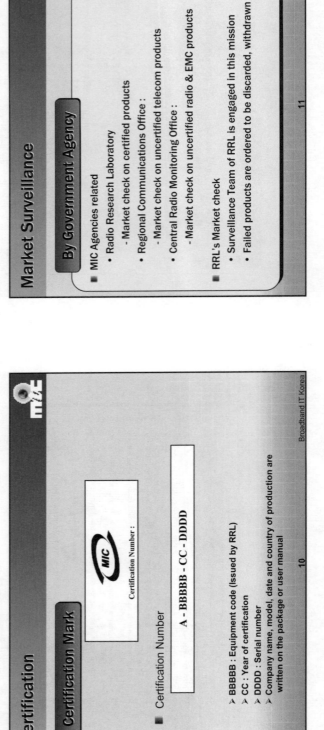

Market Surveillance

By Government Agency

- MIC Agencies related
  - Radio Research Laboratory
    - Market check on certified products
  - Regional Communications Office :
    - Market check on uncertified telecom products
  - Central Radio Monitoring Office :
    - Market check on uncertified radio & EMC products
- RRL's Market check
  - Surveillance Team of RRL is engaged in this mission
  - Failed products are ordered to be discarded, withdrawn

Certification

Certification Mark

MIC

Certification Number :

- Certification Number

A - BBBBB - CC - DDDD

- BBBBB : Equipment code (issued by RRL)
- CC : Year of certification
- DDDD : Serial number
- Company name, model, date and country of production are written on the package or user manual

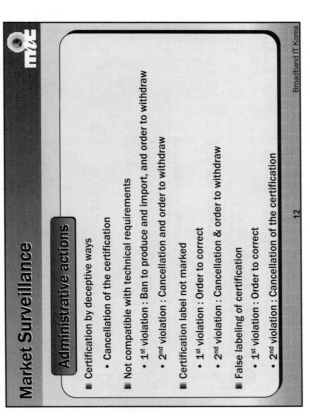

Testing Lab - Designation Procedure

Applicant

Application

Application supplement

Asking supplement

Additional submit, correction

RRL

Acceptance

Review the application — O.K.

Make up of assessment Team — O.K.

Document assessment — O.K.

On-site assessment — O.K.

Asking correction

Correction of incompatibility

Correction within 60 days

Within 60 days

Issue of designation

Testing Service

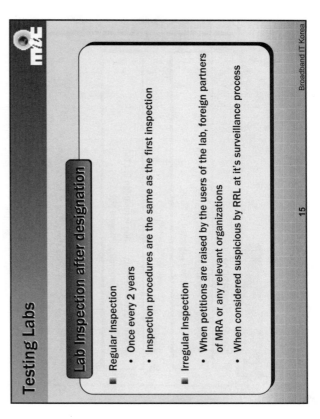

Testing Labs

Lab Inspection after designation

- Regular Inspection
  - Once every 2 years
  - Inspection procedures are the same as the first inspection
- Irregular Inspection
  - When petitions are raised by the users of the lab, foreign partners of MRA or any relevant organizations
  - When considered suspicious by RRL at it's surveillance process

Market Surveillance

Administrative actions

- Certification by deceptive ways
  - Cancellation of the certification
- Not compatible with technical requirements
  - 1st violation : Ban to produce and import, and order to withdraw
  - 2nd violation : Cancellation and order to withdraw
- Certification label not marked
  - 1st violation : Order to correct
  - 2nd violation : Cancellation & order to withdraw
- False labeling of certification
  - 1st violation : Order to correct
  - 2nd violation : Cancellation of the certification

Testing Labs

Criteria and Scope for Designation

- Designation scope for testing lab
  - Telecom
  - Radio
  - EMI
  - EMS
  - Electric Safety (for Telecommunications equipment)
  - SAR
- Criteria for Designation
  - To be a corporation(legal entity)
  - According to ISO/IEC 17025

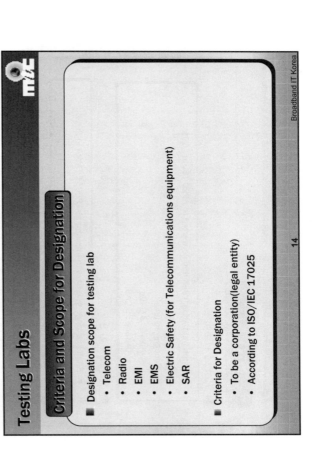

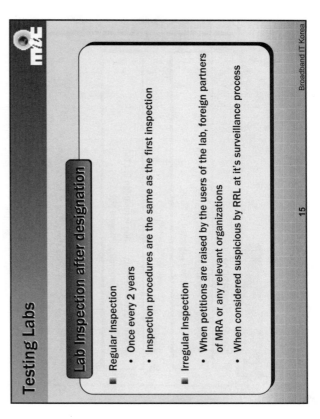

MRA

Current Status

- Korea - Canada
  - Implemented in 1998 and converted to APEC TEL in 2001
  - Phase I coverage
  - Recognized labs
    - Korea : 3 CABs
    - Canada : 5 CABs
- Korea – U.S
  - Shall exchange of letters to Implement APEC TEL MRA in 2005
  - Phase I coverage

16

MRA

Current Status

- Korea - Singapore
  - Agreed to implement Phase I of APEC TEL MRA
  - Following talks are expected in 2006
- Korea - Japan
  - MRA of Telecommunication is included in FTA
  - Talks on implementing Phase II MRA
- Korea - Vietnam
  - Talks on implementing Phase I of APEC TEL MRA

17

Basic Plan to change certification scheme

Background

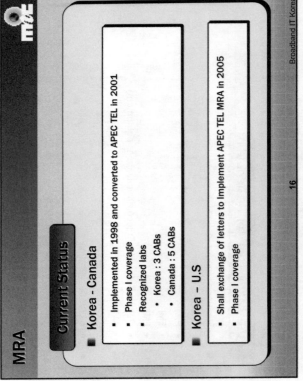

- World trend of entrusting certification to private sector
  - Shortened Life Cycle
  - More focus on surveillance than pre-regulations
- Active implementations of MRA for free trade
  - Talks on abolition of trade barriers affected by WTO/TBT
    - Acceleration of economic blocks caused by FTAs
    - Alleviation of non-tariff barriers by MRA

Helping early marketing and MRA implementation

18

Planned Changes for 2005

Certification Number

- Improvement of the way of issue
  - Now: The certification numbers are available when certification is finished
  - Changed: Advance ID numbers for manufacturers are issued by RRL
  - Industry can save in product time to market
- Certification number = RRL code + Product code
  - RRL code : Company's own identifier to be provided by RRL
  - Product code : Model number issued by company itself

19

Planned Changes for 2006

3rd Party Certification

- Plans to delegate certification authority from RRL to a private sector
- Set criteria and the procedures for designation
  - According to ISO/IEC Guide 65
- RRL would certify at limited situation such as ;
  - CB's in strikes, no designated CBs
- Scheduled beginning of Designation : late 2006

Planned Changes for 2005

Other Changes

- Using e-Documents through Network
  - Electrical Process from applying to issuing a certification
- ☐ Witness Test for Huge and Complex Product
  - Witness test at the 3rd place (manufacture's, etc.) are available for huge and complex products which are difficult to carry out.
  - Joint Sampling test under the charge of designated testing labs

---

Thank You!

Jungsuk Seo (Jsseo@rrl.go.kr)

+82-2-710-6565

www.rrl.go.kr

Planned changes for 2006

Introduction of DoC

- Introduction of DoC (Type I)
  - Tested by designated labs
  - Equipment should be registered to RRL
- Declared by : importers, manufactures
- Equipment of DoC
  - IT equipment for EMC
- Scheduled for Introduction of DoC : late 2006
  - 2005 : Prepare and confirm a draft
  - 2006 : Revise the laws

WORKSHOP: INTRODUCTION TO NUMERICAL EMC MODELING TECHNIQUES (MO-AM-WS-4)
Dr. Charles Bunting

This workshop will provide an introduction to all of the commonly used numerical EMC modeling techniques. It is intended to provide EMC engineers who are interested in learning the basics of these techniques a fundamental understanding of all the different techniques. Practicing modelers will also benefit from learning the fundamentals of modeling techniques they are currently not using. Each technique will be presented along with their strengths and weakness, so engineers can decide which techniques are appropriate for their types of problems.

Presentations:

(1) The TLM Method
David P. Johns

(2) Overview of the Partial Element Equivalent (PEEC) Method
G. Antonini

(3) Introduction to the Finite-Difference Time-Domain (FDTD) Technique
Bruce Archambeault

(4) Introduction to the Finite Element Method
Charles F. Bunting

(5) Integral Equation Methods (MOM) in Numerical Modeling
Ji Chen and Jim Drewniak

NOTES

TLM Fundamentals

Trading Time & Impedance

Link-Line Properties

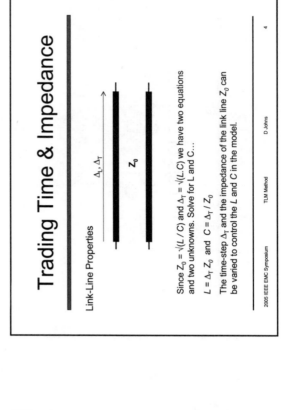

Δ_L, Δ_T

Z_0

Since $Z_0 = \sqrt{(L/C)}$ and $\Delta_T = \sqrt{(L.C)}$ we have two equations and two unknowns. Solve for L and C....

$L = \Delta_T Z_0$ and $C = \Delta_T / Z_0$

The time-step Δ_T and the impedance of the link line Z_0 can be varied to control the L and C in the model.

The TLM Method

EMC Modeling Techniques Workshop
IEEE International Symposium on EMC

Chicago, IL

Monday August 8th, 2005

David P. Johns PhD
VP EM Engineering, Flomerics Inc.
Email: david.johns@flomerics.com

TLM Divides Space & Time

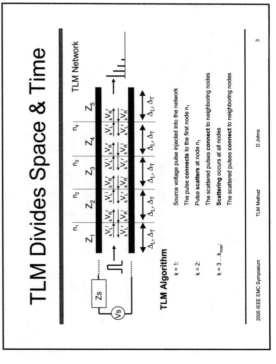

TLM Network

TLM Algorithm

k = 1: Source voltage pulse injected into the network
The pulse **connects** to the first node n_1

k = 2: Pulse **scatters** at node n_1
The scattered pulses **connect** to neighboring nodes

k = 3 ...k_{max}: **Scattering** occurs at all nodes
The scattered pulses **connect** to neighboring nodes

TLM Models of Lumped Elements and Circuits

Stub-Line Model of Inductor

$\Delta_T / 2$ (round-trip time = Δ_T)

$Z_0 = 2L / \Delta_T$ $C_p = \Delta_T^2 / 4L$

Short Circuit

The impedance is chosen to model a lumped inductor $Z_0 = 2L / \Delta_T$

The stub includes shunt capacitance given by $C = \Delta_T^2 / 4L$

If Δ_T is small Z_0 and L are large while the capacitance C is small.

Impedance of a lumped inductor is $j\omega L$.

Impedance of short-circuit stub is $jZ_0 \tan (\omega \Delta_T / 2)$

If $\omega\Delta_T$ is small then $Z_0 = 2L / \Delta_T$

Equivalent Circuits of Transmission Lines

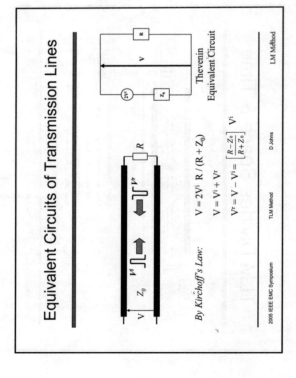

Thevenin Equivalent Circuit

By Kirchoff's Law:

$V = 2V^i\ R / (R + Z_0)$

$V = V^i + V^r$

$V^r = V - V^i = \left[\dfrac{R - Z_0}{R + Z_0}\right] V^i$

Link-Line Model of Capacitor

 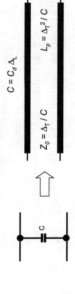

C

$C = C_d \Delta_L$

$Z_0 = \Delta_T / C$ $L_p = \Delta_T^2 / C$

The impedance of the link line is models a lumped capacitor $Z_0 = \Delta_T / C$

The model includes a distributed series inductance. This can be used to model the parasitic inductance of the capacitor $L_p = \Delta_T^2 / C$

If Δ_T is small then the parasitic inductance is small and the model approximates an ideal capacitor

2D TLM Models of Electromagnetic Fields

Scattering in 2D Shunt Node

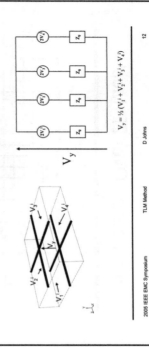

▶ Each Link-Line is replaced by its Thevenin equivalent circuit

$$V_y = \tfrac{1}{2}(V'_1 + V'_2 + V'_3 + V'_4)$$

TLM Model of Filter Circuit

Short circuit stubs are used for the inductors and an open circuit stub for the capacitor.

To synchronize the pulses, the round-trip time taken to go up and down the stub is Δ_T.

Stub Model

In TLM a transmission-line model is used for each component.

Shunt Node for 2D Space

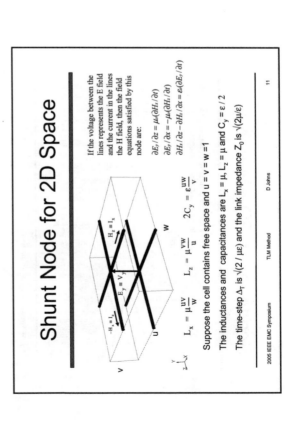

If the voltage between the lines represents the E field and the current in the lines the H field, then the field equations satisfied by this node are:

$$\partial E_y / \partial z = \mu(\partial H_x / \partial t)$$
$$\partial E_y / \partial x = -\mu(\partial H_z / \partial t)$$
$$\partial H_x / \partial z - \partial H_z / \partial x = \varepsilon(\partial E_y / \partial t)$$

$$L_x = \mu \frac{uv}{w} \qquad L_z = \mu \frac{vw}{u} \qquad 2C_y = \varepsilon \frac{uw}{v}$$

Suppose the cell contains free space and $u = v = w = 1$

The inductances and capacitances are $L_x = \mu$, $L_z = \mu$ and $C_y = \varepsilon / 2$

The time-step Δ_T is $\sqrt{(2/\mu\varepsilon)}$ and the link impedance Z_0 is $\sqrt{(2\mu/\varepsilon)}$

Scattering in 2D Shunt Node

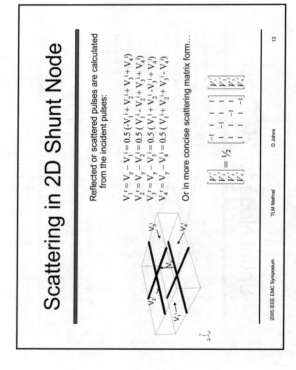

Reflected or scattered pulses are calculated from the incident pulses:

$$V_1^r = V_y - V_1^i = 0.5\,(-V_1^i + V_2^i + V_3^i + V_4^i)$$
$$V_2^r = V_y - V_2^i = 0.5\,(V_1^i - V_2^i + V_3^i + V_4^i)$$
$$V_3^r = V_y - V_3^i = 0.5\,(V_1^i + V_2^i - V_3^i + V_4^i)$$
$$V_4^r = V_y - V_4^i = 0.5\,(V_1^i + V_2^i + V_3^i - V_4^i)$$

Or in more concise scattering matrix form…

$$\begin{bmatrix} V_1^r \\ V_2^r \\ V_3^r \\ V_4^r \end{bmatrix} = \tfrac{1}{2} \begin{bmatrix} -1 & 1 & 1 & 1 \\ 1 & -1 & 1 & 1 \\ 1 & 1 & -1 & 1 \\ 1 & 1 & 1 & -1 \end{bmatrix} \begin{bmatrix} V_1^i \\ V_2^i \\ V_3^i \\ V_4^i \end{bmatrix}$$

Propagation Over 2D Mesh

Voltage Pulses Excited   Pulses Connect and Scatter   Process Repeats

Δt $2\Delta t$ $3\Delta t$

TLM Boundary Conditions

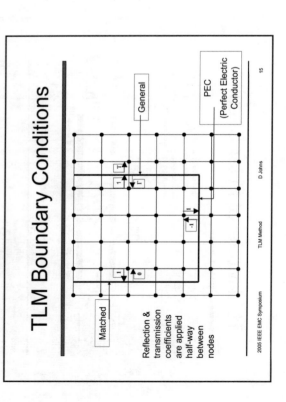

Matched

Reflection & transmission coefficients are applied half-way between nodes

General

PEC (Perfect Electric Conductor)

Irregular Cells and Materials

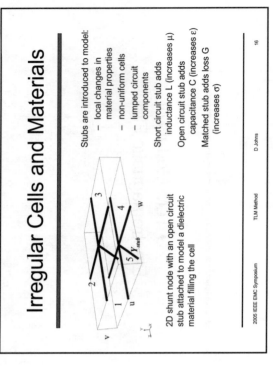

2D shunt node with an open circuit stub attached to model a dielectric material filling the cell

Stubs are introduced to model:
- local changes in material properties
- non-uniform cells
- lumped circuit components

Short circuit stub adds inductance L (increases μ)
Open circuit stub adds capacitance C (increases ε)
Matched stub adds loss G (increases σ)

Symmetrical Condensed Node

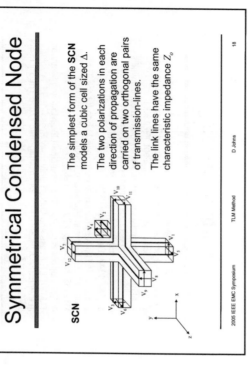

SCN

- The simplest form of the **SCN** models a cubic cell sized Δ.
- The two polarizations in each direction of propagation are carried on two orthogonal pairs of transmission-lines.
- The link lines have the same characteristic impedance Z_o.

2005 IEEE EMC Symposium   TLM Method   D Johns   18

3D TLM Models of Electromagnetic Fields

Calculating Fields in the SCN

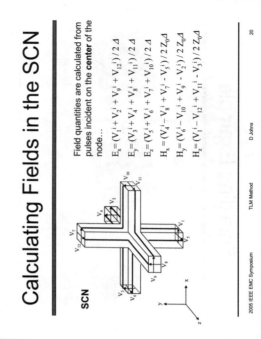

SCN

Field quantities are calculated from pulses incident on the **center** of the node....

$E_x = (V_1^i + V_2^i + V_9^i + V_{12}^i)/2\Delta$

$E_y = (V_3^i + V_4^i + V_8^i + V_{11}^i)/2\Delta$

$E_z = (V_5^i + V_6^i + V_7^i + V_{10}^i)/2\Delta$

$H_x = (V_4^i - V_8^i + V_7^i - V_5^i)/2Z_o\Delta$

$H_y = (V_6^i - V_{10}^i + V_9^i - V_2^i)/2Z_o\Delta$

$H_z = (V_1^i - V_{12}^i + V_{11}^i - V_3^i)/2Z_o\Delta$

2005 IEEE EMC Symposium   TLM Method   D Johns   20

Scattering in 3D SCN

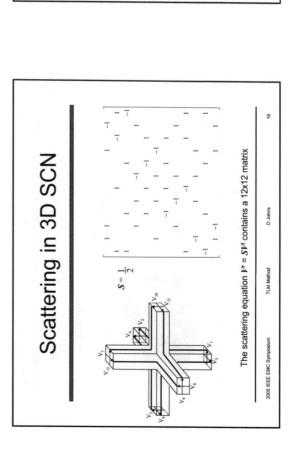

$S = \frac{1}{2}$

The scattering equation $V^r = SV^i$ contains a 12x12 matrix

2005 IEEE EMC Symposium   TLM Method   D Johns   19

Shielding Example

640 MHz 940 MHz 1660 MHz

Shielding Example

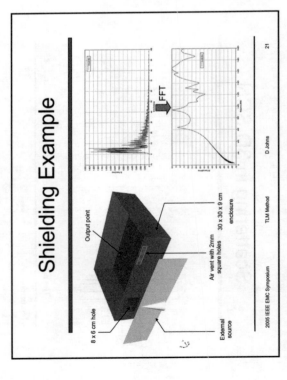

Output point

External source

8 x 6 cm hole

Air vent with 2mm square holes

30 x 30 x 9 cm enclosure

FFT

Further Reading

- 1. Johns P. B. & Beurle R. L., ' Numerical Solution of 2-Dimensional Scattering Problems Using a Transmission-Line Matrix', Proc. IEE, Vol. 118, No. 9, Sept 1971.
- 2. Akhtarzad, S. and Johns, P. B., 'The solution of Maxwell's equations in three space dimensions and time by the TLM method of numerical analysis', Proceedings IEE 122, 12, p.1344-1348, December 1975.
- 3. Johns P. B., 'A symmetrical condensed node for the TLM method', IEEE Trans. Microwave Theory and Techniques, Vol. MTT-35, No. 4, pp. 370-377, 1987.
- 4. Christopoulos C., 'The Transmission-Line Modeling Method: TLM', IEEE Press and Oxford University Press, 1995. A volume in the IEEE/OUP Series on Electromagnetic Wave Theory ISBN 0-7803-1017-9

Comparing TLM with other Techniques

- TLM uses **volume-meshing** and solves the electromagnetic fields in the **time-domain**
- Ideal for modeling complex 3D arbitrary shaped structures and well-suited to modeling mixed field-wire-circuit problems
- Time-domain response can be Fourier transformed giving wideband high-fidelity frequency-domain results, or convolved with transient waveforms (pulse train, lightning, EMP etc.)
- Surface-meshing techniques are generally better suited to modeling electrically large distances between objects
- Frequency-domain based techniques are generally better suited to modeling low-frequency (< 1 MHz) problems such as EM diffusion

IEEE International Symposium on EMC

Overview of the Partial Element Equivalent Circuit (PEEC) Method

G. Antonini

UAq EMC Laboratory

University of L'Aquila, ITALY

Acknowledgment: Albert E. Ruehli

IBM Watson Research Center

Yorktown Heights, NY, USA

Overview

- Introduction to Partial Element Equivalent Circuit (PEEC) Method
- PEEC Fundamentals
- Partial Elements Evaluation
- Assembling Equations
- Full Wave Time-Domain PEEC Models
- PEEC Model Examples
- Combined electro-thermal PEEC analysis
- New directions in PEEC modeling
- Conclusions

EM and Circuit Solution Approaches

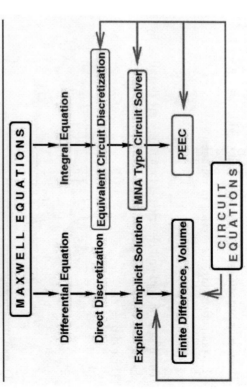

Discretization of a conductor

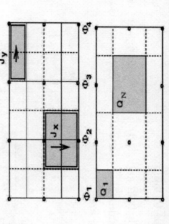

Currents are assumed flowing in volume cells running into x, y, z directions; density current is assumed constant in each volume cell. Charges are assumed on the surface of conductors; density charge is assumed constant over each surface cell.

Basic Derivation of PEEC Model

Unknowns quantities for a problem with conductors:

1. conductive currents flowing in volumes i_L;

2. potentials to infinity v.

The magnetic field and electric field couplings are described by the partial inductance and coefficient of potentials matrices. Their entries are:

$$L_{pkm} = \frac{\mu}{4\pi S_k S_m} \int_{v_k} \int_{v_m} J_{v_k} J_{v_m} \frac{\boldsymbol{u}_k \cdot \boldsymbol{u}_m}{|\boldsymbol{r}_k - \boldsymbol{r}_m|} dv_k dv_m$$

$$P_{km} = \frac{1}{4\pi\epsilon A_k A_m} \int_{A_k} \int_{A_m} \frac{1}{|\boldsymbol{r}_k - \boldsymbol{r}_m|} dA_k dA_m$$

Dense matrices!!

Basic Derivation of PEEC Model

Unknowns quantities for a problem with conductors:

1. conductive currents flowing in volumes i_L;

2. potentials to infinity v.

The magnetic field and electric field couplings are described by the partial inductance and coefficient of potentials matrices. Their entries are:

$$L_{pkm} = \frac{\mu}{4\pi S_k S_m} \int_{v_k} \int_{v_m} J_{v_k} J_{v_m} \frac{\boldsymbol{u}_k \cdot \boldsymbol{u}_m}{|\boldsymbol{r}_k - \boldsymbol{r}_m|} dv_k dv_m$$

$$P_{km} = \frac{1}{4\pi\epsilon A_k A_m} \int_{A_k} \int_{A_m} \frac{1}{|\boldsymbol{r}_k - \boldsymbol{r}_m|} dA_k dA_m$$

Dense matrices!!

August 8, 2005   *IEEE International Symposium on EMC*   Slide 5 of 24

Capacitance Model with Delay

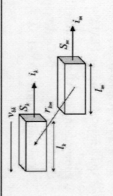

$$\Phi = PQ \; ; \; i = \frac{dQ}{dt}$$

Capacitive Coupling Source Equation:

$$i_{cm}(t) = \frac{1}{p_{mm}} \frac{\partial V_m}{\partial t} - \sum_{n \neq m}^{K} \frac{p_{mn}}{p_{mm}} i_{cn}(t'_{mn})$$

Multi-Function Element Evaluation

Example: Evaluation of Partial Inductances

- "Near" and "Far" Coefficients;

  High Accuracy Required!

$$L_{pkm} = \frac{\mu}{4\pi S_k S_m} \int_{v_k} \int_{v_m} J_{v_k} J_{v_m} \frac{\boldsymbol{u}_k \cdot \boldsymbol{u}_m}{|\boldsymbol{r}_k - \boldsymbol{r}_m|} dv_k dv_m \quad \text{Near coefficients}$$

$$L_{pkm} = \frac{\mu l_k l_m \boldsymbol{u}_k \cdot \boldsymbol{u}_m}{4\pi r_{km}} \quad \text{Far coefficients}$$

Validity of PEEC Solution

FREQUENTLY ASKED QUESTIONS

- What is a Full Wave Solution?
- Highest Frequency, F_{max} Given by Meshing
- Not Limited by Quasi Static Models

- What is a Full Spectrum Solution?
- Works for Low Frequencies, Including DC

- Limits of Lumped Circuit Element Solution?
- Same as Other Numerical Solution Techniques

- How Can We Add New Features?
- Very Flexible Circuit Based Solution Approach
- MNA (Spice) Circuit "Stamps" Technique

PEEC Model Including Finite Dielectric Blocks

Equation for Total Electric Field

- KVL: $v = \int E \cdot dl$

$$\bar{E}^i(\bar{r},t) = \frac{\bar{J}(\bar{r},t)}{\sigma} + \mu \int_{v'} G(\bar{r},\bar{r}') \frac{\partial \bar{J}(\bar{r}',t_d)}{\partial t} dv' + \frac{\nabla}{\epsilon_0} \int_{v'} G(\bar{r},\bar{r}') q(\bar{r}',t_d)$$

- KVL: Voltage = R I + s Lp I + Q/C + V_c

V_c is *Excess* Capacitance Volume Term for Dielectric

$$\bar{E}_c(\bar{r},t) = \epsilon_o(\epsilon_r-1)\mu \int_{v'} G(\bar{r},\bar{r}') \frac{\partial^2 \bar{E}(\bar{r}',t_d)}{\partial t^2} dv'$$

(Lp,P,R,τ)PEEC Equivalent Circuit Model

PEEC Equivalent Circuits For Two Basic Cells

- Best Model for MNA (Modified Nodal Analysis)
- Coupled Partial Inductances and Capacitances
- Example: 3 Node Discretization of "Metal Stick"

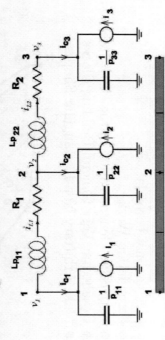

PEEC Model Complexity Reduction

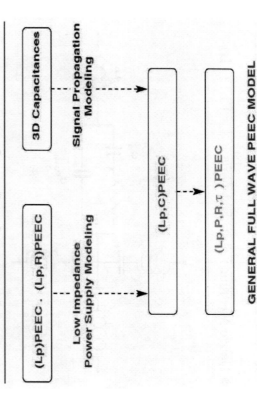

GENERAL FULL WAVE PEEC MODEL

Lossy Dielectric Example

Meandering Board Line over a Lossy Substrate

Comparison for Lossless, Debye 2 Pole and 4 Pole

Non-Orthogonal Geometry Models

Observations

- PEEC Extends Well To Non-Rectangular Geometries
- Is Consistent with Orthogonal PEEC Model
- Use Rectangular Cells Where Possible – Faster

Applications

- Connector Modeling, Wire Bonds
- First Level Packages (Chip Carriers)
- Pads, Wires on Circuit Boards

Volume Model for Dispersive Dielectrics

- Debye Medium Equivalent Circuit for PEEC Loss Model

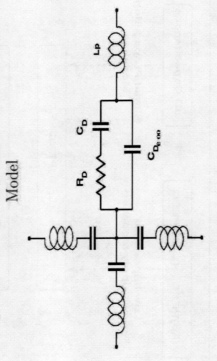

Non Orthogonal Extension

Non Orthogonal Formulation

- Formulation Work
- Extension, Generalization of the PEEC Method
- Hexahedra: Very General Building Blocks
- Make Arbitrary Non-Rectangular Shapes

Fast Time Domain Solution

Delay Differential Equation Formulation

- Delayed Modified Nodal Analysis Formulation
- Multiple Lp_{ij} Delayed Inductive Couplings
- Multiple p_{ij} Delayed Potential Couplings

$$C_0 \dot{x} + G_0 x + \sum_i G_i \, x(t - \tau_i) + \sum_i C_i \, \dot{x}(t - \tau_i) = \sum_i u_i(t - \tau_i)$$

- Sparse L/U Circuit Matrix Solver, $O(N^{1.5})$
- One Matrix Solve, Time Steps Back Substitutions
- Overall Solution Time $O(N^2)$ Not $O(N^3)$

Tested PEEC Speed Up Techniques

Matrix Sparsifications, Iterative Solution

- Multi-Function Coefficient Approximation, Sparsification
- Multi-Pole Speed-Up with Iterative Solution
- Partial Inductance Matrix L_p Sparsification L_p^{-1}
- Sparse Constant Time Step Solution
- Wavelet Basis Functions
- QR Coupling Sparsification
- Coupling Controlled Gauss-Seidel Iteration

Thin Dipole Test Example

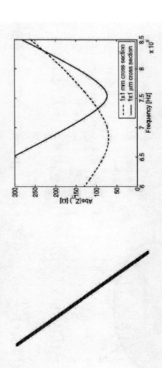

Example: 200 mm Thin Dipole Antenna - Center Gap 2mm

Theoretical Resonance Frequency is 750 MHz

Theoretical Input Impedance at Resonance 73.1 Ω

PEEC (IBMciao): Very Close to 73.0 Ω

Lossy Transmission Line Test Example

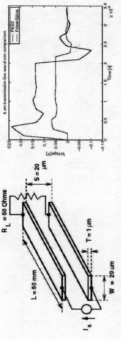

- Input Waveform Sine Square Current Source, Rise Time 100 ps, Fall Time 100 ps, Width 1.9 ns
- 20 non uniform cells along the length, 10 cells along the width, 1 cell along the thickness, largest Cell/Thickness to length ratio 1:4750
- Cross Section: VFI Skin Effect Uniform Model

Combined electro-thermal PEEC analysis

$$T(\mathbf{r},t) = \sum_{j=1}^{n} \delta_j(\mathbf{r}) T_j(t)$$

..via Galerkin procedure..

$$\int_{v_i} \nabla\cdot(-k(T_i(t),\mathbf{r})\nabla T_i(t))\,d\mathbf{r} + \int_{v_i} c(\mathbf{r})\frac{\partial T_i}{\partial t}(t)\,d\mathbf{r} = \int_{v_i} q(\mathbf{r},t)\,d\mathbf{r}$$

$$\Downarrow$$

$$\left[A G_{cond}(T(t))\,A^T + G_{conv}(T(t)) \right] T(t) + C\frac{\partial T}{\partial t}(t) = G_{conv}(t)T_a + Q_J(t) + Q$$

Summary

PEEC Model Evolution

- Excellent for Combined EM and Ckt. Modeling
- Helps Understand EM Problem Behavior
- Inductance, Capacitance, Time and Frequency Domain Solutions
- Full Wave and Full Spectrum Solution (dc to daylight)

PEEC General Purpose Modeling Future

- Need Several Models for Each Part in One Solver
- New Techniques are Evolving

Combined electro-thermal PEEC analysis

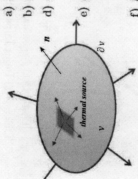

a) $k(T(t),\mathbf{r})$: thermal conductivity
b) $c(\mathbf{r})$: volumetric heat capacity
d) $q_J(\mathbf{r},t)$: heat dissipated per unit volume by Joule effect
e) $q_{ext}(\mathbf{r},t)$: heat dissipated per unit volume by known external heat sources
f) $h(\mathbf{r})$: heat transfer coefficient

$$\nabla\cdot(-k(T(t),\mathbf{r})\nabla T(\mathbf{r},t)) + c(\mathbf{r})\frac{\partial T}{\partial t}(\mathbf{r},t) = q_J(\mathbf{r},t) + q_{ext}(\mathbf{r},t)$$

$$-k(T(t),\mathbf{r})\frac{\partial T}{\partial n} = h(\mathbf{r},t)(T(\mathbf{r},t)-T_a) \quad \text{on } \partial v, \quad T_a: \text{ambient}$$

Test: chip+package

Results obtained with 150 W on 16 mm^2, after 150 ms.

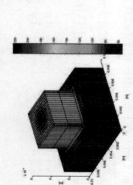

Temperature on chip surface when 150 W are dissipated on 16 mm^2.

Introduction to the Finite-Difference Time-Domain (FDTD) Technique

Dr. Bruce Archambeault

IBM

Research Triangle Park, NC

barch@us.ibm.com

Finite-Difference Time-Domain

- Electric and Magnetic Fields are found directly
- 'THE' Field found
  - No Near/Far field assumptions

Maxwell's Equations are NOT Hard!

$$\nabla \times H = J + \frac{\partial D}{\partial t}$$

$$\nabla \times E = -\frac{\partial B}{\partial t}$$

Changing to Difference Equations

$$\nabla \times E = -\frac{\partial B}{\partial t}$$

$$\frac{E_i^n - E_{i-1}^n}{\Delta x} = -(\mu)\frac{H_i^{n+1} - H_i^n}{\Delta t}$$

One-Dimensional FDTD Equations

$$H_i^{n+1} = H_i^n - \frac{\Delta t}{\mu \Delta x}\left[E_i^n - E_{i-1}^n\right]$$

$$E_i^{n+1} = \left(1 - \frac{\Delta t \sigma}{\varepsilon}\right)E_i^n + \frac{\Delta t}{\Delta x \varepsilon}\left[H_i^n - H_{i-1}^n\right]$$

FDTD Fields at Each Time Step

- Electric field found from:
  - Old electric field at that point
  - Difference in magnetic field around that point
- Magnetic field found from:
  - Old magnetic field at that point
  - Difference in electric field around that point

One-Dimensional FDTD Grid

E H E H E H E H E

Two-Dimensional FDTD Grid

E-Field

H-Field

FDTD Cells

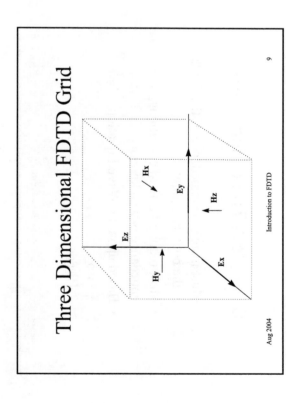

Introduction to FDTD

10

Three Dimensional FDTD Grid

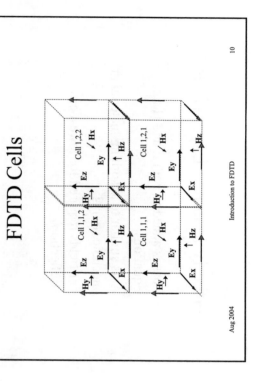

Introduction to FDTD

9

FDTD Sources

- Waveforms
  - Gaussian
  - d/dt Gaussian
  - Modulated Gaussian
  - Sinewave
- Excitation
  - Electric or Magnetic Fields
    - Currents/voltages from fields

Introduction to FDTD

12

Source Types

- Relative
  - Most common
  - Compare results from similar models for variation
- Absolute
  - Need to add 'Antenna'
  - Dipole, etc.

Introduction to FDTD

11

FDTD Model Outputs

- Monitor Points
  - Only fields directly
  - Perfect receive antennas
  - Both E and H fields
  - X,Y,Z Components individually
- Animations
  - Slice Through space
  - Provide confidence and understanding

FDTD Mesh Truncation

- FDTD Computational Domain Boundary
- Acts as if 'free-space' continues to infinity

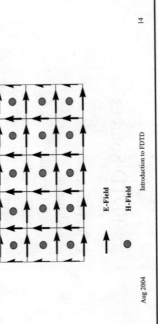

E-Field

H-Field

FDTD Mesh Truncation Types

- Must match the impedance of the fields at the boundary point.
- Most require far field conditions, so impedance is well known
- Based upon the Wave Equation
  - Liao
  - Higdon

Perfectly Matched Layer (PML)

- Loss is added to both E and H field Equations
- Acts similar to absorbing material in anechoic rooms
- Far fields required for lowest error (Reflection)

Other Considerations
Time Step Size

- Time step must be small enough so that fields do NOT propagate faster than the Speed of Light.....
- Courant's stability condition

$$\Delta t < \frac{1}{v\sqrt{\dfrac{1}{\Delta x^2} + \dfrac{1}{\Delta y^2} + \dfrac{1}{\Delta z^2}}} \qquad v = \frac{c}{\sqrt{\mu_r \varepsilon_r}}$$

Analyzing the Results
from a FDTD Model

- Monitor Points
  - Did fields decay to zero?
    - Dynamic range
    - Low frequency effects (DC Level)
  - Does relative field strengths from different monitor points, and from different polarities 'seem' correct?
  - Does source pulse frequency spectrum contain the frequencies of interest?

Complementary Operators
Method

- Based on Higdon's ABC
- Error reduced by cancellation of 1st order errors
- Average two independent solutions
- Works well for near and far fields

Total Time
(Number of Time Steps)

- Long enough for fields to propagate
- Long enough for resonances to decay
- Introduce sin(x)/x term in frequency domain if time domain truncated

FDTD
STRENGTHS AND WEAKNESSES

- *Strengths*
  - Extremely EASY to use and understand
  - Time Domain Solution Provides Wide Frequency Range With One Run
  - All Materials Possible
  - Animation Provides Insight
  - Well Suited to Inside / Outside (Shielding) Problems
  - Intuitive Technique

- *Weaknesses*
  - All Space Must Be Gridded
    - Memory Limitations
  - Far-Field Usually Requires Post-Processing
  - Difficult To Analyze Long Wires

Aug 2004   Introduction to FDTD   22

Summary -- FDTD

- FDTD is a volume based technique
  - Entire domain must be gridded
- Wide range of frequencies with one simulation
- Finds E and H Fields everywhere in domain
- Simple to learn and use
  - Brute force approach

Aug 2004   Introduction to FDTD   21

Overview

- What are we solving?
  - Variational methods
- How do we solve it?
  - Elements
  - Assembly
  - Solve
  - Post-processing
- What kinds of problems can we solve?
- References – How can I started with FEM

Integral formulation → Element matrices → Global matrix → BCs + solution → Fields, observables

OSU

Variational Methods: Example of a variational form

Integral formulation

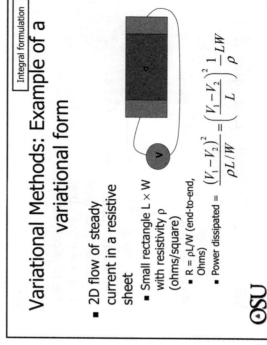

- 2D flow of steady current in a resistive sheet
  - Small rectangle L × W with resistivity ρ (ohms/square)
    - R = ρL/W (end-to-end, Ohms)
    - Power dissipated = $\dfrac{(V_1 - V_2)^2}{\rho L / W} = \left(\dfrac{V_1 - V_2}{L}\right)^2 \dfrac{1}{\rho} LW$

OSU

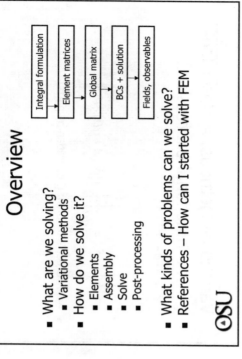

Introduction to the Finite Element Method

Charles F. Bunting, Ph.D.

Oklahoma State University

Stillwater OK USA

Variational Methods: What is a variational expression?

Integral formulation

- Parameter = SV{ some expression involving fields or potentials}

- SV = "stationary value of"

$$k_c^2 \approx \frac{\iint (\nabla \phi)^2 \, ds}{\iint (\phi)^2 \, ds}$$

Cutoff frequency of waveguide

OSU

Variational Methods: Example of a variational form

- Power extrema

$$J(\phi) = \iint \frac{1}{\rho}(\nabla\phi)^2\, ds$$

A "Functional" – or function of functions

- Try many $\phi(x,y)$ distributions

- The smallest value $J(\phi)$ will occur when (and only when) we obtain the physically correct $\phi(x,y)$

OSU

Variational Methods: Example of a variational form

- Heat loss per elementary area ds (=LW) electric field E and potential ϕ ...

$$\left(\frac{V_1-V_2}{L}\right)^2 \frac{1}{\rho} LW = (E)^2 \frac{1}{\rho}\, ds = \frac{1}{\rho}(\nabla\phi)^2\, ds$$

- Express as an extremum of power...

$$J(\phi) = \iint \frac{1}{\rho}(\nabla\phi)^2\, ds$$

OSU

Variational Methods: A closer look at a functional expression...

$\phi \to \phi + \alpha\theta$

$\theta = 0$ on boundaries

$$\delta J = \frac{d}{d\alpha}\left[\frac{1}{\rho}\iint|\nabla(\phi+\alpha\theta)|^2\, ds\right]\bigg|_{\alpha=0} = 0$$

- Apply Green's theorem (integration by parts)

OSU

Variational Methods: A closer look at a functional expression...

- In order to assess the suitability of a variational express we must "take the variation" of the functional and set to zero

- Expressed as δJ

$$\delta J = \frac{d}{d\alpha} J(\phi+\alpha\theta)\bigg|_{\alpha=0} = 0$$

Analogous with vanishing derivative for slope = 0

OSU

Integral formulation

Variational Methods: A closer look at a functional expression...

- The coefficients of θ in determine the
  - Euler Equation: This is the equation we are actually solving when we minimize the functional $\nabla^2 \phi = 0$

- Natural Boundary conditions

$$\frac{\partial \phi}{\partial n} = 0$$

Requires NO explicit enforcement

OSU

Integral formulation

Variational Methods: A closer look at a functional expression...

$$\phi J(\phi) + \nabla \cdot \nabla \phi = 0 \qquad \nabla^2 \phi + k_c^2 \phi = 0$$

$\underbrace{}_{k_c^2}$

Helmholtz equation

$$\frac{\partial \phi}{\partial n} = 0$$

TE modes: No explicit BC enforcement required

Note: For TM modes we must explicitly enforce the scalar = 0 on the boundary

OSU

Integral formulation

Variational Methods: A closer look at a functional expression...

$$\delta J = -\frac{1}{\rho} \iint_s \theta \nabla \cdot \nabla \phi \, ds + \frac{1}{\rho} \int_{\partial s} \theta \frac{\partial \phi}{\partial n} dl = 0$$

Arbitrary over S

Must be zero on boundary of S

$$\delta J = -\frac{1}{\rho} \iint_s \theta \nabla^2 \phi \, ds = 0$$

Requires: $\nabla^2 \phi = 0$ Laplace's equation (Euler equation)

OSU

Integral formulation

Variational Methods: A closer look at a functional expression...

- Cutoff frequency of a waveguide...

$$k_c^2 = J(\phi) = \frac{\iint (\nabla \phi)^2 \, ds}{\iint (\phi)^2 \, sd} \qquad \delta J = 0$$

$$-\iint_s \theta \{\phi J(\phi) + \nabla \cdot \nabla \phi\} \, ds + \int_{\partial s} \theta \frac{\partial \phi}{\partial n} dl = 0$$

Euler equation

Natural BC

OSU

Variational Methods: Some very importance consequences...

- If $\delta J = 0$ and $\delta^2 J < 0$
- Then solution is a **minimum**
  - Capacitance or cutoff frequency approximated is an upper bound to the problem – the true answer is somewhat smaller
  - The capacitance is accurate to higher order than the potential

OSU

How do we solve it? Finite Elements

The potential in an element: $\quad V_e(x,y) = a + bx + cy$

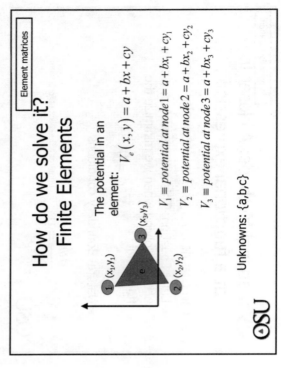

$V_1 \equiv$ potential at node 1 $= a + bx_1 + cy_1$

$V_2 \equiv$ potential at node 2 $= a + bx_2 + cy_2$

$V_3 \equiv$ potential at node 3 $= a + bx_3 + cy_3$

Unknowns: {a,b,c}

OSU

Variational Methods: A closer look at a functional expression...

- Capacitance: $\qquad F(\phi) = \frac{1}{2}\iint \varepsilon |\nabla \phi|^2 \, ds = \frac{1}{2}CV^2$

  Electrostatic Energy $\quad$ Capacitor Energy

  $C = \frac{1}{V^2}\iint \varepsilon |\nabla \phi|^2 \, ds$

  Minimization for capacitance

- Thompson's theorem: charge distribution >> minimum electrostatic energy

OSU

How do we solve it? Finite Elements

ε_0

$\varepsilon_1 = 10 \, \varepsilon_0$

Ground plane

Center conductor, V=1 V

OSU

82

How do we solve it? Finite Elements

Inverse !

The solution:

$$\begin{bmatrix} a \\ b \\ c \end{bmatrix} = \begin{bmatrix} 1 & x_1 & y_1 \\ 1 & x_2 & y_2 \\ 1 & x_3 & y_3 \end{bmatrix}^{-1} \begin{bmatrix} V_1 \\ V_2 \\ V_3 \end{bmatrix}$$

Use in:

$$V_e(x,y) = a + bx + cy$$

$$V_e = \begin{bmatrix} 1 & x & y \end{bmatrix} \frac{1}{2A} \begin{bmatrix} (x_2y_3 - x_3y_2) & (x_3y_1 - x_1y_3) & (x_1y_2 - x_2y_1) \\ (y_2 - y_3) & (y_3 - y_1) & (y_1 - y_2) \\ (x_3 - x_2) & (x_1 - x_3) & (x_2 - x_1) \end{bmatrix} \begin{bmatrix} V_1 \\ V_2 \\ V_3 \end{bmatrix}$$

Geometry !

How do we solve it? Finite Elements

Energy in an element... $\bar{E} = -\nabla V(x,y)$

$$W^{(e)} = \frac{\varepsilon^{(e)}}{2} \iint_{\Omega_e} |\nabla V_e|^2 \, d\Omega_e$$

$$\nabla V_e(x,y) = \sum_{i=1}^{3} V_i \nabla \alpha_i(x,y)$$

$$W^{(e)} = \frac{\varepsilon_0}{2} \sum_{i=1}^{3}\sum_{j=1}^{3} V_i \left[\varepsilon_r^{(e)} \iint_{\Omega_e} \nabla \alpha_i(x,y) \cdot \nabla \alpha_j(x,y) \, d\Omega_e \right] V_j$$

$$S_{ij}^{(e)}$$

Ω_e

How do we solve it? Finite Elements

Solving for {a,b,c}

"Mx=b" problem:

$$\begin{bmatrix} V_1 \\ V_2 \\ V_3 \end{bmatrix} = \begin{bmatrix} 1 & x_1 & y_1 \\ 1 & x_2 & y_2 \\ 1 & x_3 & y_3 \end{bmatrix} \begin{bmatrix} a \\ b \\ c \end{bmatrix}$$

M : can show det{M} = 2*Area of triangle

How do we solve it? Finite Elements

We can express in a shorthand notation:

$$V_e = \sum_{i=1}^{3} \alpha_i(x,y) V_i$$

where $\alpha_i(x,y) = \dfrac{1}{2A}(a_i + b_i x + c_i y)$ and

$$a_i = x_j y_k - x_k y_j$$
$$b_i = y_j - y_k$$
$$c_i = x_k - x_j$$

i	j	k
1	2	3
2	3	1
3	1	2

How do we solve it? Finite Elements

Express in matrix form:

$$S_{ij}^{(e)} = \frac{\varepsilon_r^{(e)}}{4A}\left(b_ib_j + c_ic_j\right)$$

A 3 by 3 matrix

$$\overline{\overline{W}}^{(e)} = \frac{\varepsilon_0}{2}\,\overline{V}^{T}\,\overline{\overline{S}}^{(e)}\,\overline{V} \qquad \overline{V} = \begin{bmatrix} V_1 \\ V_2 \\ V_3 \end{bmatrix}$$

The total energy is a sum over all elements

$$\overline{\overline{W}} = \sum_e \overline{\overline{W}}^{(e)}$$

OSU

How do we solve it? Finite Elements: Solution

$$\overline{\overline{W}}^{(e)} = \frac{\varepsilon_0}{2}\,\overline{V}^{T}\,\overline{\overline{S}}^{(e)}\,\overline{V} \qquad \overline{V} = \begin{bmatrix} V_1 \\ V_2 \\ V_3 \end{bmatrix}$$

We have assembled the matrices

$$\overline{\overline{W}} = \sum_e \overline{\overline{W}}^{(e)}$$

$$\delta J = 0 \;\longrightarrow\; \frac{\partial W}{\partial V_k} = 0,\; k = 1,2,\ldots,n$$

k: free potentials (not on boundary)

Matrix problem: Ku=f

OSU

How do we solve it? Finite Elements

$$S_{ij}^{(e)} = \varepsilon_r^{(e)} \iint_{\Omega_e} \nabla\alpha_i \cdot \nabla\alpha_j \, d\Omega_e$$

$$\alpha_i(x,y) = \frac{1}{2A}\left(a_i + b_i x + c_i y\right)$$

Express in matrix form:

$$S_{ij}^{(e)} = \varepsilon_r^{(e)} \iint_{\Omega_e} \left\{ \frac{\partial\alpha_i}{\partial x}\frac{\partial\alpha_j}{\partial x} + \frac{\partial\alpha_i}{\partial y}\frac{\partial\alpha_j}{\partial y} \right\} d\Omega_e = \frac{\varepsilon_r^{(e)}}{4A^2}\left(b_ib_j + c_ic_j\right)\underbrace{\iint_{\Omega_e} d\Omega_e}_{A}$$

$$S_{ij}^{(e)} = \frac{\varepsilon_r^{(e)}}{4A}\left(b_ib_j + c_ic_j\right)$$

A 3 by 3 matrix

OSU

How do we solve it? Element Assembly

$$\overline{\overline{S}} = \begin{bmatrix}
S_{11}^1 + S_{11}^2 & S_{12}^1 & S_{13}^1 + S_{12}^2 & 0 & S_{13}^2 \\
S_{21}^1 & S_{22}^1 & S_{23}^1 & 0 & 0 \\
S_{31}^1 + S_{21}^2 & S_{32}^1 & S_{33}^1 + S_{22}^2 + S_{11}^3 & S_{23}^3 & S_{12}^3 \\
S_{31}^2 & 0 & S_{32}^2 + S_{31}^3 & S_{33}^2 + S_{33}^3 & S_{32}^3 \\
0 & 0 & S_{21}^3 & S_{23}^3 & S_{22}^3
\end{bmatrix}$$

- By inspection...
- Assumes continuity of potential

OSU

Comparison of FEM with other methods

- Conformable complex boundaries
- IF Variational:
  - an upper or lower bound on an observable can be assured – specific information about error can be assured
  - Error in variational parameter an order of magnitude reduced over potential or field.
- If sparsity accounted for can be comparable to MoM in terms of computational efficiency
- More directly suited for enclosed problems but can be easily extended using ABCs
- Amenable to any partial differential equation: can couple to thermal effects and forces on mass

<OSU>

Getting started with FEM: WEB Resources

- MATLAB Based:
  - FEMLAB (www.comsol.com) $
- FEMM (femm.foster-miller.com/index.html)
- Quickfield (www.quickfield.com/free_soft.htm)

<OSU>

Microstrip Example

Unshielded

Quasi-statics:

$$\Rightarrow C_0 = 2W_e^0 = 18.84\, pF$$

$$Z_0 = \frac{\sqrt{C/C_0}}{cC} = \frac{\sqrt{\varepsilon_{eff}}}{cC} = 67.8\ \Omega$$

$$c = 3 \times 10^8\ m/s$$

Total energy = 6.41 pJ

$$W_e = \frac{1}{2}CV^2$$

$$\Rightarrow C = 2W_e = 128.2\, pF$$

$$\varepsilon_{eff} = 7.2458$$

$$Z_0 = \frac{60}{\sqrt{\varepsilon_{eff}}}\ln\left(\frac{8h}{w} + \frac{w}{4h}\right) = 61.97\ \Omega$$

<OSU>

Getting started with FEM: References

- Reddy, J.N., "An Introduction to the Finite Element Method," 2nd Edition, McGraw-Hill, 1993
- J. Jin, The Finite Element Method in Electromagnetics, 2nd Edition, John Wiley & Sons Inc, 2002
- P. P. Silvester and R.L. Ferrari, "Finite Elements for Electrical Engineers," 3rd Edition, Cambridge University Press, 1996. (Includes software)
- G. Pelosi, S. Selleri, R. Coccioli, "Quick Finite Element Method for Electromagnetic Waves" Arctech House, 1998 (Includes software)
- Y. Kwon & H. Bang, "The Finite Element Method Using MATLAB, Second Edition," CRC Press, 2000. (Includes software)

<OSU>

85

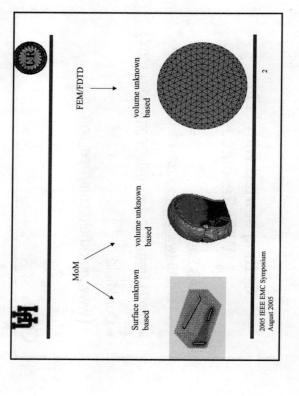

MoM

Surface unknown based   volume unknown based

FEM/FDTD

volume unknown based

Radiation in Free-Space

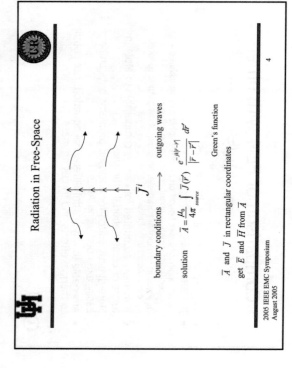

$\overline{J}^i$

boundary conditions $\longrightarrow$ outgoing waves

solution $\quad \overline{A} = \dfrac{\mu_0}{4\pi} \displaystyle\int_{source} \overline{J}(\overline{r}') \dfrac{e^{-jk|\overline{r}-\overline{r}'|}}{|\overline{r}-\overline{r}'|} \, d\overline{r}'$

Green's function

$\overline{A}$ and $\overline{J}$ in rectangular coordinates

get $\overline{E}$ and $\overline{H}$ from $\overline{A}$

Integral Equation Methods (MOM) in Numerical Modeling

Ji Chen
University of Houston

Jim Drewniak
University of Missouri-Rolla

Solutions to Maxwell's Equations

$\nabla \times \overline{E} = -j\omega\mu\overline{H}$

$\nabla \times \overline{H} = j\omega\varepsilon\overline{E} + \overline{J}_i \quad \longleftarrow$ Current source

Let $\quad \overline{H} = \dfrac{1}{\mu}\nabla \times \overline{A}$

Wave equation $\quad \nabla^2\overline{A} + k^2\overline{A} = -\mu\overline{J}_i$

+ boundary conditions $\Longrightarrow$ Solution

Green's Function

Green's function contains all boundary conditions in it

→ this makes finding a specific Green's function for an arbitrary problem very hard

→ must then go through many *contortions* to formulate the problem

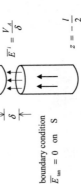

cavity

multilayer medium

Scattering Formulation-Dipole Antenna

- Let $\bar{E}^i$ be the incident field resulting from the applied voltage V_A
  → it will drive a surface current $\bar{J}_s$ on the antenna conductor

- Let $\bar{E}^s$ be the field that results from $\bar{J}_s$:

$$\bar{E}^i + \bar{E}^s(\bar{J}_s) = 0 \quad on \ S \qquad (EFIE)$$

where

$$\bar{E}^s = -j\omega\bar{A} - j\frac{1}{\omega\mu\varepsilon}\nabla(\nabla\cdot\bar{A})$$

and $\bar{A}$ is as given previously

$\bar{A}$ is solution to the wave equation **problem solution**

fields satisfy boundary conditions

the antenna conductor has been removed and replaced with a Maxwellian source for $\bar{J}_s$, so we can use the previous $\bar{A}$

Green's Function (Free-Space)

The Green's function is a spatial impulse response

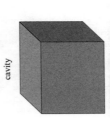

$$\bar{J}_i = \delta(\bar{r})\,\hat{z}$$

$$\bar{A} = \frac{\mu}{4\pi}\frac{e^{-jkr}}{r}\,\hat{z}$$

Scattering Formulation - Dipole Antenna

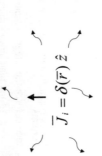

antenna conductor surface S

$\bar{E}^s(\bar{J}_s)$

$z = +\frac{l}{2}$

$\bar{J}_s$

$\bar{E}^i = \frac{V}{\delta}$

$z = -\frac{l}{2}$

incident electric field drives a surface current $\bar{J}_s$ on the antenna conductor

boundary condition
$\bar{E}_{tan} = 0$ on S

but the previous solution is for free-space, and do not have the spatial impulse response for this problem that includes the antenna conductors

Integral Equation

dipole antenna:

$$E_z^i(z) \cong -\frac{1}{j\omega\varepsilon} \int_{-l/2}^{l/2} J_z(z') \underbrace{\left[\frac{\partial^2}{\partial z^2} + k^2\right] G(z,z')}_{K(z,z')}\, dz'$$

$$G(z,z') = \frac{e^{-jk|\vec{r}-\vec{r}'|}}{|\vec{r}-\vec{r}'|}$$

- exact integral representation of solution
- solve for the current $J_z(z)$ on the antenna
  → then can get $\bar{E}, \bar{H}, Z_{in}$

Approximating the Solution

Sub-domain basis functions

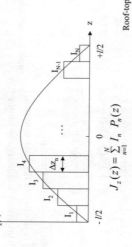

$$J_z(z) = \sum_{n=1}^{N} I_n P_n(z)$$

$$P_n(z) = \begin{cases} 1 & z \text{ in } \Delta z_n \\ 0 & \text{else} \end{cases}$$

basis functions →

Roof-top

Discretizing the Integral Equation

$$E_z^i(z) \cong -\frac{1}{j\omega\varepsilon}\int_{-l/2}^{l/2}\sum_{n=1}^{N} I_n P_n(z') K(z,z')\, dz'$$

$$= -\frac{1}{j\omega\varepsilon}\sum_{n=1}^{N} I_n \int_{\Delta z_n} K(z,z')\, dz'$$

this is 1-equation in N-unknowns – discretized unknown currents

then enforce the integral equation on each segment at
$z = z_m$ (point matching) – discretized the entire problem

$$E_z^i(z_m) \approx -\frac{1}{j\omega\varepsilon}\sum_{n=1}^{N} I_n \int_{\Delta z_n} K(z_m,z')\, dz'$$

over each pulse to get N-equations in N-unknowns

Matrix Equation

$$\begin{bmatrix} Z_{11} & Z_{12} & \cdots & Z_{1N} \\ Z_{21} & \cdots & & \\ \vdots & & & \\ Z_{N1} & \cdots & \cdots & Z_{NN} \end{bmatrix} \begin{bmatrix} I_1 \\ \cdots \\ \cdots \\ I_N \end{bmatrix} = \begin{bmatrix} V_1 \\ \cdots \\ \\ V_N \end{bmatrix}$$

$$Z_{mn} = -\frac{1}{j\omega\varepsilon} \int_{\Delta z_n} K(z_m,z')\, dz' \quad \leftarrow \text{numerical integration}$$

$$V_m = E_z^i(Z_m) = \begin{cases} \dfrac{V_s}{\delta} & \text{at the gap} \\ 0 & \text{else} \end{cases}$$

I_n → unknowns

solve for I_n and get approximate $J_z(z)$

The Method of Moments

Electric Field Integral Equation → expand unknown current in basis functions → enforce the IE with testing functions → get a matrix equation → solve, compute E, H, Zin etc.

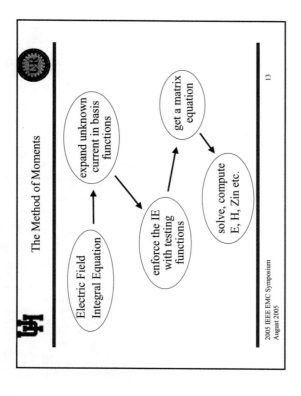

MOM Considerations

- Increasing N is used to improve the quality of the solution (but appropriate sampling rate is required, 10-20 points/wavelength)
- Enforcing the integral equation (weak form)
  - used point matching here (enforced IE at a point)
  - Galerkin's procedure uses testing functions to enforce the integral equation in a weighted integral sense – "best" solution approach
- There are many things that can easily go wrong – must be aware of problem physics

---

MOM Attributes

- Advantages
  - generalized meshing
  - very efficient when Green's functions are known
  - physics incorporated into the integral representation of the solution
- Disadvantages
  - inhomogeneous media challenging
  - full matrices are computationally burdensome
- Research: Fast algorithms

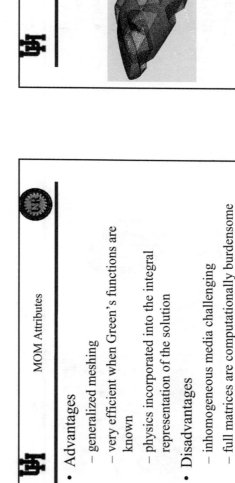
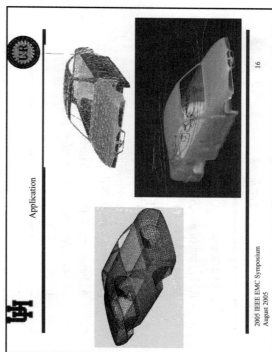

Application

References

- **References**
  - R. F. Harrington, *Field Computation by Moment Methods*, Krieger Publishing, 1968.
  - B. Archambeault, O. Ramahi, and C. Brench, *EMI/EMC Modeling Handbook*, Kluwer, 1998.
  - C. A. Balanis, *Advanced Engineering Electromagnetics*, Wiley, 1989, Ch. 12.
  - A. Peterson, S. Ray, R. Mittra, *Computational Methods for Electromagnetics*, IEEE Press, 1998.

2005 IEEE EMC Symposium
August 2005

18

Application

Ideal Applications: Large, open structures   ???

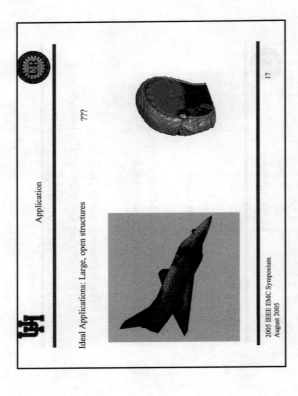

2005 IEEE EMC Symposium
August 2005

17

TUTORIAL: NANOTECHNOLOGY AND ADVANCED MATERIALS (MO-AM-WS-5)

Christopher L. Holloway *(co-chair)*
NIST, Boulder, CO, USA
Maria Sabrina Sarto *(co-chair)*
University of Rome "La Sapienza", Rome, Italy

Nanotechnology is functional engineering on an extremely small scale that can be used to develop innovative advanced materials (e.g. metamaterials, frequency selective surfaces, photonic band gap, etc.) components and devices, implants for numerous industrial applications. It involves the control of materials with a nanoscale fine structure, and with the manipulation of tiny objects at the dimension of molecules and atoms. The potential benefits of nanotechnology are revolutionary. Nanotechnology is currently exploited in microelectronics, optoelectronics, material science, but its application in EMC is still not very wide. Advanced nanostructured materials can be designed and optimized to realize frequency-selective smart surface to be used for shielding, or as substrate for PBC and antenna applications. Carbon nanotubes can be used to realize nano-scale components and circuits, low-reflection materials. The workshop will cover various aspects of nanotechnology and advanced materials. The workshop will overview various aspects of nanotechnology, including interconnection problems between nanostructured systems and sub-nano or micro-size devices (as well as medical and bio related topics), and on advanced artificial materials, such as metamaterials.

Presentations (all but (5) not available for publication):

(1) Introduction and Overview of the Workshop
   Dr. C.L. Holloway, NIST

(2) Overview of Nanotechnology and the National Nanotechnology Initiative
   Dr. C. Teague, Director, National Nanotechnology Coordinating Office

(3) An Overview of Recent Developments in Nanotechnology
   Dr. M. Meyyappan, NASA Ames Research Center

(4) NCI Alliance for Nanotechnology in Cancer- Breakthrough Technologies for recognition and Therapy of Cancer
   Dr. P. Grodzinski, Program Director for Nanotechnology in Cancer, National Cancer Institute

(5) Electromagnetic Properties of Nanostructured Thin Films *(published)*
   Prof. M.S. Sarto, University of Rome "La Sapienza"

(6) Development of Negative Index Materials for Breakthrough Applications
   Dr. C.G. Parazzoli, Boeing Phantom Works

(7) Emerging Nanoelectronic Device Technologies
   Prof. W. Porod, Center for Nano Science and Technology, University of Notre Dame

(8) UIC's Microfabrication Applications Laboratory (MAL), a Regional Resource for Developing Nano Devices and Materials
   Prof. A. Feinerman, Microfabrication Applications Laboratory (MAL), University of Illinois at Chicago

---

NOTES

---

e m c L — University of Rome La Sapienza electromagnetic compatibility Laboratory — http://w3.uniroma1.it/emclab

2005 IEEE International Symposium on EMC
Chicago (CA), Aug.8-12, 2005

Workshop on Nanotechnology and Advanced Materials

Nanostructured Thin Films: EM Modeling, Characterization and Applications to EMC

Maria Sabrina Sarto
Univ. of Rome "La Sapienza"
Department of Electrical Engineering

---

e m c L — University of Rome La Sapienza electromagnetic compatibility Laboratory — http://w3.uniroma1.it/emclab

OUTLINE

NANOSTRUCTURED THIN FILMS:

- **Transparent metals**
- **CNT loaded thin films**
- **Sculptured thin films**

APPLICATIONS TO EMC:

- **Passive transparent shields for radio frequency EM fields**
- **Active transparent shields for low-frequency magnetic fields**
- **Frequency selective surfaces**

---

e m c L — University of Rome La Sapienza electromagnetic compatibility Laboratory — http://w3.uniroma1.it/emclab

Design and realization of transparent metal samples

CHOICE OF TARGET MATERIALS:

- **Ag:** high electrical conductivity ($\sigma_{Ag\,(bulk)}$=1.59·10^6 S/m);
  plasma resonance at 320 nm
- **TiO$_2$:** very high refractive index in the visible range;
  high relative permittivity at microwave

MEASURED ELECTRICAL CONDUCTIVITY OF Ag FILMS DEPOSITED BY DIBS

Thickness [nm]	17	63	400	bulk
Electrical Conductivity [S/m]	7.75·10^6	12.8·10^6	15.6·10^6	66.7·10^6

---

e m c L — University of Rome La Sapienza electromagnetic compatibility Laboratory — http://w3.uniroma1.it/emclab

Design constraints

1) **High shielding effectiveness (SE) at radio frequency:**

SE ≥ 40 dB   for   30 MHz ≤ f ≤ 6 GHz

Since: $\lim_{f \to 0} SE = 45.51 + \log d_{Ag}\,\sigma_{Ag}$ S/m

$\sigma_{Ag} \cong 7.75 \cdot 10^6$ S/m   → $\boxed{d_{Ag} = 68 \text{ nm}}$

2) **High transparency (T) in the visible range:**

$T_{max}(0,\lambda_c) \geq 70\%$ (λ_c = 550 nm)

$$T_{av}(0) = \frac{\int_{\lambda_{min}}^{\lambda_{max}} T(\lambda;0)\exp\left[-4\,^{\lambda-\lambda_0}{}^2/W^2\right]d\lambda}{\int_{\lambda_{min}}^{\lambda_{max}}\exp\left[-2(\lambda-\lambda_0)^2/W^2\right]d\lambda} \geq 60\%$$

with: λ_{min}=400 nm, λ_{max}=700 nm, λ_0=555 nm, W=83 nm

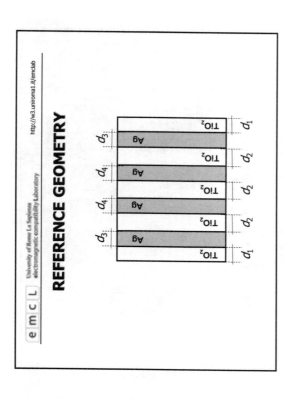

REFERENCE GEOMETRY

The D.I.B.S. system at ENEA Research Center "La Casaccia" Rome, Italy

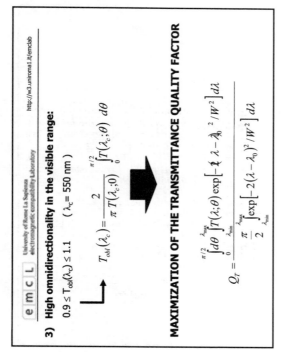

3) High omnidirectionality in the visible range:

$0.9 \leq T_{obl}(\lambda_c) \leq 1.1$ ($\lambda_c = 550\,nm$)

$$T_{obl}(\lambda_c) = \frac{2}{\pi\, T(\lambda_c;0)} \int_0^{\pi/2} T(\lambda_c;\theta)\, d\theta$$

MAXIMIZATION OF THE TRANSMITTANCE QUALITY FACTOR

$$Q_T = \frac{\int_0^{\pi/2} d\theta \int_{\lambda_{min}}^{\lambda_{max}} T(\lambda;\theta)\exp\left[-4\left(\lambda-\lambda_0\right)^2/W^2\right] d\lambda}{\frac{\pi}{2}\int_{\lambda_{min}}^{\lambda_{max}}\exp\left[-2(\lambda-\lambda_0)^2/W^2\right] d\lambda}$$

Total Ag thickness:

$$d_{Ag} = 2(d_3 + d_4) = 68\,nm$$

NARROW-BAND FILTERS   **BROAD-BAND FILTERS**

$d_3 = 12\,nm,\ d_4 = 22\,nm$ $d_3 = d_4 = 17\,nm$

The thickness d_1 and d_2 of the external and internal TiO$_2$ layers results from the optimisation of the optical properties of the coating

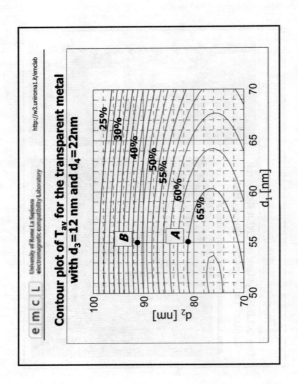

Contour plot of T_{av} for the transparent metal with d_3=12 nm and d_4=22nm

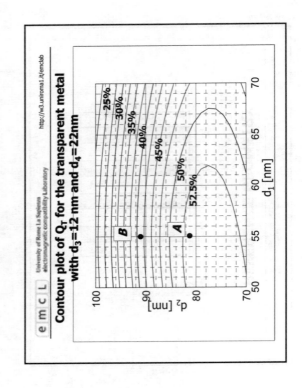

Contour plot of Q_T for the transparent metal with d_3=12 nm and d_4=22nm

REALIZED SAMPLES

Transparent Metal	d_1 [nm]	d_2 [nm]	d_3 [nm]	d_4 [nm]
A (narrow-band; high transmittance)	55	81	12	22
B (narrow-band; high omnidirectionality)	62	91	12	22
C (broad-band)	32	64	17	17

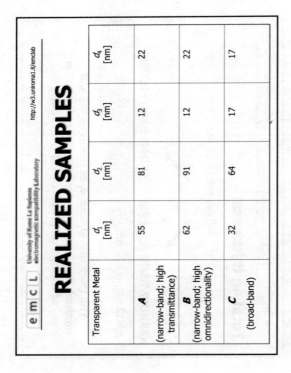

Contour plot of T_{obl} for the transparent metal with d_3=12 nm and d_4=22nm

Contour plot of T_{obl} for the transparent metal with $d_3=d_4=17$ nm

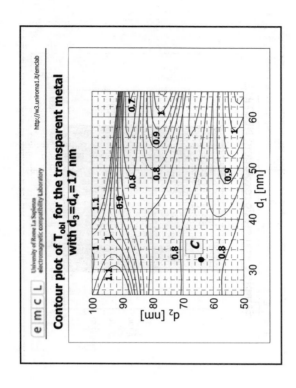

COMPUTED TRANSMITTANCE SPECTRUM
(TF Calc, Software Spectra Inc.)

NORMAL INCIDENCE

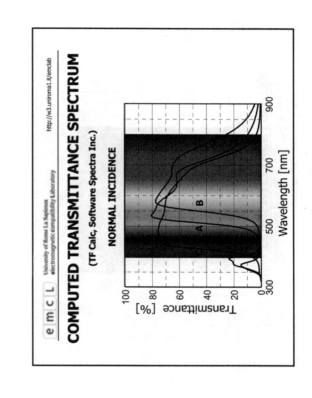

Contour plot of T_{av} for the transparent metal with $d_3=d_4=17$ nm

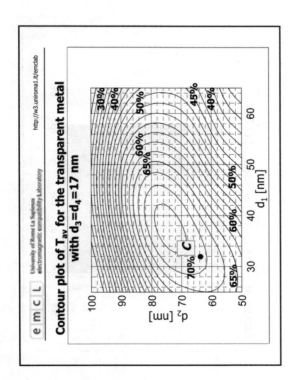

Contour plot of Q_T for the transparent metal with $d_3=d_4=17$ nm

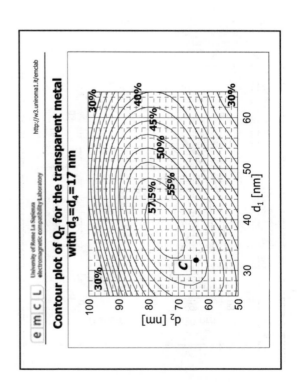

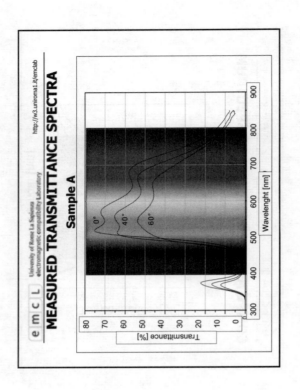

MEASURED TRANSMITTANCE SPECTRA
Sample A

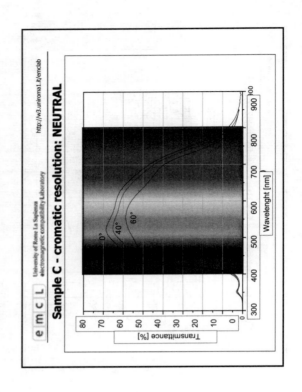

Sample C - cromatic resolution: NEUTRAL

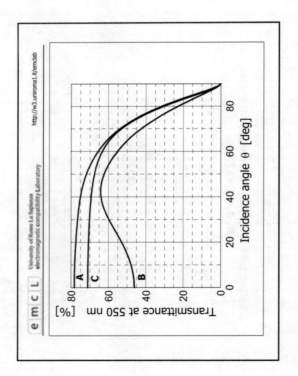

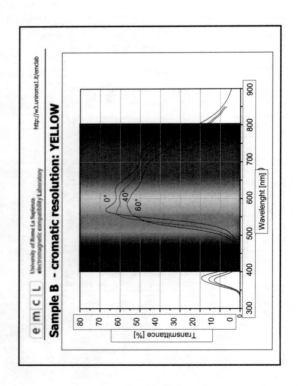

Sample B - cromatic resolution: YELLOW

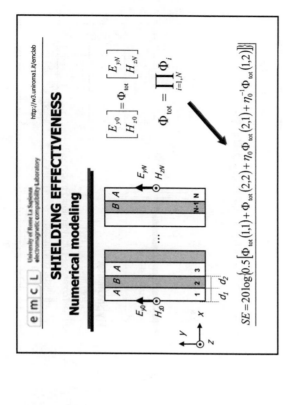

SHIELDING EFFECTIVENESS

Numerical modeling

$$\begin{bmatrix} E_{y0} \\ H_{z0} \end{bmatrix} = \Phi_{tot} \begin{bmatrix} E_{yN} \\ H_{zN} \end{bmatrix}$$

$$\Phi_{tot} = \prod_{i=1,N} \Phi_i$$

$$SE = 20\log\left\{0.5\left[\Phi_{tot}(1,1) + \Phi_{tot}(2,2) + \eta_0\Phi_{tot}(2,1) + \eta_0^{-1}\Phi_{tot}(1,2)\right]\right\}$$

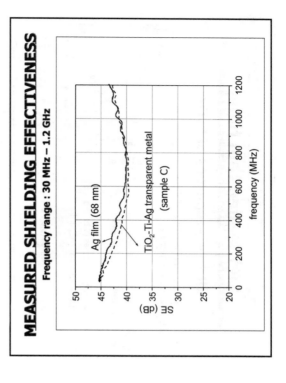

MEASURED SHIELDING EFFECTIVENESS

Frequency range : 30 MHz – 1.2 GHz

Ag film (68 nm)

TiO$_2$-Ti-Ag transparent metal (sample C)

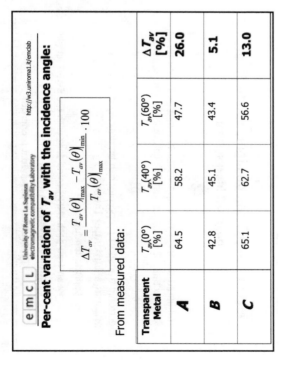

Per-cent variation of T_{av} with the incidence angle:

$$\Delta T_{av} = \frac{T_{av}(\theta)|_{max} - T_{av}(\theta)|_{min}}{T_{av}(\theta)|_{max}} \cdot 100$$

From measured data:

Transparent Metal	$T_{av}(0°)$ [%]	$T_{av}(40°)$ [%]	$T_{av}(60°)$ [%]	ΔT_{av} [%]
A	64.5	58.2	47.7	**26.0**
B	42.8	45.1	43.4	**5.1**
C	65.1	62.7	56.6	**13.0**

Experimental Tests

SE measurement: modified ASTM 4935/89

Frequency range : 30 MHz – 6 GHz

Slide 1

CNT loaded thin films

Electric properties of CNTs

The electrical properties of CNT depends on chirality:

- Armchair SWNT with indexes (n,n): **metallic** ($\Delta E_F \approx 0.1$ eV)

- Chiral SWNT with indexes (a,b), b-a $\neq$ 3N: **semiconductor** ($\Delta E_F \approx 1$ eV)

- Chiral SWNT with indexes (a,b), b-a = 3N: **semimetal** ($\Delta E_F \approx 0$ eV)

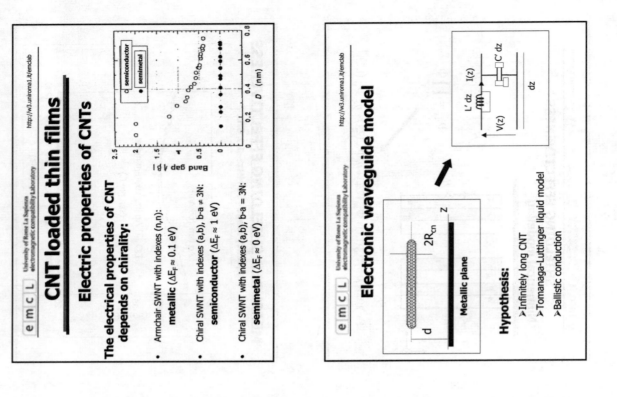

Slide 2

Electronic waveguide model

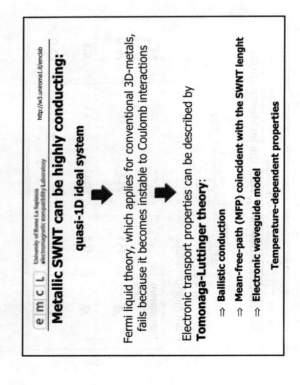

Hypothesis:

- Infinitely long CNT
- Tomanaga-Luttinger liquid model
- Ballistic conduction

Slide 3

Frequency range : 30 MHz – 6 GHz

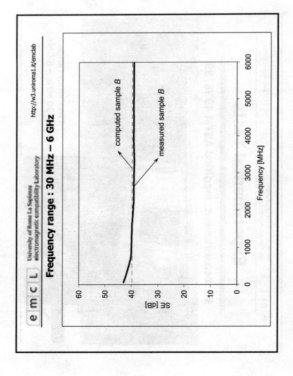

Slide 4

Metallic SWNT can be highly conducting: quasi-1D ideal system

Fermi liquid theory, which applies for conventional 3D-metals, fails because it becomes instable to Coulomb interactions

Electronic transport properties can be described by **Tomanaga-Luttinger theory:**

- $\Rightarrow$ **Ballistic conduction**
- $\Rightarrow$ **Mean-free-path (MFP) coincident with the SWNT lenght**
- $\Rightarrow$ **Electronic waveguide model**

Temperature-dependent properties

L' = L'e + L'k

p.u.l. inductance

external inductance
$$L'_e = \frac{\mu_0}{2\pi} \ln \frac{2d}{R_{cn}}$$

kinetic inductance
$$L_k = \frac{R_0}{2 v_F}$$

C' = C'e C'q / (C'e + C'q)

p.u.l. capacitance

external capacitance
$$C'_e = \frac{2\pi \varepsilon_0}{\ln(2d/R_{cn})}$$

quantic capacitance
$$C_q = \frac{2}{R_0 v_F}$$

with:

$$R_0 = \frac{\pi \hbar}{e^2}$$

v_F : Fermi velocity
$\hbar$: Plank constant
e : Electronic charge

Telegrapher's equations:

$$\partial V(z,t) / \partial z = -L' \; \partial I(z,t) / \partial t$$
$$\partial I(z,t) / \partial z = -C' \; \partial V(z,t) / \partial t$$

I(z,t) : *common mode* current   V(z,t) : *common mode* voltage

G. Ya. Slepyan, S. A. Maksimenko, A. Lakhtakia, O. Yevtushenko, A. V. Gusakov, "Electrodynamics of carbon nanotubes: Dynamic conductivity, impedance boundary conditions, and surface wave propagation", Physical Review B - 15 Dec. 1999-II, Vol. 60, No.24.

J.O. Wesstrom. "Signal propagation in electron waveguides: transmission-line analogies", Physical Review B, Vol.54, No. 16, Oct. 15, 1996.

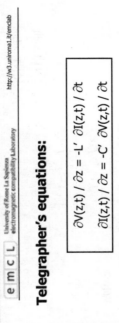

Film of aligned CNTs

Equivalent axial conductivity of a metallic CNT

$$\sigma_{zz}(\omega) = i \frac{2\sqrt{3} e^2 \gamma_0}{m \pi \hbar^2 (\omega + i v)} \qquad \text{Zigzag}$$

$$\sigma_{zz}(\omega) = i \frac{2 e^2 \gamma_0}{m \pi \hbar^2 (\omega + i v)} \qquad \text{Armchair}$$

$$\sigma_{zz}(\omega) = i \frac{2\sqrt{3} e^2 \gamma_0}{\pi \hbar^2 \sqrt{m^2 + mn + n^2}\,(\omega + i v)} \qquad \text{Chiral}$$

$\hbar$: Plank constant τ : mean time of electron free path
$v = 1/\tau$: relaxation frequency $\gamma_0 = 2.7$ eV

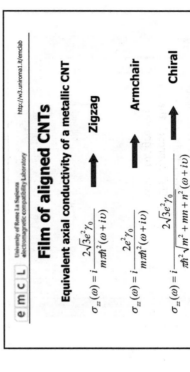

S. A. Maksimenko, G. Y. Slepyan, "Electrodynamic properties of Carbon Nanotubes", in "Electromagnetic Fields in unconventional materials and structures" edited by Singh and Lakhtakia, ISBN0-471-33656-1, 2000 John Wiley & Sons, Inc.., pp.217-255.

Electromagnetic performances of thin films with CNTs inclusions

1) CNTs randomly dispersed in polymeric matrix
   - SE measurements

2) CNTs powders randomly deposited on glass substrate
   - SE measurements

3) Film of aligned CNTs
   - **Electrical conductivity**
   - **Simulation model**
   - **SE calculation**

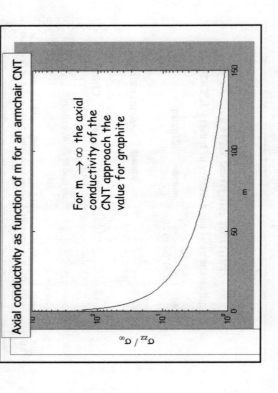

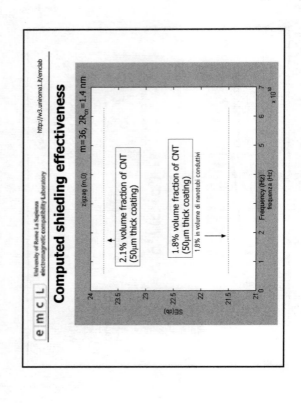

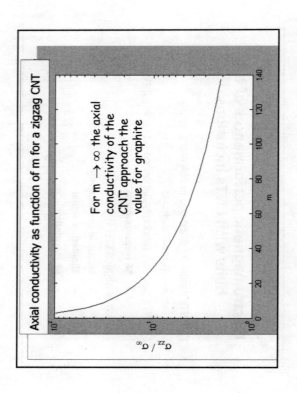

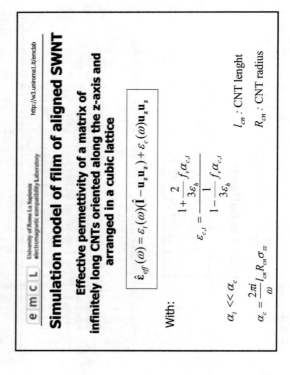

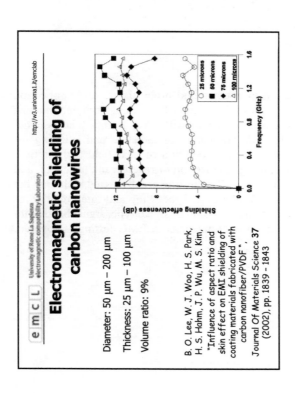

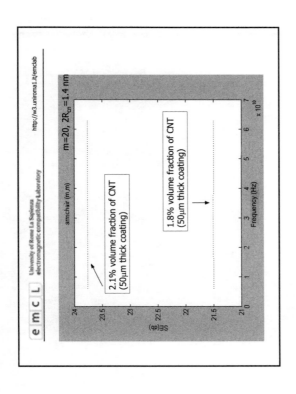

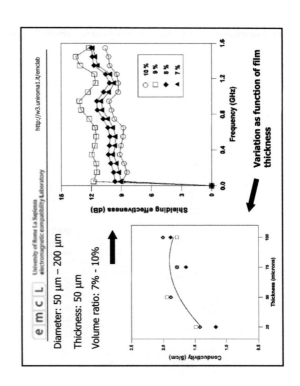

WORKSHOP: BASIC ANTENNA AND PROBE USE IN EMC
(MO-PM-WS-7)
C. R. Suriano, PhD.
Suriano Solutions

Antenna and Probe Fundamentals provides an introduction to antenna and probe theory and application relevant to EMC. This workshop covers fundamental principles of operation for various common antenna and field probe configurations covering the frequency spectrum associated with EMC testing. The essential descriptive characteristics of antennas and probes are defined. The nature of radiation and coupling for various types of antennas is described and illustrated including consideration of near field and far field effects. The use of antennas in EMC testing is covered including comparison of reverberant, anechoic, and open air testing. The implications of the antenna characteristics on EMC testing are discussed including the nature and use of antenna factors, gain, radiation resistance, VSWR, etc. Processing and interpretation of antenna signals by receivers and analyzers is discussed including discussion of signal type, signal bandwidth and filtering of signals. The use of soft ferrites in conjunction with antennas in EMC testing is covered. Unintentional radiators/receptors will also be discussed.

Presentations (not available for publication):

(1) Antenna and Probe Basics
Zhong Chen

(2) Antenna Regions (Near and Far Field)
Qin Yu

(3) Antenna and Probe Measurements (Signal Processing and Equipment)
Tom Holmes and Candace Suriano

(4) Soft Ferrite use with Antennas
Paul Zdanowicz

NOTES

[handwritten notes:]

mark Steffka

m steffka@ umd. umich.edu

model software { NECK 2 n 4 / NICK 2 n 4 / Ansoft antenna modeling

Specify Cal of antenna - Vert. HORIZONAL & height above floor

102

Antenna and Probe Basics

Zhong Chen

ETS-Lindgren
1301 Arrow Point Drive
Cedar Park, TX 78613
Zhong.Chen@ets-lindgren.com

Outline

- Antennas
  - Review of antenna terms and definitions
  - Typical EMC Antennas and – Why so many antennas?
  - How to calibrate
  - Applications
- Probes
  - Definitions and terms
  - How does it work
  - Applications and Usage

Applications in EMC testing

- Antennas convert time-varying voltages to a **radiated** electromagnetic field, or vice versa.

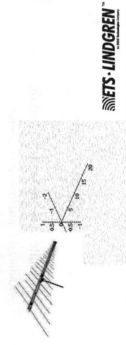

Is this an antenna?

- Field generators such as
  - TEM cells, parallel plates, and E/H field generators are, strictly speaking, not antennas.

A Review of Terms

- Gain
- VSWR (return loss)
- Antenna factor
- Radiation (reception) pattern, Beamwidth
- Line of Sight
- Bandwidth (frequency of operation)
- Phase center
- Polarization
- Near/Far field

Applications

- EMC antennas are mainly used for
  - Radiated Emissions Measurement
  - Radiated Immunity Testing
  - Site qualification test (Normalized site attenuation)
  - Other applications, such as exciting a reverberation chamber

---

Voltage Standing Wave Ratio

- VSWR (reflection coefficient/return loss)
  - They all describe the same physical phenomenon.
  - VSWR defines how a device is matched to the measuring instrument (normally at 50 ohms).
  - Analogy: water (RF signal) flows through pipes with unequal diameters. Some goes through, and some is reflected.

  - A perfect match (everything goes through) is when VSWR=1:1, reflection coefficient is 0, and return loss is infinite.

- Directivity (gain)
  - Specifies an antenna's ability to concentrate a transmitted signal in a desired direction, or receive a signal from this direction.
  - A passive antenna can not amplify a signal. Directivity is defined by comparing to a theoretically omni-directional antenna with the same input power.
  - In some cases gain is interchangeable with directivity. Sometimes gain also includes the mismatch factor between the antenna and its feed.
  - By reciprocity, transmit gain is the same as receive gain

Antenna Factor (AF)

- Antenna Factor (AF)
  - AF is a function of antenna gain, VSWR, and frequency.
  - Provides a receiving antenna the relationship between the incident EM field and the voltage on a 50 ohm load connected to the antenna.
    - AF=E/V
  - AFs are normally provided by antenna manufactures or calibration labs. The accuracy/uncertainty of AFs directly affects radiated emission measurements.

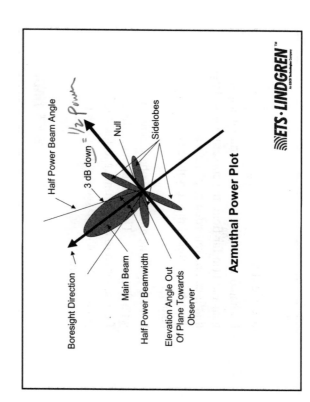

Azmuthal Power Plot

(labels: Half Power Beam Angle, 3 dB down = ½ Power, Null, Sidelobes, Boresight Direction, Main Beam, Half Power Beamwidth, Elevation Angle Out Of Plane Towards Observer)

Example:

- Example:
  - VSWR=2:1
  - Reflection coefficient is 1/3
  - Return loss is 9.5 dB
  - 11% of the power is reflected, or 89% of the power is delivered to the load.

100w like low reflected

Antenna Radiation Pattern & Beamwidth

- Antenna Radiation Pattern & Beamwidth
  - Is the response of an antenna as a function of viewing angle.
  - Beamwidth is typically measured when power received has fallen half (3 dB down) of the boresight direction. This is called half-power beamwidth or 3 dB beamwidth.

100w like a flashlight if to side its strongest off to side like a flashlight its strongest measure

what is near field
vs far field
is near field is
circular... far constant
field 20s constant

• **Phase Center**

– Radiated wavefront has a curvature when in near field (in far field, the curvature is so large that it can be regarded as plane wave). The apparent center of the curvature is the phase center.

– For log periodic antennas, phase center moves with frequency. The measurement distance from antenna to device under test is unclear. It is often chosen at a fixed position as an approximation.

• **Near Field/ Far Field**

– Far field and near field boundaries can be seen:

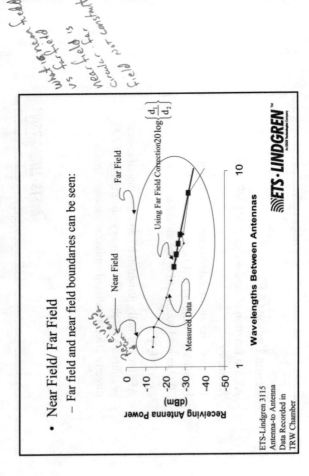

ETS-Lindgren 3115
Antenna-to Antenna
Data Recorded in
TRW Chamber

• **Line of Sight**

– This is especially important for horn antennas. The boresight of the transmitting antenna needs to line up with boresight of the receiving antenna.

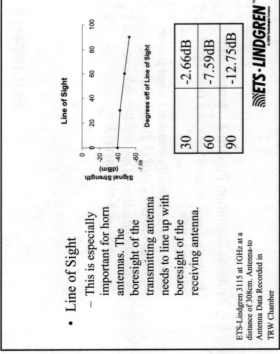

30	-2.66dB
60	-7.59dB
90	-12.75dB

ETS-Lindgren 3115 at 1GHz at a distance of 308cm. Antenna-to Antenna Data Recorded in TRW Chamber

---

• **Polarization**

– Linear/circular/elliptical

– It has to do with radiated vector field traced out as a function of time

– Most EMC antennas are linearly polarized, such as log periodic dipole antennas, biconical antennas, and dipoles. Some are circularly polarized, as required by MIL-STD 461.

Balun

- *Balanced*-to-*Unbalanced* transformer.
- Provides low impedance to differential current, and high impedance to common mode current.
- Coaxial cables are unbalanced, because they are unsymmetrical with respect to ground plane
- Unbalanced antennas have different responses depending on which side is up when vertically polarized. This causes large measurement uncertainties.

‽ETS·LINDGREN ™

Typical EMC Antennas

Insulator

Conductive

- Loop & Magnetic Field Coil
  - Low frequency from 20 Hz to 30 MHz for measuring H field.
  - Most are shielded loops with a gap to prevent a shorting turn.

‽ETS·LINDGREN ™

Bandwidth

- "The range of frequencies within which the performance of the antenna, with respect to some characteristic, conforms to a specific standard" – (Balanis- Antenna Theory)
- The "characteristics" normally include:
  - **VSWR**
  - **Beamwidth**
  - **Radiation pattern**

‽ETS·LINDGREN ™

Why so many antennas?

- Magnetic *vs.* electric antennas
- Emissions *vs.* immunities
- Frequency range
- Accuracy *vs.* speed (convenience) of testing
- Polarization requirement
- Because standards say so!

‽ETS·LINDGREN ™

Biconical Antenna

- Biconical Antenna
  - Typical 20 MHz to 300 MHz.
  - All biconical elements on market have similar sizes and shapes, because they are based on MIL-461 spec from the 1960s.
  - Due to high VSWR (more than 5:1) at <50 MHz, balun performance is important for bicons.
  - Common mode current can be induced on the feed cable. Ferrite beads are often used to suppress it. Cable should be extended out from the antenna before dropping.

ETS·LINDGREN™

Log Periodic Dipole Arrays

- Log Periodic Dipole Arrays
  - Typical 80 MHz to a few GHz
  - Phase center of a log antenna moves from the back of the antenna boom to the front as frequencies go up.
  - For emissions measurement, center of the boom is typically used to measure distance to an EUT as an approximation
  - For immunity measurement, the front of the boom is typically used to measure distance.
  - Gain is typically around 5 dB, which provides a good compromise between beamwidth and sensitivity (or power requirement).

ETS·LINDGREN™

Dipole

- Dipole
  - Tuned to a specific frequency, approximate between 30 MHz to a few GHz. Narrow band.
  - Often used as reference antenna because performance can be theoretically calculated, even for near-field effects. Note: balun impedance has an effect on AF. Antenna performance can only be calculated if the balun is known.
  - Seldom used in everyday measurement, due to the need for individual tuning at each frequency.

ETS·LINDGREN™

Calculable Biconical Antenna

- Calculable Biconical Antenna
  - Combines the best of bicon and dipole antennas
  - Calibrated balun
  - Numerically computed element response
  - Theoretically computed antenna factors for site validation testing or free space antenna factors for product emissions testing
  - Accuracy is better than a Roberts dipole, because the balun performance is calibrated.
  - Uncertainty is better than 0.25 dB for its antenna factor.

ETS·LINDGREN™

Slide 1 (top-left): Bicon/Log Hybrid

- Bicon/Log Hybrid
  - Sometimes called biconilog/bilog etc.
  - Combines the frequency range of a bicon and a log antenna (typically ~20 MHz to a few GHz).
  - At 30 MHz, $\lambda/2=5$ m. Hybrid antennas are electrically short. Some antennas use loading techniques to compensate for the size. These antennas should typically only be used for <u>immunities</u> test. (Z. Chen "Understanding the measurement uncertainties of the bicon/log hybrid antenna", ITEM 1999)

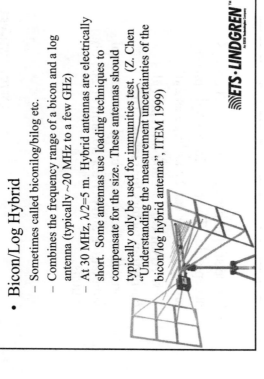

Slide 2 (top-right): Standard Gain Horn antenna

- Standard Gain Horn antenna
  - ~900 MHz to GHz
  - Gains can be calculated.
  - Many horns are needed to cover a broad frequency range.

Slide 3 (bottom-left): Conical Log-Spiral Antenna

- Conical Log-Spiral Antenna
  - Mostly used for MIL standard measurements.
  - Frequency range 100 MHz ~ 1000 MHz
  - Circularly polarized field, so there is no need for horizontal and vertical measurements separately.
  - There is a 3 dB factor (1/2) for measuring linearly polarized field.

Slide 4 (bottom-right): Broadband ridged waveguide horn

- Broadband ridged waveguide horn
  - 700 MHz to 18 GHz
  - Versatile and broadband. Make sure beamwidth meets your measurement requirement.

- Basic setups for standard site method:
  - Conducting ground plane
  - One antenna is at a fixed height (e.g. 1m, 1.5 m)
  - The other antenna is scanned from 1 to 4 m in height
  - Minimum SAs are recorded (or maximum response).
  - Calculations are then performed to derive the antenna factors.
  - Although ground plane is used, the aim of C63.5 is to obtain free space AF by theoretically removing the ground plane effect.

ETS·LINDGREN™

- These simple assumptions are not always acceptable. The error for a single bicon antenna factor can be as large as 2 dB.
- New ANSI C63.5-2000 draft provides correction factors for bicons. The correction factors are based on numerical simulation, and perfect 50 ohm or 200 ohm baluns.

ETS·LINDGREN™

Antenna Calibration

- Standard Site Method:
  - For "dipole-like" antennas, such as dipole, bicon, log antennas, and bicon/log hybrid, ANSI C63.5 specifies the method based on Normalized Site Attenuation (NSA).
  - Site Attenuation (SA): basically is the insertion loss between transmit and receive antenna
    - NSA (in dB) =SA-AF1-AF2

ETS·LINDGREN™

- Some assumptions made in the standard site method
  - Antennas have radiation patterns of a point dipole (i.e. Uniform in H-plane, and $\sin(\theta)$ in the E-plane): donut shape.
  - No mutual couplings among transmit, receive antennas and ground plane.
  - Physical size of the antenna does not affect the AF (i.e. Antennas are immersed in a uniform field)

ETS·LINDGREN™

Reference Antenna Method

- Antennas with known AFs are used (standard Roberts dipole)
  - Basically is a substitution method
  - Two know antennas are measured, and the unknown antenna is placed to substitute one of them.
  - Error attributors:
    - Roberts dipole baluns are not well characterized
    - Mutual coupling coefficient will vary drastically when comparing two dipoles with, a dipole and an antenna under test.

ETS·LINDGREN™

Use of Antennas for Radiated Emission Testing

- Test setup per ANSI C63.4 or equivalent EN standards.
- Metal ground plane
- Very similar to antenna calibration setup, except for turntable. EUT is set on a table top (80 cm high). Receive antenna scans from 1 to 4 m for both horizontal and vertical polarization. Maximum reading is recorded and compared to standards.

ETS·LINDGREN™

- For log antennas, there is currently no correction table provided. These major factors contribute to errors:
  - Non-stationary phase center with respect to frequency
  - Non-dipole-like pattern. Log antennas have approximately 5 dBi gains.
- It is not practical to have unified correction factors for log antennas due to the diverse designs.
- Research is in progress to develop a new method based on a complex fit NSA scheme. (Z. Chen, M. Foegelle "An improved method for determining normalized site attenuation using log periodic dipole arrays", IEEE symposium 2000 and several follow-up papers, including one in this symposium)

ETS·LINDGREN™

- Calibrations for High frequency Antennas (Horn antennas)
  - Horns typically have high gains (10 dBi or more), thus have narrow beamwidth.
  - Antennas do not see ground plane at close distances. Calibration is in free-space condition.

ETS·LINDGREN™

EN Typical Radiated Emissions Limits - EN 55022

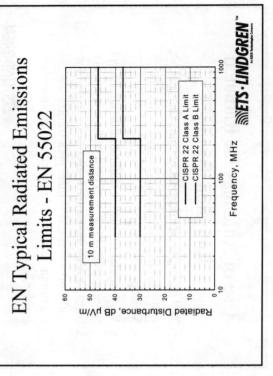

FCC part 15 Radiated Specification Limits - ITE

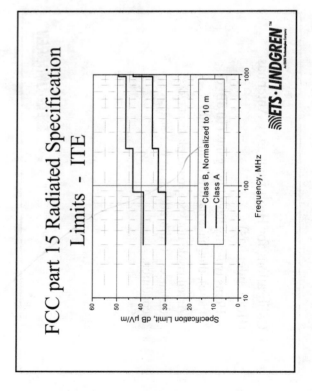

Use of Antennas for Radiated Immunity testing

- No US requirements. Most tests are performed per EN 61000-4-3.
- Requires the establishment of a uniform field plane where EUT would be located. Absorbing materials are likely to be necessary between the antenna and the uniform plane to neutralize the ground reflection.

Use of Antennas for Site Validation Testing

- Reverse of antenna calibration process.
- Requirement is within +/- 4 dB of theoretical NSA
- What AFs to use
  - Geometry specific (golden site): this is equivalent to comparing the site where antennas are calibrated to the site under test.
  - Free space AF: Inherent errors due to the simplistic assumptions in the NSA model. how to correct for the errors?

Idealized Immunity Test System Equipment Function according EN 61000-4-3

- **Signal Generator** – Source of test signal, amplitude and frequency, 80 - 1000 MHz, 80% AM
- **Amplifier** – Increases level of test signal to achieve desired test field values
- **Forward/Reverse power Coupler** – Samples forward and reflected power to radiating device
- **Power Meter** – Reads power values in forward and reverse channels, allows calculation of forward power to antenna
- **Antenna** – Generates test field at 3 m
- **Field Meter** – Reads generated field levels, provides feedback loop

EM field Probes/Sensors

- Definitions and Terms
- Types of probes
- Basic theory of operation
- Calibration/Application

Typical Immunity Test setup

EM field Probes/Sensors

- Terms
- Types of probes
- Basic theory of operation
- Calibration/Application

Term Definition

- Frequency Response
- Linearity Response(dynamic range response)
- Isotropic Response (Isotropicity)
- Difference from antennas

Typical EMC probes

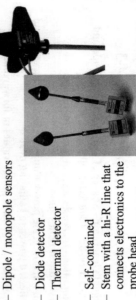

- Electric probes
  - Dipole / monopole sensors

  - Diode detector
  - Thermal detector

  - Self-contained
  - Stem with a hi-R line that connects electronics to the probe head

---

— Active

Definition (IEEE 1309)

- Field Probe
  - An electrically small field sensor or set of multiple field sensors with various electronics (for example, diodes, resistors, amplifiers, etc.). The output from a field probe cannot be theoretically determined from easily measured physical parameters
- Field Sensor
  - An electrically small device without electronics (passive) that is used for measuring electric or magnetic fields, with a minimum of perturbation to field being measured.
  - Can be theoretically determined, and traceable to NIST

EM field Probes/Sensors

- Terms
- Types of probes
- Basic theory of operation
- Calibration/Application

Probes

Magnetic Field Probes

- Magnetic Field Probes
  - Loop sensors
  - Typically work at low frequencies (below 1 GHz)
  - E field rejection is critical

ETS·LINDGREN™
An ESCO Technologies Company

Basic Theory of Operation

- Diode Sensor/Probe
- Thermal (thermistor) Sensor/Probe

ETS·LINDGREN™
An ESCO Technologies Company

E field probes

z-h-x

- Typically works from 10 KHz to GHz range (40 GHz)
- EMC probes are designed to have a flat frequency response.
- EMC probes are typically designed with three orthogonal sensors for isotropic response
- Broadband device (respond to signals at all frequencies in their operating band)
- Minimal disturbance device (Fiber optical link)

ETS·LINDGREN™
An ESCO Technologies Company

EM field Probes/Sensors

- Definitions and Terms
- Types of probes
- Basic theory of operation
- Calibration/Application

Probes

ETS·LINDGREN™
An ESCO Technologies Company

Expensive

How does an Electric Field Sensor work?

- Antenna elements (resistive loaded)
- Diode rectifier or thermal sensor
  - Linear region (proportional to E-field)
  - Square-law (proportional to field density)
- DC Filter
- Gain blocks - adjustable for wide dynamic ranges, such as 0.5 V/m to 900 V/m
- A/D conversion
- Micro-processor, and serial optical interface

≋ETS·LINDGREN™
An ESCO Technologies Company

Know your power amplifier

- What you see is not always what you get
  - Max output power
  - 1 dB gain compression point
  - Harmonics
  - Third Order Interception Point
  - Noise Figure
  - Immunity tests (IEC61000-4-3) involve one tone tests, and harmonic contents can be significant (typically no intermods)

≋ETS·LINDGREN™
An ESCO Technologies Company

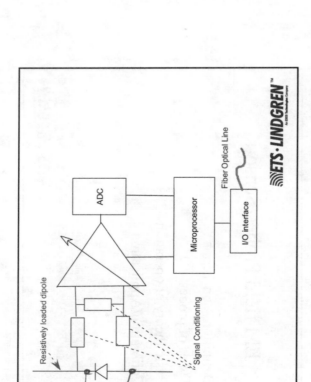

≋ETS·LINDGREN™
An ESCO Technologies Company

Pay Attention to...

- Range Switch (how its handled)
- Linearity
  - Internal lookup table.
  - Calibration procedure SHOULD adjust the linear response of a probe. (calibration vs. characterization)
  - Unlike thermal probes, diodes are typically NOT true RMS detectors (under large signals), but are calibrated such that probes read correctly under CW conditions.
- Broadband device
  - No frequency discrimination in band

≋ETS·LINDGREN™
An ESCO Technologies Company

Isotropic Response

- Probes are typically designed to be isotropic. There are three orthogonal axes. The field are summed based on:

$$E_{Total} = \sqrt{E_x^2 + E_y^2 + E_z^2}$$

- Figure of merit: Anisotropy

$$A = 10\log_{10}\left[\frac{S_{max}}{\sqrt{S_{max} S_{min}}}\right]$$

ETS·LINDGREN™
An ESCO Technologies Company

Probe Holder/Fixture

- They are in close vicinity of the probe. These factors are important:
  - Material property (dielectric constant, dissipation factor)
  - Size
  - Position
- How about placing probe directly on the tabletop? Tripod?

ETS·LINDGREN™
An ESCO Technologies Company

- Correctly size an amplifier for output power based on the transmit antenna and test environments
  - Typically biconical antennas can be quite inefficient (and poor match to 50 Ω) below ~60 MHz. Pushing the amp hard can mean large harmonics
  - Commercial EMC standards start at 80 MHz, but can be important for medical devices immunity tests.
- Making sure the spectral purity of the output signal (may need harmonic low pass filters) _ACTIVE_
- AM modulation: how would a probe react? OKAY ~ ?
- Again, probes do not know frequencies and signal purity. Engineers must check the test conditions.

ETS·LINDGREN™
An ESCO Technologies Company

Otho-Angle

Rotating around the ortho-angle will align each sensor axis successively with a linear incident electric field

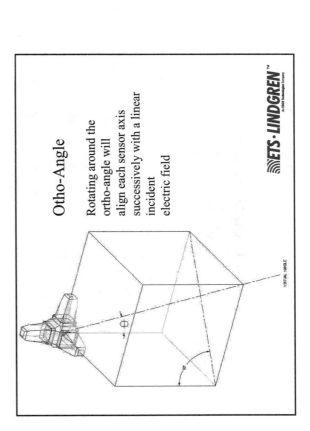

VIRTUAL HANDLE

ETS·LINDGREN™
An ESCO Technologies Company

Frequency response of a HI-6005

3"x2"x0.75" Delrin Block
Er=3.7

frequency (Hz)

ETS·LINDGREN™
An ESCO Technologies Company

- calibrate probes in the same orientation as will be used – this can be a misleading proposition.
- Fixtures and chambers can have significant impact on the measurements – they are typically different at calibration and during usage.
- In an actual immunity test setup, field structure in a chamber can be quite complex (due to the partial lining on the ground plane, non-ideal performance of the absorbers, limited size chambers, in near-field of the transmitting antenna etc.). The advantage of an **isotropic** probe is to measure the field accurately regardless the non-ideal factors. A calibration does not repeat all these factors.

ETS·LINDGREN™
An ESCO Technologies Company

EM field Probes/Sensors

- Definitions and Terms
- Types of probes
- Basic theory of operation
- Calibration/Application

Probes

ETS·LINDGREN™
An ESCO Technologies Company

- Probes are calibrated with minimal size, low dielectric supports
- Users should do the same during immunities testing to minimize measurement uncertainties.
- Anechoic chambers used for calibration should be rigorously tested so that they do not introduce additional errors. (periodic ripples in frequency response may indicate non-ideal measurement conditions)

ETS·LINDGREN™
An ESCO Technologies Company

Temperature Effects

- Temperature affects the probe readings
  - Diode temperature response
  - Electronics (gain blocks) in the probe
- At low field levels (below about 3 V/m), effects are larger.
- For most EMC measurements, they are performed in lab environments. So this effect is small.

Self-contained vs. Probe on a Stem

- State of the art self-contained probe, such as HI-6005 has a upper frequency limit of 6 GHz. The whole probe is immersed in the field during calibration and application.
- Probes on stems can be used to as high as 40 GHz. For some calibration setups, not all parts of a probe is in a field (such as in a TEM cell devices). If this is the intended usage, there will be no additional uncertainties. Otherwise, additional uncertainties need to be assessed. Some orientation of the probe is not recommended.

- The best calibration is to qualify each axis thoroughly, and minimize the uncertainties during calibration **and** actual usage.

Interpolation in Frequency and Linearity Response)

- In the gigahertz range, probe frequency response may not be as smooth. Make sure enough frequency points are obtained.
- Probe linearity response is a weak function of frequency. Comprehensive calibration in linearity responses at different frequencies can be collected, but there will be a tremendous amount of data.

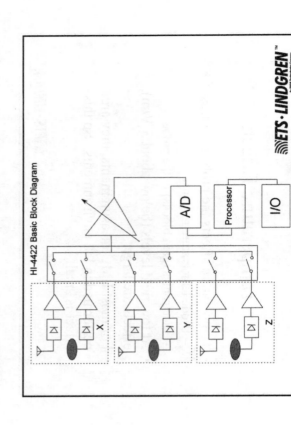

HI-4433-GRE Frequency Response

Legend:
— X axis aligned
— Y axis aligned
— Z axis Aligned
— head on 1
— head on 2
— head on 3
— head on 4
— head on 5

(y-axis: dB, values 2, 1, 0, -1, -2, -3, -4, -5)
(x-axis: frequency (GHz), values 1, 1.5, 2, 2.5, 3, 3.5, 4)

ETS·LINDGREN™

HI-4422 Basic Block Diagram

A/D

Processor

I/O

X   Y   Z

ETS·LINDGREN™

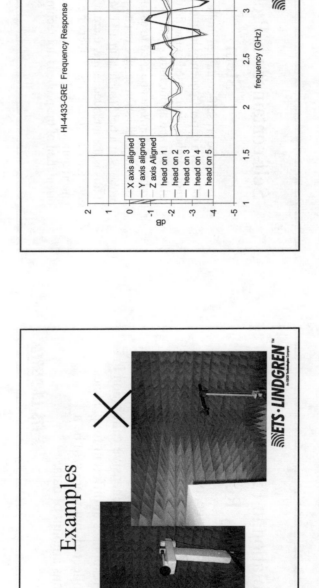

Examples

ETS·LINDGREN™

Range Setting/Switching

- Older probes require manual switching between ranges. Errors can (and often) occur by using probes outside the dynamic range of a specific setting.

- Modern probes provide seamless range switching which is transparent to the end user.

ETS·LINDGREN™

Summary

- Many factors affect probe calibrations and applications, including signal purities, fixtures, isotropicity, linearity, temperature, test setups etc... Care must be taken during each step.
- Probe calibrations involves more than characterizations. Follow the recommended practices by manufactures.
- Modern probes can save time and reduce measurement errors (no manual switching between ranges).

ETS·LINDGREN™

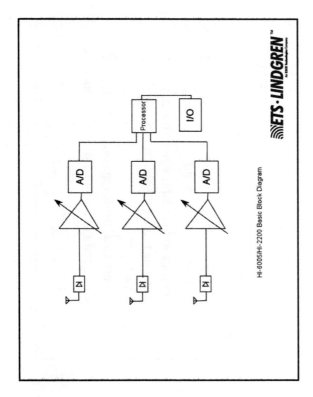

HI-6005/HI-2200 Basic Block Diagram

ETS·LINDGREN™

Q&A for Antennas and Probes

ETS·LINDGREN™

121

Antenna Regions

- Motivation
- Definitions
- Examples
- Conclusion

Antenna Regions

Qin Yu
qy@lucent.com
Lucent Technologies, Inc.

CR Suriano
SurianoSolutions@comcast.net
Suriano Solutions

Motivation

- FCC CFR 47, Part 15.31(f), clearly states:
  1. At frequencies at or above 30 MHz, measurements may be performed at a distance other than what is specified provided: measurements are not made in the near field except where it can be shown that near field measurements are appropriate due to the characteristics of the device;
  2. At frequencies below 30 MHz, measurements may be performed at a distance closer than specified in the regulations; however, an attempt should be made to avoid making measurement in the near field.

Motivation

- Far field / near field determination integral to EMC measurements
- Rules and Standards determine in which antenna region measurements are to be made
- Aperture antenna regions are determined differently than wire antenna regions

Definitions

- Far field and near field boundaries are not fixed. They depend on:
  - Radiation frequency.
  - Sizes of the transmitting and receiving antennas.
  - Type of antenna.
  - Accuracy that an application requires.
  - Shield or antenna design application.

Motivation

- Since the radiation pattern does not change in the far field, radiated emissions from EUT measured in a far field region have a better correlation with other test data. For example:

  In an EMC radiated emission measurement, when the formula, $20\log\left\{\dfrac{d_1}{d_2}\right\}$ is used to adjust the radiated emission limit specified at d_1 to what the value would be at d_2, both d_1 and d_2 must be in the far field.

Definitions

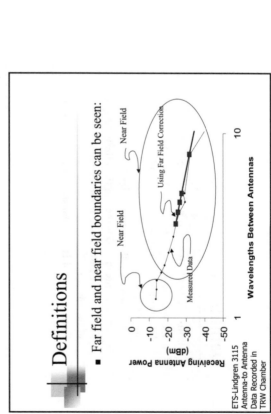

Radiating Near-Field Region

Far Field Region

Region Boundaries:
- $-\lambda/2\pi$
- $-5\lambda/2\pi$
- $-(d+D)^2/\lambda$ (D>.4d)
- $-50D^2/\lambda$
- -3λ
- $-2D^2/\lambda$
- $-5D$
- -1.6λ

R

Receiving Antenna

**Reactive Near-Field Region
Transmitting Antenna**

Definitions

- Far field and near field boundaries can be seen:

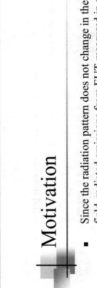

Near Field

Near Field

Using Far Field Correction

Measured Data

Receiving Antenna Power (dBm)

0, -10, -20, -30, -40, -50

1 — 10

Wavelengths Between Antennas

ETS-Lindgren 3115
Antenna-to Antenna
Data Recorded in
TRW Chamber

Definitions

- Field regions may have two or three designations
- For the two region designation, there is the far and near field
- Near field- $1/r^3$ and $1/r^2$ terms dominate
- Other names for near field include, Fresnel Zone, Quasistatic Field
- Far field – $1/r$ terms dominate and the pattern in the far field is independent of the distance to the antenna
- Other names for far field include, Fraunhoffer Zone and Radiation Zone

Definitions

- Radiating near field: $1/r^2$ terms dominate in field equations. (Derivation later in Definitions.)
- Radiation fields dominate and distance from antenna determines angular field distribution.
- Other names: Induction Field, Transition Region, Fresnel Region.
- Using Huygens' Principle, where each point on a radiator is considered to be a source of spherical waves, this region has spherical wavefronts.
- Radial energy flow exists.
- Radial field components not zero.

Definitions

- Terms used defining near and far field:
  - Electrically Large Antenna — $D > \lambda$, where D is the largest dimension of the antenna and λ is the wavelength.
  - Electrically Small Antenna — $D << \lambda$.
  - For wire antennas, D is the length of the wire.

  Dipole

  Magnetic Loop

  - For aperture antennas, D is the diagonal dimension of the aperture.

  Aperture

  - Receiving antennas, similar dimensions are referred to as d.

Definitions

- Three radiation zones, consist of the reactive near field, radiating near field, and far field.
- Reactive near field- $1/r^3$ terms dominate in field equations. (Derivation later in Definitions.)
- Reactive fields dominate over radiative fields
- Other names: Quasistatic or Static field,
- Using Huygens' Principle, where each point on a radiator is considered to be a source of spherical waves, this region has spherical wavefronts
- No radial energy flow- energy is mostly stored.
- Radial field components not zero.

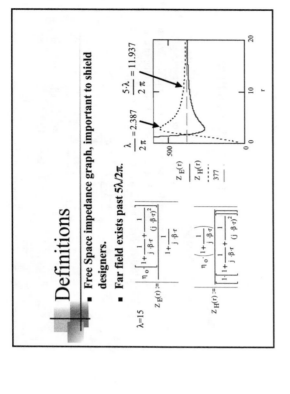

Definitions

- **Free Space impedance graph, important to shield designers.**
- **Far field exists past $5\lambda/2\pi$.**

$\lambda = 15$

$$Z_E(r) := \eta_o \left[\frac{1 + \frac{1}{j \cdot \beta \cdot r} + \frac{1}{(j \cdot \beta \cdot r)^2}}{1 + \frac{1}{j \cdot \beta \cdot r}} \right]$$

$$Z_H(r) := \frac{\eta_o \cdot \left(1 + \frac{1}{j \cdot \beta \cdot r}\right)}{1 + \left[\frac{1}{j \cdot \beta \cdot r} + \frac{1}{(j \cdot \beta \cdot r)^2}\right]}$$

$\dfrac{\lambda}{2\pi} = 2.387$ $\dfrac{5\lambda}{2\pi} = 11.937$

$Z_E(r)$

$\dfrac{Z_H(r)}{377}$

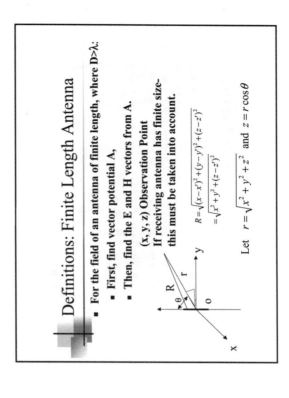

Definitions: Finite Length Antenna

- **For the field of an antenna of finite length, where $D > \lambda$:**
  - **First, find vector potential A,**
  - **Then, find the E and H vectors from A.**
    - **(x, y, z) Observation Point**
    - **If receiving antenna has finite size- this must be taken into account.**

$$R = \sqrt{(x-x')^2 + (y-y')^2 + (z-z')^2}$$
$$= \sqrt{x^2 + y^2 + (z-z')^2}$$

Let $r = \sqrt{x^2 + y^2 + z^2}$ and $z = r\cos\theta$

Definitions

- **Far field or Fraunhoffer Region: $1/r$ terms dominate in field equations. (Derivation later in Definitions.)**
  - **Field distribution pattern in independent of distance to antenna.**
  - **Using Huygens' Principle, where each point on a radiator is considered to be a source of spherical waves, this region has planar wavefronts.**
  - **Energy is radiated.**
  - **Radial field components zero.**
  - **Wave impedance in free space, $\eta_o = 377$Ohms**

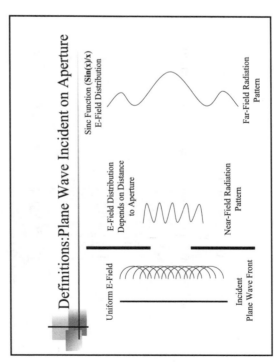

Definitions:Plane Wave Incident on Aperture

Sinc Function (Sin(x)/x)
E-Field Distribution

E-Field Distribution Depends on Distance to Aperture

Far-Field Radiation Pattern

Near-Field Radiation Pattern

Uniform E-Field

Incident Plane Wave Front

Definitions: Finite Length Antenna

- For the field of an antenna of finite length

$$\vec{A}(x,y,z) = \frac{\mu}{4\pi}\int \vec{J}_e(x',y',z')\frac{e^{-j\kappa R}}{R}dl'$$

$$\vec{E}_A = -j\omega\vec{A} - j\frac{1}{\omega\mu\varepsilon}\nabla(\nabla\bullet\vec{A})$$

$$\vec{H}_A = \frac{1}{\mu}\nabla\times\vec{A}$$

Using binomial expansion, R is written as a series:

$$R = r - z'\cos\theta + \frac{1}{r}\left(\frac{z'^2}{2}\sin^2\theta\right) + \frac{1}{r^2}\left(\frac{z'^3}{2}\cos\theta\sin^2\theta\right) + \cdots$$

Definitions: Finite Length Antenna

- **Provided $r \gg z'$, then the higher order terms become less significant. Some approximations on R can be made. The approximation of R in the phase needs to be more accurate than the amplitude of R.**

- **For amplitude, let R = r.**

- **For phase, let R = r - z'cosθ.**

$$\therefore \frac{e^{-j\kappa R}}{R} = \frac{e^{-j\kappa r}}{r}\cdot e^{jz'\kappa\cos\theta}$$

Definitions: Finite Length Antenna

- **Then the most significant term neglected in the phase is the third term. It can be found that when $\theta=\pi/2$, the third term reaches the maximum and the fourth term is zero.**

- **$\therefore$ the maximum error of the third term is:**

$$\frac{z'^2}{2r}$$

Definitions: Finite Length Antenna

- It has been shown by many studies that for most practical antennas, with overall lengths greater than a wavelength $(D>\lambda)$, a maximum total phase error of $\pi/8$ rad (22.5°) can be considered negligible and has little effect on the overall far field radiation characteristics in pattern calculations or predictions

$$\therefore \frac{\kappa(z')^2}{2r} \leq \frac{\pi}{8}$$

$$\Rightarrow r \geq \frac{2D^2}{\lambda}$$

Definitions: Finite Length Antenna

- ∴In order to maintain the maximum phase error less than $\pi/8$ rad (22.5°), the 3rd term in R needs to be kept, that is,

$$R \approx r - z'\cos\theta + \frac{1}{r}\left(\frac{z'^2}{2}\sin^2\theta\right).$$

- The most significant term in R being ignored is the 4th term: $\left[\frac{1}{r^2}\left(\frac{z'^3}{2}\cos\theta\sin^2\theta\right)\right]_{max} \leq \frac{\pi}{8}.$

Definitions: Finite Length Antenna

- Therefore, when $0.62\sqrt{\frac{D^3}{\lambda}} \leq r < \frac{2D^2}{\lambda}$, this region is designated as radiating near field or Fresnel region.

- When $0 < r < 0.62\sqrt{\frac{D^3}{\lambda}}$, this region is designated as reactive near field region.

- Thus, for an antenna where D>λ:

Reactive near-field: $0 < r < \left[0.62\sqrt{D^3/\lambda}\right]$,

Radiating near-field: $\left[0.62\sqrt{D^3/\lambda}\right] \leq r < 2D^2/\lambda$,

Far-field: $2D^2/\lambda \leq r < \infty.$

Definitions: Finite Length Antenna

- ∴ For an antenna whose maximum dimension is D, the far field approximation is valid provided the observations are made at a distance

$$\frac{2D^2}{\lambda} \leq r \leq \infty$$

- When $r < \frac{2D^2}{\lambda}$, the maximum phase error by using $R \cong r - z'\cos\theta$ is greater than $\pi/8$ rad (22.5°).

Definitions: Finite Length Antenna

- The 4th term becomes maximum when,

$\theta = \tan^{-1}(\pm\sqrt{2})$ and $z' = \frac{D}{2}.$

$\boxed{4^{th}\ \textbf{term}} \Rightarrow \frac{\kappa z'^3}{2r^2}\cos\theta\sin^2\theta = \frac{\pi}{12\sqrt{3}}\left(\frac{D^3}{\lambda r^2}\right) \leq \frac{\pi}{8}$

$\Rightarrow r \geq 0.62\sqrt{\frac{D^3}{\lambda}}.$

Definitions: Infinitesimal Dipole

- So when $\kappa r = 1$, that is, $r = \lambda/2\pi$, the $1/r$, $1/r^2$ and $1/r^3$ terms in equations for H_ϕ, E_r and E_θ are equal;
- For $r < \lambda/2\pi$, that is, $\kappa r < 1$, the $1/r^2$ and $1/r^3$ terms in equations for H_ϕ, E_r and E_θ are larger than the $1/r$ term. When $r \ll \lambda/2\pi$, the $1/r^3$ terms begin to dominate.
- For $r > \lambda/2\pi$, that is, $\kappa r > 1$, the $1/r$ term is larger than the $1/r^2$ and $1/r^3$ terms; when $r \gg \lambda/2\pi$, the $1/r^2$ and $1/r^3$ terms in equations for H_ϕ, E_r and E_θ become negligible and the $1/r$ term dominates. $\Rightarrow E_r \cong 0$, $E_\theta \neq 0$, and $H_\phi \neq 0$.

Example 1

- EMCO 3160-09 Pyramid Horn antenna has a working frequency range of 18-26GHz.
- Aperture size is 3.5cm x 2.6cm.
- Diagonal dimension D = 4.36cm.
- At 18GHz, λ = 1.7cm and at 26GHz, λ = 1.1cm.
- D > λ – electrically large, but not physically large.
- Note: Most aperture antennas are electrically large antennas.

Definitions: Infinitesimal Dipole

- The fields of an infinitesimal dipole are:

$$H_r = H_\theta = 0, \quad E_\phi = 0,$$

$$H_\phi = \frac{j\kappa^2 I_o l \sin\theta}{4\pi}\left[\frac{1}{\kappa r} + \frac{1}{j(\kappa r)^2}\right]*e^{-j\kappa r},$$

$$E_r = \frac{\kappa^3 I_o l \cos\theta}{2\pi\omega\varepsilon_o}\left[\frac{1}{(\kappa r)^2} + \frac{1}{j(\kappa r)^3}\right]*e^{-j\kappa r},$$

$$E_\theta = \frac{\kappa^3 I_o l \sin\theta}{4\pi\omega\varepsilon_o}\left[\frac{1}{\kappa r} + \frac{1}{j(\kappa r)^2} - \frac{1}{(\kappa r)^3}\right]*e^{-j\kappa r}.$$

Definitions: Infinitesimal Dipole

- Thus, for an infinitesimal dipole or for an electrically small antenna,

  $r \ll \lambda/2\pi$, reactive near-field region,

  $r \cong \lambda/2\pi$, transition region,

  $r \gg \lambda/2\pi$, far-field region.

- The $\lambda/2\pi$ boundary is derived from the infinitesimal dipole, but it also applies to small dipole antennas.

Example 1

- EMCO 3160-09 Pyramid Horn antenna has a working frequency range of 18-26GHz.
- Diagonal dimension D = 4.36cm. At 18GHz, λ = 1.7cm and at 26GHz, λ = 1.1cm.
- 3λ = 5.1cm to 3.3cm
- $(5\lambda)/2\pi$ = .812cm to .525cm
- $(50D^2)/\lambda$ = 5.59m to 8.64m
- $(2D^2)/\lambda$ = 22.36cm to 34.56cm
- $\lambda/2\pi$ = .271cm to .175cm

Example 2

- EMCO 3301B Rod antenna has a working frequency range of 30Hz-50MHz.
- D = 1.1m. At 30Hz, λ = 107m and at 50MHz, λ = 6m
- 3λ = 321m to 18m
- $(5\lambda)/2\pi$ = 85.14m to 4.77m
- $(50D^2)/\lambda$ = .565m to 10.08m (Not a precision antenna!!)
- $(2D^2)/\lambda$ = .023m to .403m (Not electrically large!)
- $\lambda/2\pi$ = 17.03m to .955m

Example 2

- EMCO 3301B Rod antenna has a working frequency range of 30Hz-50MHz.
- D = 1.1m.
- At 30Hz, λ = 107m and at 50MHz, λ = 6m
- $D \ll \lambda$ – electrically small, but not physically small.
- Note: Most rod antennas and many wire antennas are electrically small antennas.

Example 3

- EMCO 3115 Double Ridged Waveguide antenna has a wide frequency range of 1GHz-18GHz.
- Aperture dimensions are 14cm x 24cm, so the diagonal D = 28cm.
- For an aperture antenna, its effective aperture is not necessarily the same as its physical size.
- For a broadband aperture antenna, gain is sacrificed to create a broad frequency range. D_e, effective aperture size, is less than D. Sometimes D_e is given.
- Since $D_e < D$, $(2D^2)/\lambda$ will give the maximum nominal far field distance.

Example 3

- **EMCO 3115 Double Ridged Waveguide antenna has a wide frequency range of 1GHz–18GHz.**
- **In order to avoid mutual coupling between Tx antenna and EUT, a few wavelengths of separation are needed.**

F(GHz)	3λ(cm)	λ/2π(mm)	F(GHz)	3λ(cm)	λ/2π(mm)
3	30	15.9	11	8.18	4.3
5	18	9.5	13	6.92	3.6
7	12.9	6.8	15	6.00	3.1
9	10	5.3	18	5.00	2.6

Example 3

- **EMCO 3115 Double Ridged Waveguide antenna has a wide frequency range of 1GHz–18GHz.**
- **Diagonal, D = 28cm. D_e, effective aperture size, is less than D.**

F(GHz)	λ(cm)	(2D²)/λ(m)	F(GHz)	λ(cm)	(2D²)/λ(m)
3	10	1.57	11	2.7	5.75
5	6.0	2.61	13	2.3	6.79
7	4.3	3.66	15	2.0	7.84
9	3.3	4.70	18	1.7	9.41

Summary

- Far field and near field boundaries are not fixed. They depend on:
  - Radiation frequency.
  - Sizes of the transmitting and receiving antennas.
  - Type of antenna.
  - Accuracy that an application requires.
  - Shield or antenna design application.

Agenda

- Classes of Signals
- Instrumentation
- Signal Strength Measurements
- Windowing Concepts
- Test Sites

Classes of Signals

Broadband

The signal has energy spread across the spectrum, beyond the bandwidth of the receiver. Doubling the receiver bandwidth doubles the measured signal power.

Example: A brush type DC motor creates a broadband signal.

Measurements

Tom Holmes   Candace Suriano

Agilent Technologies   Suriano Solutions

tom_holmes@agilent.com SurianoSolutions@comcast.net

August 9, 2005

Classes of Signals

Narrowband

The signal energy is concentrated at one frequency, narrower than the receiver bandwidth. Doubling the receiver bandwidth does not double the measured signal power.

Example: Unmodulated carrier, radio station signal

Agenda

- Classes of signals
- **Instrumentation**
- Signal strength measurements
- Windowing concepts
- Test Sites

Antenna

- There are four types of antennas:
  - resonant,
  - electrically small,
  - aperture antennas
  - broadband antennas.
- Antennas/feedlines exhibit resonant behavior

Classes of Signals

Why is this distinction important?

- Narrowband signals can often completely block a communications channel

- Broadband signals tend to raise the noise floor, reducing signal to noise ratio

Instrumentation For Measuring Signals

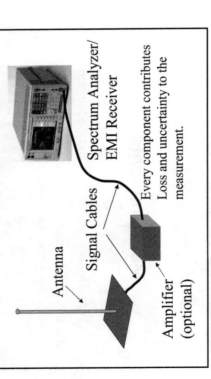

Spectrum Analyzer/
EMI Receiver

Signal Cables

Antenna

Amplifier
(optional)

Every component contributes Loss and uncertainty to the measurement.

Spectrum Analyzer

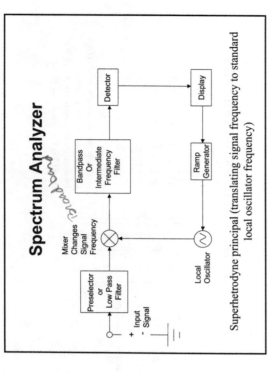

Mixer Changes Signal Frequency

Preselector or Low Pass Filter

+ Input
- Signal

Local Oscillator

Bandpass Or Intermediate Frequency Filter

Ramp Generator

Detector

Display

Superhetrodyne principal (translating signal frequency to standard local oscillator frequency)

Agenda

- Classes of signals
- Instrumentation
- **Signal strength measurements**
- Windowing concepts
- Test Sites

Antenna Polarization

- Maximum response occurs when antenna E-field aligns with incident wave E-field.

- If the E-field is parallel to the ground, then the polarization is considered horizontal.

- If E-field is perpendicular to ground, then it is vertical polarization.

- Vehicle whip antennas are vertically polarized

EMI Receiver/ Spectrum Analyzer

- Similar Architecture

- EMI Receiver/ Spectrum Analyzer display signal amplitude versus frequency

- Spectrum Analyzer is high performance swept frequency receiver – considered more versatile than EMI Receiver. Has tracking filter in front end- sees more energy than EMI receiver

- EMI Receiver specifications defined in CISPR 16

pre-selector

CISPR 14

EMC Measurement Terms

- Peak Detector- records peak value of signal

- Quasi-Peak Detector- an RC filter that weights the repetition rate of a signal. As the duty cycle approaches 100% it approaches the level found by a Peak Detector.

- Average Detector- designed to zero in on narrowband signal contributions and suppress broadband signal contributions.

Comparison of Measurements

All of these values are defined by CISPR 16.

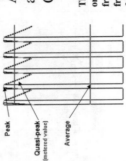

Peak

Quasi-peak
(metered value)

Average

The Quasi-Peak Detector was originally based on radio interference from certain pulse repetition frequencies determined in the 1930's for a CISPR Radio-Noise Meter.

Electromagnetic Field Measurements

- Energy radiated from a source manifests itself as a power density in Watts / square meter.

- Measuring power density is difficult, but measuring the associated electric field (the E-field) is relatively easy. The E-field is measured in Volts/m. (H-field is Amps/m)

- The simplest antennas are easy to calibrate for the E-field.

Peak and Quasi-Peak

Input   Output

Peak Detector

Input   Output

Quasi-Peak Detector

What is CISPR 16 ?

- **Title: Specification for radio disturbance and immunity measuring apparatus and methods.**

- **CISPR is the International Special Committee on Radio Interference**

- **The initials come from the French version of the name.**

- **The specification is published through the IEC (International Electrotechnical Commission).**

- **3rd edition published in 1993.**

CISPR 16 RECEIVER

- **+/- 2 dB accuracy for sine wave measurements.**

- **Defines Peak, Quasi-Peak, Average, and RMS measuring receivers from 9 kHz to 1 GHz.**

- **6 dB measurement BW's are tightly toleranced:**
  - **200 Hz (9 kHz to 150 kHz), +20,-30 Hz,**
  - **9 kHz (150 kHz to 30 MHz), +/- 2 kHz and**
  - **120 kHz (above 30 MHz), +/- 20 kHz.**

- **Receiver must have < 1 dB error while operating in 3 Volts / meter electric field.**

Comparison of Measurements

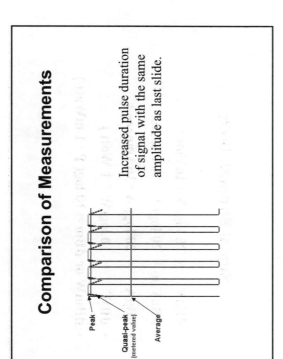

Peak

Quasi-peak
[metered value]

Average

Increased pulse duration of signal with the same amplitude as last slide.

What is CISPR 16 ?

- **It defines the critical characteristics of the measurement device, as well as various ancillary devices, such as antennas.**

- **It also includes procedures for building and validating an Open Air Test Site(OATS).**

- **It runs 220 pages, with French and English versions on facing pages.**

- **Today, we will just talk about the measurement apparatus (receiver), and antenna sections.**

Relationships 101

$$P = \frac{V^2}{R} = I^2R$$

$$\frac{P_1}{P_2} = \frac{V_1^2/R}{V_2^2/R} = \frac{I_1^2R}{I_2^2R}$$

$$10LOG(\frac{P_1}{P_2}) = 20LOG(\frac{V_1}{V_2}) = 20LOG(\frac{I_1}{I_2})$$

Relation of Measurement Units

1 Watt = 0 dBW

1 mWatt = 0 dBm

1 uVolt = 0 dBuV

1 uAmp = 0 dBuA

CISPR 16 RECEIVER

- Emphasis on pulse response of receivers

- Rejection of signals at the IF and image frequencies specified; typically –40 dB to tuned frequency.

- No explicit requirement for a preselector is called out, except in the section on spectrum analyzers used above 1 GHz (6.2 d).

- Scan time range: 0.1 to 10 seconds

Signal Strength Units

- **dBμV** = 20 log(V / 1uVolt)
- **dBuV/m** = 20 log(V / 1uV/meter)
- **dBμA** = 20 log(A / 1uAmpere)
- **dBW** = 10 log(W / 1 Watt)
- **dBmW or dBm** = 10 log(P / 1 mWatt)

Relation of Measurement Units

For 1 uVolt in a 50 Ohm system :

20 log(1 uV) - 10 log(R) = -137 dBW

Since 0 dBW = +30 dBmW

Then: dBmW = dBuV - 107

For a 75 Ohm system:

dBm = dBuV - 108.8

Agenda

- Classes of signals
- Instrumentation
- Signal strength measurements
- **Windowing concepts**
- Test Sites

Relation of Measurement Units

In logarithmic form, $P = V^2 / R$ becomes:

10 log P = 10 log V^2 - 10 log R

Or:

10 log P = 20 log V - 10 log R

Relation of Measurement Units

Similarly, $P = I^2 R$, so:

10 log W = 10 log A^2 + 10 log R

Or:

10 log W = 20 log A + 10 log R

In 50 ohms, 1 uA (0 dBuA) = -73 dBm

And in 75 Ohms, 1 uA = -71.25 dBm

Gaussian Filter Shape in Receiver

Remember: by definition impulsive signal with zero width has signal across all frequencies.

Therefore you must understand IF filter response to broadband signal!! See Amendment 2 to CISPR 16 Part 1.

Window Size & Signal Class

Consider the previous signal. A window is 24 kHz wide, again centered at 20 kHz.

The signal strength is: 10 log(3x) dBmW = 14.8 dBmW, where x is the individual signal amplitude.

Since this is more than 3 dB higher than the previously measured 10 dBmW, this is considered a broadband signal.

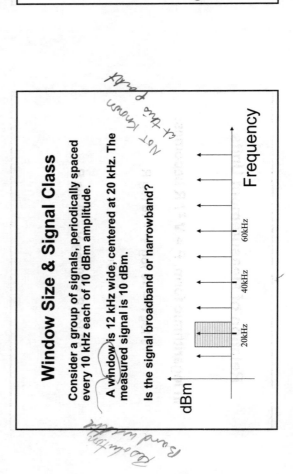

Gaussian Filter Shape in Receiver

Window Size & Signal Class

Consider a group of signals, periodically spaced every 10 kHz each of 10 dBm amplitude.

A window is 12 kHz wide, centered at 20 kHz. The measured signal is 10 dBm.

Is the signal broadband or narrowband?

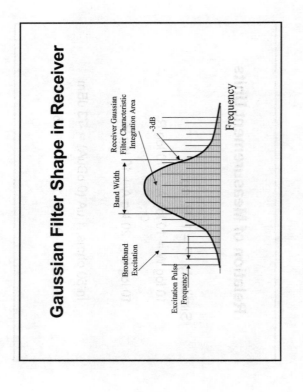

Window Size & Signal Class

In this example, the components are again spaced every 10 kHz, each with 10 dBmW strength.

The window is 4 kHz wide, centered at 20 kHz. The measured signal strength is 10 dBmW.

Is the signal broadband or narrowband?

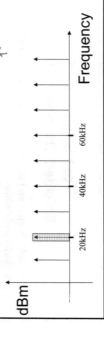

dBm — Frequency — 20kHz 40kHz 60kHz

Window Size & Signal Class

- The "window" is the resolution bandwidth (RBW) of the measurement receiver.

- A typical rule of thumb for NB vs. BB is to increase the RBW by 10X. If the measured level increases by 8 dB or more, then there is a BB signal present.

- A real RBW filter has a Gaussian shape; specified BW is at -3 dB points.

Signal Strength Calculation

Although rather unusual except for certain contrived circumstances, all of these signals have exactly the same amplitude.

10 dBm= 10 mWatt

How to add the three signals together?
10 + 10 + 10 = 30 mW;
10 log(30) = 14.8 dBmW

Window Size & Signal Class

This time, the window is 4 kHz wide, centered at 20 kHz.

The signal strength is the same, for there is only one component of the signal within the window.

This is certainly less than a 3dB increase over 10 dBmW, so this must be a narrowband signal.

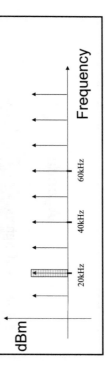

dBm — Frequency — 20kHz 40kHz 60kHz

Test Sites

- Open Air Test Site (OATS)
- Anechoic Chamber
- Semianechoic Chamber
- Reverberation Chamber
- TEM Waveguides
- On Site

Agenda

- Classes of signals
- Instrumentation
- Signal strength measurements
- Windowing concepts
- Test Sites

Test Sites
Shielded Chamber

- Anechoic, Semi-Anechoic, and Reverberation Chambers are shielded chambers

- Shielded chamber attenuates ambient signals, typically 100-115 dB from 100 KHz to 10 GHz, after 10 GHz falls off to about 80-90 dB unless certain precautions are taken. Fall off is due to openings in chamber. (per Garth D'Abreau ETS-Lingren)

- HVAC and fire protection required.

Test Sites
Open Air Test Site (OATS)

- NIST and FCC Preferred site for RE

- Intent is no reflected signals from DUT and no ambient signals to interfere.

- Precipitation can cause reflections.

- Real world has MANY ambient signals at the desirable locations, like your parking lot.

- FCC allows ambient interferers to be subtracted from DUT spectrum.

Test Sites
Semianechoic Chamber

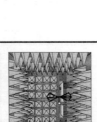

- Same as an anechoic with conductive floor.
- Can be modeled as an open air test site in the frequency range where absorbers are functional.
- Same intent as OATS, with lower ambient.
- Physical size set by DUT, lowest frequency of test, absorber capability and technology.
- Expensive to build, validate, and operate.

Less cost than Anechoic to build maint about same

Test Sites
Anechoic Chamber

- Absorber on all walls and floor.
- Used for EMC testing, to generate antenna patterns and radar cross section measurements.
- Physical size set by DUT, lowest frequency of test, absorber capability and technology.
- Very expensive to build, validate, and operate. Absorber cones may need to be rotated.

Test Sites
TEM Waveguides

GTEM

- TEM Cell (GTEM Cells are a variant of TEM Cells) have the TEM designation because the transverse electromagnetic mode (TEM) is the dominate field produced in the operating portion of the cell.
- TEM Cell specified in ISO 11452-3 and SAE J1113/24
- TEM Cell consists of an enclosed transmission line, with RF power in one end and load resistance in other end. TEM wave travels down the transmission line and sets up a field between the conductors.

Test Sites
Reverberation Chamber

- Random modes generated by changing boundary conditions (wall moving, paddle turning, etc.) result in less time needed to find worse radiated emissions case and statistical field uniformity for immunity testing.
- Small amounts of power generate large field.
- New standards need chamber's time constant.
- Most often used for immunity testing and thresholding.
- Less expensive than anechoic or semianechoic.

mostly for immunity

↓ then make deadspots mode stirrer

A few inches can make a diff

Test Sites
TEM Open Waveguides

- Stripline and Triplate are similar to TEM Cells, they consist of an open transmission line, with RF power in one end and load resistance in other end.

- Must be located in shielded room because of generated fields.

- Stripline test is defined in ISO 11452-5 and   SAE J1113/25.

- Triplate test is defined in SAE J1113/23.

- Lower cost than TEM Cell.

Summary

- Measurements are affected by type of signal (NB or BB) and signal processing

- CISPR 16 sets standards for measuring instruments

- Test site characteristics influence measurements and are specified by test standards

Test Sites
TEM Waveguides

- Expanded waveguide section to fit EUT, where field is uniform and known.

- TEM Cell upper operating frequency limit is inversely proportional to size. Above frequency limit, undesirable modes occur.

- Can be used for radiated emissions.

- TEM Cell is a shielded enclosure.

- Lower cost than a chamber.

Test Sites
On Site

- Sometimes, it is necessary to test on the site where the DUT is used; every site is unique.

- Antenna calibrations are for specific distances and heights above ground; may not be usable on site.

- Inverse square law can be used to correct for distance; use a reference source to verify.

- Time is often short; planning is critical.

•F1

Soft Ferrite Use With Antennas

Paul Zdanowitz
Fair-Rite Products Corp.
zdanowiczp@fair-rite.com

August 9, 2005

Fair-Rite Products Corp. •1

"Your Signal Solution"

•F1

Outline

1. Ferrite overview
   What are ferrites?
   How do they work?
2. Ferrite Applications
3. EMI Suppression Application
   Material Characteristics
   Selecting the Right Core
   Material Selection / Control Performance
4. Cable Shield Current Suppression Example
5. Conclusions

Fair-Rite Products Corp. •2

"Your Signal Solution"

•F1

What Is A Ferrite?

Ferrite is a ceramic material formed by reacting metal oxides into a magnetic material.

- Soft magnetic material is one that can be both easily magnetized and demagnetized, so that it can store or transfer magnetic energy in alternating or other changing wave forms (sine, pulse, square, etc).

CHEMICAL COMPOSITION
(metal oxides) + (iron oxide)

$(MnO + ZnO)$ **Manganese - Zinc**
    $+ (Fe_2O_3) =$
$(NiO + ZnO)$ **Nickel - Zinc**

Fair-Rite Products Corp. •3

"Your Signal Solution"

•F1

What Makes Ferrite Tick

– <u>Ferrite Rod</u> (internal structure)

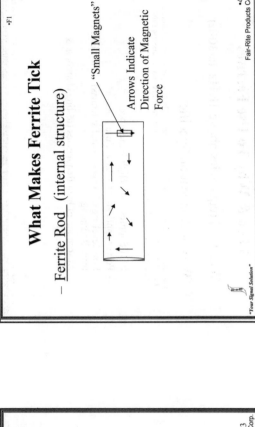

"Small Magnets"

Arrows Indicate
Direction of Magnetic
Force

Fair-Rite Products Corp. •4

"Your Signal Solution"

When & Why To Use Ferrites

When – Frequencies above 1KHz (to 3GHz)

Why – Application Specific

Ferrites are used to process electronic signals. These signals can be filtered, transformed, absorbed, attenuated or concentrated. A broad classification of the product applications are:

- EMI Suppression – High Impedance
- Power applications – Low Core Loss
- Low level signals (Sensors and antennas) – Stop Cables from Radiating
- Absorption of high frequencies (testing chambers & shielding)

"Your Signal Solution" Fair-Rite Products Corp. •6

EMI Suppression
Cable Filtering Applications

- Largest application of suppression ferrites.
- Industrial, computer, telecom, medical, aerospace applications
- Materials: #43; #44; #31; #61; #73; #51, #46
- Shield beads, snap-on cores and flat cable beads

"Your Signal Solution" Fair-Rite Products Corp. •8

What Makes Ferrite Tick
continued

- Excitation Of Ferrites

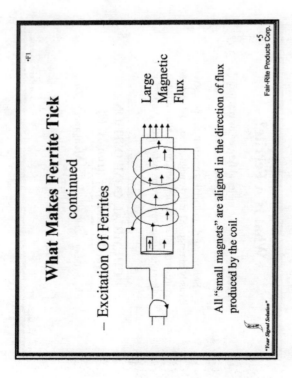

Large Magnetic Flux

All "small magnets" are aligned in the direction of flux produced by the coil.

"Your Signal Solution" Fair-Rite Products Corp. •5

Feedlines/Cables

- There is loss/uncertainty associated with all feedlines/transmission lines
- Loss is defined per unit measure for cables
- Balun is **balanced** to **unbalanced**- adds impedance between antenna and feedline
- Common Mode currents (shield currents) crawl about on feedlines creating unbalanced condition and need to be decreased

"Your Signal Solution" Fair-Rite Products Corp. •7

Intrinsic Characteristics/Applications

EMI Suppression Applications

Intrinsic Characteristics
Complex Permeability [u' & u'']
High Impedance

Applications
Antennas
Computers and peripherals
Communication Systems
Automobiles
Switch Mode Power Supplies
dc-dc converters
ignition coils

"Your Signal Solution" Fair-Rite Products Corp. •9

Material Characteristics

(handwritten: after saturation slope helping; μ = 1; sweet spot; Nickel Zinc)

43 Material

Property	Unit	Symbol	Value
Initial Permeability @ B < 10 gauss		μ_i	850
Flux Density @ Field Strength	gauss oersted	B H	2000 10
Residual Flux Density	gauss	B_r	1300
Coercive Force	oersted	H_c	.45
Temperature Coefficient of Initial Permeability (20-70 C)	%/C		1.25
Loss Factor @ Frequency	10^{-6} MHz	$\tan\delta/\mu_i$	250 1.0
Curie Temperature	°C	T_c	>130
Resistivity	Ω cm	ρ	$1 \cdot 10^5$
Recommended Frequency Range EMI Applications	MHz		20 - 250

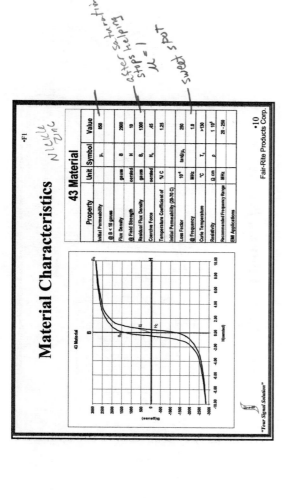

"Your Signal Solution" Fair-Rite Products Corp. •10

SELECTING THE RIGHT FERRITE CORE

THE SOURCE of EMI

FREQUENCY of DESIRED SIGNAL VS. NOISE

CIRCUIT IMPEDANCE [LOAD and SOURCE]

ENVIRONMENTAL CONDITIONS

ALLOWABLE SPACE

Fair-Rite Products Corp. •11

Impedance Math

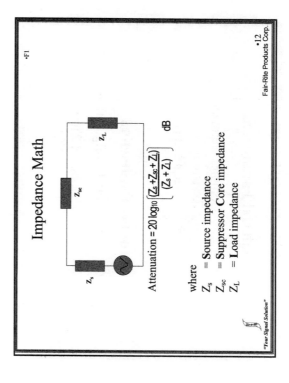

$$\text{Attenuation} = 20 \log_{10}\left[\frac{Z_s + Z_{sc} + Z_L}{Z_s + Z_L}\right] \quad dB$$

where
Z_s = Source impedance
Z_{sc} = Suppressor Core impedance
Z_L = Load impedance

"Your Signal Solution" Fair-Rite Products Corp. •12

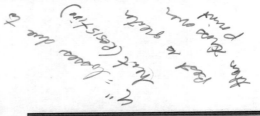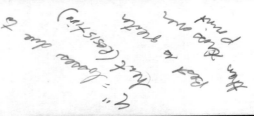

Material Parameters

μ_s' & μ_s'' — Complex Permeability
ρ — Resistivity
T_c — Curie Temperature

Product Parameters

C_1 — Core Configuration
N^2 — Number of Turns

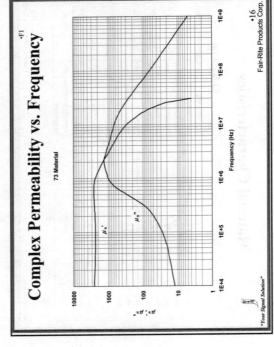

Complex Permeability vs. Frequency

73 Material

μ_s' μ_s''

Frequency (Hz): 1E+4, 1E+5, 1E+6, 1E+7, 1E+8, 1E+9

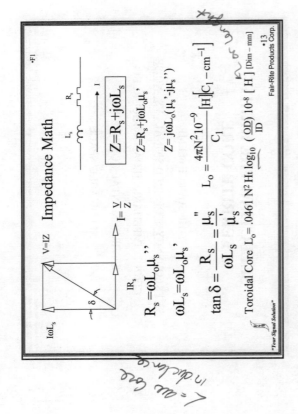

Impedance Math

$$Z = R_s + j\omega L_s$$

$V = IZ$, $I = \dfrac{V}{Z}$

$Z = R_s + j\omega L_o \mu_s'$

$Z = j\omega L_o(\mu_s' - j\mu_s'')$

$R_s = \omega L_o \mu_s''$

$\omega L_s = \omega L_o \mu_s'$

$\tan\delta = \dfrac{R_s}{\omega L_s} = \dfrac{\mu_s''}{\mu_s'}$

$L_o = \dfrac{4\pi N^2 10^{-9}}{C_1}\,[\mathrm{H}]\,\big[C_1 - \mathrm{cm}^{-1}\big]$

Toroidal Core $L_o = .0461\,N^2\,Ht\,\log_{10}\left(\dfrac{OD}{ID}\right)10^{-8}\,[\mathrm{H}]\,[\mathrm{Dim-mm}]$

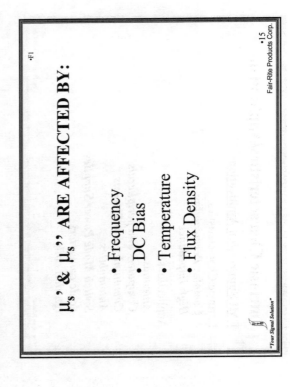

μ_s' & μ_s'' ARE AFFECTED BY:

- Frequency
- DC Bias
- Temperature
- Flux Density

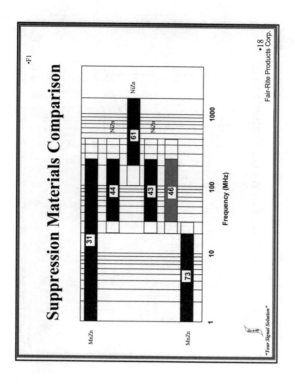

Impedance vs. Frequency

2773009112 Bead On Lead (1 turn)

•F1

Fair-Rite Products Corp.

•17

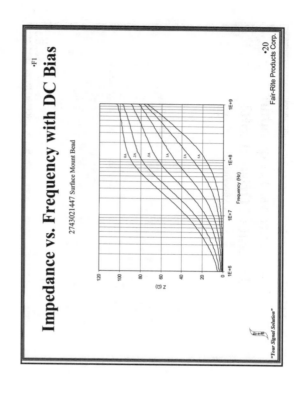

Suppression Materials Comparison

•F1

Fair-Rite Products Corp.

•18

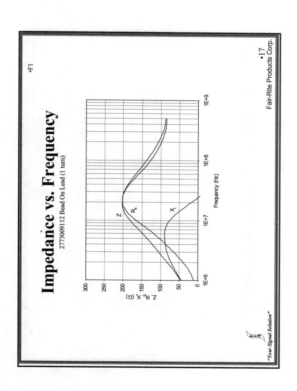

Comparison Impedance vs. Frequency

26–000301

•F1

Fair-Rite Products Corp.

•19

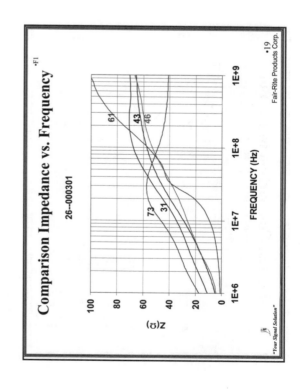

Impedance vs. Frequency with DC Bias

2743021447 Surface Mount Bead

•F1

Fair-Rite Products Corp.

•20

Impedance vs. Temperature
Percent of Original 25ºC
73 Material

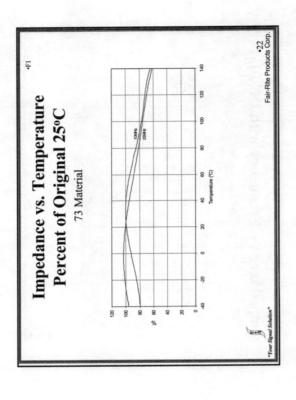

The Effect of Turns on Impedance

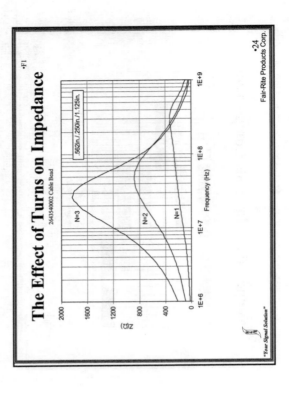

Material Comparison w/ DC Bias

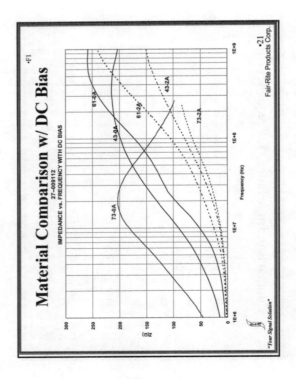

Amplitude Permeability vs. Flux Density

43 Material

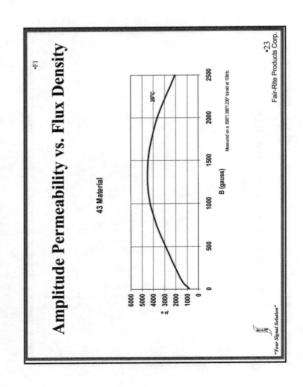

Slide 25

Review – Desirable Material Properties For EMI Suppression [F1]

(handwritten: Good)

- High core loss (u'') in the intended frequency range (magnetic losses)
  Note: low eddy current loss (high resistivity)

- High permeability at the low frequency range (high u')

- Resistance to dc-bias (i.e. high incremental permeability vs. H)

- Good thermal stability (Z vs. T)

- High Curie Temperature (Tc)

- Resistance to thermal shock

"Your Signal Solution"

Fair-Rite Products Corp. •25

Slide 26

Various Ferrite Configurations [F1]

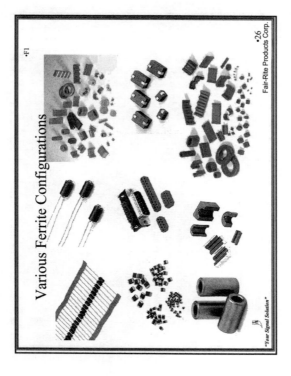

"Your Signal Solution"

Fair-Rite Products Corp. •26

Slide 27

Why So Many Different Shapes? [F1]

Answer: Each shape has unique feature(s) which are required in each specific application.

- Low cost   - Easy to wind the coil
- Simple to assemble   - Good magnetic shielding
- Availability of standard sizes

Why So Many Different Materials?

Answer: Each material has unique properties which are required for a specific application

- High permeability   - High saturation
- Low losses (except in EMI) -Low variability (temp & time)
- High Curie temperature

"Your Signal Solution"

Fair-Rite Products Corp. •27

Slide 28

Common-Mode vs Differential-Mode [F1]

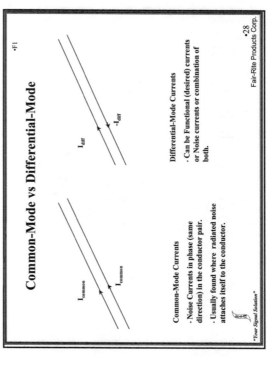

Common-Mode Currents

- Noise Currents in phase (same direction) in the conductor pair.

- Usually found where radiated noise attaches itself to the conductor.

Differential-Mode Currents

- Can be Functional (desired) currents or Noise currents or combination of both.

"Your Signal Solution"

Fair-Rite Products Corp. •28

Common-Mode Choke

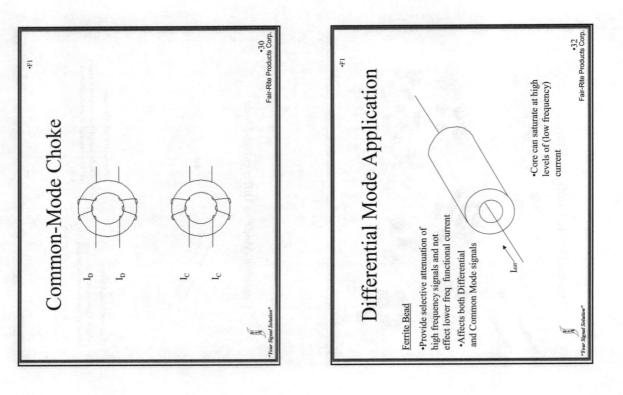

"Your Signal Solution"

Fair-Rite Products Corp.

Differential Mode Application

Ferrite Bead

•Provide selective attenuation of high frequency signals and not effect lower freq functional current

•Affects both Differential and Common Mode signals

I_{diff}

•Core can saturate at high levels of (low frequency) current

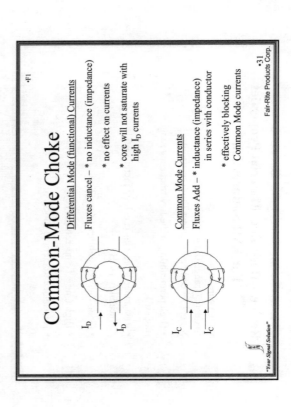

"Your Signal Solution"

Fair-Rite Products Corp.

Common-Mode Application

I_{diff}

$-I_{diff}$

$I_{Common-Noise}$

$I_{Common-Noise}$

"Your Signal Solution"

Fair-Rite Products Corp.

Common-Mode Choke

Differential Mode (functional) Currents

Fluxes cancel – * no inductance (impedance)
  * no effect on currents
  * core will not saturate with high I_D currents

Common Mode Currents

Fluxes Add – * inductance (impedance) in series with conductor
  * effectively blocking Common Mode currents

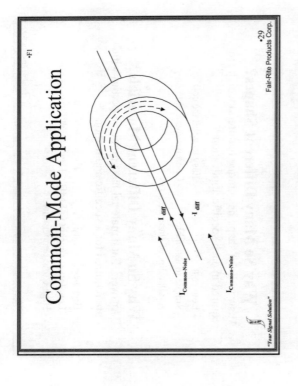

I_D I_D

I_C I_C

"Your Signal Solution"

Fair-Rite Products Corp.

Soft Ferrite Common Mode Chokes for Cables

- Cable Suppression Core

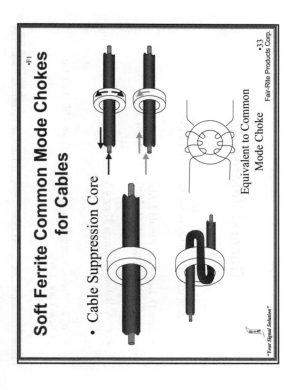

Equivalent to Common Mode Choke

•33   Fair-Rite Products Corp.

Need for Ferrite Example

•F1

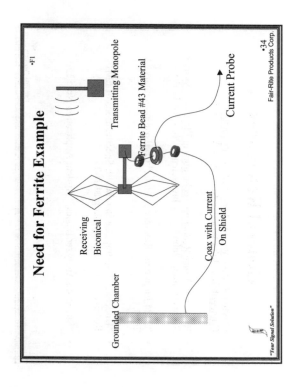

Transmitting Monopole

Ferrite Bead #43 Material

Current Probe

Receiving Biconical

Coax with Current On Shield

Grounded Chamber

•34   Fair-Rite Products Corp.

Need for Ferrite Example

•F1

Current Probe + 2 Beads

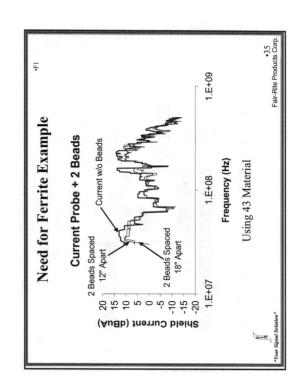

Using 43 Material

•35   Fair-Rite Products Corp.

Need for Ferrite Example

•F1

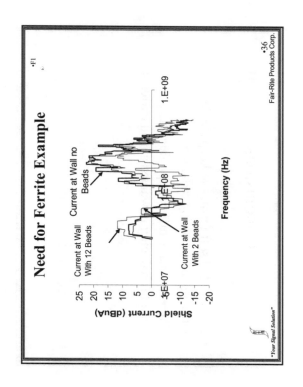

•36   Fair-Rite Products Corp.

151

Conclusions

- Cables need soft ferrites to keep shield currents from causing radiation
- There are many different products to choose from for reducing unwanted shield currents

"Your Signal Solution" — Fair-Rite Products Corp. •38 •F1

Suppression Materials Comparison

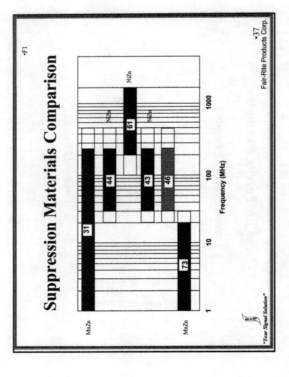

"Your Signal Solution" — Fair-Rite Products Corp. •37 •F1

General References

- W. L. Stuzman and G. A. Thiele, <u>Antenna Theory and Design</u> 2nd Edition, John Wiley & Sons, Inc, N.Y., 1998.

- John D. Kraus and Ronald J. Marhefka , <u>Antennas</u>, McGraw-Hill Science / Engineering / Math; 3rd Edition, 2001.

- C. A. Balanis, <u>Antenna Theory Analysis and Design</u> 2nd Edition, Wiley 1996.

- W. L. Weeks, <u>Antenna Engineering</u>, McGraw-Hill Book Co., New York, 1968.

"Your Signal Solution" — Fair-Rite Products Corp. •39 •F1

General References

- Clayton R. Paul, <u>Introduction to Electromagnetic Compatibility</u>, John Wiley & Sons, New York, 1992.

- H. W. Ott, <u>Noise Reduction Techniques in Electronic Systems</u>, Second Edition, John Wiley Interscience, New York, 1988.

- "2004 Engineers' Reference Guide," *Conformity*, January 2004.

- "Understanding Impulse Bandwidth Specifications of EMI Receivers," *Conformity*, August 2005.

- "Spectrum Analyzer Basics," Agilent Application Note 150

"Your Signal Solution" — Fair-Rite Products Corp. •40 •F1

WORKSHOP: INTENTIONAL EMI (MO-PM-WS-8)
Dr. Bill Radasky
Metatech Corporation, US

This tutorial is intended to provide a broad overview of the problem of Intentional EMI (IEMI) covering the definitions of terms, the examination of the threats, the types of effects that may occur, the methods of protection, and the work ongoing to standardize society's response to this new threat.

This half-day presentation will begin with a historical background of the problem with emphasis on the international organizations and conferences that have dealt with this area. Next we will introduce the different types of threat waveforms that may be generated (with actual examples provided) and the terminology involved with narrowband and wideband threats. A major portion of this tutorial will examine the types of effects that have been noted experimentally by leading researchers in the field, including the impacts of IEMI on computer systems and networks. The tutorial will conclude with a discussion of mitigation methods and efforts that are progressing in standardization.

This tutorial will be useful for those who wish to understand this new threat to electronic systems in general and for those who are concerned about security threats to their offices and factories and the products that they produce.

This tutorial will be presented by two leading researchers in the field: Dr. Bill Radasky of Metatech Corporation, US and Mr. Richard Hoad of QinetiQ, UK.

Presentations (not available for publication):

(1) Introduction to Intentional Electromagnetic Interference (IEMI)
    Bill Radasky and Richard Hoad

(2) The Effect of IEMI on Equipment and Systems
    Richard Hoad and Bill Radasky

(3) Mitigation Concepts and Approaches for IEMI
    Bill Radasky and Richard Hoad

(4) Standardisation Activities in the IEC
    Richard Hoad and Bill Radasky

NOTES

OUTLINE

- Introduction to the Threat of IEMI
- Types of IEMI Threat Environments
- Examples of IEMI Generators
- IEMI Protection Approach
- The International Electrotechnical Commission (IEC) Standardization Program in High Power EM
- Summary

Metatech

INTRODUCTION TO THE IEMI THREAT-2

- Electromagnetic (EM) weapons possess an energy source (e.g. battery, capacitors) and an antenna
- They are designed to produce and propagate a high power EM field to a significant distance from the weapon
- These weapons have mainly been designed for military purposes
- The technology is not difficult to apply for a qualified engineer
- Commercial electronics equipment is typically not protected against these types of threats
- A new term has been used over the past 6 years to describe this threat and its effects on commercial equipment – IEMI (Intentional Electromagnetic Interference)

Metatech

Introduction to Intentional Electromagnetic Interference (IEMI)

Metatech

Dr. William A. Radasky, Ph.D., P.E.
Metatech Corporation, USA
wradasky@aol.com

Mr. Richard Hoad
QinetiQ, UK
rhoad@QinetiQ.com

8 August 2005

Metatech

INTRODUCTION TO THE IEMI THREAT-1

- High Power Electromagnetics (HPEM) has been defined to describe high level electromagnetic fields and their effects on systems, including
  - Lightning EM Pulse fields (sometimes referred to as LEMP)
  - Electrostatic Discharge (ESD)
  - Radar fields (sometimes referred to as HIRF)
  - EM pulsed fields in power substations due to arcing events
  - High altitude Electromagnetic Pulse (HEMP)
  - Intentional use of EM weapons against civil systems (IEMI)
- Our interest in this tutorial is to primarily describe the threat of IEMI with some discussion of the HEMP

Metatech

Metatech

WHAT IS INTENTIONAL EMI (IEMI)?

Definition:

Intentional malicious generation of electromagnetic energy introducing noise or signals into electric and electronic systems, thus disrupting, confusing or damaging these systems for terrorist or criminal purposes

(Zurich EMC Symposium, February 1999; Also IEC 61000-2-13:2005)

Metatech

5

WORLDWIDE SCIENTIFIC ACTIVITY IN IEMI

- URSI published a resolution in 1999 dealing with the criminal activities of EM "tools" and the need to protect against the emerging threat
- The International Electrotechnical Commission (IEC) SC77C (EMC: High Power Transient Phenomena) is writing standards to deal with this problem
- The IEEE EMC Society published a special issue on IEMI in August 2004 and is working on a standard to protect publicly accessible computers from IEMI
- Many EMC and HPEM Conferences are dealing with the subject of IEMI
- Private companies are developing methods of threat assessments, protection methods, and monitors

Metatech

6

WHY IS IEMI OF INTEREST?

- Terrorist threats are increasingly of concern world-wide
- Intentional EMI is a new threat dimension
- Attractiveness of covert operations outside of physical barriers
- Technological advances in higher energy RF sources and antennas
- Increasing proliferation of IEMI sources and knowledge world-wide
- Increasing dependence on information and on automated mission-critical and safety-critical electronic systems
- Increasing EM susceptibility for new high density IT systems working at higher frequencies and lower voltages

Metatech

7

AUGUST 1999 TORONTO: THE URSI RESOLUTION -- 1

The URSI Resolution of Criminal Activities using Electromagnetic Tools was intended to make people aware of:

- The existence of criminal activities using electromagnetic tools
- The fact that criminal activities using electromagnetic tools can be undertaken covertly and anonymously
- The potential serious nature of the effects of criminal activities using electromagnetic tools on the infrastructure
- The possible disruption on the life, health and economic activities of nations could have a major consequence

Metatech

8

COMPARISON OF HPEM ENVIRONMENTS

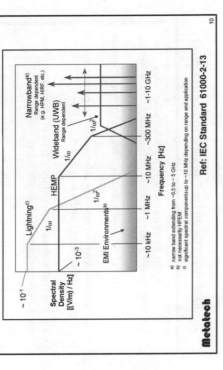

Ref: IEC Standard 61000-2-13

10

NARROWBAND WAVEFORMS AND SPECTRA (~1 GHz)

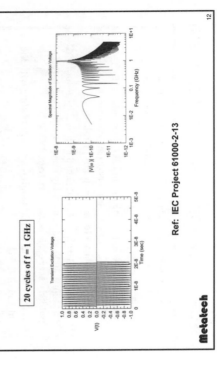

20 cycles of f = 1 GHz

Ref: IEC Project 61000-2-13

12

AUGUST 1999 TORONTO: THE URSI RESOLUTION -- 2

The URSI Council resolved that URSI should recommend to the scientific community in general and the EMC community in particular to take into account this threat and to undertake the following actions:

- Perform additional research to establish appropriate levels of vulnerability
- Investigate techniques for appropriate protection to protect the public
- Develop high-quality testing and assessment methods
- Provide reasonable data regarding the formulation of standards of protection

9

NARROWBAND IEMI WAVEFORMS

- Nearly single frequency (percent BW < 1%) high power and energy signal in a pulse with duration up to microseconds and usually radiated within the band 0.3 – 3 GHz

- Pulses can be repetitive and frequency can vary with time and/or be modulated. Maximum coupling occurs if tuned to a significant resonance in system transfer function. May cause permanent damage when system communication frequencies are matched

- Many systems have significant resonance susceptibilities at only particular frequencies, thereby limiting the threat from a single frequency IEMI generator

11

156

WIDEBAND IEMI WAVEFORMS

- A single pulse produces frequency and energy content over a wide range of frequencies. The pulse may be repeated.

- Main frequency content and power is spread over a very broad spectrum usually within 0.3 – 3 GHz. Bandratio (90% of energy) is used instead of percent bandwidth.

- Multiple resonances can be stimulated simultaneously
  - Energy produced in a single pulse is spread over many frequencies
  - It takes typically an order of magnitude more peak field than a properly tuned narrowband device to cause harm
  - More likely to cause interference than permanent damage as coupling is through unintentional (and indirect) coupling paths

---

WIDEBAND WAVEFORM AND SPECTRA (~1 GHz)

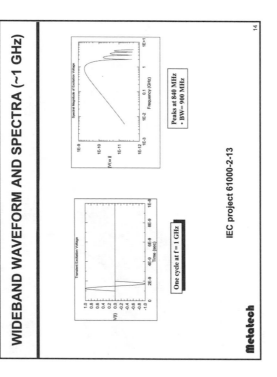

One cycle at f = 1 GHz

Peaks at 840 MHz
- BW= 900 MHz

IEC project 61000-2-13

IEMI BANDWIDTH DEFINITIONS (IEC 61000-2-13)

	Percentage Bandwidth	Bandratio
hypoband or narrowband	< 1%	< 1.01
mesoband	1% < pbw ≤ 100%	1.01 < br ≤ 3
sub-hyperband	100% < pbw < 163.4%	3 < br ≤ 10
hyperband	163.4% < pbw < 200%	br ≥ 10

$$\text{band ratio} = br = \frac{f_h}{f_l}$$

$$\text{band ratio decades} = brd = \log_{10}(br)$$

$$pbw = 200 \frac{(br-1)}{(br+1)}$$

$$br = \frac{\left[1 + \dfrac{pbw}{200}\right]}{\left[1 - \dfrac{pbw}{200}\right]}$$

COUPLING PATHS FOR RADIATED IEMI FIELDS

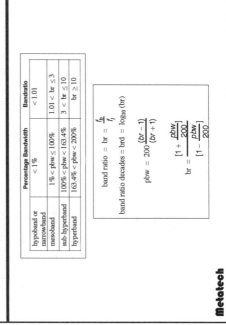

Mobile EM Transmitter

Communication & Data lines

Window

Network

Commercial Power

CONDUCTED IEMI THREAT ENVIRONMENT WAVEFORM TYPES

- Conducted threats include same two basic waveform types
  - Narrowband and wideband
  - Lower frequencies reach sensitive equipment more easily since propagation along lines have lower losses
  - Created from radiated field coupling and direct injection
- Narrowband
  - Frequency range of a few hertz to 1 GHz
  - High power concentrated in narrow bandwidth
- Wideband
  - Single pulse has frequency content between 1 kHz and 1 GHz
  - High rep rate possible for faster waveforms (up to 1 MHz)

Metatech

17

EM THREAT DEVICES

- High power briefcase/suitcase-sized EM devices are commercially available from Diehl Munitions in Germany
- Scientists have built laboratory devices (source and antenna) that are approximately 0.5 by 0.5 meters in size
- Other EM device kits are available on the Internet and can even be constructed from microwave ovens and surplus radars
- Technically qualified personnel can develop sources

Metatech

18

DIEHL EM EMITTER

- Diehl Munitions Systeme is marketing a small interference source (including antenna)
  - 350 MHz damped sine field
  - 120 kV/m at 1 meter (omni-directional antenna)
  - 30 minute continuous operation (5 pulses per second) or 3 hours in bursts
  - 20 x 16 x 8 inches and 62 pounds
  - Price per unit = 150,000 Euros
- Demonstration in Summer 2004

Metatech

19

LABORATORY UWB EMITTER

Parameters	Values
Amplitude at 20 m distance	2 kV/m
Pulse duration	0.2 ns
Pulse repetition rate	Up to 1000 Hz
Antenna aperture	0.35 m × 0.35 m

Metatech

20

JOLT IRA UWB EMITTER

21

- AFRL has developed an extremely powerful IRA system that produces UWB pulses
  —E*R = 5.3 MV
  —pulse width ~100 ps

Metatech

IEMI PROTECTION APPROACH

22

- Due to the nature of the threat of Intentional EMI, there are two separate aspects to be considered to provide adequate protection for the example of a building
  —Security approach
  —Electromagnetic approach

- A combination of both approaches is usually most cost effective

- This topic is discussed later in this tutorial

Metatech

IEC STANDARDIZATION DEALING WITH IEMI

23

- The International Electrotechnical Commission (IEC) has been developing HEMP standards and reports since the late 1980s
  —IEC SC 77C began work in 1992

- Initial emphasis was to provide the means to protect civil electronics equipment from the effects of high-altitude (generally above 30 km) nuclear bursts (HEMP)
  —Scope of work in Subcommittee 77C expanded in June 1999 to include all high-power EM transient threats, including IEMI

- More details will follow later in this tutorial

Metatech

IEMI INTRODUCTION SUMMARY

24

- The definition of IEMI and different types of threat environment waveforms have been established

- Information about IEMI emitters has indicated their likely size and power thereby allowing the development of threat field levels for different system classes

- Significant work in the area of equipment susceptibility has been accomplished and is discussed later in this tutorial

- Given the threat environment and the susceptibility levels of commercial equipment, mitigation needs and levels can now be determined -- discussed later in this tutorial

- Standardization work is well underway in the IEC
  —More details later in this tutorial

Metatech

The Effect of IEMI on Equipment and Systems

Richard Hoad, QinetiQ
E-mail: rhoad@qinetiq.com
Dr. Bill Radasky, Metatech Corp.
E-mail: wradasky@aol.com

Content

- Background
  - A short film
  - Environment
- System Effects
  - Case Studies
    - Impact
  - Experimental data
    - Test Methods
    - Published data
    - Detailed example
- Summary

A short film

Environment

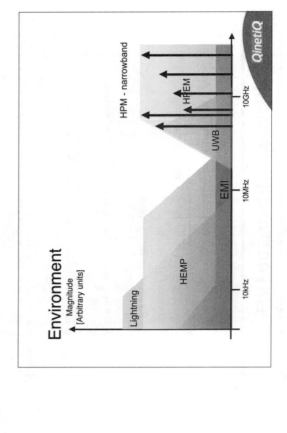

System Effects – Case Studies

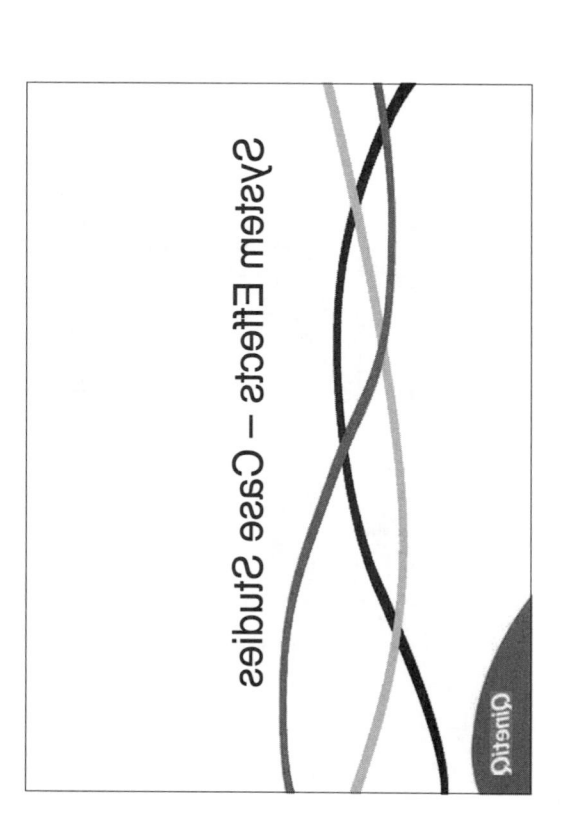

QinetiQ

HEMP Effects

- First reported during Starfish test conducted by the US in 1962
  - Johnston Atoll
  - 1400km to Oahu, Hawaii
  - Exo-atmospheric
  - 400km burst altitude
  - 1MT yield

Honolulu: fireball viewed from Starfish, 800 miles away

Source : The US EMP Congressional Commission – Executive Summary

QinetiQ

HEMP Effects

- In Hawaii:
  - Estimated field strength of 5.6kV/m
  - Burglar alarms and air raid sirens went off
  - Some streetlights extinguished while others came on
  - A string of 30 lights failed in one area
  - Several fuses blown

Source : IEC 61000-1-3 The effects of high-altitude EMP (HEMP) on civil equipment and systems

QinetiQ

Reality!

- All electronics will be upset or damaged by EM fields providing the power is high enough

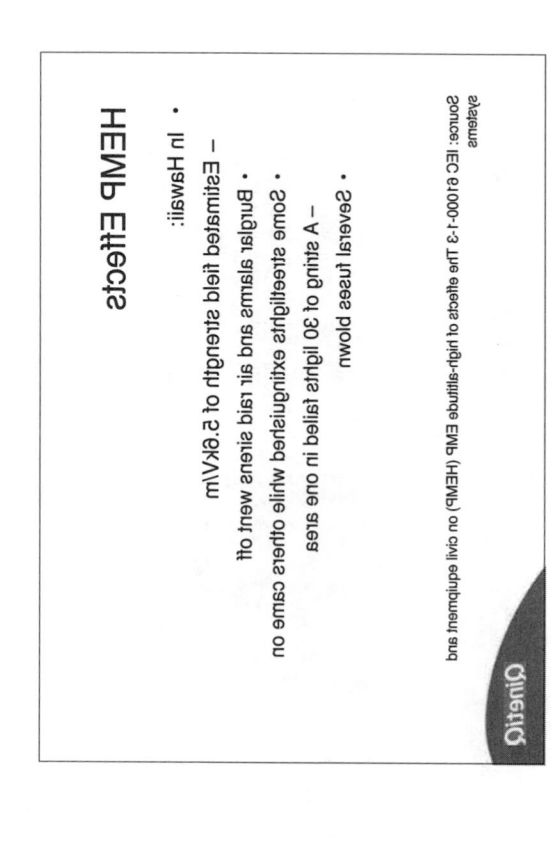

Source: IEC – www.iec.ch

QinetiQ

EMP Congressional Commission

EMP Commission
Public Law 106-398,
Title XIV

Vulnerability of US Military and Civilian Systems

- One or a few high-altitude nuclear detonations can produce EMP, simultaneously, over wide geographical areas
- Unprecedented cascading failure of our electronics-dependent infrastructures could result
  - Power, energy transport, telecom, and financial systems are particularly vulnerable and interdependent
  - EMP disruption of these sectors could cause large scale infrastructure failures for all aspects of the Nation's life
- Both civilian and military capabilities depend on these infrastructures
- Without adequate protection recovery could be prolonged—months to years

Source: The US EMP Congressional Commission – *Executive Summary*

Horror Stories:

- The *Apache* helicopter, EMI triggered an over-speed condition that could have resulted in double engine failure.
- In mid-May 1984, a Soviet ammunition depot exploded. The cause of the accident, according to the Soviets, was an over-the-horizon radar that had illuminated the depot.
- B-52 Bomber, use of the HF radio resulted in the uncommanded activation of all rear empennage flight control surfaces

Source: NASA Reference Publication 1374

HEMP Effects

Observed EMP Anomalies During USSR Atmospheric Testing October 1962

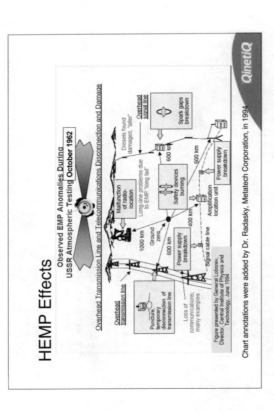

Chart annotations were added by Dr. Radasky, Metatech Corporation, in 1994.

Horror Stories

- NASA published an unclassified report documenting various EMC related vulnerabilities.
- The following are extracts from this document.

System Effects – Experimental data

Test Methods [2]

- 'Hybrid' EMC tests
  - FAR Immunity type tests
  - Reverberation chamber
  - Advantages
    - Wide range of environments
    - Better repeatability
    - Lower Uncertainty
  - Disadvantages
    - Match to true IEMI waveforms
    - Less realistic environment?

Horror Stories: USS Forrestal

- 1967 off the coast of Vietnam
- Uncommanded release of munitions that struck a fully armed and fueled fighter on deck.
- The results were explosions, the deaths of 134 sailors, and severe damage to the carrier and aircraft.

Test Methods [1]

- Open air - High Power Simulator testing, such as:
  - HPM, Magnetron sources
  - Specialised Test Environments (TEM cell)
  - Advantages
    - Closest match to true IEMI waveforms
    - Platform level illumination
  - Disadvantages
    - Narrow range of environments
    - Expensive
    - Unique facilities
    - Difficult to compare contrast results with other facilities
    - Repeatability
    - Uncertainty of measurement

Susceptibility Levels for a Computer Motherboard for Radiated EM Pulse Variations

Susceptibility level of the 233 MHz MB

Legend: HPRF, MPRF, LPRF

Pulse risetime/pulsewidths:

WIS EMP10 - 10/200 ns
WIS EMP1 - 1/80 ns
WIS UWB up - 90/2500 ps
Rheinmetall UWB - 200/500 ps
WIS UWB bp - 100/350 ns

Note: Small variations are seen for different pulse repetition rates

Source: Daniel Nitsch, et. al., IEEE EMC Transactions, Aug. 2004

Programmable Logic Controller (PLC) Analog Input Injection Test (5/50 ns)

- Arcs observed, at about the 3 kV pulse level
- Upset: A/D output (digital reading) does not respond to analog input (reset with off/on power cycle) at 2.5 kV pulse level (analog current input)
- Permanent damage: 3.5kV for unit 1, 4.5kV for unit 2 (analog voltage input). Output bits permanently stuck; all 4 ports damaged (all share a single A/D converter)
- Shot 74, 4.5kV, A/D unit damaged; peaks: 3890V (blue), 54.6A (red)

Source: Savage, et. al., Metatech Corp., Zurich EMC Symposium, February 2005

Component Susceptibility data

Example of measured susceptibility thresholds for a TTL component as a function of frequency:

DM74LS00N [TTL] Quad 2-Input NAND Gate

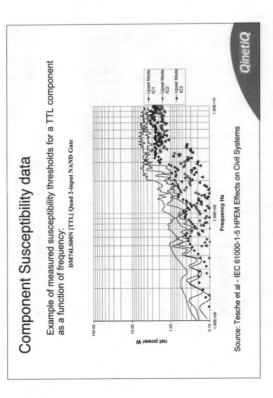

Source: Tesche et al - IEC 61000-1-5 HPEM Effects on Civil Systems

---

10 Base-2 Semiconductor Damage

Damage to chip caused by 500 V 10/700 microsecond Telecom Pulse (IEC 61000-4-5) injected on cable

Source: M. Messier, Metatech, Zurich 2001

Susceptibility Of Automobiles, Narrowband Radiated Fields

- Fixed frequencies between 1.3 – 15 GHz were tested

- Most prominent effects at the lower test frequencies, also when the car was not operating. Types of damage observed included: engine control units, relays, speedometer, revolution counter, burglar alarm, and a video camera.

- Upset (engine stop): 500 V/m

- Permanent damage: 15 kV/m at 1.3 GHz
  24 kV/m at 2.86 GHz

Source: Dr. Mats Bäckström, Zürich 1999

Detailed Investigation

- Compare EMI susceptibilities of Modern IT equipment :
  - Same Brand and specification Computers (Batch testing)
  - Different Brand same specification Computers (Brand testing)
  - Trends in different specification Computers
  - Computer Networks

Results of Electronic Cash Machine (ECM) Tests With UWB Radiated Fields

TABLE 1: Upset levels

ECM type	SAMSUNG ER-4615RF	SAMSUNG ER-250RF
Critical level of UWB field, kV/m	2.3–2.5	2.2–2.4

TABLE 2: Level of damage

Level of UWB field, kV/m	2.5	3.1	3.9	4.4	4.8	5.1
Result	Upset	Upset	Upset	Upset	Upset	Damage

Source: Dr. Yuri Parfenov, IHED, Russia, Presented at EUROEM 2004

System Effects – Experimental data – Detailed Example

Reverberation Chamber

One of three reverberation chambers at QinetiQ

Equipment Under Test

- 5 Modern desktop PCs selected for testing
  - 1 off Brand C 1.4GHz, Pentium IV
  - 1 off Brand I 1.4GHz, Pentium IV
  - 3 off Brand D 667MHz, Pentium III
- Historical data on EM vulnerability of 486 computers
- Computer Network equipment

Failure mode	During EM	Impact	After EM
Monitor	Temporary blanking or severe interference	Monitor not usable	Returns to normal
Mouse	Random movement of pointer	Mouse not usable	Returns to normal
Program close	Mouse deflection and input closes program	possible loss of unsaved data	Soft program restart required
Crash - (SR)	Computer stops and latches up	Likely loss of unsaved data	Soft program restart required
Crash - (MR)	Computer stops and latches up	Needs hard reset– extended downtime	Recycle mains, illegal shutdown detected
Shutdown - (SR)	Computer switches off startup screen appears	Extended downtime – loss of confidence	illegal shutdown detected
Shutdown - (MR)	Computer switches off and stays off	Extended downtime – loss of confidence	Recycle mains, illegal shutdown detected
Damage	Physical damage to hard disk or othecomponent	Long term outage	Repair

SR = Self Restart   MR = Manual Restart

Test Configuration

- Equipment Under Test (EUT) mounted on copper test bench
- Equipment cables on 50mm spacers above bench
- All EUTs powered via Line Impedance Stabilising Networks (LISN)
- Pulse modulated RF carrier
  - 30us pulse width 1kHz p.r.f.
- Mode stirring used - tuner speed 1 rpm
- DO160D Equation used

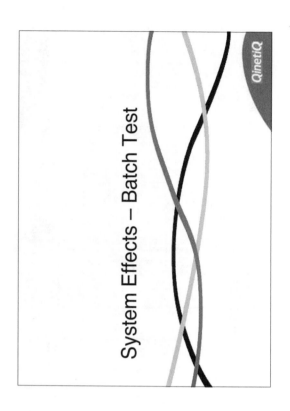

System Effects – Batch Test

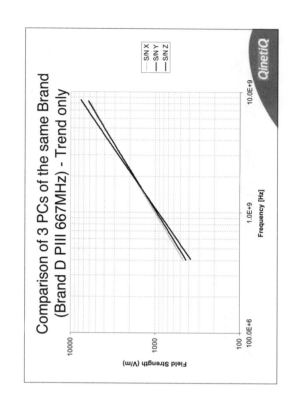

Comparison of 3 PCs of the same Brand (Brand D PIII 667MHz) - Trend only

Observed Effects

- Screen Interference
- Mouse deflection
- 'Pop ups'
- Program Crash
- Shutdown

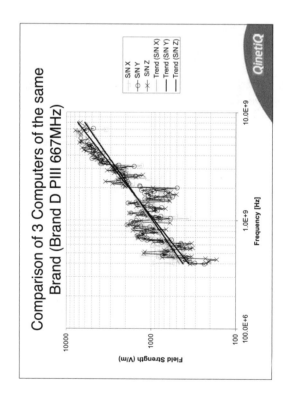

Comparison of 3 Computers of the same Brand (Brand D PIII 667MHz)

Summary of PIII 667MHz (batch test) results

- Results indicate that for susceptibility batch variation is within ± 3dB
- The types of failure observed were similar

Comparison of 2 PCs of the same Specification (PIV 1.4GHz) - Trend only

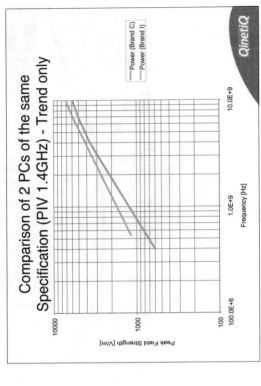

Comparison of 3 PCs of the same Brand (Brand D PIII 667MHz) - with error bars

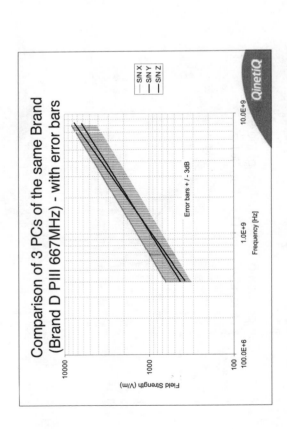

System Effects – Brand Test

Summary of Brand Test results

- Results indicate that Brand C is more vulnerable than Brand I, this is probably due to build quality
- The failures observed were more severe for Brand C
- Permanent damage to Brand C hard drive occurred
- It was necessary to re-install the windows environment (approx. 1.5hrs downtime)

Expectation

- Newer PCs are *more* susceptible than older PCs because:
  - Faster operating speeds
  - Faster edge transition speeds
  - Lower switching Voltages

Courtesy of the International Technology Roadmap for Semiconductors (ITRS) 2003

Comparison of 2 PCs of the same Specification (PIV 1.4GHz) - with error bars

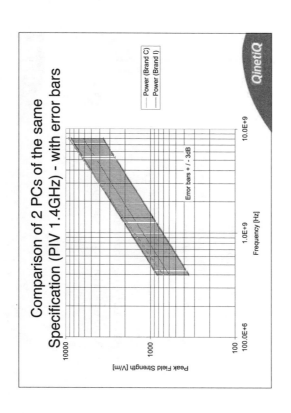

System Effects – Trend

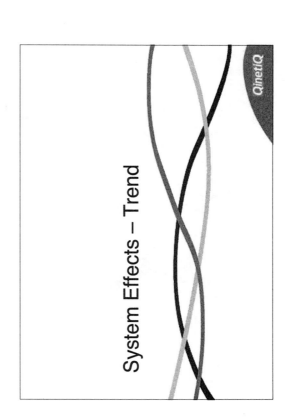

Trends

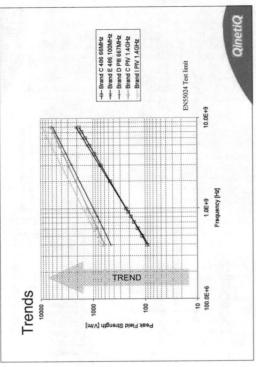

Legend:
- Brand C 486 66MHz
- Brand E 486 100MHz
- Brand D PIII 667MHz
- Brand C PIV 1.4GHz
- Brand I PIV 1.4GHz

TREND

Peak Field Strength [V/m]

Frequency [Hz]

EN55024 Test limit

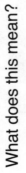

Fair test ? - Operating Parameters

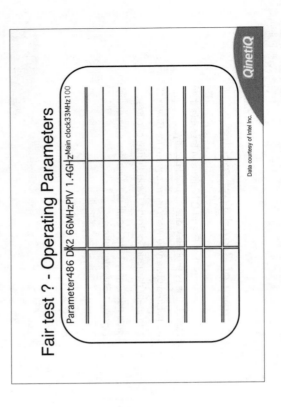

Parameter 486 DX2 66MHz PIV 1.4GHz Main clock 33MHz 100

Data courtesy of Intel Inc.

Trends

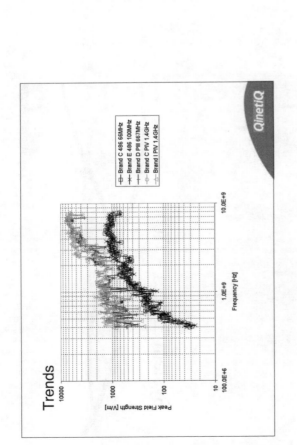

Legend:
- Brand C 486 66MHz
- Brand E 486 100MHz
- Brand D PIII 667MHz
- Brand C PIV 1.4GHz
- Brand I PIV 1.4GHz

Peak Field Strength [V/m]

Frequency [Hz]

What does this mean?

- Indications are that modern, high speed computers are harder (less susceptible) than their predecessors - *Goes against expectation*

- But the impact of the effect is more severe (longer down times)

- Batch testing has shown minimal differences

- Brand testing has shown some differences which are probably due to build quality

Techniques used to mitigate Emissions/ aid signal integrity

- Mechanical means
  - Finger stock on PC case
  - Grounded heat-sink (Faraday Cage)
  - Motherboard ground ring pads
  - Multi-layer PCBs (P4 = 6 layers)
  - Edge stitching
- Other means
  - Dithered (Spread Spectrum) Clock oscillators
  - Differential clock drivers
  - Selective clock gating

Emission Mitigation methods (heat-sink)

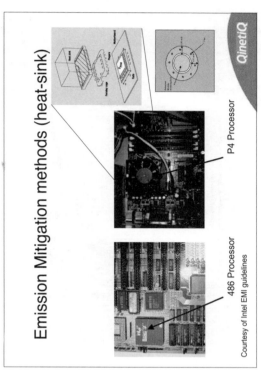

P4 Processor

486 Processor

Courtesy of Intel EMI guidelines

What's changed? Emission and immunity limits

- Commercial and military emission and immunity limits haven't changed significantly over the period (5 years) of development
- (CISPR16, CISPR22, EN61000, EN55022)

- However, emissions and especially signal integrity of concern to PC manufacturers

Emission mitigation methods (Case)

Upper cover

Overlap margin
An overlap is created on each edge of the upper and lower covers so that no gap exists between them.

Lower cover

Fingers
The fingers are installed so that the upper and lower covers maintain good contact with each other.

Courtesy of Intel EMI Guidelines

171

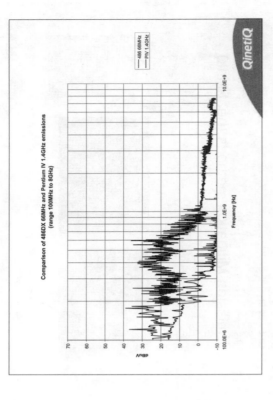

Comparison of 486DX 66MHz and Pentium IV 1.4GHz emissions
(range 100MHz to 8GHz)

486 66MHz
PIV 1.4GHz

System Effects – Networks

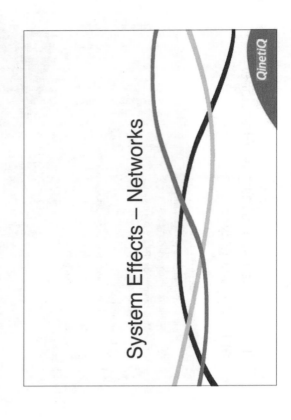

Emission mitigation methods (clock conditioning)

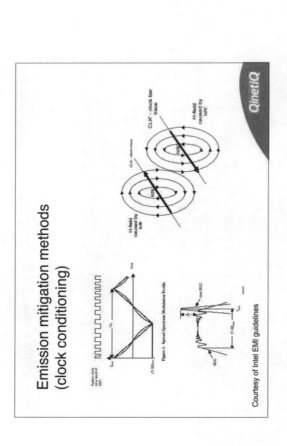

CLK - clock trace

CLK* - clock bar trace

H-field caused by Iclk

H-field caused by Iclk*

Figure 1. Spread Spectrum Modulation Profile

Courtesy of Intel EMI guidelines

Summary of Brand Test results

- Modern, high speed computers are harder than their predecessors

  Probably because

- Manufacturers are getting smarter about controlling signal condition, emissions, and interference

Networked Computers - Ethernet LAN

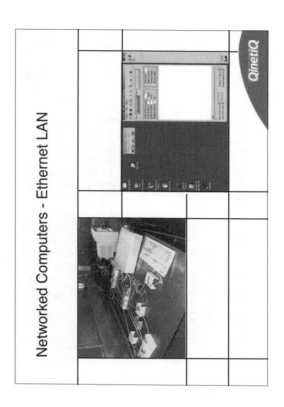

QinetiQ

Network- Two Computers under test

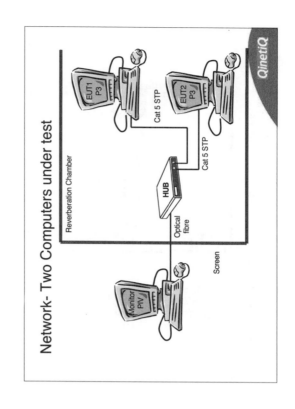

QinetiQ

Basic Network

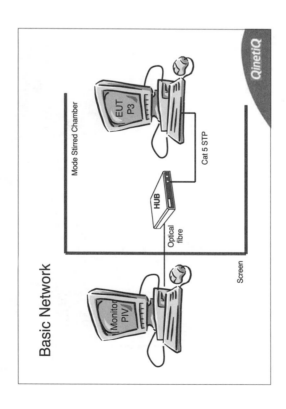

QinetiQ

Network Effect vs Computer Effect

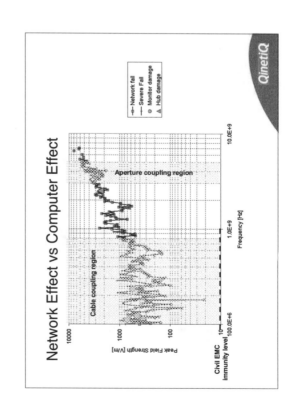

QinetiQ

Networked PCs - PC, Hub, and Router

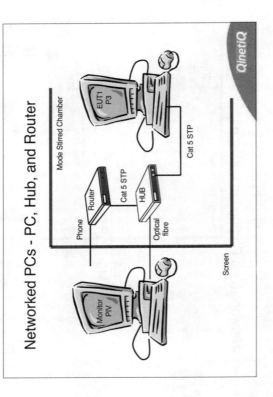

Summary of Network Test results

- Network failure (Denial of Service) generally occurs at a lower susceptibility level than Computer severe failure
- When Denial of Service occurs it is necessary to cycle the power supply of the hub/switch to re-start communications
- Networks - Monitor, Hub and Router Power supplies vulnerable to damage
- Computer susceptibility threshold unaltered by network connection

Severe fail (1PC) Vs Severe fail (2PCs)

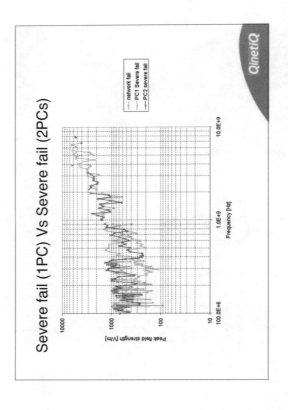

Networked PCs - PC, Hub, and Router

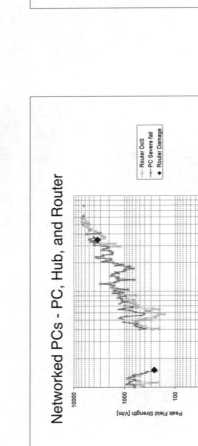

Summary

- IEMI has the potential to cause a wide range of effects to systems
- The impact of the effect is dependent on the function of the system
- Computer systems pervade all levels of society
- Computer systems have been shown to be susceptible to IEMI
- Further work is required to assess the threat of IEMI and advise on protection of civil systems

QinetiQ

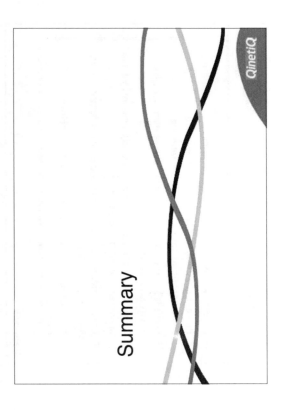

Summary

QinetiQ

MITIGATION CONCEPTS AND APPROACHES FOR IEMI

Dr. William A. Radasky, Ph.D., P.E.
Metatech Corporation, USA
wradasky@aol.com

Mr. Richard Hoad
QinetiQ, UK
rhoad@QinetiQ.com

8 August 2005

Metatech

IEMI PROTECTION APPROACH

- Due to the nature of the threat of Intentional EMI, there are two separate aspects to be considered to provide adequate protection for the example of a building
  - Security approach
  - Electromagnetic approach
- A combination of both approaches is usually most cost effective

Metatech

2

SECURITY APPROACH FOR PROTECTION

- Develop a "keep out" or buffer zone around your building
- Prevent unauthorized access to all power and communications cables entering the building
- Prevent IEMI emitters from being placed near sensitive electronic systems
- Keep important internal electronics equipment away from the outer walls of the building
- Use redundancy and diverse routing for important wiring inside the building
- Ensure that backup power is available for critical operations

Metatech

3

ELECTROMAGNETIC APPROACH FOR PROTECTION

- Monitor building rooms with external exposure and building wiring for unusual transients
  - Provide alarms to security personnel if high levels and/or repetitive transients are detected
- Provide EM shielding for critical equipment
- Provide surge protection and filters for cables connected to critical equipment
- Use non-metallic fiber optic cables for internal communications when possible
- Ensure that the grounding system is properly designed
- Develop an IEMI verification program to periodically test the facility at low levels (CW and pulse)

Metatech

4

EXAMPLES OF IEMI HARDENING AND PROTECTION CONCEPTS

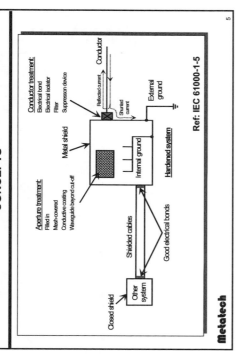

Ref: IEC 61000-1-5

Aperture treatment:
Filled in
Mesh-covered
Conductive coating
Waveguide beyond cut-off

Conductor treatment:
Electrical bond
Electrical isolator
Filter
Suppression device

Closed shield

Other system

Shielded cables

Good electrical bonds

Metal shield

Internal ground

Hardened system

Reflected current

Shunted current

Conductor

External ground

Metatech

5

CAN OUR PAST HEMP EXPERIENCE BE USEFUL?

- **Experience with high altitude EMP (HEMP) has shown that EM shielding and POE protection are the best defenses against external EM threats**

- **HEMP has significant frequency content below 100 MHz**

- **IEMI environments may possess significant energy above 1 GHz**

- **To leverage from HEMP experience**
  — **Improve EM shielding above 100 MHz**
  — **Improve POE filtering above 100 MHz**

Metatech

6

THE ROLE OF EM MONITORS - 1

- **For many cases the threat of IEMI is one of disruption of operation as opposed to permanent damage**

- **Many IEMI threat generators have battery capabilities that can last for hours**

- **Monitoring for high level radiated and conducted transients can be useful to evaluate system malfunctions**
  — Radiated field monitors can establish that a facility or its subsystems are under attack
  — Conducted transient monitors can be used to monitor critical data lines

- **Portable radiated IEMI monitors can also be useful to locating a threat generator quickly by security personnel**

Metatech

7

THE ROLE OF EM MONITORS - 2

- **Desirable monitor features – radiated EM**
  — Ability to detect both narrowband and wideband threats inside and outside of a facility
  — Narrowband from 0.3 to 3 GHz (basic requirement)
  — Wideband for pulsewidths wider than 200 ps
  — Peak detection should have some ability to adjust

- **Desirable monitor features – conducted EM**
  — Ability to detect both narrowband and wideband threats mainly inside a facility
  — Narrowband from 1 - 100 MHz (basic requirement)
  — Wideband for pulsewidths wider than 10 ns
  — Peak detection should have ability to adjust

Metatech

8

OVERALL IEMI ASSESSMENT APPROACH

- Each commercial facility can be assessed against IEMI threats
  - Examine basic geometry of a building and locations where IEMI threats could be present
  - Determine the critical systems/sub-systems that need to be protected
  - Evaluate the balance between security measures and EM monitoring and protection
  - Determine the balance between mitigation and cost relative to the criticality of the system functions
  - Develop overall mitigation plan including test methods to validate the protection (before, after, and during maintenance/surveillance)

Metatech

10

IEMI RADIATED FIELD MONITOR

Portable "Canary" EM detector developed by QinetiQ

Metatech

9

Slide 1

QinetiQ

Standardisation Activities in the IEC

Richard Hoad, QinetiQ
E-mail: rhoad@qinetiq.com

Dr. Bill Radasky, Metatech Corp.
E-mail: wradasky@aol.com

1

Slide 2

QinetiQ

Content

* Structure of SC's within the TC
* Objective and Background of SC77C
* Active Projects
* Summary

2

Slide 3

QinetiQ

Structure of TC 77: Electromagnetic Compatibility

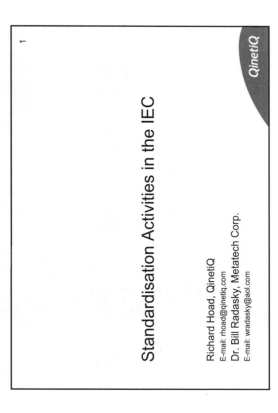

TC 77 SCOPE: PREPARE EMC STANDARDS AND REPORTS WITH EMPHASIS ON BASIC IMMUNITY AND EMISSION STANDARDS. SUPPORT PRODUCT COMMITTEES ON REQUEST.

3

Slide 4

QinetiQ

Organisation of work in SC 77C

* Objective is to provide voluntary standards for civil systems to protect against all man made high power EM transients including a HEMP event

* Secretariat is held by UK: Richard Hoad is Secretary

* Chairman is Dr. William Radasky, USA

* Participating Nations (P-members)
  – Austria, Bulgaria, China, Finland, France, Germany, Italy, Japan, Korea (Republic of), Mexico, Norway, Poland, Romania, Russian Federation, Sweden, Switzerland, Thailand, United Kingdom and USA (19)

  –

* Observing Nations (O-members)
  – Belgium, Brazil, Canada, Croatia, Czech Republic, Denmark, Ireland, Israel, Netherlands, Portugal, Slovakia, Spain, Turkey, and Ukraine (14)

4

Background

- The IEC has been developing High-altitude Electromagnetic Pulse (HEMP) Standards and reports since the late 1980s
  - SC77C was formed in 1992
- Initial emphasis was to provide the means to protect civil electronics equipment from the effects of HEMP generated by high-altitude nuclear bursts
- Scope of work in subcommittee SC77C expanded in June 1999 to include all High Power EM transient threats (HPEM)
- High Power generally refers to radiated fields or conducted voltages and currents which have the capability to disrupt electronic systems (e.g. greater than 100V/m and greater than 100V)
- Work comprises 17 projects of which 16 are published

QinetiQ

5

Major Structure of IEC TC 77 Standards

- Seven Parts defined for 61000 Series
  - 1: General
  - 2: Environment
  - 3: Limits
  - 4: Testing and measuring techniques
  - 5: Installation and mitigation guidelines
  - 6: Generic standards
  - 9: Miscellaneous

QinetiQ

6

SC 77C Project Organisation

61000-1- (General)	-3 HEMP EFFECTS ON SYSTEMS	-5 HPEM EFFECTS ON SYSTEMS

61000-2- (EM Environment)	-9 HEMP RADIATED ENVIRONMENT	-10 HEMP CONDUCTED ENVIRONMENT	-11 CLASSIFICATION OF HEMP ENVIRONMENTS	-13 HPEM ENVIRONMENTS

61000-4- (Testing and Measuring Techniques)	-23 TEST METHODS RADIATED	-24 TEST METHODS CONDUCTED	-25 HEMP IMMUNITY TESTS	-32 HEMP SIMULATOR COMPENDIUM	-33 HPEM MEASUREMENT METHODS

61000-5- (Installation and Mitigation Guidelines)	-3 HEMP PROTECTION CONCEPTS	-4 SPECIFICATIONS FOR RADIATED PROTECTION	-5 SPECIFICATIONS FOR CONDUCTED PROTECTION	-6 MITIGATION OF EXTERNAL EM INFLUENCES
	-7 EM CODE			

61000-6- (Generic Standards)	-6 GENERIC STANDARD FOR HEMP IMMUNITY

QinetiQ

7

What is HEMP? - IEC 61000-2-9

- High-altitude Electromagnetic Pulse (HEMP)
  - Exo-atmospheric nuclear detonation (>30km)
  - There are three time portions of the HEMP waveform
- Nuclear Radiation interacts with the atmosphere
  - Gamma Rays produce Compton electrons
  - Electrons are deflected by the earth's magnetic field
  - Transverse electron currents produce transverse electric fields
- HEMP is the *only* nuclear effect of concern at Ground Level (i.e. Blast, Thermal, Ionising radiation not an issue)

QinetiQ

8

Description of HEMP Environment IEC 61000-2-9

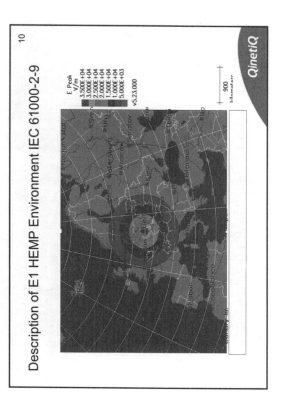

Description of E1 HEMP Environment IEC 61000-2-9

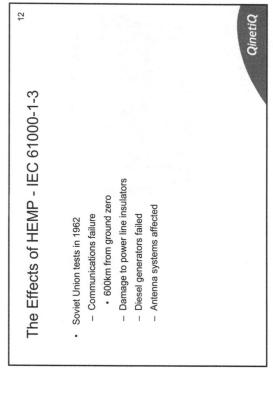

The Effects of HEMP - IEC 61000-1-3

- First reported during Starfish test conducted by the US in 1962
  - Johnston Atoll (1400km to Oahu, Hawaii)
  - 400km burst altitude (exo-atmospheric)
  - 1MT yield
- In Hawaii:
  - Estimated field strength of 5.6kV/m
- Burglar alarms and air raid sirens went off
- Some streetlights extinguished while others came on
  - A string of 30 lights failed in one area
- Several fuses blown

The Effects of HEMP - IEC 61000-1-3

- Soviet Union tests in 1962
  - Communications failure
    - 600km from ground zero
  - Damage to power line insulators
  - Diesel generators failed
  - Antenna systems affected

HEMP Simulator Compendium: 61000-4-32

13

- This report summarizes the characteristics of the large HEMP simulators throughout the world
  - Test volume size
  - Polarization
  - Peak field in test volume
  - Rise and fall time of pulse

- 39 simulators from 13 countries are included

HEMP Simulator Compendium: 61000-4-32

14

Example: QinetiQ Guided Wave HEMP simulator

- Only UK simulator
- 4m x 4m x 4m volume
- Vertical E-Field
  - Max. 90kV/m
- Separate shielded instrumentation chamber

HEMP Protection concepts 61000-5-3

15

- The report describes basic HEMP protection concepts for civil facilities
  - Covers both existing and new facilities
  - Defines specific HEMP protection classes
- Protection principles covered
  - Zoning
  - Radiated environment protection
  - Conducted environment protection
  - Wiring and installation guidelines
  - Relationship of HEMP and lightning protection principles

- HEMP protection concepts and classes are described for buildings and enclosures

HPEM Radiated Environments IEC 61000-2-13

16

- The objective of this standard was to develop a set of electromagnetic environments that are able to create interference in commercial electronic systems. These form the basis for protection methods.
  - Wideband waveforms (single plus bursts) -- "UWB"
  - "Single" frequencies formed into pulses -- "HPM"
  - Both types may occur under radiated or conducted conditions

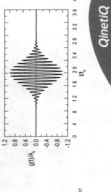

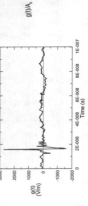

182

Measurement Methods IEC 61000-4-33

17

- Standard provides information on the development of complete measurement systems for time domain transients

  - Overall measurement concepts
  - Measuring equipment (sensors, attenuators, baluns, integrators, recording equipment)
  - Measurement procedures
  - Data processing

Sensor · Balun · Attenuator · Integrator · Fiber optic transmitter · Fiber optic receiver · Waveform digitizer · Data acquisition and control · Coaxial cable · Fiber optic cable

QinetiQ

IEC SC 77C Publications and Active Projects

Title	Number	Stage	Project Leader
Part 1: GENERAL			
The effects of high-altitude EMP (HEMP) on civil equipment and systems	61000-1-3	PUB	W. Radasky, USA
High power electromagnetic (HPEM) effects on civil systems	61000-1-5	PUB	W. Radasky, USA
Part 2: EM ENVIRONMENT			
Description of HEMP environment: radiated disturbance	61000-2-9	PUB	G. Champiot, France
Description of HEMP environment: conducted disturbance	61000-2-10	PUB	W. Radasky, USA
Classification of HEMP environment	61000-2-11	PUB	W. Radasky, USA
High power electromagnetic (HPEM) environment - radiated and conducted	61000-2-13	PUB	N. J. Carter, UK

QinetiQ

IEC SC 77C Publications and Active Projects

Title	Number	Stage	Project Leader
Part 4: TESTING AND MEASUREMENT TECHNIQUES			
Test methods for protective devices: HEMP and other radiated disturbance	61000-4-23	PUB	F. Tesche, USA
Test methods for protective devices: HEMP conducted Disturbance	61000-4-24	PUB	W. Büchler, Switzerland
HEMP immunity test methods for equipment and systems	61000-4-25	PUB	P. Barnes, USA
HEMP simulator compendium	61000-4-32	PUB	C. Giles, USA
Measurement methods for high-power-transient parameters	61000-4-33	FDIS	A. Kaelin, Switzerland
Part 5: INSTALLATION AND MITIGATION GUIDELINES			
HEMP protection concepts	61000-5-3	PUB	M. Ianoz, Switzerland
Specification of protective devices: HEMP radiated Disturbance	61000-5-4	PUB	J. Delaballe, France
Specification of protective devices: HEMP conducted Disturbance	61000-5-5	PUB	W. Büchler, Switzerland
Mitigation of external EM influences	61000-5-6	PUB	W. Radasky, USA
Degrees of protection by enclosures (EM code)	61000-5-7	PUB	C. Jones, USA
Part 6: GENERIC STANDARDS			
Generic standard for HEMP immunity for indoor equipment	61000-6-6	PUB	P. Barnes, USA

QinetiQ

IEC SC77C Summary

- The IEC has established a subcommittee to develop standards for protecting civil systems from HEMP and other high-power EM HPEM Environments. This will help manufacturers and facility owners to protect their equipment from the effects of these disturbances

  - Presently seventeen documents are part of the formal program
  - Sixteen publications are now complete
  - Remaining publication is expected late 2005
  - Maintenance cycle begins
  - New projects anticipated (HPEM simulator compendium)

QinetiQ

WORKSHOP: BPL: THE ISSUES (MO-PM-WS-9)
Don Heirman, Tom Fagan, and Bob Scully

This workshop is intended to provide an introduction and to present signal measurements for the new broadband access of internet services using the power line as the transport medium and the send/receive connection provided by simply connecting a PC to the AC power line. For short this is called BPL or Broadband access over Power Lines. The focus will be on describing the BPL systems under development and in field trial and the EMC impact of such transmissions over the power line. Speakers will represent hardware manufacturers, users, regulators and those interested in the RFI potential to existing radio services.

Presentations:

(1) Technical Overview of Broadband Powerline (BPL) Communication Systems
   Robert G. Olsen

(2) EMC Factors Applicable to Broadband Over Power Line Systems
   Ed Hare

(3) Report on Standard P1675 - Broadband Over Power Line Hardware
   Terry Burns

(4) Overview of FCC Requirements for Broadband Over Powerline
   William Hurst

(5) NATO and Power Line Telecommunications
   Arto Chubukjian

NOTES

Technical Overview of Broadband Powerline (BPL) Communication Systems

Robert G. Olsen
School of Electrical Engineering and Computer Science
Washington State University
Pullman, WA, USA
bgolsen@wsu.edu

Abstract -- **The use of the electric power transmission and distribution system as a transmission medium for broadband powerline (BPL) communications is considered. Since the power system was not designed for this purpose, it is useful to identify any significant technical hurdles to be overcome before BPL systems can be successfully implemented. Two are discussed here. The first is the relatively high channel attenuation rate due to discontinuities such as taps, transformers and other devices connected to the system. The second is system unbalance and its effect on meeting government regulated limitations on electromagnetic emissions. The potential profitability of a BPL system is affected by both phenomena**

I. INTRODUCTION

The possible use of the power transmission and distribution system as a waveguiding structure for high data rate or broadband communications (e.g., internet connection) will be examined in this paper. Generally, the higher the rate of information transfer (i.e., data rate measured in bits per second (B/sec)), the larger the signal bandwidth and the higher the range of frequencies used will be. Since internet connections may require bandwidths well in excess of 1 MHz, the use of frequencies up to 30 MHz will be considered.

The fundamental question to be asked is how the power system (designed to be operated at 50/60 Hertz) responds to signals in the 2 – 30 megahertz range. Clearly, the power system was not designed for this application.

The most significant advantage of broadband power line (BPL) communication systems over their wired competition (e. g., xDSL and cable modem) is that they do not require an entirely new infrastructure. The most serious technical challenges to BPL systems are first, channel attenuation due to junctions such as taps, connected elements such as transformers and the lack of matched transmitter/receiver impedances and second, system unbalance and its effect on meeting legal limits on electromagnetic emissions from these unlicensed systems. The first causes the attenuation rate for high frequency signals to be quite high and very frequency dependent and (together with background noise and input power limitations due to the latter) results in possibly unacceptable limits on the range of the system. Reduction of the attenuation and/or emissions to more reasonable levels through system conditioning may require a financial investment that is incompatible with the requirement that the system be profitable.

II. CHANNEL ATTENUATION

There are two major causes of high frequency attenuation in a power line communications channel. The first is attenuation due to ohmic absorption in the materials that make up the physical channel. This absorption varies with frequency and leads to attenuation rates of approximately 1 dB/km. The second (and by far most important) is attenuation due to reflections from abrupt discontinuities and mismatched impedances (e.g., underground to overhead risers, taps, transformers and capacitors) that occur along the power line. These reflections cause part of the signal to be diverted away from the receiver and absorbed in other parts of the system. This phenomenon can lead to attenuation rates of 40 dB/km or more.

A. Transformers

The effect of transformers on the propagation of high frequency signals is complex. This is evident from an examination of the high frequency equivalent circuit for a single phase transformer shown in Fig. 1. It is clear that the capacitances and inductances may resonate and present low or high impedances for various frequencies. One result of this is that the transmission of signals through a transformer is a very strong function of frequency.

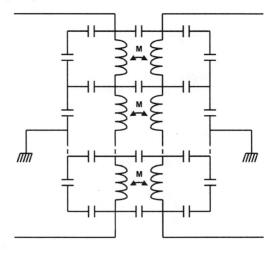

Fig. 1. High frequency equivalent circuit for a single phase transformer

The best way to characterize transformers is to measure their impedance matrix (i.e. the set of complex valued self and mutual impedances needed to characterize a four port network) or scattering parameters (amplitude and phase) [1]. These data can be incorporated into computer programs that are used to model propagation of communication signals on power lines. In the absence of such data, a "rule-of-thumb" is that attenuation of high frequency signals across transformers ranges from 10 – 20 dB and is strongly dependent on frequency.

B. Attenuation Due to Junctions

Consider a single phase overhead power line that consists of two parallel wires of radius "a" and spacing "d." As mentioned earlier, the attenuation of a signal with frequency less than 30 MHz is 1 dB/km or less. If, however, there is a tap along the line as shown in Fig. 2, the situation is significantly different.

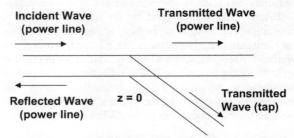

Fig. 2. Transmitted and reflected waves at a power line tap.

In this case it is assumed that the line geometry for the power line and its tap is the same so that the characteristic impedance and propagation constant of each line is Z_0 and $\gamma = \alpha + j\beta$ respectively. When a wave is incident upon the junction, two things happen. First, there is a reflected wave generated. A second effect of the junction is that transmitted waves are created beyond the junction on both the transmission lines and the tap. Because there is more than one path for the transmitted wave, it is split into two (in this example) and hence has smaller amplitude than it would have if there were only one path for the transmitted wave.

Since the transmission lines carrying the signal beyond the junction are in parallel, the input impedance for the incident wave equals $Z_0/2$. It can then be shown that the transmission coefficient (T) which is the ratio of the signal voltage amplitude on the power line for $z > 0$ to the incident signal voltage amplitude is

$$T = 2/3 \qquad (1)$$

Thus, the two transmitted waves are attenuated by 3.5 dB. It can also be shown that there is a reflected wave that is 9.5 dB below the incident wave amplitude.

A second example of a discontinuity along the power line is a change in line type. One common change is from overhead to underground as shown in Fig. 3.

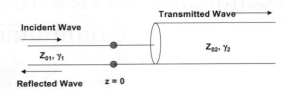

Fig. 3. Overhead to underground line transition.

It can be shown that the transmission coefficient for this junction is

$$T = \frac{2Z_{02}}{Z_{01} + Z_{02}} \qquad (2)$$

where Z_{01} and Z_{02} are the characteristic impedances of the overhead and underground lines. Since typical values of Z_{01} and Z_{02} are 500Ω and 50Ω respectively, the transmitted wave would be attenuated by 15 dB. It is clear that such a transition can have a significant effect on the propagation of communication signals. It can also be shown that if the transmitted wave is small, the reflected wave is large. The desire to reduce these effects is one reason that networks are sometimes conditioned by adding components to "match" the junction (i.e., reduce reflections).

C. Connected Devices, Mismatches and System Attenuation

Until this point, the loss has been estimated by calculating the transmission and/or reflection coefficients at specific types of junctions. In fact, the calculation of total system attenuation is more complicated than this because waves traveling in each direction are reflected and transmitted many times from each junction. To study this, it is necessary to examine an entire system. To this end, consider the very simple 1 km long single phase power system shown in Fig. 4. The power line in this system has a wire radius and spacing of 1 cm and 1 m respectively. The resulting characteristic impedance of this line is 636 Ω.

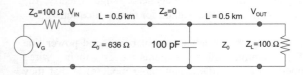

Fig. 4. Uniform transmission line with a shunt 100 pF capacitor at its center and mismatched at transmitter and receiver since each has a 100 Ω input impedance

In this system there is a 100 pF shunt capacitance halfway along the line that might represent a simple tap or possibly a connected device such as a shunt capacitor (although the actual equivalent circuit for a real shunt capacitor would be much more complex than this). Note that the impedance of a 100 pF capacitor at 1 MHz is approximately 1600 Ω and decreases with frequency beyond 1 MHz. Further, neither the transmitter nor the receiver is "matched" to the transmission line's characteristic impedance. It cannot generally be expected that matching will occur without some conditioning of the system.

The system "attenuation" (i.e. the ratio V_{out}/V_{in}) is shown in Fig. 5. Between 0.1 and 1 MHz, the average attenuation is about 10 dB. Beyond that, the attenuation can exceed 40 dB. In addition, it is clear that the attenuation is strongly frequency dependent.

It can be concluded that even simple models with mismatches, junctions and connected devices result in attenuations far in excess of the 1 dB/km expected for matched uniform transmission lines with no connected devices or junctions.

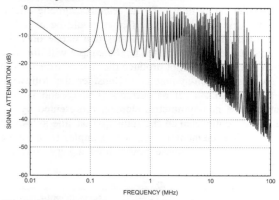

Fig. 5. The attenuation (i.e. V_{out}/V_{in}) for the system shown in Fig. 4

Extensive modeling of real systems has been reported in [2]. These results have also been compared to measurements on real power systems.

D. Results from Field Measurements

Recent experience with BPL systems installed on overhead distribution lines with relatively few (i.e., fewer than roughly one per 100 m) devices such as transformers, capacitors, taps, and underground risers suggests typical attenuation rates on the order of 30 dB/km. For the same lines, the maximum distance between repeaters is approximately 600 m for a communication rate of at least 10 Mbps. Note that the communication rate available to any one user may be smaller than this since the transmission system is shared by all of its users. Overhead distribution lines with a larger density of attached devices may exhibit similar attenuation rates and maximum distances between repeaters, but there can be no guarantee of this. Underground distribution lines typically exhibit attenuation rates that are three times as high as those for overhead lines. However, this is often compensated for by the substantially lower noise levels on most underground lines, since they do not tend to pick up radio broadcast signals.

Experiments on sub-transmission lines (i.e., 69 kV) have shown that repeaters may be spaced as far as 1200 m or more apart for a communication rate of 10 Mbps. It can be inferred from this result that attenuation rates on higher-voltage lines may be even lower. The reason for this is likely related to the smaller number of attachments, and more uniform dimensions. Reducing this attenuation would appear to be an important goal for BPL designers.

III. SYSTEM UNBALANCE

A. Introduction

All of the systems that we have considered to this point are inherently "balanced" systems because two conductor lines have been assumed and (except for the capacitance between conductors) displacement currents have been ignored. Thus the current that flows on one conductor is equal and opposite to that flowing on the other conductor. In fact, most systems are unbalanced for at least two reasons. First, power lines usually consist of more than two conductors. Hence, there is more than one path for return current and one of these paths may carry the current at a considerable distance from the forward current. Second, at higher frequencies it is found that "open circuited" conductors can carry currents. To analyze these, however, it is necessary to explicitly consider stray capacitances or (at even higher frequencies) analyze the system using a full wave electromagnetic analysis. Unbalance is important since (as will be shown later) the electromagnetic emissions of a power system are very sensitive to exactly where the return current is located compared to the forward current. The electromagnetic emissions will be considerably larger if the two currents are widely spaced.

Here, two cases for which currents are unbalanced are described. In the first, a system with multiple return paths is considered. For simplicity and to avoid obscuring insight with complicated mathematics, only a two phase with neutral line (i.e. N = 3) that supports 2 modes of propagation (i.e., differential and common modes) will be considered. The ideas generated, however, can easily be extended to cases for which there are more than two modes.

B. Systems with more than one return path

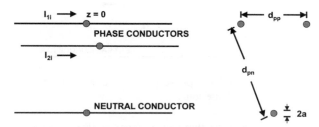

Fig. 6. symmetric two phase power line with neutral

The first issue to consider is that of excitation. In the single-phase case, the source and its internal impedance are simply connected between the phase and neutral conductors. As discussed in the last section, this causes a differential mode to be generated that travels toward the load. In the multiphase case the situation is more complicated. Consider the simple symmetric two-phase transmission line shown in Fig. 6. This line consists of two-phase conductors and a neutral wire (the explicit effect of the earth is neglected although it can be added if desired). As shown in Fig. 6b, the spacing between phase conductors is d_{pp}. The spacing between each phase and neutral is d_{pn} and each conductor has a radius of a. The two currents at z = 0 that flow on the line are I_{1i} and I_{2i} respectively.

Given the symmetry of this line, it can be shown that the currents on the conductors can be decomposed into "common" and "differential" modes as

$$[I_i] = \begin{bmatrix} i_{1i} \\ i_{2i} \end{bmatrix} = i_{Ci} \begin{bmatrix} 1 \\ 1 \end{bmatrix} + i_{Di} \begin{bmatrix} 1 \\ -1 \end{bmatrix} \qquad (3)$$

where i_{Ci} and i_{Di} are the amplitudes of the common and differential current modes respectively.

The common mode consists of wire currents that are equal in amplitude and direction with a return current through the neutral wire. The differential mode consists of wire currents that are equal in amplitude and opposite in direction. Since these currents add to zero, there is no return current through the neutral wire. This difference will have an impact on the level of electromagnetic fields generated. Since the neutral wire is usually further from the phase conductors than the interphase spacing (i.e. $d_{pn} \gg d_{pp}$), the common mode will usually generate higher electromagnetic fields for a given mode amplitude. Since the magnitude of these fields is limited by law, there is reason to reduce the common mode contribution to the current.

There are at least two ways to inject high frequency signals on this line. One is via magnetic coupling that has been used by several companies and can be modeled as a voltage source in series with the line. The other is capacitive coupling that can be modeled by shunt voltage source in series with impedance. Here, for simplicity, the source impedance is neglected and the system looks like the one shown in Fig. 7.

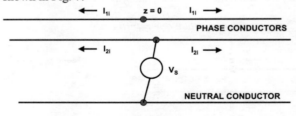

Fig. 7. symmetric two phase power line with neutral excited with a voltage source

The first observation that can be made is that currents are generated in both directions. By symmetry, the magnitudes of these two currents are the same. Of course, the same thing would happen on a single-phase line. But what is not clear is how to calculate the amplitudes of the currents generated in wires numbers 1 and 2. To do this, it is necessary to consider the relationship between the voltages and the currents. The wire voltages can also be expanded into common and differential modes and are

$$[V_i] = \begin{bmatrix} v_{1i} \\ v_{2i} \end{bmatrix} = v_{Ci} \begin{bmatrix} 1 \\ 1 \end{bmatrix} + v_{Di} \begin{bmatrix} 1 \\ -1 \end{bmatrix} \qquad (4)$$

where v_{Ci} and v_{Di} are the amplitudes of the common and differential voltage modes. Further, the mode amplitudes for the voltages and currents are related by

$$i_{Ci} = v_{Ci}/Z_{OC} \quad \text{and} \quad i_{Di} = v_{Di}/Z_{OD} \qquad (5)$$

where Z_{OC} and Z_{OD} are respectively the characteristic impedances of the common and differential modes and are equal to

$$Z_{0D} = 60\ln\left(\frac{d_{pp}}{a}\right)\Omega \quad \text{and} \quad Z_{0C} = 120\ln\left(\frac{d_{pn}^2}{\sqrt{d_{pp}a}}\right)\Omega \qquad (6)$$

Clearly, both the common and differential modes are excited. As mentioned above, this will have implications in terms of the amplitude of the electromagnetic fields generated. One could conclude that it would be useful to develop alternative excitation schemes that excite only the differential mode. However, the next example will illustrate that such a scheme may not produce the desired effect given other sources of non-symmetry. Consider the following issue. Suppose that a set of currents (i.e., i_{z1} and i_{Z2}) is incident upon a non-symmetric element represented by the impedance Z_L connected to the transmission line as shown in Fig. 8. This element might, for example, be a single phase load on a three phase power line; a very common element.

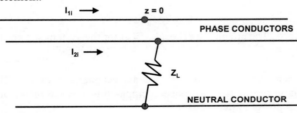

Fig. 8. Unsymmetrical load on a two-phase power line with neutral.

It can be shown that if $Z_L \ll (Z_{OC} + Z_{OD})/4$, then the transmitted modal current amplitudes (i.e., i_{Ct} and i_{Dt})

$$i_{Ct} \cong \frac{Z_{OD}}{Z_{OC} + Z_{OD}}(i_{Ci} + i_{Di})$$

$$i_{Dt} \cong \frac{Z_{OC}}{Z_{OC} + Z_{OD}}(i_{Ci} - i_{Di}) \qquad (7)$$

If the incident wave is a differential mode, then (assuming that the two characteristic impedances are approximately the same) the differential mode suffers a 6 dB loss on passing through the junction. Further, a common mode signal is created in the process. Thus, even if the source creates only a differential mode, a common mode signal will be created by essentially every junction passed by the signal.

C. Systems with Significant Displacement Currents

Consider next another source of unbalanced currents. A simple two-wire transmission line is shown in Fig. 9. If the vertical wires are removed, the wires carry equal and opposite (i.e. balanced or differential mode) currents. At low frequencies it can be shown that no currents pass through the vertical wires since they are open circuited. This is the expected result. At higher frequencies, however, the vertical wire current can be significant as shown in Figure 10. These unbalanced currents generate electromagnetic fields that can dominate the emissions from balanced systems.

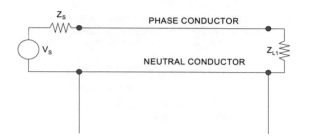

Fig. 9. Simplified circuit for studying the effect of displacement currents on system balance

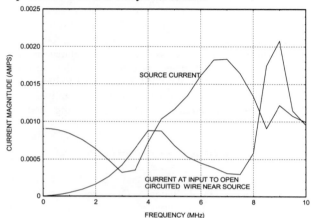

Fig. 10. High frequency source and left vertical wire input current

IV. ELECTROMAGNETIC EMISSIONS

A. Balanced Systems

Consider a two-wire transmission line with a phase to phase spacing of 1 meter (refer to Fig. 6 with the neutral conductor eliminated). If the wires carry equal and opposite (i.e. balanced) continuous wave (i.e., single frequency) currents, then the "equivalent" electric field (i.e. the magnetic field multiplied by the impedance of free space = 120π) is 30 μV/m or 29.5 dBμV/m (i.e., the US Federal Communications Commission (FCC) limit between 1.705 and 30 MHz) at 30 meters from the power line for a wire current of only 447 μA! Further, if the characteristic impedance of the parallel wire transmission line is Z_0 = 550Ω, then the maximum single frequency power flowing (without violating the US FCC limit) on the transmission line is 109 μW or –9.6 dBm! European limits are even more stringent. This is one reason why it has been more difficult to operate BPL systems in Europe

Although 109 μW is extremely small, it should be noted that the calculation was made for a single frequency signal. The use of broadband modulation techniques effectively reduces because the FCC emission limits are based on measurements employing a CISPR quasi-peak detector with a 9 kHz bandwidth. Such a receiver will respond to only the small fraction of a broadband signal that appears within the 9 kHz

bandwidth that surrounds the center frequency of the receiver.

Of more concern, however, is the fact that the currents on a real power line may not be balanced as assumed here. There are two reasons for this. First, unbalance can lead to significantly higher radiated fields. Second, they can affect the rate of decay of fields away from the power line. This is important since the FCC makes certain assumptions about the rate of decay that must be used to extrapolate measurements and that may or may not be valid.

B. Unbalanced Systems

Consider again a three conductor power line. Here, however, all three conductors are in a line as shown in Fig. 11. This is done in order to simplify the calculations so that the mathematics not obscure the ideas that will be developed. In this figure, the two phase wires are again separated by a distance d_{pp} while the return current is assumed to be in a neutral wire that is separated from the nearest phase conductor by a distance d_{pn}. The phase wires carry constant currents I_1 and I_2 respectively while the neutral wire carries a current I_3. It is assumed here that there is no current in the ground so that

$$I_1 + I_2 + I_3 = 0. \tag{8}$$

Fig. 11 Geometry for calculating the fields of differential and common mode currents.

It can be shown that the azimuthal magnetic field on the x axis due to these currents is

$$H_\phi = \frac{2\pi}{4j\lambda} \left\{ I_1 H_1^{(2)}[\frac{2\pi}{\lambda}(x - d_{pp})] \right.$$
$$\left. + I_2 H_1^{(2)}[\frac{2\pi}{\lambda}x] + I_3 H_1^{(2)}[\frac{2\pi}{\lambda}(x + d_{pn})] \right\} \tag{9}$$

where $H_1^{(2)}(x)$ is the Hankel function of second kind, order 1 and argument x and λ is the free space wavelength. At 1 and 30 MHz, λ is equal to 300 and 10 meters respectively.

The result in (9) does not give much insight into the lateral behavior of the fields. But, it becomes much simpler at "low" frequency (i.e., near field) which is defined as

$$x, (x-d_{pp}), (x+d_{pn}) \ll \lambda.$$

In this case $H_1^{(2)}(q) \approx 2j/(\pi q)$ and

$$H_\phi \cong \frac{1}{2\pi} \left\{ I_d \frac{d_{pp}}{x(x - d_{pp})} \right.$$
$$\left. + I_c \frac{x(2d_{pn} + d_{pp}) - d_{pp}d_{pn}}{x(x - d_{pp})(x + d_{pn})} \right\} \tag{10}$$

189

where the currents I_1, I_2 and I_3 have been written in terms of the common and differential mode currents that are defined as

$$I_c = \frac{I_1 + I_2}{2}, \quad I_d \frac{I_1 - I_2}{2} \tag{11}$$

If $I_c = 0$ (i.e., there is no common mode), then the magnetic field reduces to

$$H_\phi \cong \frac{1}{2\pi} \left\{ I_d \frac{d_{pp}}{x(x - d_{pp})} \right\} \tag{11}$$

If, in addition, $x \gg d_{pp}$ (usually true), the field decays as $1/x^2$. This attenuation is equivalent to the "near field" attenuation factor $40\log_{10}(d(\text{meters})/3)$ from FCC Section 15.31(f) that is used to extrapolate BPL field measurements made at 3 meters to other locations. A similar result (i.e., $1/x^2$ field decay) can be obtained if $I_c \neq 0$ (i.e., there is a common mode) when $x \gg d_{pp}, d_{pn}$. This corresponds to the case for which all return currents are in a neutral conductor (i.e., not in the earth) that is relatively close to the phase conductors.

It is not, however, usually reasonable to assume that BPL currents either consist of only differential mode currents or that all return currents are in a neutral conductor close to the phase conductors. If return currents are deep in the ground (modeled here as $d_{pn} \gg x$), it can be shown that

$$H_\phi \cong I_d \frac{d_{pp}}{2\pi x^2} + I_c \frac{1}{\pi x} \tag{12}$$

For comparable differential and common mode currents the fields from the common mode currents (i.e., those that decay as $1/x$) dominate. When valid, this result could be used to justify using an attenuation factor of $20\log_{10}(d(\text{meters})/3)$ rather than the factor $40\log_{10}(d(\text{meters})/3)$ specified by the FCC. Note again, however, if $x \gg d_{pn}$ (such as when all return current is in a neutral wire that is not too far away from the phase conductors) the magnetic field again decays as $1/x^2$.

Finally, it is possible to approximate (8) at higher frequencies for which $x >$ approximately $\lambda/3$ and $x \gg d_{pp}$. This is done using an asymptotic expansion for the Hankel function $H_1^{(2)}(q) \approx j(2j/\pi q)^{1/2} e^{-jq}$. The result is (13)

$$H_\phi \cong \sqrt{\frac{j}{4\lambda}} e^{-j2\pi x/\lambda} \left\{ I_d \frac{j2\pi d_{pp}}{\lambda \sqrt{x}} + 2I_c \left[\frac{1}{\sqrt{x}} - \frac{e^{-j2\pi d_{pn}}}{\sqrt{x + d_{pn}}} \right] \right\}$$

Again, in this case, it is not justified to use the attenuation factor specified by the FCC.

V. OTHER US GOVERNMENT REGULATIONS

In addition to meeting the standards mentioned above, CFR47-15 requires that:

(a) persons operating intentional or unintentional radiators shall not be deemed to have any vested or recognizable right to continued use of any given frequency by...

(b) Operation of an intentional, unintentional, or incidental radiator is subject to the conditions that no harmful interference is caused....

(c) The operator of a radio frequency device shall be required to cease operating the device upon notification by a Commission representative that the device is causing harmful interference.

The "harmful interference" clause here is a real "wild card" for BPL because the FCC has yet to publicly define how it will handle complaints of this type.

VI. SOME ENGINEERING RESPONSES

A. Reducing Emissions to Acceptable Levels

The most important fact to note is that the CISPR receiver required by the FCC is a narrowband receiver with a bandwidth of 9 kHz. If the power of a modulated signal is spread out over a wide bandwidth (as is usually the case), the signal power within the CISPR receiver bandwidth will be reduced. Other methods for improving system balance to reduce emissions require system conditioning and are expensive.

B. Modulation schemes for very complex channels

As mentioned above, the power line channel presents some very difficult design challenges. One specific problem is that channel attenuation, input impedance and background noise have significant time and frequency variations. The challenge to the designer is to select a modulation scheme that works well in this environment. One scheme that has been successfully used in this environment is Orthogonal Frequency Division Multiplexing (OFDM). With OFDM the signal is transmitted on a large number of operating frequencies (i.e., carriers) within the usable spectrum. The data rate for the signal on each carrier is equal to the overall data rate divided by the number of carriers. Given this, the symbol length can be made longer and the effects of delay spread due to multiple reflections minimized. Another advantage of such a system is that carriers on sensitive portions of the spectrum (e.g., amateur radio bands) can simply be turned off to avoid interference.

VII. REFERENCES

1. F. M. Tesche, "Investigation of Measured S- Parameters of an Allis-chambers 1.2 kV – 120/240V Power Transformer," A report to Lawrence Livermore National Laboratory, May 1993

2. F.M. Tesche, B.A. Renz, R.M. Hayes, and R.G. Olsen, "Development and Use of a Multiconductor Line Model for PLC Assessments," 15th International Zurich Symposium on EMC, February 2003

EMC Factors Applicable to Broadband Over Power Line Systems

Ed Hare

Laboratory Manager

ARRL, the National Association for Amateur Radio

225 Main St,

Newington, CT 06111

Email: W1RFI@arrl.org, Tel: 860-594-0318

Abstract— **This paper outlines the parameters that impact the ability of BPL systems to operate compatibly with nearby radio receivers. Emission levels that will protect most radio reception are discussed. The mechanisms by which BPL that is operating at the present US FCC emissions limits can cause interference are described. The impact of signals operating at the FCC limits on HF communications at power levels typical of the Amateur Service is demonstrated with a VOACAP propagation study. The paper includes a comparison of BPL signal levels against the present FCC conducted emissions limits below 30 MHz.**

Keywords-BPL; PLC; EMC; interference; modeling; immunity; ingress; propagation

I. BROADBAND OVER POWER LINE SYSTEMS COMPARED TO OTHER DEVICES DEPLOYED UNDER UNLICENSED RULES

Broadband over Power Line systems (BPL – Also known as Power Line Communications – PLC) are generally regulated by rules that apply to unlicensed devices. In the US, they are regulated by Part 15 of the FCC rules [1]. Although the FCC has recently written rules that apply specifically to BPL, in general [2], BPL is subject to the same emissions limits and requirements not to cause interference that apply to most types of unlicensed emitters.

Although there have been interference problems associated with unlicensed devices[1], the present FCC rules have worked to a degree to control interference from unlicensed devices. BPL, especially access BPL, has posed a significantly different interference potential than many other devices, due to the ways that BPL is inherently different in kind than many types of devices.

A. The Rules Function by Controlling Probability of Interference

The rules regulating unlicensed emitters control interference by controlling the probability that interference will occur. As will be discussed later in this paper, the levels of emissions permitted to unlicensed devices are high enough that

interference to nearby devices is a very real possibility. Most unlicensed emitters, however, do not emit strong signals (e.g., more than a few dB higher than the ambient noise floor) continuously across a wide range of spectrum. A computer device, for example, typically has strong emissions on only a few frequencies across a wide frequency range.

Most emitters do not emit signals all of the time, and most of the licensed radio operation that is protected by the rules governing unlicensed devices are not in continuous operation. This offers an additional layer of probability against the occurrence of harmful interference. Most unlicensed emitters have a limited geographical area over which their emissions are strong enough to cause harmful interference. Buildings, for example, generally offer some attenuation of radiated signals from devices located within them and most conducted emissions are radiated by the wiring directly connected to them (ac mains or other system wiring, for examples). For interference to occur, the device must be operating near a radio receiver being used at the same time.

B. BPL Systems

Most BPL systems, especially access BPL systems using overhead medium-voltage (MV) lines to distribute signals, do not operate in a way that allow these factors to prevent most interference. BPL systems are broadband, fully occupying the spectrum they are using, typically using on the order of tens of MHz. BPL systems feeding neighborhoods, or those conducting functions such as streaming video monitoring cameras, will produce radiated and conducted signals over long or continuous time periods. Access BPL systems that use overhead MV lines conduct and radiate their signals over a large geographical area up and down the lines, from radiators that are located high and in the clear.

C. Probability of Interference and Nearby Radio Services

Whether BPL carries a high or a low probability of interference can depend on perspective. Whether interference occurs at all depends on whether there are nearby receivers using the same spectrum as the emissions from a BPL system. Most of the time, that is not the case. If BPL were operated near a station licensed in the Amateur Service, for example, interference could only occur when that station was in use on any spectrum where the emissions from BPL were stronger

---

[1] See
http://www.arrl.org/tis/info/HTML/plc/FCC_enforcement/Part15_Enforcement_Letters.html

than the signals that the Amateur station was trying to receive. At times when the Amateur station is off the air, there is no interference. In that sense, the likelihood of interference could be characterized as being low.

However, from the perspective of the Amateur station used in this example, the probability of interference is high if every time that station attempts to make use of its primary access to the spectrum that BPL is using, the strong BPL emissions obstruct the ability of that station to communicate with other licensed stations. The same high probability of interference would exist from nearby Citizens Band (CB) stations or receivers trying to listen to international shortwave broadcasts from other countries, as other examples.

D. Harmful Interference and the Rules

Using FCC rules as an example, at least in theory, these stations are protected. Under these rules, if harmful interference to a licensed station should occur (and this does include CB or the reception of international shortwave broadcast signals), the operator of the unlicensed device must take those steps that are necessary to address the interference. So the scenario that has a "low" probability of interference does has a "high" probability any time a nearby station uses the same spectrum that the unlicensed emitter may be using at or near the emissions limits in the rules. And under those rules, the operator of the unlicensed emitter has an unconditional requirement to correct harmful interference.

E. Unlicensed Emissions Generally Must Avoid Using Locally Used Spectrum

To avoid causing interference, unlicensed emitters that operate at or near the FCC emissions limits must avoid using spectrum that is in use locally. In some cases, this may be relatively easy. In many cases, an emitter that is near a station licensed to use a particular frequency can determine the location and frequency of the station from public records and potentially could design the system not to use that spectrum

However, in other cases, this may not be as simple as this may appear. The locations of many receivers that need to be protected are unknown. Public records for some stations – those operating in the Amateur Service, for example – may show a mailing address, but not necessarily a station location. In the Amateur Service, mobile and portable operation is common, often forming a vital part of that service's ability to meet is obligations under the rules to provide emergency and public-service communications. In other cases, such as CB stations or people trying to receive international shortwave broadcast stations, the location of receivers cannot be determined.

Under the rules, irrespective of probability, should harmful interference to any of these stations occur, the operator of the unlicensed device is required to correct the interference. It is not effective for this to be complaint-driven. In the case of mobile operation, it would not be possible to correct interference "on the fly" as the station changed locations. In other cases, such as people listening to international shortwave broadcasts within nearby homes, is it not reasonable to expect

that they could properly identify the source of an interfering emission and know how to complain. In residential areas, best practice would be to avoid operating in spectrum allocated to the following primary users:

- CB

- Amateur Radio

- International Shortwave broadcast

In addition to these best-practices requirements, in the US, FCC rules prohibit access BPL using overhead medium-voltage distribution lines from operating at all on a list of prohibited bands described in the FCC Part-15 rules.

BPL uses a wide swath of spectrum continuously over time, and when a commercial deployment is built, it could be as large as an entire state. This is clearly an EMC challenge if the requirements of the rules prohibiting interference are to truly be met.

Appendix A shows a table of the spectrum that best practice would require BPL systems to avoid in residential neighborhoods.

II. RADIATED EMISSIONS LIMITS AND HARMFUL INTERFERENCE

A. Part-15 Emissions Compared to Ambient Noise Levels and Signals

This section of the paper will use the US FCC Part-15 rules as an example. The Part-15 limits are generally much higher than the limits in other countries, but the principles apply to any limits that could be greater than the signal a particular licensed station is trying to receive.

Under the Part-15 rules, BPL is classified as an unintentional emitter. It is, however, a carrier-current device that conducts its signals on the ac power mains, so Part 15 requires it to meet the radiated emissions limits for intentional emitters or the applicable radiated limits for Class A or Class B environments. (In general, the conducted emissions limits in Part 15 do not apply to carrier-current devices below 30 MHz.)

The radiated limits are defined in Part 15 rules. Between 1.705 and 30 MHz, a limit of 30 μV at 30 meters from the source applies. Above 30 MHz, BPL devices must meet the radiated emissions limits for digital devices. Access BPL using MV lines meets the limits for Class A computing devices and other BPL must meet the Class B radiated limits. On 30-88 MHz, this would be a limit of 90 μV/m at 10 meters from the source for access BPL systems. On HF, the quasi-peak-detected radiated emissions from these systems are measured in a 9-kHz bandwidth; on VHF a 120-kHz bandwidth is used. Above 1 GHz, an average detector is used in a 1 MHz bandwidth.

B. Levels Needed to Protect Stations Operating in the Amateur Service

By radiocommunications standards, especially on HF, these are strong signals. ARRL and FCC measurements [3, 4] show that ambient noise level field strengths of 0 dBμV/m to –10 dBμV/m (or lower) are common. The levels of man-made noise that are generally accepted as the *median* values are several dB higher than this. In many instances, especially with a radio service that has frequency agility such as the Amateur Service, operators generally use the quiet spectrum in between the specific man-made sources that constitute that median value. Amateur operation typically uses minimum signal levels that are only a few dB higher than the ambient noise levels, so it is necessary to protect to these minimum values to avoid obstructing these communications.

To protect mobile amateur stations, the field strength at the mobile antenna should be lower than –10 dBμV/m, but not to exceed 0 dBμV/m in any case. To protect fixed amateur stations, it may be necessary not to exceed –20 dBμV/m at the amateur antenna. In some types of amateur operation, higher BPL signal levels may be tolerated, but not those that operate at or anywhere near the FCC emissions limits.

III. PART-15 EMISSIONS SIGNALS AND RECEIVED SIGNAL LEVELS

The Part-15 limits are high enough that signals from unlicensed emitters operating at these limits will be strong by nearby antennas. The strength and effect of these signals is related to the following factors:

- Strength of the emission

- Frequency of the emission (the path and receive antenna capture area vary as -20 log [frequency])

- Distance between the source and receiving antennas[2]

- Gain of the receive antenna

- Noise figure (sensitivity) of the receiver

- Ambient noise level from other sources

- Frequency distribution and nature of the emitted signal

- Receiver bandwidth

- The strength of the signal being received

The analyses in this paper assumes that the radiated emissions from most BPL systems will be at or near the permitted FCC limits. The amount of signal an antenna will pick up if it is placed in a specific radiated field would be defined by the following formulas in the far-field region of the two antennas involved, where *RSL* is the received signal level:

$$RSL_{dBW} = -107.2 + dB\mu V/m - 20log_{10}(F_{MHz}) + RcvAntGain_{dBi} - dB_{losses}^{3} \qquad (1)$$

This formula assumes that the RSL is in the same bandwidth as the measurement bandwidth to determine the level in dBμV/m. If the bandwidths are different, then for uncorrelated signals (i.e., noiselike) the following correction must be made to the RSL to obtain an approximation of the bandwidth in the appropriate measurement bandwidth:

$$RSL_{actual} = RSL_{measurement} - 10log \text{ (measurement bandwidth / receiver bandwidth)} \qquad (2)$$

These received signal levels are many dB higher than the receiver sensitivity for receivers typically used on HF or than the minimum signal levels typically used by stations in many HF radio Services.

In-situ, radiated fields include the effects of earth ground and other scattering conductors, so to be conservative, this paper uses the free-space gain of typical amateur receive antennas for its calculations.[4] Using the formulas above, assuming dB$_{losses}$ = 0 dB, the received signal levels in Table I above are calculated if the antenna is in a field of 30 μV/m.

To amateur radio communications, the received BPL signals are noise. The increase in noise level calculated and shown in Table II below is a conservative calculation of the RSLs that will occur from fields that are at the FCC Part 15 limits for intentional emitters. The FCC found similar degradation in its measurements made in a number of areas where BPL was deployed.

IV. DEGRADATION OF COMMUNICATIONS CAPABILITY FROM BPL OPERATION

One of the major factors in determining whether an external noise source will cause harmful interference is the signal-to-noise ratio of the desired signal. On HF, and to some extent on VHF, propagation between any two points can vary considerably. In general, on HF, radiocommunications circuits are analyzed by assessing the reliability of the circuit – the percentage of time that the path is expected to be open with a

TABLE I. RECEIVED SIGNAL LEVELS FROM A 29.54 DBμV/M FIELD TO TYPICAL ANTENNAS USED ON HF

Frequency	Amateur antenna type	Amateur antenna gain	Receive system BW	BPL signal RSL at 30 meters[1]	BPL signal RSL at 10 meters[1]
3.5 MHz[1]	Half-wave dipole	2.14 dBi	2500 Hz	-92 dBW	-82.5 dBW
3.5 MHz	Array	8.0 dBi	2500 Hz	-86.1 dBW	-76.6 dBW
14 MHz	3-element Yagi	8.0 dBi	2500 Hz	-98.1 dBW	-88.6 dBW
14 MHz	Stacked array	13 dBi	2500 Hz	-93.1 dBW	-83.6 dBW

---

[2] In the far field region, the strength of the electric and magnetic fields varies as 20log$_{10}$(distance). This is only approximately true in the near-field regions.

[3] Losses include the receive antenna feed line, connectors, etc.

---

[4] This is conservative because antennas located close to ground will lose some of their gain due to impedance mismatch and mutual coupling with the lossy earth.

necessary signal-to-noise margin.

ARRL used the HFWIN32 VOACAP "Inverse Area" software program[5] to predict communications-circuit reliability on 14 MHz and 5 MHz under the conditions shown in Table II below for various man-made noise levels:

- A sunspot number of 50, to represent reasonable, but not maximum, world-wide propagation conditions[6]

- The dates of January 1, April 1, July 1 and October 1

- Times of 0000, 0400, 0800, 1200, 1600 and 2000 UTC

- A transmitter EIRP of 30 dBW (1 kW)

- A receive antenna gain of 7.5 dBi on 14 MHz and 2.14 dBi on 5 MHz

- A receiver system for 2K50J3E emissions (2.5 kHz bandwidth SSB)

- Various levels of man-made noise

The results of this study were outlined in a paper ARRL presented to the FCC in the BPL rulemaking proceedings, "Impact of Man-Made Noise From Broadband Over Power Line Systems Operating at the FCC Part-15 Radiated Emissions Limits on Worldwide HF Communications." [5]

In the VOACAP simulation, a worldwide grid of transmitters is set up in the program. They were programmed at a power level of 1000 watts to an isotropic radiator, representing about 200 watts and a typical 3-element Yagi

TABLE II.   THE AMOUNT OF DEGRADATION OF TYPICAL LOCAL AMBIENT NOISE LEVELS ON DIFFERENT FREQUENCIES AND ANTENNAS

Frequency	Antenna type	Receive system ambient[1]	BPL RSL dB level relative to ambient, 30 meters distance	BPL RSL dB level relative to ambient, 10 meters distance
3.5 MHz	Half-wave dipole	-135 dBW	43 dB	52.5 dB
3.5 MHz	Array	-135 dBW	48.9 dB	58.4 dB
14 MHz	3-element Yagi	-145 dBW	46.9 dB	56.4 dB
14 MHz	Stacked array	-149 dBW	55.9 dB	65.4 dB
50 MHz	5-element Yagi	-160 dBW	32.3 dB	41.8 dB
50 MHz	¼-wave ground plane	-152 dBW	24.2 dB	33.7 dB

---

[5] This program is part of the HFWIN32 suite of software freely available from the Institute for Telecommunication Sciences, Boulder, CO at http://elbert.its.bldrdoc.gov/pc_hf/hfwin32.html.

[6] ARRL has repeated these calculations for other frequencies and sunspot numbers and concludes that the results described in this paper generally apply to HF communications circuits.

antenna for the transmitters. The program then calculates the received signal level at a specified location and compares it to a specified level of man-made noise. The graph shows circuit reliability – the percentage of time that the signal will exceed the specified signal-to-noise ratio.

This is typical of signals in the Amateur Service. For that reason, a low signal-to-noise ratio was chosen The required signal-to-noise ratio referenced to dBW/Hz used in VOACAP was conservatively based on a receive bandwidth of 2500 Hz, plus a modest 10 dB signal/noise ratio, for a value of 44 dB required SNR.

The man-made noise levels chosen for this study are:

- The RF environment at ARRL Headquarters, located in a residential neighborhood in Newington, Connecticut. This location was measured by ARRL in 1996 at a minimum ambient-noise level of –170 dBW/Hz at 14 MHz.

- The "residential" environment described in ITU-R Recommendation P.372-8, "Radio Noise." This is –163.5 dBW/Hz on 14 MHz (extrapolated from –145 dBW/Hz on 3 MHz using the formula described in the document).

- An environment with an ambient man-made noise level of –140.5 dBW/Hz on 14 MHz, calculated from the Part-15 HF radiated emissions limits for carrier-current devices and isotropic receive antenna gain.

These noise levels were determined from the following sources and methods shown in Table III below:

The results of all of ARRL's modeling can't be reproduced here in their entirety, but these graphs on the following pages are representative of the calculated data.

Figure 1 on the following page shows the results of calculations made of man-made noise levels at those of the measurements made by ARRL in 1996 at several typical residential amateur stations. The VOACAP software combines the programmed man-made noise level with the predicted

TABLE III.   LEVELS OF MAN-MADE NOISE USED IN ARRL VOACAP CALCULATIONS

Noise level dBW/Hz at 3 MHz as entered into the VOACAP program[1]	Noise level measured or extrapolated to 14 MHz	Environment
-153 dBW/Hz	-170.0 dBW/Hz	Best case measurements made by ARRL in a typical residential environment on quiet frequencies with minimal interference[1].
-145 dBW/Hz	-163.5 dBW/Hz	Residential environment described in ITU-R P.372-8.
-122 dBW/Hz	-140.5 dBW/Hz	Noise level at 14 MHz, calculated from the FCC Part-15 radiated emissions limits.

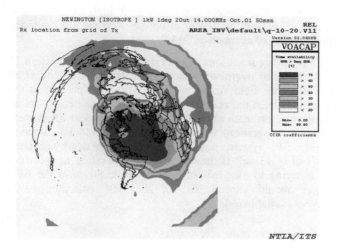

Figure 1. This shows the calculated reliability in percent for an ambient man-made noise level of −170 dBW/Hz on 14 MHz. The station in this model is using a 3-element Yagi to receive signals from world-wide stations transmitting +30 dBW EIRP. This station is capable of worldwide communication at various times of day. Date: Oct 01 2000 UTC SSN = 50.

natural-noise levels for the geographic location, time of year, time of day and frequency and calculates reliability of a circuit, using the parameters provided. Amateur station capability can be significantly more sensitive and use much lower power than the conservative parameters chosen for this paper.

Figure 2 shows that at the man-made noise levels in ITU-R P.372-8, there is a demonstrable degradation to the reliability and range of worldwide HF communications, compared to the results from a quieter location shown in Figure 1.

The ITU-R P378.2 recommendation describes an ambient man-made noise level of −145 dBW/Hz. This is somewhat

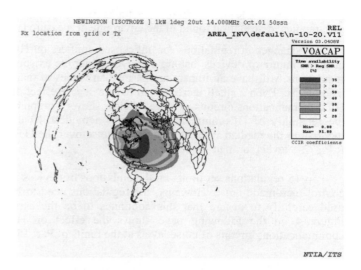

Figure 3. This shows the calculated reliability in percent for an ambient man-made noise level of −153.5 dBW/Hz on 14 MHz, a modest 10 dB higher than the ITU-R P372-8 noise level for "residential" environments at 14 MHz. The station in this model is using a 3-element Yagi to receive signals from worldwide stations transmitting 30 dBW EIRP. This modest change in noise levels from the present environment has changed the 14-MHz spectrum region from a worldwide to a regional band. Date: Oct 01 2000 UTC SSN = 50.

higher than the levels ARRL used for its Figure-1 calculation. The ITU-R level is the median value of the measured results. The nature of much man-made noise is such that all devices that radiate noise do not all radiate at the same time, or even all the time. Most do not radiate equally on all frequencies. For example, a computer system may be a prolific generator on RF, but much of that energy if found on specific frequencies, with most spectrum being relatively clear. Nonetheless, ITU-R P.372-8 does represent the worldwide consensus of the present

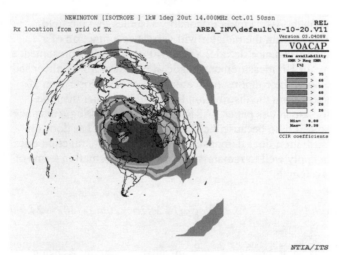

Figure 2. This shows the calculated reliability in percent for an ambient man-made noise level of −163.5 dBW/Hz, the ITU-R P372-8 level for "residential" environments at 14 MHz. The station in this model is using a 3-element Yagi to receive signals from worldwide stations transmitting 30 dBW EIRP. Although still capable of worldwide communications, the present level of man-made noise is just starting to have a noticeable effect on the capability of this station to establish reliable communications. Date: Oct 01 2000 UTC SSN = 50.

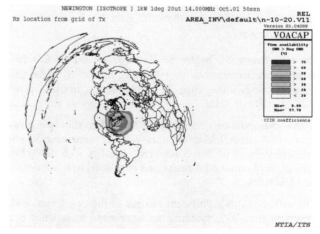

Figure 4. This shows the calculated reliability in percent for an ambient man-made noise level of −140.4 dBW/Hz on 14 MHz, the level of signal that would be received by an isotropic antenna placed in a field at the present level of HF Part-15 radiated emissions for carrier-current devices. The station in this model is using a 3-element Yagi to receive signals from worldwide stations transmitting +30 dBW EIRP. The range and reliability of this station on 14 MHz has been reduced to the point where this frequency range is no longer useful for any long-distance communication. Date: Oct 01 2000 UTC SSN = 50.

level of man-made noise from the types of devices and geographical distribution found in the environment measured.

Any changes in regulations for unlicensed emitters on HF, or in the nature of devices that are deployed under the existing regulations, will have an impact on the median values of man-made noise. Even a small increase can have a severe effect on HF communications circuits. Figure 3 below shows a graph of the reliability of HF communications with a modest 10 dB increase in the median value of man-made noise over the ITR-R P.372-8 levels for man-made noise.

Part 15 regulations set limits on the emissions of devices to control man-made noise. However, the regulations need to be used carefully to ensure that this continues to be the case. Figure 4 on the following page shows the effect on HF communications circuits of noise levels at the limits of Part 15.

V. BPL and Conducted Signals

As a carrier-current device, BPL generally does not have to meet the conducted emissions limits. It is usually tested for radiated emissions as a means of establishing compliance.

However, in order for BPL to work reliably on power lines, it must operate at a higher level than the existing noise on the lines. This means that its conducted signal must be greater than he conducted emissions from other devices connected to the ac mains.

In the rulemaking, information about the conducted signal levels of BPL equipment was made available to the FCC. In its filing, Ambient, an access BPL manufacturer, noted that its equipment used a power level of –50 dBm/Hz, and that its couplers had an insertion loss of about 6 dB [6]. This level of –56 dBm/Hz will be used for the following calculations and estimations.

A. BPL Conducted Levels and FCC Part 15 Conducted Limits Compared [7]

On HF, below 30 MHz, Sec. 15.107 of the FCC's rules limits conducted emissions to 1000 µV, measured quasi-peak in a 9-kHz bandwidth. In a 50-ohm system, this is a power level of –47 dBm/9 kHz.

If one extrapolates –56 dBm/Hz to 9 kHz, this is a power level of –16.5 dBm/9 kHz. If this voltage were in a 50-ohm system, the voltage of this conducted signal is 30.5 dB greater than the present conducted emissions permitted to other devices by the FCC rules.

The effect of this significant change in the conducted EMC environment that BPL systems are connected to has not been studied to any extent at all.

VI. Ingress

EMC is a two way street. Any system that can leak signals out will also leak signals in. BPL must function in an environment that may contain strong radiated signals. In the case of the Amateur Service, it would not be uncommon to find nearby radio transmitters using power as high as 1500 watts transmitter power, with an effective isotropically radiated power (EIRP) of as much as 20 kW.

These amateur stations would typically be located within 15 to 50 meters of overhead power lines. It would not be at all unusual to see field strengths above 100 V/m present at the power lines from the operation of nearby transmitters. A more conservative estimate of 30 V/m would be typical of amateur stations in operation, either fixed or mobile. To function properly, BPL systems must be able to tolerate nearby radiated signals of this level. If these signals are operating in spectrum BPL is trying to use, the required dynamic range of the BPL receiver would exceed that of the best communications receivers available today.

A. Estimates of Induced Signals

A good estimate of this coupling from a 1500-watt amateur station can be obtained by using the free-space path-loss formula and the gain of the transmit antenna:

$$Coupled\ power = 31.8\ dBW - path\ loss + transmit\ antenna \\ gain + receive\ antenna\ gain \qquad (3)$$

$$Path\ loss = -27.55 + 20log_{10}(F_{MHz}) + 20log_{10}(distance \\ meters) \qquad (4)$$

The induced power will increase as the frequency decreases, but a calculation done at 14 MHz provides a good example that is in the frequency range being used in the BPL trial areas at this time. The following calculation conservatively assumes that the amateur antenna is located 30 meters from the distribution lines.

The path loss formula reasonably assumes that the field strength from the radiator will vary at as a function of a $20log_{10}$(distance decade). (If the $40log_{10}$(ratio) is presumed, as it is for HF measurements made of emission from unlicensed devices, the coupling from antennas located closer than 30 meters from the distribution lines will be higher than the estimate in this paper.) ARRL is not using a $40log_{10}$(distance decade) ratio because the antenna modeling it has done on distribution lines demonstrates that the $40log_{10}$ function does not apply well to radiators that are not very small in terms of wavelength.

$$Path\ loss\ = -27.55 + 20log_{10}(14\ MHz) + 20log_{10}(30) = 24.9\ dB \qquad (5)$$

If is it presumed that an amateur station is using a 3-element Yagi antenna with a gain of 7.5 dBi:

$$Coupled\ power = 31.8\ dBW - 24.9\ dB + 7.5\ dBi + 0\ dBi = \\ 14.4\ dBW = 27.5\ W \qquad (6)$$

Signals from nearby transmitters couple onto building wiring, too, but building wiring is generally not as effective a receive antenna as are overhead distribution lines. The electrical wiring in a building is generally uses a combination of star and daisy-chain techniques, with numerous electrical loads that absorb RF power. In general, the amount of power coupled into each of those loads is considerably less than the 27.5 W from ARRL's calculation of the amount of power that will be coupled into overhead wiring.

B. Limited Testing

There has been only limited testing of the immunity of BPL systems to nearby radio transmitters [8]. Most of this testing has been done by operators in the Amateur Service.

Testing done in Potomac, MD by amateur operator members of AMRAD on November 9, 2003 showed that the system there was seriously degraded by a mobile amateur station parked on the street near the house carrying BPL. When the station was parked on the street in front of the house, the download was stopped with power level ranging from 5 to 15 watts on amateur bands between 3.5 and 21 MHz.

At 0.1 miles distance along the overhead power line carrying access BPL to that home, the download stopped at 10 watts to 60 watts, depending on frequency. At 0.5 miles, the data was affected from 100 watts on the 3.5 MHz band in once case and unaffected by that power level in another.

Similar tests[7] done by the Old Virginia Hams, an amateur club in Manassas, VA showed similar results, with transmitter power of 40 watts to a nearby mobile station causing stoppage or significant slowdown of test data being downloaded by one of their users.

This is an area where considerably more study should be done. To date, ARRL offers to help conduct or coordinate such testing have not resulted in any utility or BPL manufacturer willing to look at this aspect of BPL systems' operation.

VII. Conclusions

In the US, BPL is regulated by the same FCC rules that control interference from many types of devices. BPL is different than most devices, however, in that it emits continuously vs frequency, usually emits over long periods of time and, when used for access BPL on overhead electrical wring, is a distributed radiator that emits signals along significantly long sections of line. These factors mean that the statistical effects that allow the present rules to control interference for many devices do not apply well to BPL.

To avoid interference, BPL systems must avoid locally used spectrum. In residential areas, this generally means Amateur, CB and international shortwave broadcasting.

The radiated emissions from BPL operating at the FCC emissions limits will be many dB stronger than ambient noise levels and many desired signals that are routinely used on HF

and VHF. When BPL is stronger than desired signals, local harmful interference is virtually certain. This will generally be manifest as degradation in range and decreased communications circuit reliability.

The conducted signals from BPL are tens of dB higher than the FCC conducted-emissions limits for most devices. The effect of this significant change in the conducted EMC environment on other systems is not well understood and needs to be studied further.

There has been only limited testing done on the effect of ingress on BPL systems, but nearby transmitters operating legally under the FCC's rules can create fields near the wiring conducting BPL signals in excess of 30 V/m. Testing done to date by operators in the Amateur Service has shown that as little as 4 watts of transmitter power from a nearby mobile station was sufficient to degrade or disrupt BPL systems. This is another area that needs significant study.

ARRL has prepared a number of papers and engineering analyses on BPL. They are listed on the ARRL web page at http://p1k.arrl.org/~ehare/bpl/ARRL_BPL_Papers.html.

References

[1] US Title 47 Code of Federal Regulations, Part 15. These are available at http://www.access.gpo.gov/nara/cfr/waisidx_04/47cfr15_04.html for download.

[2] FCC Report and Order, FCC 04-25, Docket numbers ET-03-104 and 04-37. These are available for download from the FCC Electronic Filing System at http://gullfoss2.fcc.gov/prod/ecfs/retrieve.cgi?native_or_pdf=pdf&id_document=6516882767 and http://gullfoss2.fcc.gov/prod/ecfs/retrieve.cgi?native_or_pdf=pdf&id_document=6516882769.

[3] E. Hare, C. Imlay, "Calculated Levels from Broadband Over Power Line Systems and their Impact on Amateur Radio Communications Circuits", ARRL, as filed as Comments in the FCC BPL rulemaking proceedings, July, 2003. http://www.arrl.org/announce/regulatory/et03-104/Calculated_Part15_levels.doc.

[4] ARRL Staff, "Amateur Service Protection Requirements," ARRL, as filed as Reply Comments in the FCC BPL rulemaking proceedings, August, 2003. http://gullfoss2.fcc.gov/prod/ecfs/retrieve.cgi?native_or_pdf=pdf&id_document=6516182983.

[5] E. Hare, "Impact of Man-Made Noise from Broadband Over Powerline Systems Operating at the FCC Part-15 Limits on Worldwide HF Communications", as filed as Reply Comments in the FCC BPL rulemaking proceedings, August, 2003. http://gullfoss2.fcc.gov/prod/ecfs/retrieve.cgi?native_or_pdf=pdf&id_document=6514683434.

[6] G. Wheeler, Esq, "Comments of Ambient Corporation", as filed as Comments in the FCC BPL rulemaking proceedings, July, 2003. http://gullfoss2.fcc.gov/prod/ecfs/retrieve.cgi?native_or_pdf=pdf&id_document=6514284539

[7] E.Hare, "Exhibit B: Broadband Over Power Line Devices and Conducted Emissions", as filed as Comments in the FCC BPL proceedings, July , 2003. http://gullfoss2.fcc.gov/prod/ecfs/retrieve.cgi?native_or_pdf=pdf&id_document=6514683434.

[8] ARRL Staff, "BPL is Sseriously Degraded by Nearby Radio Transmitters", ARRL web page, updated May, 2005. http://www.arrl.org/tis/info/HTML/plc/degrade.html

---

[7] http://www.target-eng.com/bpl/bplweakness.html

Appendix A – Best Practices For BPL to Avoid Locally Used Spectrum in Residential Environments

Frequencies Not Available for BPL		Frequencies Available for BPL	
Bands (kHz)	Reason	Bands (kHz)	Bandwidth (kHz)
1,700 – 30,000	See 47 CFR 15.615(f)(3)(i) for certain 4 km Coordination Areas		
1,700-38,250	See 47 CFR 15.615(f)(3)(ii) for certain 4 km Coordination Areas		
1,700-80,000	See 47 CFR 15.615(f)(3)(iii) for certain 1 km Coordination Areas		
1700-30000	See 47 CFR 15.615(f)(3)(iv) for 37 km radar Coordination Areas		
		1,700 – 1,800	100
1,800 – 2,000	Amateur 160 m Band		
		2,000 – 2,173.5	173.5
2,173.5 – 2,190.5	Mobile (Distress and Calling) See 47 CFR 15.615(f)(2) for Exclusion Zones	2,173.5 – 2,190.5 outside Exclusion Zones	17
2,300 – 2,495	Tropical Broadcast Band	2,300 – 2,495 outside Tropical Zone	195
2,495 – 2,501	Standard Frequency and Time Signals		
		2,501 – 2,850	349
2,850 – 3,025	Excluded Frequency Band (Aeronautical Mobile (R)) See 47 CFR 15.615(f)(1)		
		3,025 – 3,400	375
3,400 – 3,500	Excluded Frequency Band (Aeronautical Mobile (R)) See 47 CFR 15.615(f)(1)		
3,500 – 4,000	Amateur 80 m Band		
		4,000 – 4,650	650
4,650 – 4,700	Excluded Frequency Band (Aeronautical Mobile (R)) See 47 CFR 15.615(f)(1)		
		4,700 – 4,995	295
4,995 – 5,003	Standard Frequency and Time Signals		
		5003 – 5,330.5	327.5
5,330.5 – 5,406.5	Amateur 60 m Band		
		5,406.5 – 5,450	
5,450 – 5,680	Excluded Frequency Band (Aeronautical Mobile (R)) See 47 CFR 15.615(f)(1)		
		5,680 – 5,990	310
5,990 – 6,200	HF Broadcasting		
		6,200 – 6,525	325
6,525 – 6,685	Excluded Frequency Band (Aeronautical Mobile (R)) See 47 CFR 15.615(f)(1)		
		6,685 – 7,000	315
7,000 – 7,300	Amateur 40 m Band		
7,300 – 7,350	HF Broadcasting		
		7,350 – 8,815	1,465
8,815 – 8,965	Excluded Frequency Band (Aeronautical Mobile (R)) See 47 CFR 15.615(f)(1)		
		8,965 – 9,400	435
9,400 – 9,900	HF Broadcasting		
		9,900 – 9,995	95
9,995 – 10,005	Standard Frequency and Time Signals		
10005 – 10100	Excluded Frequency Band (Aeronautical Mobile ®) See 47 CFR 15.615(f)(1)		
10,100 – 10,150	Amateur 30 m Band		
		10,150 – 11,275	125
11,275 – 11,400	Excluded Frequency Band (Aeronautical Mobile (R)) See 47 CFR 15.615(f)(1)		
		11,400 – 11,600	200
11,600 – 12,100	HF Broadcasting		
		12,100 – 13,260	1,160
13,260 – 13,360	Excluded Frequency Band (Aeronautical Mobile (R)) See 47 CFR 15.615(f)(1)		
		13,360 – 13,570	210
13,570 – 13,870	HF Broadcasting		

Frequencies Not Available for BPL		Frequencies Available for BPL	
		13,870 – 14,000	130
14,000 – 14,350	Amateur 20 m Band		
		14,350 – 14,990	640
14,990 – 15,005	Standard Frequency and Time Signals		
		15,005 – 15,100	95
15,100 – 15,800	HF Broadcasting		
		15,800 – 17,480	1,600
17,480 – 17,990	HF Broadcasting		
17,900 – 17,970	Excluded Frequency Band (Aeronautical Mobile (R)) See 47 CFR 15.615(f)(1)		
		17,970 – 18,068	98
18,068 – 18,168	Amateur 17 m Band		
		18,168 – 18,900	732
18,900 – 19,020	HF Broadcasting		
		19,020 – 21,000	1,980
21,000 – 21,450	Amateur 15 m Band		
21,450 – 21,850	HF Broadcasting		
		21,850 – 21,924	74
21,924 – 22,000	Excluded Frequency Band (Aeronautical Mobile (R)) See 47 CFR 15.615(f)(1)		
		22,000 – 24,890	2,890
24,890 – 24,990	Amateur 12 m Band		
		24,990 – 26,960	1,970
26,960 – 27,410	Citizens Band		
		27,410 – 28,000	590
28,000 – 29,700	Amateur 10 m Band		
		29,7 – 50 MHz	20.3 MHz
50.0 – 54.0 MHz	Amateur 6 m Band		
	(TV channels 2 – 4)	54 – 74.8 MHz	20.8 MHz
74.8 – 75.2 MHz	Excluded Frequency Band (Aeronautical Radionavigation) See 47 CFR 15.615(f)(1)		
	(TV channels 5 – 6)	75.2 – 80 MHz	4.8 MHz

Report on Standard P1675 – Broadband over Power Line Hardware

Terry Burns
Communications Engineering
Arizona Public Service Co.
Phoenix, Arizona

Abstract—**P1675 is a standard being developed by the IEEE Power Engineering Society to address specifications for hardware used in the Broadband over Power Line industry. The Standard will also cover installation methods for the safe and reliable operation of the both the BPL and distribution systems.**

Key Words – Broadband over Power Line Hardware, couplers, grounding and bonding

I. INTRODUCTION

The concept of injecting broadband signals on distribution lines has been a topic of discussion at IEEE Power Engineering Society (PES) meetings for a number of years. The European academic community has been researching this topic since the early 90's and is far ahead of similar efforts in the US. At the annual PES meeting in Toronto in July of 2003, the Communications Committee was directed by the PES Technical Council to begin standards work on the Broadband over Power Line (BPL) technology. At that time, only one person on the committee had an involvement in BPL.

Not long after the Toronto meeting, the author became the chair of a study group to begin work on a yet to be defined BPL Standard. The IEEE Standards Association (IEEE-SA) had simultaneously assigned a person to incubate the project, realizing the technical significance of BPL to the IEEE community. Together, the topic was researched and companies were found that were involved in the technology. Prospects were contacted and plans were made for a meeting. The first meeting of what was to become the BPL Standards Working Group was in San Diego in January 2004. There was a good representation of vendors and other interested people. The group's primary task was to determine the subject area most needing a Standard. Several topics were discussed including interference, modem design and a number of other BPL related topics. It was decided that the biggest impact to the BPL community would occur if efforts were concentrated on the hardware used by BPL to connect to distribution lines and the associated installation topics.

During the spring of 2004, efforts began to complete a PAR (Project Authorization Request) [1], the necessary document to begin work on a standard. This work progressed via e-mail and conference calls. Just after the Working Group's meeting in early June of 2004, the PAR was submitted to the Standards Association and was approved at their June 18, 2004, meeting.

This provided the charter required to proceed with the Standard and made the group an official Standards Working Group.

II. BPL BASICS

To fully comprehend the topics the standard covers, an understanding of Broadband over Power Line installation is essential. The basic principle of BPL is the use of distribution lines as communications cables for high-speed Internet. Distribution voltages are commonly 12.5 kV, 13.8 kV and sometimes as high as 34.5 kV. The RF signal that carries the Internet traffic must be coupled onto one of the phase conductors of the line, and coupled in such a manner that the line voltage is isolated from the BPL equipment. There are two common types of couplers. Capacitive couplers connect directly to the distribution conductor and provide isolation through the capacitance of the device. An inductive coupler wraps around the conductor and induces the RF signals into the conductor through an electro-magnetic field. As an inductive coupler doesn't touch the conductor, the only source of connectivity to high voltage is through tracking on the jacket of the cable connecting the BPL equipment to the coupler or possible degradation of the insulation. The BPL equipment, commonly referred to as a node or repeater, is usually mounted in an enclosure. The enclosure is attached to the pole in an overhead environment. In an underground installation, the enclosure is either mounted inside the pad mounted transformer housing, or in a pedestal placed near the transformer. The BPL equipment is basically a computer that converts Ethernet signals into RF pulses in one direction and RF pulses into Ethernet signals in the other direction.

The distance the BPL RF signal can travel down the line is limited by the amount of transmit power, the impedance match in the coupler, and the RF conductivity properties of the distribution line. If the location of a node is too far from the next location for proper operation of the system, a repeater is installed. A repeater simply decouples the signal on one side of a pole (in an overhead environment) and recouples it on the other side, using a different set of frequencies to prevent interference.

As the signals approach a residence, or other location that requires high-speed Internet, the RF will encounter a step-down transformer. The transformer reduces the distribution voltage down to 120/240V normally seen in a residence. Because the RF signal is not strong enough to penetrate the core of the transformer without an unacceptable loss, it is decoupled off the distribution line and into the node. The node then recouples the signal onto the service drop conductors running into the residence or residences. This will allow the homeowner to connect his computer into a BPL modem, plug the modem into an outlet, and receive high-speed Internet anywhere in his house that has an electrical outlet.

III. THE BASIC COMPONENTS OF THE STANDARD

A. The Standard as it Applies to Hardware

The primary concern of a distribution engineer, when confronted with a BPL installation, is having equipment installed on the line that could potentially provide a path to ground for a distribution phase conductor or induce some other failure mode into the system. The owner of the BPL equipment would have a similar worry. Having distribution voltages surge through the sensitive BPL electronic equipment would not be in their best interest. The easiest method for either the distribution engineer or the BPL equipment owner to be confident their installation is adequate is to purchase and install equipment that conforms to a standard written specifically with line and equipment protection in mind.

The standard therefore covers attributes of BPL hardware, primarily the couplers, that if adhered to by the hardware manufacturer, will prevent most mishaps from occurring. See Table I for a list of proposed attributes for couplers. The standard will describe the various attributes the hardware should be designed to, and then what testing method must be used to verify the equipment meets those requirements.

The primary requirements of BPL coupler hardware standards are prevention of failures that would allow the hardware to provide distribution voltage a path to ground. As such, Basic Insulation Level (BIL) is an important parameter. Let's assume that BPL equipment is mounted on a 12.5 kV phase to phase line. The voltage between the top of the insulator and ground would then be 7200 volts. This puts the coupler attached to the phase wire at a potential of 7200 volts. The repeater, if properly grounded, would be at zero potential, or ground. Metallic wire is used to connect the coupler to the node. Even though the metallic wires do not touch the phase conductors, they must have adequate insulation. The minimum amount of isolation needed is 7200 volts since the difference in potential from the coupler (7200 volts) to the node (0 volts) is 7200 volts. The metallic wire connecting the coupler to the node must be capable of entering and leaving the 7200 volt field without the insulation being penetrated and causing a fault to ground.

TABLE I.   COUPLER ATTRIBUTES

Couplers
▪ BIL
▪ Surge withstand characteristics
▪ Weather resistance
▪ Environmental
▪ Temperature range
▪ Humidity
▪ Water proof
▪ Shock/vibration
▪ Dielectric
▪ Contamination
▪ Mounting
▪ RIV
▪ Compatibility with existing hardware
o   Corona
o   Short circuit current
o   Labeling/nameplate information
o   Mechanical
▪ Weight
▪ Size
▪ Spacing
▪ Attachment
▪ Failure mode
▪ Flammability
▪ Liquid vs. dry
o   Grounding
o   Testing
▪ Impulse withstand
▪ Vibration
▪ Environmental
•   Sunlight Resistance
▪ Short circuit withstand
▪ RIV
▪ HV tests
▪ Power quality
▪ Impact resistance

Providing enough insulation to prevent voltage on the phase wire from traveling on the coupler wires satisfies the situations where the cable is dry and there are no impurities on the jacket that will allow voltage migration down it. When the line becomes saturated with a conductive material, the results of a rainstorm for example, the voltage on the line will have the ability to track down the jacket of the coupler wire into the BPL node. So the standard must address situations where pollution and inclement weather can compromise the insulation ability of jacketed conductors. Should the insulation level not be sufficient, the voltage on the distribution conductor will track down the coupler cable and go to ground at the node, causing a fault on the line. This will obviously impact the node negatively, but it will also cause the feeder circuit recloser to trip, causing, at least momentarily, an interruption in power to the customers on the feeder.

Because distribution lines, and even service entrances, do not always operate in a steady-state mode, that is, at their fundamental voltage, BPL hardware must meet further criteria to prevent a failure in a non-normal environment. For example, if a BPL coupler meets the standard for surge withstand characteristics, it will then survive most voltage spikes on a line, caused by faults in substations, lightening strikes, or similar occurrences.

To ensure that a manufacturer's equipment meets the parameters described in the standard, a test is prescribed for each criterion in the standard. Usually, only a sample of the device is tested for compliance. For some tests, it must be done on every device manufactured. The testing method is often found in another standard, which has been developed to specify how a test is to be accomplished, and what the criteria is for passing.

B. The Standard as it Applies to Installation

The installation of BPL equipment would be more straightforward if it only consisted of line-type hardware. BPL melds two technologies, high voltage distribution with highly sensitive electronic equipment, providing numerous opportunities for problems and concerns. Grounding is of primary concern in a BPL installation. Where a repeater is installed on a pole, normally the only ground available is the pole ground. A pole ground is installed as one of many ground points on a multi-grounded neutral. The National Electric Safety Code (NESC) [2] requires that the resistance of a pole ground be no more than 25 ohms. In a BPL installation, the repeater needs to be grounded. The pole ground is not only the obvious choice, but the only choice. But in the case of a three-phase system with an unbalance between phases, a portion of the unbalance current flows through the pole ground down to earth. This could be multiple amps. It would not take a very large difference in potential for a person in a parallel path to receive a lethal amount of current. Therefore, the designers, installers, and technicians working on the equipment must all take precautions and adhere to good work practices when designing and installing this equipment. The utility should provide adequate instructions for personnel working with the BPL equipment.

As a node or repeater requires power to operate, most BPL installations require a 120 Volt connection. If there isn't a distribution transformer on the pole the node or repeater is mounted on, a 120 Volt cable is run from the nearest transformer. The 120 Volt cable should include a neutral and a ground conductor. The ground must be bonded, not only to the cabinet for the BPL equipment, but also the pole ground. This will improve the ground resistance at the pole. It is imperative that all the grounds and any metallic equipment, such as equipment cabinets, be bonded together. The installation of a computer powered by household AC, even if it is in a box on a pole, has the expectation of being inherently safe. The installation procedures and attention to detail when installing it will go a long ways toward making this happen.

The installation of BPL equipment on poles has generated many debates on the proper methods and locations of these installations. The primary guide the Standards Working Group is using to answer many of these questions is the National Electric Safety Code (NESC). The code, as it is written today, has no provisions for running cables vertically on a pole. As the BPL couplers are required to be in the distribution voltage area of the pole, can the cables attached to them be run out of the distribution voltage area into the joint use area where communications cables for telephones and cable TV are attached? Or must the BPL equipment remain in the distribution voltage area, and therefore only be accessible by qualified linemen?

Not all BPL installations will be on poles. Most utilities have underground distribution, especially in newer residential areas. In underground situations, the location for installing equipment is much easier to get to, but the 12,500 volt environment is much closer also. Because most pad mounted transformers are installed in public right-of-way, they are accessible to the public and are much more likely to be tampered with. Therefore, keeping people away from harmful voltages is desirable.

From a BPL installation perspective, coupling to the primary and secondary voltages inside a pad-mounted transformer is an obvious necessity. Even though pad mounted transformers are considered "dead-front" meaning no live voltages are present when the front of the cabinet is open, utilities still consider them hazardous. Therefore, only authorized personnel are allowed in a pad mounted transformer. As the jacket on the primary voltage cable is at or near ground potential, a coupler attached to it is not in a high voltage field and therefore tracking on the coupler wiring should not be an issue. Precautions must be taken however, to prevent a fault on the primary side of the transformer from migrating through the BPL equipment to the secondary side, allowing high voltage to be coupled to house wiring.

The placement of the BPL equipment is another factor that must be addressed. Some existing installations place a small node or repeater inside of the transformer housing. Others have designed a pedestal that is installed beside the transformer and connected to the transformer by conduit run to it from underneath. In the latter case, BPL technicians should be able to work on the BPL equipment without assistance from a lineman, or other qualified utility worker. If the node is in the transformer, a qualified lineman would be required to do any work on it.

As described up to this point in the paper, the purpose of the Standard has appeared to be for the benefit of the distribution system and protection of personnel. From another perspective, the effectiveness of the BPL hardware is only as good as its installation. Good installation practices will enhance the operability of the BPL system. With proper installation and good grounding and bonding techniques, the BPL signal will better couple to the distribution line and stray signals will not potentially interfere with other users in the frequency band.

These are the primary examples of what this standard sets out to do. That is, provide a known source for what constitutes a safe device that will be attached to a distribution line. From a standards perspective, the methodology used is irrelevant. There is no intent of the Standard to enforce a particular vendor or design. What the Working Group wishes to ensure is that whatever methodology is used, it be properly tested and verified by an unbiased entity and that it will provide all the protection utilities think they need to protect themselves and their customers.

IV. BENEFITS OF THE STANDARD

What the Working Group hopes to accomplish with this standard is to increase the viability and availability of the BPL technology. Some examples:

To aid utilities – Utilities are, by nature, risk adverse. When a utility begins researching the viability of installing a BPL system, the potential risk and impact to the distribution network will weigh heavily in the decision to pursue this new technology. The availability of an IEEE Standard would most likely alleviate some of the concerns in this area.

To aid BPL vendors – When a BPL vendor approaches a utility with a proposal to use the utilities lines to install a system, or just to sell the utility BPL hardware; the fact that their product meets an approved standard will give considerable credence to their sales pitch.

Reduce invested engineering time – To install BPL equipment without a standard, a large amount of engineering time must be invested to determine whether the equipment the vendor is proposing would impact the distribution system. Most utilities do not have the time or the in-house expertise to fully evaluate specifications and test results, or the in-depth knowledge needed to determine if the proposed installation has the potential of a hazardous work environment. A standard puts this knowledge at the front end of the process, alleviating the distribution engineer from having to become familiar with the elements needed to ensure a sound installation.

Increase the integrity of installations – When a utility designs a project and performs the construction, they do it with every intention of ending up with a sound and responsible installation. Yet, in most cases, the combined knowledge of a utility is far less than that of an IEEE standards body given a particular topic. By using the combined engineering expertise of IEEE and lessons learned from those who have already started down the BPL road, the utility can gain the benefit of the experience of others.

V. CONCLUSIONS

P1675 – Standard for Broadband over Power Line Hardware, will provide the BPL industry with a much-needed tool for the safe and functional installation of BPL devices. This standard, while being developed under the auspices of the IEEE Power Engineering Society Communications Committee, will be a combined effort of many other groups and individuals. The goal is to have this standard completed within the next year allowing the BPL industry to benefit from its contents.

REFERENCES

[1] IEEE-SA Standards Board Project Autorization Request (PAR) Form (2002), Standard for broadband over power line hardware. Project Number – P1675, 18 June 2004.

[2] Insitute of Electrical and Electronic Engineers, Inc., National Electric Safety Code, 2002 Edition. 1 August 2001, P. 24.

Overview of FCC Requirements for Broadband over Powerline

William Hurst
Laboratory Division
Federal Communications Commission
Columbia, Maryland

Abstract: **The Federal Communications Commission (FCC) has historically permitted the use of carrier current systems for the transmission of radio frequency (RF) signals on the powerline. The FCC recently issued a Report and Order covering equipment known as Access Broadband over Powerline (BPL). Access BPL is a new type of carrier current system. This paper gives an overview of this recent FCC decision.**

Keywords: Access Broadband over Powerline, In-house Broadband over Powerline, Carrier Current Systems, Part 15, Radio Frequency Interference

I. INTRODUCTION

On October 28, 2004 the Federal Communications Commission (FCC) adopted a Report and Order (*Order*), which established new rules for Access Broadband over Power Line (Access BPL) systems [1]. Access BPL is a new type of carrier current technology that provides access to high speed broadband services using electric utility companies' power lines. The FCC has adopted rules that provide both technical and administrative procedures for the mitigation of interference to licensed radio services from BPL systems.

II. BACKGROUND

A. Carrier Current Systems

Historically the FCC has permitted the use of carrier current systems for the transmission of Radio Frequency (RF) signals over alternating current (AC) electric power lines to carry communications by coupling very low power RF signals onto the AC electrical wiring. A carrier current system is defined as a "system, or part of a system, that transmits radio frequency energy by conduction over an electric power line to a receiver also connected to the same power line."[1] Traditionally, these systems have included amplitude modulated (AM) radio systems on school campuses and devices intended for the home, such as intercom systems and remote controls for electrical appliances and lamps. Campus radio systems have been operating for over fifty years in the United States at many universities as unlicensed broadcast radio stations in the AM Broadcast band.[2] Carrier current systems operate on an

---

1 47 C.F.R. § 15.3(f), Carrier Current System
2 47 C.F.R. § 15.221, Operation in the Band 525-1705 kHz

unlicensed basis under Part 15 of the Commission's rules. As a general condition of operation, Part 15 devices may not cause harmful interference to authorized radio services and must accept any interference that they receive.

Until recently, carrier current devices generally operated on frequencies below 2 MHz and with relatively limited communications capabilities. In the last few years, the availability of faster digital processing capabilities and the development of sophisticated modulation schemes have allowed the development of new designs for carrier current devices that are capable of overcoming earlier technical obstacles caused by the inherent noise and impedance mismatch of power lines. These new designs have led to the development of BPL systems that use spread spectrum or multiple carrier techniques with highly adaptive algorithms to overcome the noise on the AC powerline. These new BPL systems provide high speed digital communications capabilities by coupling RF energy onto either the power lines inside a building (In-House BPL) or onto the medium voltage power delivery lines (Access BPL).

In-House BPL uses the 110 volt power wiring inside a residence or business to carry information within a structure. Access BPL typically uses the medium voltage exterior power distribution network lines (carrying between 1,000 to 40,000 volts) as a transmission medium to bring high-speed communications services, *e.g.*, the Internet and other broadband services, to neighborhoods from where they are delivered to users. In-House BPL systems use the electrical wiring in a building to transfer information between computers and other home electronic devices, eliminating the need to install new wires between these devices.

Access BPL systems deliver high speed Internet and other broadband services to homes and businesses. In addition, electric utility companies can use Access BPL systems to monitor, and manage their electric power distribution operations. Because Access BPL capability can be made available in conjunction with the delivery of electric power, it may also be used to provide for the "last-mile" delivery of broadband services to homes and businesses.

B. Interference Concerns

The interference concern regarding BPL operation arises from the fact that electric power lines are not shielded and therefore a portion of the conducted RF energy will result in radiated emissions being generated. This "signal leakage," which has for years made possible the reception of carrier current radio stations at colleges, universities and other institutions without a connection to the power line, can become harmful interference if not carefully managed. That is, radio systems using the same frequency bands as those on which local Access BPL signals are transmitted could possibly receive harmful interference from such signal leakage if adequate safeguards are not in place.

Most Access BPL systems that are currently deployed operate in the range from 2 MHz to 50 MHz, with very low-power signals that are spread over a broad range of frequencies. These frequencies are also used by licensed radio services that must be protected from harmful interference under the Commission's Part 15 rules for unlicensed devices. In the radio spectrum below 50 MHz, incumbent authorized radio services include fixed, land mobile, aeronautical mobile, maritime mobile, radiolocation, broadcast radio, amateur radio terrestrial and satellite, and radio-astronomy. Users of this spectrum include, for example, public safety and Federal government agencies, aeronautical navigation licensees, amateur radio operators, international broadcasting stations, and citizens band radio operators.

C. Existing Requirements for Carrier Current Systems

The requirements for carrier current systems specify radiated and conducted emission limits for devices operating both below 30 MHz and above 30 MHz. Carrier current systems operating from 9 kHz to 30 MHz are subject to radiated emission limits on emissions from any part of the wiring or power network connected to the RF power source. For carrier current systems that contain their fundamental emission within the standard AM broadcast band of 535 to 1705 kHz and are intended to be received using standard AM broadcast receivers, there is no limit on conducted emissions. All other carrier current systems operating below 30 MHz are subject to a conducted emission limit only within the AM broadcast band. Carrier current devices operating above 30 MHz must meet the radiated emission limits of Section 15.109(a), (b) or (g) for digital devices, which are further divided into two types. Class A equipment includes devices marketed for use in a commercial, industrial or business environment, excluding devices which are marketed for use by the general public or are intended to be used in the home. Class B equipment includes devices marketed for use in a residential environment, notwithstanding use in commercial, business and industrial environments. The rules require Access BPL systems to comply with the limits for Class A or B devices depending on whether they are marketed for use in a commercial, industrial or business environment on the one hand or for use by the general public or in the home on the other. Under this Class A/Class B designation, Access BPL systems that operate on medium voltage lines external to residential environments are considered Class A devices. Carrier current devices that do not operate on frequencies below 30 MHz are subject to the general conducted emission limits below 30 MHz. The existing Part 15 rules also address power line carrier systems, which are low-speed carrier current systems operating between 10 kHz and 490 kHz, used by an electric public utility entity for protective relaying, telemetry, etc., for general supervision of the power system. Because of their specialized use and operating frequency range, power line carrier systems are not subject to specific emission limits as are general carrier current systems.

III. OVERVIEW OF RULEMAKING

A. Definition of Access BPL

For purposes of the Part 15 rules, Access BPL was defined as a carrier current system operating on any electric power transmission line owned, operated, or controlled by an electric power provider. Although the *Order* does not generally address In-House BPL, clarification was given as to the differences between these two types of BPL.

Two new definitions were added to Section 15.3 of the rules:

"Access Broadband over Power Line (Access BPL).[3] A carrier current system installed and operated on an electric utility service as an unintentional radiator that sends radio frequency energy on frequencies between 1.705 MHz and 80 MHz over medium voltage lines or over low voltage lines to provide broadband communications and is located on the supply side of the utility service's points of interconnection with customer premises. Access BPL does not include power line carrier systems as defined in Section 15.3(t) of this part or In-House BPL as defined in Section 15.3(gg) of this part."

"In-House Broadband over power line (In-House BPL).[4] A carrier current system, operating as an unintentional radiator, that sends radio frequency energy by conduction over electric power lines that are not owned, operated or controlled by an electric service provider. The electric power lines may be aerial (overhead), underground, or inside the walls, floors or ceilings of user premises. In-House BPL devices may establish closed networks within a user's premises or provide connections to Access BPL networks, or both." [5]

B. Emission Limits

Radiated Emission Limits – For Access BPL, emission limits are given only for radiated emissions. Access BPL systems that operate in the frequency range of 1.705 kHz to 30 MHz over medium voltage power lines are required to comply with the radiated emission limits for intentional radiators provided in Section 15.209 of the rules. Access BPL systems that operate in the frequency range above 30 MHz over medium voltage power lines are required to comply with the radiated emission limits provided in Section 15.109(b) of the rules.

Access BPL systems that operate over low-voltage power lines, including those that operate over low-voltage lines that are connected to the in-building wiring, are required to comply

---

3 47 C.F.R. § 15.31(ff), Access Broadband over Power Line (Access BPL)
4 47 C.F.R § 15.31(gg), In-House Broadband over power line (In-House BPL)

with the radiated emission limits provided in Section 15.109(a) and (e) of the rules, unless the building is in a commercial or industrial environment, in which case the requirements of Section 15.109(b) apply.

Conducted emission limits –Access BPL devices are not subject to the conducted emission limits of Section 15.107.

C. *Interference Mitigation*

Access BPL systems are required to incorporate capabilities to modify their systems' operations and performance to mitigate or avoid potential harmful interference to radio services and to deactivate specific units found to actually cause harmful interference. This approach is intended to provide Access BPL equipment manufacturers and operators with flexibility to design and implement a broad range of products and system designs, while ensuring that systems have the capabilities to make operational changes to avoid any interference that may arise. Access BPL systems are required to follow the same requirements for addressing interference complaints as other types of unlicensed devices. Access BPL is subject to the procedures of Section 15.5(c) of the rules. Under this rule, parties who believe they are experiencing interference from an unlicensed device are first expected to bring the matter to the attention of the operator of the unlicensed device. If that action does not resolve the interference, the party may then seek intervention by the Commission.

(1) *Frequency Avoidance* – Access BPL systems incorporate the capability to avoid the use of specific frequency bands. The ability to alter a system's operation to notch-out transmissions from specific frequencies where interference is occurring is a necessary feature for resolving interference without disrupting service to BPL subscribers.

(2) *Shut down requirement* – Access BPL systems are required to incorporate a remote-controllable shut-down feature to deactivate, from a central location, any unit found to cause harmful interference, if other interference mitigation techniques do not resolve the interference problem.

D. *Access BPL Notification and Database Requirements*

The *Order* requires that an Access BPL notification and database be maintained to ensure that any potential interference to licensed services from BPL operations can be adequately identified and addressed. The primary intention of the notification and database requirements is to ensure that licensed users of the spectrum have a publicly accessible and centralized source of information on BPL operations to determine whether there may be Access BPL operations on particular frequencies within their local area so that any incident of harmful interference can be resolved should it occur. The information contained in the notification database need only be sufficient to determine whether there may be a BPL operation in the local area, the nature of the BPL operations, whether the BPL system is operating on frequencies that could potentially be a source of harmful interference to the licensed user and to identify an appropriate contact person who can work directly with the complainant to resolve the harmful interference if it is determined to be caused by the local BPL operations. Additional or more detailed relevant information needed by a radio operator may be requested via the contact person indicated in the data base, as appropriate.

E. *Equipment Authorization*

The FCC uses three different equipment authorization procedures depending on the type of equipment and as specified in the rules. The procedure to which a device is subject depends on the risk of interference that the equipment poses to licensed radio services. The three equipment authorization procedures are as follows:[5]

(1) *Verification* requires that equipment be tested either by the manufacturer or at an independent test laboratory to ensure that it complies with the technical requirements. The FCC is not notified by the manufacturer for this equipment authorization type and does not maintain a database of equipment subject to verification.

(2) *Declaration of Conformity* (DoC) is a manufacturer's self-approval procedure where the responsible party, who could be the manufacturer, the grantee or the importer of the equipment, as defined in 47 C.F.R. § 2.909, makes measurements at a recognized accredited test laboratory to ensure that the equipment complies with the appropriate technical standards. The FCC is not notified of this equipment authorization and does not maintain a database of equipment subject to DoC.

(3) *Certification* is an equipment authorization issued by the Commission or its designated entities, known as Telecommunication Certification Bodies (TCBs), based on representations and test data submitted by the applicant. The FCC is notified when products are certified. A complete copy of the application for certification is maintained in the FCC database. See www.fcc.gov.

Access BPL systems are not typical unintentional radiators, and it was recognized that the equipment authorization, for such systems, is critical in determining their interference potential. Due to the newness of the Access BPL measurement procedures it was decided that a review of measurement reports by a third party is warranted. Therefore, it was determined that Access BPL systems be required to be approved using the Certification equipment authorization procedure. At the present time TCBs are not permitted to authorize Access BPL devices. This will change once the Commission has determined that adequate procedures are in place and that TCBs are able to perform the authorizations.

There was consideration given as to whether the equipment authorization should be performed by the system operator, rather than the Access BPL equipment manufacturer. It was determined that the requirement for equipment authorization not be placed on the system operator. However, it was strongly recommended that operators perform initial installation and

---

5 47 C.F.R §2.907

subsequent periodic testing on their systems in order to ensure that the systems maintain compliance with the emission limits.

IV. BPL MEASUREMENT PRINCIPLES

In order to ensure that emissions from Access BPL systems are accurately measured specific measurement principles for both Access BPL and all other carrier current systems were included in the *Order,* as appendix C [2]. The following highlights some of those principles and the reader is referred to [2] for a complete copy of the measurement principles.

For Access BPL systems in underground installations, the guidelines use the common method of measuring radiated fields along a number of radials at a specified distance from the periphery of the transformer pad, which is mounted above the ground, where the Access BPL equipment is located. For Access BPL systems installed on overhead lines, in order to take into account the effect of the long power line, the measurement guidelines specify measurements at fixed horizontal distances from the power line where the Access BPL signal injection source is installed. Thus, rather than finding the maximum emissions across a number of radials, as currently performed for other Part 15 emitters, the measurement guidelines specify that the receive antenna be moved down-line, parallel to the power line, starting from the Access BPL signal injection equipment location, to find the maximum emissions at each frequency within the requisite frequency range of the Access BPL device; the minimum down-line distances at which measurements are to be taken in this sequence are specified in terms of the wavelength of the Access BPL mid-band frequency. The measurement guidelines also allow the use of the existing distance extrapolation factors for measurements made at distances other than the specified distance in the rules.

A. General Measurement for Access BPL, In-House BPL and CCS

General guidance is given for the different types of BPL systems, including Access BPL, In-House BPL and Carrier Current Systems. The procedure calls for measurements to be taken at the highest power settings of the equipment under test (EUT) and using the maximum RF injection duty factor and burst rate. The procedure specifies that for frequencies below 30 MHz that an active or passive magnetic loop be used to make the measurements. For emissions above 30 MHz, an electric field sensing antenna is to be used.

B. Access BPL Measurement Principles

Testing is to be performed at distance of 0, ¼, ½, ¾, and 1 wavelength down the line from the BPL injection point on the power line. Wavelength spacing is based on the mid-band frequency used by the EUT. In addition, if the mid-band frequency exceeds the lowest frequency injected onto the power line by more than a factor of two, testing shall be extended in steps of ½ wavelength of the mid-band frequency until the distance equals or exceeds ½ wavelength of the lowest frequency injected.

Measurements are normally performed at a horizontal separation distance of 10 meters from the overhead line. If necessary, due to ambient emissions, measurements may be performed a distance of 3 meters. Distance corrections are to be made in accordance with Section 15.31(f).

The distance correction for the overhead-line measurements are to be based on the slant range distance, which is the line-of-sight distance from the measurement antenna to the overhead line. (See fig. 1) For example, if the device injects frequencies from 3 to 27 MHz, the wavelength corresponding to the mid-band frequency of 15 MHz is 20 meters, and wavelength corresponding to the lowest injected frequency is 100 meters. Measurements are to be performed at 0, 5, 10, 15, and 20 meters down line—corresponding to zero to one wavelength at the mid-band frequency. Because the mid-band frequency exceeds the minimum frequency by more than a factor of two, additional measurements are required at 10-meter intervals until the distance down-line from the injection point equals or exceeds ½ of 100 meters. Thus, additional measurement points are required at 30, 40, and 50 meters down line from the injection point.

For frequencies above 30 MHz, an electric field sensing antenna, such as a biconical antenna is used. The signal shall be maximized for antenna heights from 1 to 4 meters, for both horizontal and vertical polarizations, in accordance to ANSI C63.4-2003 procedures [3]. For Access BPL measurements only, as an alternative to varying antenna height from 1 to 4 meters, these measurements may be made at a height of 1 meter provided that the measured field strength values are increased by a factor of 5 dB to account for height effects.

For frequencies below 30 MHz, an active or passive magnetic loop is used. The magnetic loop antenna should be at 1 meter height with its plane oriented vertically and the emission maximized by rotating the antenna 180 degrees about its vertical axis.

C. In-House BPL and Carrier Current Measurement Principles

In-House BPL devices are typically composite devices consisting of two equipment classes (Carrier current system and personal computer peripheral (Class B)). While carrier current systems require Verification, personal computer peripherals require Declaration of Conformity (DoC) or Certification, as specified in Section 15.101 of the Rules. Appropriate tests to determine compliance with these requirements shall be performed.

In-House BPL devices present a similar measurement challenge as Access BPL systems. What arrangement can be used to represent a typical installation? Historically the FCC has required that carrier current systems be tested *in-situ*. The FCC has determined that *in-situ* measurements are still required for carrier current and In-House BPL devices. The buildings selected for testing In-House BPL devices must not have metal siding or shielded wiring. The building wiring must meet the current United States building codes.

When the Equipment under Test (EUT) is both a carrier current device and a computer peripheral, the device shall also be tested in a laboratory environment to demonstrate compliance with the digital devices requirements in accordance with the measurement procedures in C63.4-2003 [8].

D. BPL Technical Report Requirements

Access BPL devices are subject to the equipment procedure known as certification. Applications for certification of Access BPL devices are required to be accompanied by a technical report in accordance with Section 2.1033 of the Rules. Each device used in an Access BPL system requires its own Certification.

For Access BPL devices, the statement describing how each device operates shall include the following information: modulation type, number of carriers, carrier spacing, channel bandwidth, notch capability/control, power settings/control, and range of signal injection duty factors.

For Access BPL devices, the measurement report is also required to include representative emissions spectrum plot(s) of the reported data.

E. Responsibility of BPL Operator

Although it is not anticipated the equipment authorization of an Access BPL device will be normally performed by the BPL operator, it is recommended that a BPL operator perform testing on the initial installation and periodic testing of Access BPL systems on his power lines. These tests need to be performed to ensure that the system in conjunction with the installation site complies with the appropriate emission limits. The BPL operator is not required to submit the test results. In the instance that the Access BPL system was tested on the operator's network for certification purposes, the initial installation tests do not need to be repeated. However, periodic testing of installed Access BPL systems is recommended to

ensure that the system maintains compliance with Part 15 emission limits.

V. MEASUREMENT DATA

For Access BPL systems installed on overhead power lines, calculation of the measurement distance is performed using a "slant range". Fig. 1 illustrates the "slant range" calculation method to be used in determining the measurement distance in order for comparison of the emission to the limit. Fig. 2 gives an example of data taken on an access BPL system installed on an overhead power line.

Access BPL systems are required to incorporate the capability to avoid the use of specific frequency bands. The ability to alter a system's operation to notch-out transmissions from specific frequencies where interference is occurring is a necessary feature for resolving interference without disrupting service to BPL subscribers. Fig. 3 gives examples of data taken showing a notch in the BPL emission at 18 MHz.

VI. CONCLUSION

In the Report and Order on BPL, the FCC recognized the significant concerns of licensed radio service users regarding the potential of Access BPL systems to cause interference to their operations. The rule changes in the *Order* establish specific technical and administrative requirements for Access BPL equipment and operators to ensure that interference does not occur and, should it occur, to provide for a timely resolution of that harmful interference without disruption of service to Access BPL subscribers. The *Order* also sets forth procedures to measure the radio frequency (RF) energy emitted by Access BPL equipment.

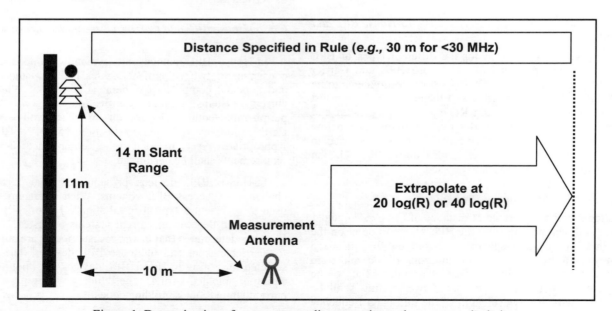

Figure 1. Determination of measurement distance using a slant range calculation.

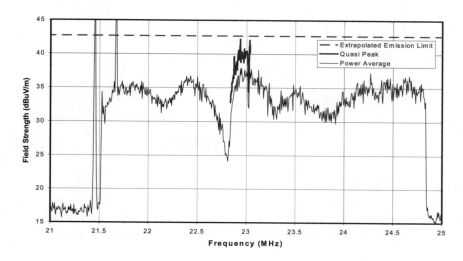

Figure 2: Measurement of Access BPL System showing measurement data
for both average and quasi-peak detectors.

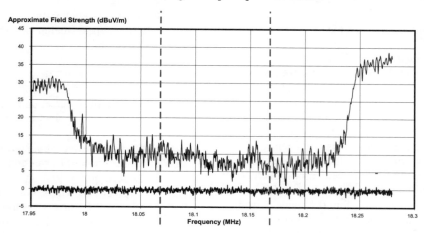

Figure 3. Spectrum Analyzer plot showing notch in the
Access BPL signal at 18 MHz.

REFERENCES

[1] FCC 04-245, ET Docket No. 04-37, *Amdment of Part 15 regarding new requirements and measurement guidelines for Access Broadband over Power Line Systems*

[2] FCC 04-245, Appenix C, *Measurement Guidelines for Broadband Over Power Line (BPL) Devices Or Carrier Current Systems (CCS) and Certification Requirements For Access BPL Devices*

[3] ANSI C63.4-2003, *American National Standard for Methods of Measurement of Radio-Noise Emissions from Low-Voltage Electrica and Electronic Equipment in the Range of 9 kHz to 40 GHz*

[4] ET Docket No. 03-104, 18 FCC Rcd 8498 (2003), *Inquiry Regarding Carrier Current Systems, including Broadband over Power Line Systems, Notice of Inquiry*

[5] ET Docket Nos. 03-104 and 04-37, 19 FCC Rcd 3335 (2004), *In the Matter of Carrier Current Systems, including Broadband over Power Line Systems and Amendment of Part 15 regarding new requirements and measurement guidelines for Access Broadband over Power Line Systems, Notice of Proposed Rulemaking*

NATO and Power Line Telecommunications

Arto Chubukjian
Communications Research Centre
Ottawa, Ontario, Canada
Arto.Chubukjian@ieee.org

BACKGROUND

Concerned with the evolving technology of Power Line Telecommunications (PLT, PLC, BPL) and its possible effects on the HF spectrum, NATO's Research and Technology Organization (RTA) has formed IST-050/RTG-022, a research task group (RTG) on HF Interference, Procedures and Tools, under its Information Systems Technology (IST) Panel. Several nations are participating in this activity. The inaugural meeting was held in March 2004 and the work must be completed by March 2007.

JUSTIFICATION (Relevance to NATO)

Power Line Telecommunications (PLT) and various forms of Digital Subscriber Line (xDSL) transmissions are recent and rapidly evolving technologies using the existing electricity power or telephone lines for data transmission with rates higher than 1 MBit/s. As these lines were not designed for transmission of high data rates, they will produce noiselike interference in the HF-range. The intensity depends on the electrical characteristics of the lines (balance, match, screening) as well as on the density and area coverage of these new systems. Exact calculations are impossible at this time because of missing models for the new wire-line communication systems with respect to emission of radio noise in the HF band. First measurements and estimations show that radio noise from PLT and xDSL will bring up big problems for military HF radio communications and Communication Intelligence (COMINT) in all NATO countries. HF is still, and will be further, used for near (ground wave) and far (sky wave) distance communications, as its equipment is easily and rapidly deployable. It permits fully military-controlled command links across long distances with secured transmissions without additional costs and easy frequency co-ordination. Any degradation in the quality of the HF spectrum would have adverse consequences to this capability.

OBJECTIVE

The objective of this task group will be to find out procedures, models and tools for being able to calculate and measure radio noise produced by PLT and xDSL systems in the HF range. This will then enable NATO and its countries to determine the threat to military HF radio communications and COMINT systems by PLT and xDSL and to take the appropriate steps.

TOPICS

The topics to be covered are:

- Identify the effects of PLT and xDSL systems contributing to HF radio noise.
- Find out technical characteristics of PLT and xDSL systems that may be modelled as HF radio noise sources.
- Establish the corresponding models including procedures and tools for determination of the technical parameters describing the HF radio noise sources (power, antenna characteristic, gain, etc).
- Determine these technical parameters theoretically and by measurement.

PROGRAMME OF WORK

The programme of work set up by RTA allows the work to be subdivided into nine distinct tasks:

Task 1: Radiation effects by PLT/xDSL,
Task 2: Description of power and telephone lines,
Task 3: Description of PLT/xDSL techniques/systems,
Task 4: Typical PLT/xDSL systems (for modeling),
Task 5: PLT/xDSL noise measurement methods,
Task 6: Propagation path loss models,
Task 7: Modeling techniques for PLT/xDSL noise sources,
Task 8: Models and results of typical PLT/xDSL systems,
Task 9: Measurements and model verification.

In addition, Task 1 includes a review of international regulatory activities and limits, and Task 7 includes EMC analysis techniques or methods in addition to computational models.

The work to be carried out is quite involved, especially given the three-year life of this RTG. A significant portion of the work involves the review of various technical studies and published literature, monitoring of the regulatory activities, and keeping abreast of the commercial developments involving this technology. A final report will be submitted to the IST Panel at the conclusion of the work in early 2007.

GLOSSARY

It is worthwhile here to include a short list of organizations and acronyms involved.

EC – *European Commission*
CENELEC – *European Committee for Electrotechnical Standardization*
ETSI – *European Telecommunication Standards Institute*
CEN – *European Standardization Committee*
ECC – *European Communications Committee*
CEPT – *European Conference of Postal and Telecommunications Administrations*
ERC – *European Radiocommunications Committee within CEPT*
JWG – *Joint Working Group of CEN, CENELEC and ETSI for PLT and VDSL (EC mandate M313)*
BBC – *British Broadcasting Corporation*
EBU – *European Broadcasting Union*
ITU – *International Telecommunication Union*
CISPR – *International Special Committee on Radio Interference*
NTIA – *National Telecommunications and Information Administration*
FCC – *Federal Communications Commission*

CURRENT STATUS OF WORK

The current status (March 2005) of the major areas and/or tasks of the RTG are summerized below in no particular order of importance. In terms of the tasks listed above, Tasks 1, 2, and 3 are approaching completion, Tasks 4, 5, and 7 are in the initial stages, Task 6 has been completed, and finally, some work has been carried out under Task 8.

Power line infrastructures

There are some differences in power line infrastructrure between North American and European power systems, that will impact the modeling and the EMC analyses activities of the RTG. For instance, where the power distribution lines are located underground, the emissions from house wirings and attached modems would be the major sources of interference, and where the power distribution lines that are located above ground, an additional concern would be the emissions from these lines.

xDSL infrastructures

Normally, these systems are of a lesser concern, especially in North America, as the transmission medium is mostly shielded. Another reason for the lesser concern is based on the fact that for xDSL, the HF signal is only fed to the customer's lines while for PLT, it is fed to all of the electrical infrastructure around the local interface. Nevertheless, because the xDSLs are included within the terms of reference of the RTG, they are included in the work programme.

PLT and xDSL device types and technical characteristics

The compilation of the specific information is an on-going activity for the foreseeable future, in order to account for any new devices coming unto the market.

EMC studies

There have been quite a few EMC studies and papers (on cumulative effects and on sharing) published on the subject of PLT, in various NATO countries. The RTG is evaluating them as part of its work. In addition, the spectrum management office of NATO is also involved in developing sharing and interference mitigation techniques, and is collaborating with the RTG.

Noise level

In all radio communications, the limiting factor is the ability to receive weak signals against the background noise. However, because of the characteristics of the HF band, this background noise is not the noise generated in the receiver (as it is on VHF and higher frequencies), but the ambient noise in the external environment. In effect this noise enters the receiver via the antenna along with the wanted signals, so that the radio environment is part of the receiving process.

The ambient noise environment consists of two parts, the irreducible residual ambient noise which is more or less constant in any particular location, and incidental noise from local man-made sources. The combination of these two determines the minimum usable signal level.

Contributing to the ambient noise environment are:

a) Natural noise sources:

- Atmospheric noise, a major source of which is almost continuous lightning activity around the equator (ca. 100/s have been measured) from which interference is propagated to the rest of the world by ionospheric reflection. The overall noise level depends on frequency, time of day, season of the year, sunspot number and location. In temperate zones, noise from this source is relatively low, compared to the equatorial zone, although there will be short bursts of noise from local electrical atmospheric activity (thunderstorm) at certain times.

- Cosmic noise originates from outer space. The main generator of radio noise is the sun, along with atmospheric gases and star clusters. In the HF band the cosmic noise reaching the antenna depends on the screening effect of the ionosphere. At lower HF frequencies (<10 MHz), it is impractical to distinguish between cosmic noise and the general background noise from other sources.

b) Man-made noise sources:

- Man-made noise derives from electrical, electronic or radio equipment and exhibits two effects. Firstly, there is the contribution from a large number of relatively distant sources. This noise is effectively "white" and one of the constituents of the ambient noise floor. Secondly, there is incidental noise from local sources the level of which varies, depending on the type of environment. Environments are classified as business, residential, rural and quiet rural.

From the radio users point of view, the difference between these environments is the level of the noise and the length of time for which it persists.

As the sensitivity of HF receiving systems in general is determined by the ambient noise, the protection requirements are derived from the ambient noise levels specified in ITU-R P.372-8, as well as from the minimum noise measured in Europe.

PLT and xDSL will cause unintentional radiofrequency emissions which may increase the established radio noise floor directly nearby or by cumulative propagation far away from many such sources. This type of emission is quite different from that produced by electronic devices and equipment: it is broadband noise, most of the time with a high level, and extending over the HF band.

Emission limits

Currently, there are several existing/proposed electric field strength emission limits for wire-line communications, specified at a distance of 3 metres, and in peak values. In the HF band of 1.6 – 30.0 MHz, these limits range between 0 to 70 dBμV/m, depending on the country or the organization.: Germany (NB 30), Norway, United Kingdom, BBC/NATO/EBU, JWG, United States (FCC Part 15, 33 dB/decade), ITU-T SG5, and Guelleman.

While the subject of emission limits are within the responsibility of the national and international spectrum management authorities, from the perspective of NATO, it is desirable that these be eventually harmonized, for the following reasons:

a) emissions from wire-line communications travel long distances and past international boundaries, therefore, differences in emission limits introduce additional difficulties to the interference assessement and mitigation functions; and,

b) different emission levels, thus different noise ambients, have the potential to affect interoperability within NATO.

The incidental noise generated even by devices and equipment compliant with relevant EMC standards can greatly exceed the natural noise floor. Then, reception of low-level HF signals is possible only because of the statistical nature of this incidental noise. Many devices radiate near the limit of their standard on only a few discrete frequencies, or on a narrow band of frequencies. In addition most incidental noise is relatively short lived. HF communication services are opportunistic, i.e. frequencies and time are chosen to optimise the probability of a satisfactory signal-to-noise ratio. If incidental noise prevents communication at any particular time, the transmission is repeated at a later time when the interference has ceased. In automatic systems this is built into the operating protocol, but it doesn't work with a broadband noise floor steadily increased by PLT and/or xDSL.

Therefore it is necessary to find worldwide harmonized standards covering EMC aspects of wire-line telecommunication networks including their in-house extensions. These standards should ensure that broadband wire-line telecommunications will not degrade HF radio reception

- directly in the immediate vicinity of the wire-lines, as well as,

- far away from mass-deployed telecommunication networks by cumulative interference.

Propagation path loss models

The RTG reviewed the existing HF propagation path loss models and identified the appropriate prediction models to be used in the EMC studies involving wire-line communications. This task is now considered to have been completed.

There are two major radio wave propagation mechanisms in the HF frequency range: *sky waves*, in which the radio waves are refracted in the ionosphere, and *ground waves*, propagating along the ground. Generally, sky waves can reach farther, but there is a loss associated with the refraction and also by D-layer absorption. The RTG recommends one model for each propagation type, and proposes relevant input parameters (not included here) when the models are used to predict propagation of PLT/xDSL signals.

In the case of sky waves, the RTG recommends to use one of the programs of the *IONCAP* family. This recommendation is based on the facts that these programs are well-proven in practice by many users. Among the three programs of the *IONCAP* family the use of *ICEPAC* is recommended, because it is the newest and therefore most advanced model, and has been used for frequency planning by the administrations of several of the countries involved in the RTG.

In the case of ground waves, the RTG recommends *GRWAVE*, since it has been thoroughly verified and does not require any detailed terrain information. The limiting factor in predictions will often be the available data, meaning that a more sophisticated model cannot necessarily give significantly more accurate predictions, even though such a model may be more accurate in isolated cases. However, one should be aware of the limitations of *GRWAVE*, and use caution when utilizing it outside its validity range. In certain cases, such as mixed sea/land paths, where there is a need for more than one ground conductivity/permittivity, the RTG recommends using *Millington's* method. Simple Matlab scripts has been developed by the group that extend on *GRWAVE* to deliver *Millington* functionality within the Matlab environment.

Measurement methods

In the RTG's case, the measurement issue mainly involves radiated rather than conducted emissions. The RTG is currently evaluating several comprehensive methods prepared by various administrations and organizations. Included among these are those from Industry Canada (Canada), RegTP (Germany), FCC (United States), ETSI, and others. Some of the contentious issues with respect to methodology involve:

a) the measurement location specifics such as whether it is carried out at line height or below, and at what distance away from the line, and at what longitudinal intervals;

b) the measurement geometry (measurement points around the line, movement of the antenna, etc);

c) the measurement instrumentation and the settings;

and so on.

This is one issue that is undergoing a fair amount of discussion in international and national organizations, and it may be a while before it is resolved.

PLT system trials/measurements

As part of the work, RTG is also reviewing an extensive set of documents on trials and measurements carried out by various authorities in many countries. The review of available documents indicated that indeed PLT are significant sources of interference. For instance, measurements carried out at an unnamed German city where frequency-hopping PLT systems were installed, the interference effects ranged all the way up to 20 MHz, and in some cases even higher. It was noticed that, even at very low data rates (or in stand-by mode), the harmful effects of these PLT systems were immediately apparent on all radio systems operating within the same band. In another example of the effect of PLT on the spectrum, it is mentioned that in the city of Mannheim, Germany, shortwave broadcast reception in parts of the city is seriously affected or not possible at all. Similar examples exist in other countries.

Modeling activities

The main instrument for modeling and simulations is the computational electromagnetics tool. Some work has been carried out in this area, notably by the NTIA and by the Communications Research Centre (CRC) in Canada. In the latter case, emissions from above ground power lines with connected PLT devices were modeled, and assessed with respect to FCC Part 15 radiated limits. The following is a brief outline of the CRC work.

A medium voltage (MV) power line distribution network within a neighborhood generally comprises three-phase wiring, and geometrically could be very complex. The MV power wires run from a substation, and these wires may be physically oriented on the utility pole in a number of configurations (e.g., horizontal, vertical, or triangular). One or more phase lines may branch out from the three phase lines to serve a number of customers. The devices associated with a power distribution system itself and PLT equipment include the transformers, line branches and turns, the injected signal source, etc. These all cause impedance discontinuities along the power line.

To characterize the PLT power networks, the electromagnetic parameters and geometric configurations of the power line have to be modeled in a way to reflect the actual power line structure over ground and its wide range of characteristics: insulated wires, transformer(s), branches or sharp turns off the lines, various injection locations of electromagnetic excitation in the structure, and structures in dielectric media.

With the above consideration, a basic MV power line model was designed. Its configuration consists of three-phase parallel perfectly conducting lines (horizontal phase configuration) 10 meters above a good soil ground. The lines with a total length of 540 metres are mounted on 19 poles with the steel bar holders and insulators; the horizontal separation between the lines being one metre. The lines are straight for 360 metres and turn right at the 10th pole at a 60 degree angle for 180 metres. At both ends, the three phase lines are terminated with transformers and arranged in a Y-type configuration.

Many factors could impact the radiated emissions of the PLT system. However, the turn points or sections of the MV lines, the source location, the number of the transformers (or equivalent devices) and their locations implemented with the PLT systems are the three basic factors to cause the impedance discontinuities. These discontinuities can produce radiation directly or cause signal reflections in the power line that produce standing waves and associated radiation along the line. In this study, based on the basic model, several PLT models were developed by varying the locations of the signal source and adding more transformers. These models exhibit the various scenarios of impedance discontinuities, and thereby the analyses of the models will provide us with a good understanding of the unintentional radiation arising from the real PLT systems.

Phase 1 of this study has been completed, and the analyses indicated the following results (partial set):

- The measurements taken at distances along the power lines that are fractions of a wavelength, as proposed by FCC guidance, will fail to reveal the peak field strength in many cases. However, the analysis indicates that more than 80 percent of the local field strength peaks will be within 5 dB of the peak electric field strength measured along the power line at a height of two metres above the ground.

- Numerical results calculated with the maximum radiated power of 0.5 watt source significantly exceeded the FCC limits. This indicates that the source power level used in this simulation was too high.

- By reducing the source power level by 30 dB, the maximum output power of the signal source will be 0.5 mW. For the frequencies below 30 MHz, the maximum emission values for the Cases of 1, 2, 5 and 6 would be below the FCC limit while the values for the Cases of 3 and 4 at most frequencies would be below the FCC limit but on the margin. However, for the frequencies greater than 30 MHz, almost every case exceeds the FCC limit. This could suggest that for a PLT system operating at high frequency, its output power should be further reduced (Cases are referring to the different scenarios of connecting the PLT and line terminations, and so on).

- In the evaluation of the S_{11} parameter, at certain frequencies where S_{11} values are very small, the power line could possibly radiate the PLT signal efficiently at those frequencies. Nevertheless, the probability of the power line structures acting as efficient radiators is very small. Statistically, the probability could be evaluated as the ratio of the number of the data points with very small S_{11} values (< -10 dB) over the total number of data points (1200 in this case). This ratio was found to be 20 out of 1200 (or ~2%). Therefore, in a real PLT installation, there is a small probability that on a particular line and at a particular operating frequency, the PLT (or part of it) will radiate efficiently. It was also found that the reflection coefficient is highly dependent on the details of each power line configuration, such as the location of PLT source and transformer loading.

One cautionary point needs to be made with respect to the results. Certain general assumptions were made in the modeling scenario, due to the lack of specific information on the following items:

- Power distribution network configuration, and the geometric structure,
- PLT connection details such as on which of the three lines (left, centre, right),
- Impedance matching network details,
- Impedance data of the PLT devices (coupler, decoupler, repeater) and the power utility transformer over the entire frequency range of 1 – 40 MHz.

The importance of first two bullets is that it will affect the transmission mode – differential or common. In addition, with respect to the last two bullets, some uncertainty exists over the actual behaviour of the impedance data throughout the frequency range, compared to the assumption.

Therefore, the modeling results stated above should still be considered as an initial outcome to be refined further as more specific data on the PLT devices and power distribution network transformers will become available.

FINAL COMMENTS

The main concern for NATO as a major user of the HF band is the possible degradation of the spectrum quality as a result of the uncontrolled emissions (interference) from wire-line communications systems.

Given that these wire-line systems are interference-causing equipment as opposed to radio communications systems, the normal spectrum management approaches such as sharing studies, or applying limits to transmitter output power, antenna gain, and bandwidth, or specifying emission masks, etc can not be utilized. Rather, the regulators need to impose proper emission limits on the wire-line communications systems, preferably harmonized throughout the NATO countries.

As outlined above, the work programme of this RTG is quite involved, given the short time frame. Nevertheless, significant progress has been made thus far, and it is expected that the pace will continue.

Finally, sincere appreciations are extended to the members of the RTG for their solid work, to their respective national authorities, to NATO RTA organization and staff, and to colleagues at work and in the IEEE EMC Society who are also dealing with the subject of PLT.

TUTORIAL: FUNDAMENTALS OF SIGNAL INTEGRITY
(MO-PM-WS-10)
Dr. Jim Drewniak

This tutorial will provide an introduction to some fundamentals of signal integrity. Power distribution network design for high-speed digital systems will be addressed, as well as device modeling, including IBIS models. Basics of measurements for signal integrity in both time- and frequency-domain will also be covered. Finally, modeling the complete signal path for SI analysis will be discussed.

Presentations:

(1) Aspects of Signal Integrity
Jim Drewniak, Jun Fan, Jim Nadolny, Vittorio Ricchiuti and Ted Dibene

(2) DC Power Bus Design in Multilayer PCBs: Concepts, EMI and SI Implications, SMT Decoupling, and Modeling
Jim Drewniak

(3) Measurements for Signal Integrity
Vittorio Ricchiuti

(4) Basics in SPICE & IBIS Modeling of IC
J. Ted DiBene II and Giuseppe Selli

(5) High Speed Link Design and Simulation
Jim Nadolny

(6) Understanding Transmission-Line Loss
Jun Fan, Kai Xiao and James L. Knighten

NOTES

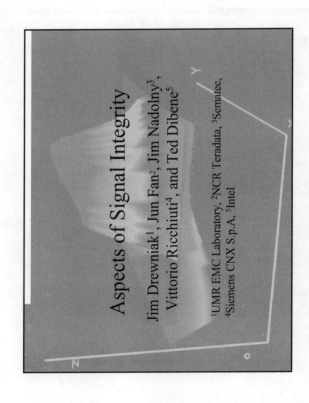

Overview

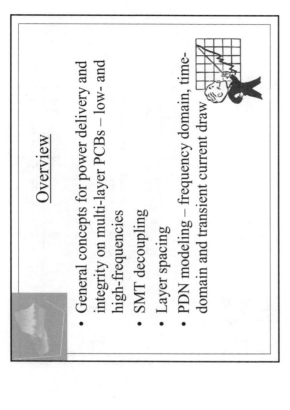

- General concepts for power delivery and integrity on multi-layer PCBs – low- and high-frequencies
- SMT decoupling
- Layer spacing
- PDN modeling – frequency domain, time-domain and transient current draw

Logic Transitions

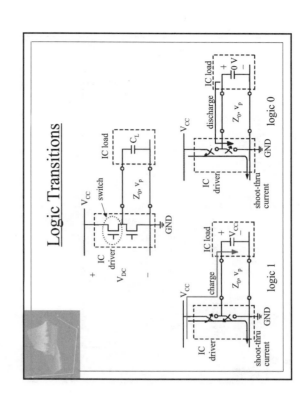

DC Power Bus Design in Multilayer PCBs: Concepts, EMI and SI Implications, SMT Decoupling, and Modeling

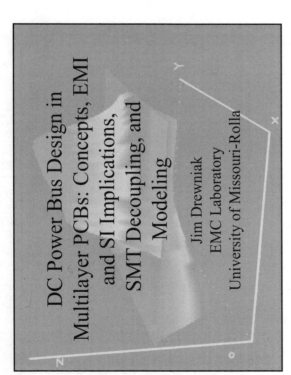

Jim Drewniak
EMC Laboratory
University of Missouri-Rolla

PDN Design: General Concepts

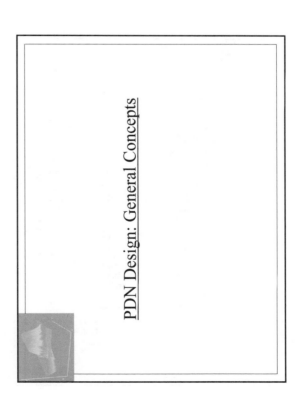

Equivalent Circuit Model

Equivalent low-frequency circuit model:

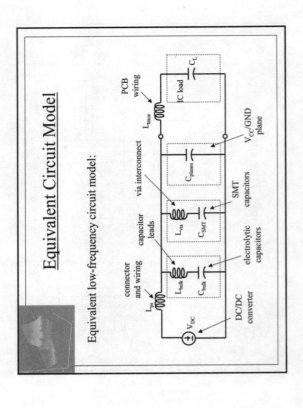

Effect of Inductance

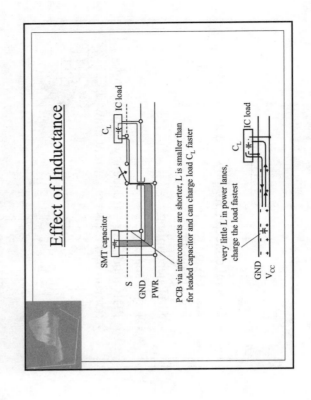

PCB via interconnects are shorter, L is smaller than for leaded capacitor and can charge load C_L faster

very little L in power lanes, charge the load fastest

Multilayer PCB Power Bus

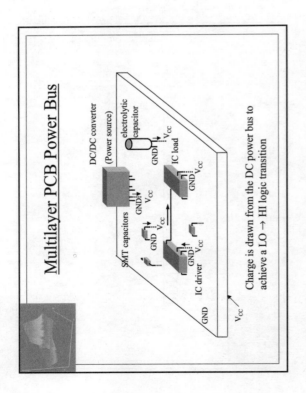

Charge is drawn from the DC power bus to achieve a LO → HI logic transition

Effect of Inductance

Inductance – impedes the flow of current (charge) to the load that will charge it to achieve a logic 1

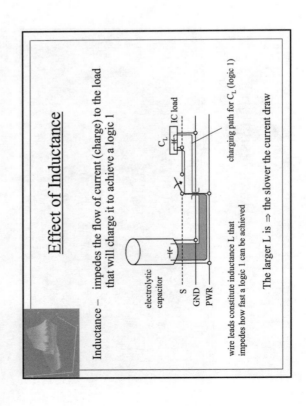

charging path for C_L (logic 1)

wire leads constitute inductance L that impedes how fast a logic 1 can be achieved

The larger L is ⇒ the slower the current draw

218

A Hydraulic Analogy

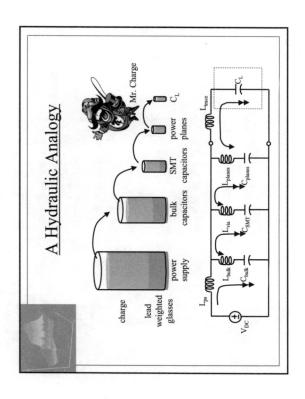

V$_{CC}$ Plane Disturbance

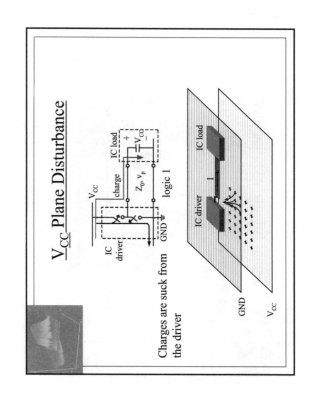

Charges are suck from the driver

Power Bus Charging Hierarchy

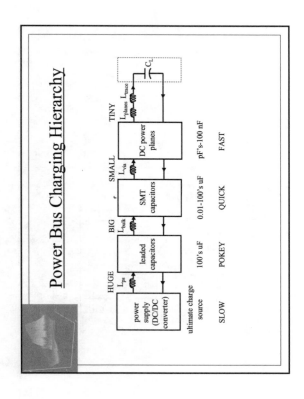

Consequence of Drawing Charge

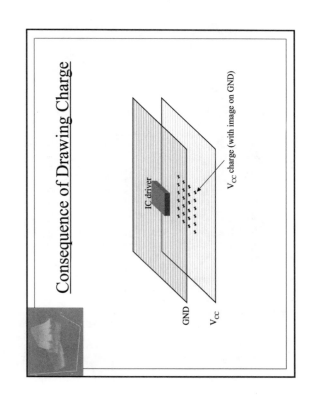

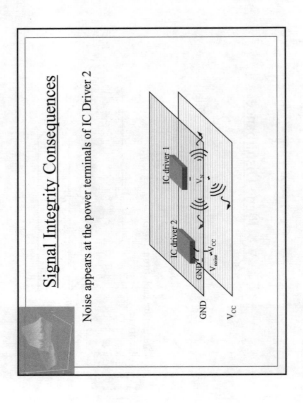

Signal Integrity Consequences

Noise appears at the power terminals of IC Driver 2

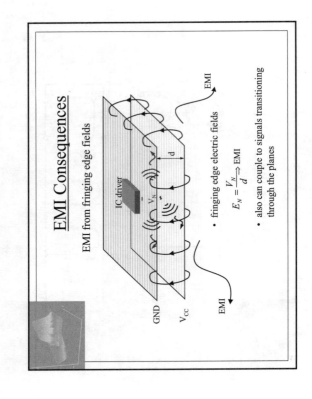

EMI Consequences

EMI from fringing edge fields

- fringing edge electric fields

$$E_N = \frac{V_N}{d} \Rightarrow EMI$$

- also can couple to signals transitioning through the planes

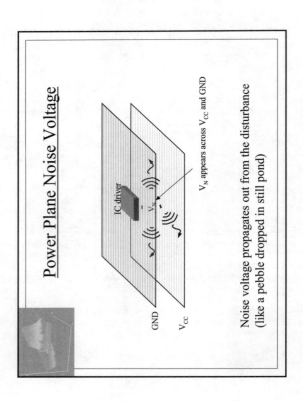

Power Plane Noise Voltage

V_N appears across V_{CC} and GND

Noise voltage propagates out from the disturbance (like a pebble dropped in still pond)

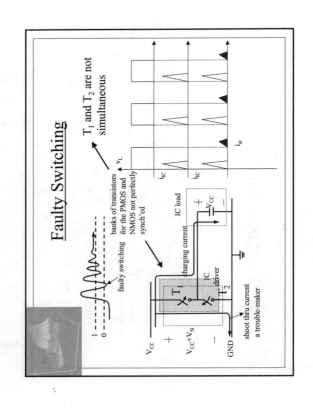

Faulty Switching

T_1 and T_2 are not simultaneous

Transfer Impedance

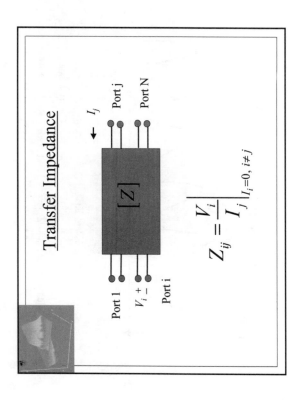

$$Z_{ij} = \frac{V_i}{I_j}\bigg|_{I_i = 0,\ i \neq j}$$

Input Impedance of the board

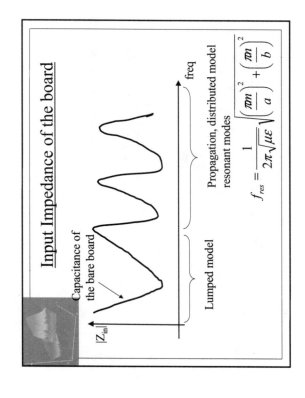

$$f_{res} = \frac{1}{2\pi\sqrt{\mu\varepsilon}}\sqrt{\left(\frac{\pi m}{a}\right)^2 + \left(\frac{\pi m}{b}\right)^2}$$

DC Power Bus Parallel Planes

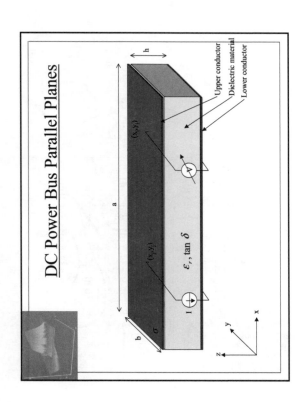

Input Impedance

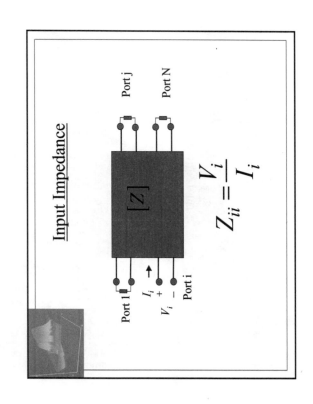

$$Z_{ii} = \frac{V_i}{I_i}$$

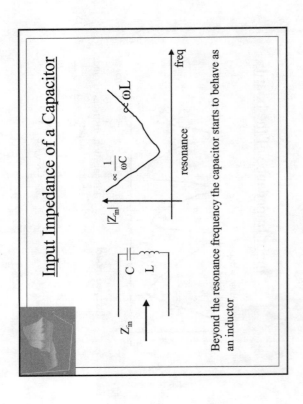

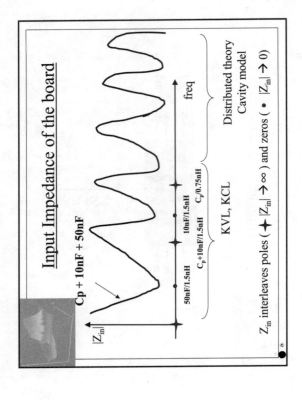

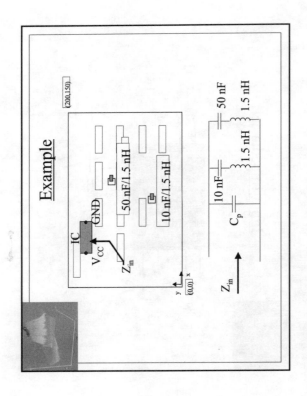

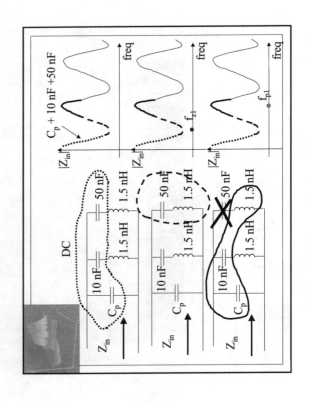

Power Bus Design Issues

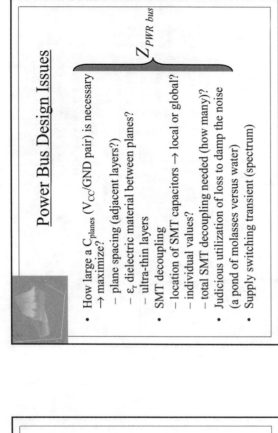

$Z_{PWR\ bus}$

- How large a C_{planes} (V_{CC}/GND pair) is necessary → *maximize?*
  - plane spacing (adjacent layers?)
  - ε_r dielectric material between planes?
  - ultra-thin layers
- SMT decoupling
  - location of SMT capacitors → local or global?
  - individual values?
  - total SMT decoupling needed (how many)?
- Judicious utilization of loss to damp the noise (a pond of molasses versus water)
- Supply switching transient (spectrum)

SMT Placement

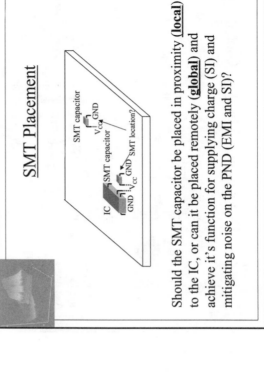

Should the SMT capacitor be placed in proximity **(local)** to the IC, or can it be placed remotely **(global)** and achieve it's function for supplying charge (SI) and mitigating noise on the PND (EMI and SI)?

Power Bus Design Strategy

- Source of charge needed in short time for fast switching to charge logic state —
  - power planes (V_{CC}/GND)
  - SMT decoupling capacitors
- Must be adequate to charge C_L (in light of the shoot-thru current)
- Fastest source of charge ⇒ smallest inductance (connections to V_{CC}/GND)
- Recharge smaller capacitances (SMTs, power planes) with large, "bulk" charge storage capacitors
- Work to minimize the noise voltage distribution on the V_{CC}/GND plane pair (for both EMI and SI)
- Largest value of decaps in a given package size

SMT Decoupling on Multi-Layer Printed Circuit Boards

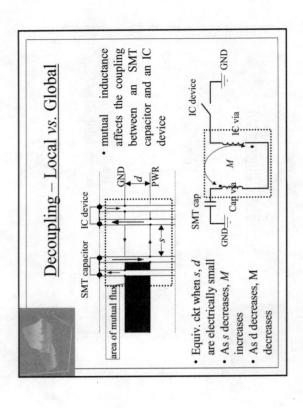

Decoupling – Local *vs.* Global

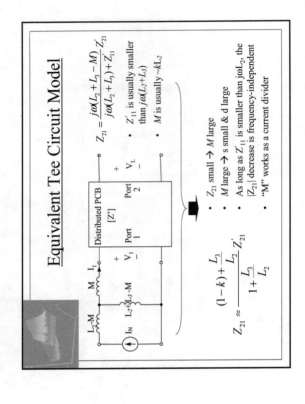

Equivalent Tee Circuit Model

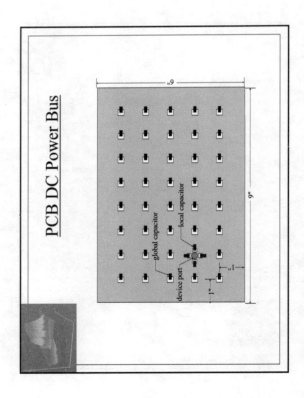

PCB DC Power Bus

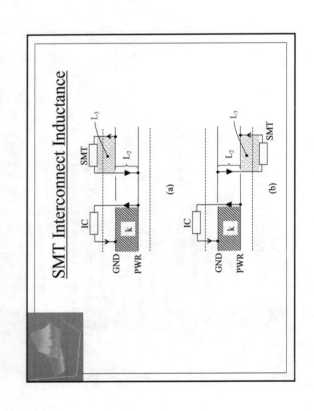

SMT Interconnect Inductance

Closed-Form Expressions

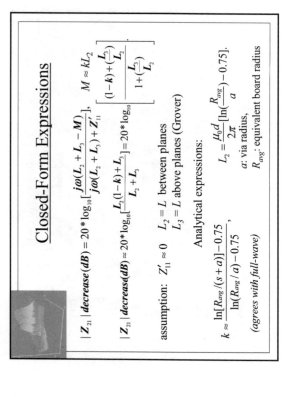

$$|Z_{21}| \, decrease(dB) = 20*\log_{10}\left[\frac{j\omega(L_2+L_3-M)}{j\omega(L_2+L_3)+Z'_{11}}\right], \qquad M \approx kL_2 \frac{(1-k)+\left(\frac{L_3}{L_2}\right)}{1+\left(\frac{L_3}{L_2}\right)}$$

$$|Z_{21}| \, decrease(dB) \approx 20*\log_{10}\left[\frac{L_2(1-k)+L_3}{L_2+L_3}\right] = 20*\log_{10}$$

assumption: $Z'_{11} \approx 0$ $L_2 = L$ between planes
  $L_3 = L$ above planes (Grover)

Analytical expressions:

$$k \approx \frac{\ln[R_{avg}/(s+a)]-0.75}{\ln(R_{avg}/a)-0.75}, \qquad L_2 = \frac{\mu_0 d}{2\pi}\left[\ln\left(\frac{R_{avg}}{a}\right)-0.75\right].$$

a: via radius,
R_{avg}: equivalent board radius

(agrees with full-wave)

PCB Configuration Studies

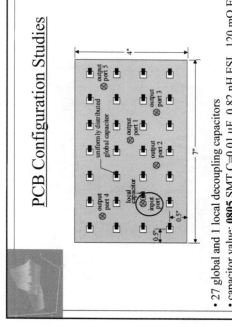

- 27 global and 1 local decoupling capacitors
- capacitor value: **0805** SMT C=0.01 μF, 0.82 nH ESL, 120 mΩ ESR
- $\varepsilon_r = 4.7$, tan δ = 0.02

Measured |Z₂₁|

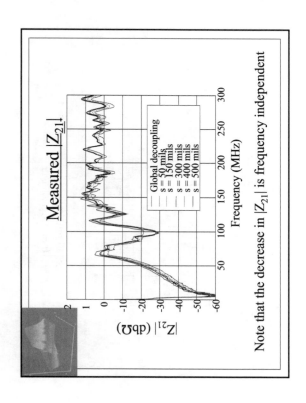

Note that the decrease in $|Z_{21}|$ is frequency independent

SMT Decoupling Conclusions

- Mitigation benefit of local decoupling was verified by the test board – and is frequency independent
- The equation derived from the equivalent circuit model provides a means to estimate the Z_{21} decrease
- Closed-form formulas for via inductance and coupling coefficient have been developed – benefits of local decoupling are achieved for a large ratio of inter-plane L_2 to above plane L_3
- Local SMT decoupling applicable only for thick power/ground plane pairs

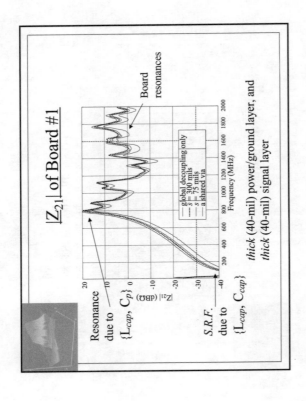

$|Z_{21}|$ of Board #1

Board resonances

Resonance due to $\{L_{cap}, C_p\}$

S.R.F. due to $\{L_{cap}, C_{cap}\}$

global decoupling only
$s = 300$ mils
$s = 75$ mils
a shared via

thick (40-mil) power/ground layer, and *thick* (40-mil) signal layer

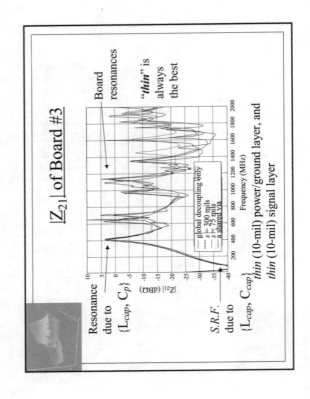

$|Z_{21}|$ of Board #3

Board resonances

"thin" is always the best

Resonance due to $\{L_{cap}, C_p\}$

S.R.F. due to $\{L_{cap}, C_{cap}\}$

global decoupling only
$s = 300$ mils
$s = 75$ mils
a shared via

thin (10-mil) power/ground layer, and *thin* (10-mil) signal layer

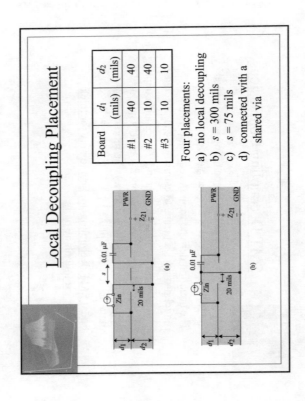

Local Decoupling Placement

Board	d_1 (mils)	d_2 (mils)
#1	40	40
#2	10	40
#3	10	10

Four placements:
a) no local decoupling
b) $s = 300$ mils
c) $s = 75$ mils
d) connected with a shared via

0.01 μF

PWR

GND

Zin

Z_{21}

20 mils

(a)

0.01 μF

PWR

GND

Zin

Z_{21}

20 mils

(b)

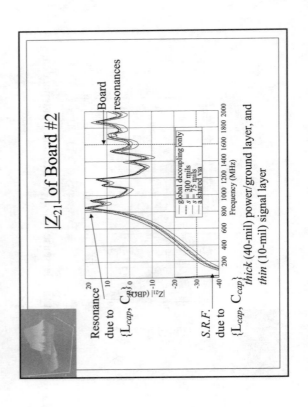

$|Z_{21}|$ of Board #2

Board resonances

Resonance due to $\{L_{cap}, C_p\}$

S.R.F. due to $\{L_{cap}, C_{cap}\}$

global decoupling only
$s = 300$ mils
$s = 75$ mils
a shared via

thick (40-mil) power/ground layer, and *thin* (10-mil) signal layer

DC Power Bus Design Implications

- Local decoupling is beneficial for thick power/ground layers (30 mils or greater)
- The decoupling capacitor is effective beyond its series resonant frequency due to the mutual inductance
- There is little benefit of local decoupling for thin power/ground layer (10 mils or less)
- The decrease of power bus noise is more than 10 dB with a thin PCB core (40 mils -> 10 mils)
- Implications for PCB design:
  - use a thin power/ground plane spacing in the stackup
  - for thick PCBs, place decoupling close to PWR/GND pins
  - minimize the interconnect inductance for decoupling effectiveness

E-Field at 3m for Varying Board Thickness

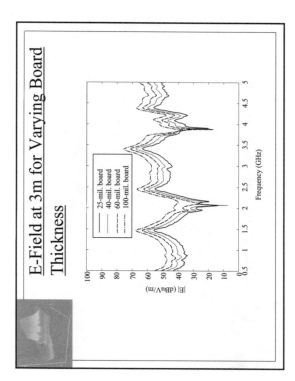

Power Bus Noise Decrease

Case (d) – a shared via vs. (a) - no local decoupling	Modeled $|Z_{21}|$	Calculated R
Board #1 (40/40)	-3.9 dB	- 3.0 dB
Board #2 (10/40)	-4.5 dB	-4.6 dB

$$R \approx \frac{(1-k) + \dfrac{L_3}{L_2}}{1 + \dfrac{L_3}{L_2}} \quad \text{where}$$

$L_2 = 1.14$ nH

$L_{3,10} = 0.19$ nH

$L_{3,40} = 1.12$ nH

$k \approx 0.8$ for a shared via

- ESL of the capacitor was included in L_3

Impact of Layer Spacing on PCB Layer Impedance and Noise Voltage

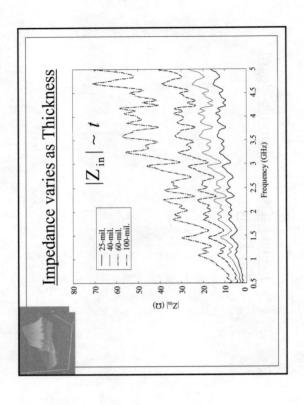

Impedance varies as Thickness

$$|Z_{in}| \sim t$$

Power Distribution Network Modeling in Multi-Layer PBCs

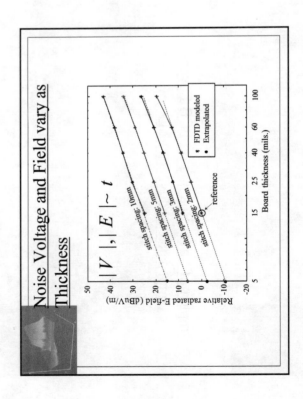

Noise Voltage and Field vary as Thickness

$$|V|, |E| \sim t$$

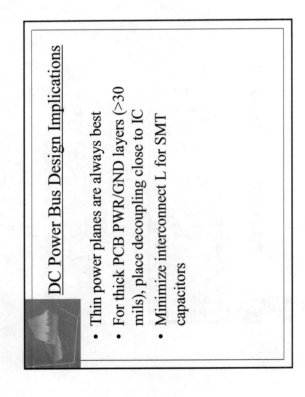

DC Power Bus Design Implications

- Thin power planes are always best
- For thick PCB PWR/GND layers (>30 mils), place decoupling close to IC
- Minimize interconnect L for SMT capacitors

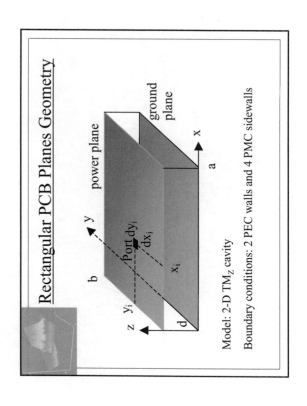

Rectangular PCB Planes Geometry

Model: 2-D TM_z cavity

Boundary conditions: 2 PEC walls and 4 PMC sidewalls

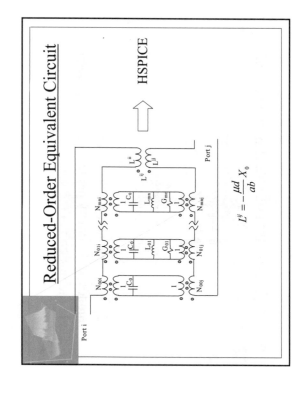

Reduced-Order Equivalent Circuit

$$L^{ij} = -\frac{\mu d}{ab} X_0$$

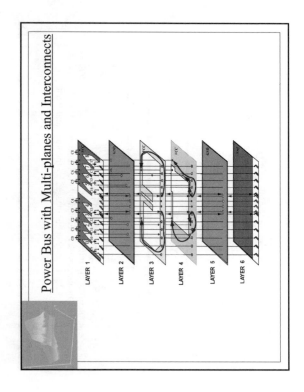

Power Bus with Multi-planes and Interconnects

LAYER 1
LAYER 2
LAYER 3
LAYER 4
LAYER 5
LAYER 6

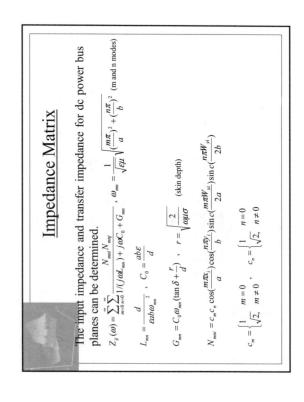

Impedance Matrix

The input impedance and transfer impedance for dc power bus planes can be determined.

$$Z_{ij}(\omega) = \sum_{m=0}^{\infty}\sum_{n=0}^{\infty} \frac{N_{mni} N_{mnj}}{1/(j\omega L_{mn}) + j\omega C_0 + G_{mn}} , \quad \omega_{mn} = \frac{1}{\sqrt{\varepsilon\mu}}\sqrt{(\frac{m\pi}{a})^2 + (\frac{n\pi}{b})^2} \quad \text{(m and n modes)}$$

$$L_{mn} = \frac{d}{\varepsilon ab\omega_{mn}^2} , \quad C_0 = \frac{ab\varepsilon}{d}$$

$$G_{mn} = C_0 \omega_{mn}(\tan\delta + \frac{r}{d}) , \quad r = \sqrt{\frac{2}{\omega\mu\sigma}} \quad \text{(skin depth)}$$

$$N_{mni} = c_m c_n \cos(\frac{m\pi x_i}{a})\cos(\frac{n\pi y_i}{b})\text{sinc}(\frac{m\pi W_{xi}}{2a})\text{sinc}(\frac{n\pi W_{yi}}{2b})$$

$$c_m = \begin{cases} 1 & m=0 \\ \sqrt{2}, & m\neq 0 \end{cases} , \quad c_n = \begin{cases} 1 & n=0 \\ \sqrt{2}, & n\neq 0 \end{cases}$$

Calculation of Parasitic Inductance L_1

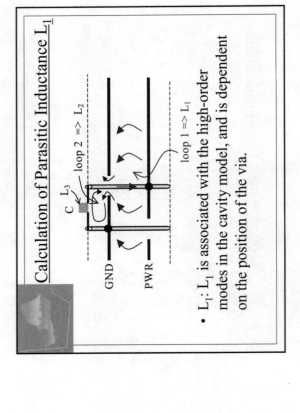

- L_1: L_1 is associated with the high-order modes in the cavity model, and is dependent on the position of the via.

Calculation of Parasitic L_2

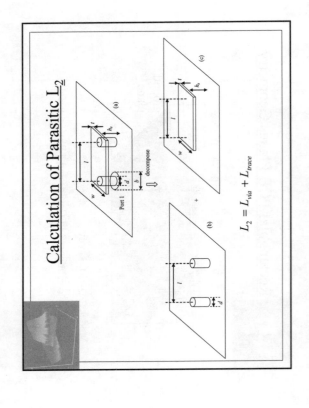

$$L_2 = L_{via} + L_{trace}$$

Parasitic Inductances

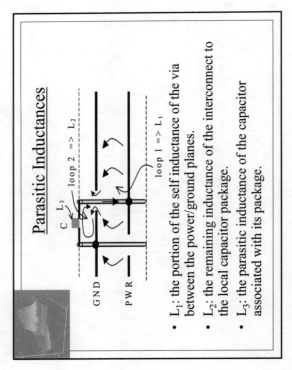

- L_1: the portion of the self inductance of the via between the power/ground planes.
- L_2: the remaining inductance of the interconnect to the local capacitor package.
- L_3: the parasitic inductance of the capacitor associated with its package.

Calculation of Parasitic L_2

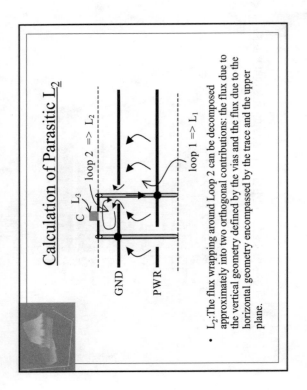

- L_2: The flux wrapping around Loop 2 can be decomposed approximately into two orthogonal contributions: the flux due to the vertical geometry defined by the vias and the flux due to the horizontal geometry encompassed by the trace and the upper plane.

S-parameters of the Power Bus (S21)

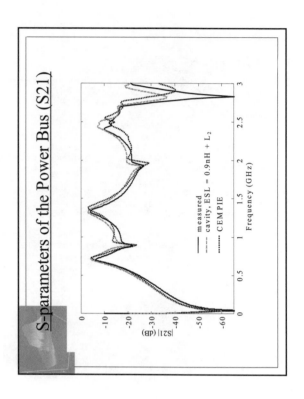

Multi-Plane Coupling - Vias

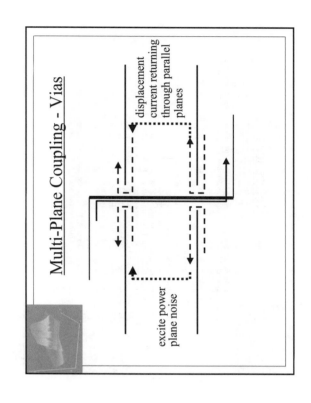

Power Bus with Global Decoupling Capacitors

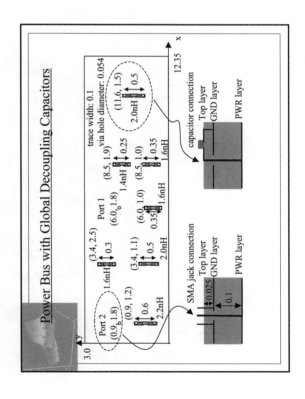

Multi-Plane Coupling – Cavity Modes

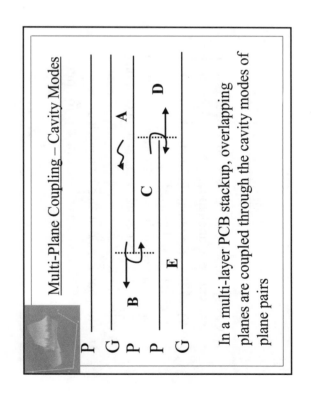

In a multi-layer PCB stackup, overlapping planes are coupled through the cavity modes of plane pairs

References

- J. Fan, J. L. Drewniak, and J. L. Knighten, "Lumped circuit model extraction for vias in multi-layer substrates," *IEEE Trans. Electromagn. Compat.*, vol. 45, pp. 272-280, May 2003.

- W. Cui, J. Fan, Y. Ren, H. Shi, J. L. Drewniak, and R. E. DuBroff, "DC power bus noise isolation with power plane segmentation," *IEEE Trans. Electromagn. Compat.*, vol. 45, pp. 436-443, May 2003.

- J. Fan, W. Cui, J. L. Drewniak, T. P. Van Doren, and J. L. Knighten, "Estimating the noise mitigation effect of local decoupling in printed circuit boards", *IEEE Trans. on Advanced Packaging*, vol. 25, pp. 154-165, May 2002.

- Chen Wang, Jingkun Mao, Giuseppe Selli, Shaofeng Luan, Lin Zhang, Jun Fan, James L. Drewniak, David J. Pommerenke, and Richard E. DuBroff, "An efficient approach for power delivery network design with closed-form expressions for parasitic interconnect inductances," accepted for publication in the *IEEE Trans. on Advanced Packaging*, 2005.

- J. Fan, J. L. Drewniak, J. L. Knighten, N. W. Smith, A.. Orlandi, T. P. Van Doren, T. H. Hubing, and R. E. DuBroff, "Quantifying SMT decoupling capacitor placement in DC power bus design for multi-layer PCBs, *IEEE Trans. Electromagn. Compat.*, vol. 43, pp. 588-599, November 2001.

- T. H. Hubing, J. L. Drewniak, T. P. VanDoren, and D. Hockanson, "Power bus decoupling on multi-layer printed circuit boards," *IEEE Trans. Electromagn. Compat.*, vol. 37, pp. 155-166, May 1995.

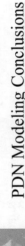

PDN Modeling Conclusions

- Cavity model can be used to model power bus with regular shape.

- With the segmentation method, the fast approach can be used to model irregular shaped power delivery networks on multiple layers with shorting vias and decoupling capacitors.

- Slots and gaps can also be modeled.

- A SPICE model can be extracted for time-domain simulations.

Measurements for Signal Integrity

2005 IEEE International Symposium on
Electromagnetic Compatibility
8 - 12 August 2005, Chicago, IL

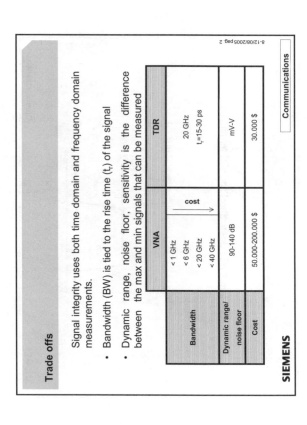

Vittorio Ricchiuti
Siemens CNX S.p.A., Loc. Boschetto, 67100 L'Aquila, Italy
e-mail: vittorio.ricchiuti@siemens.com

SIEMENS | Communications

Trade offs

- Signal integrity uses both time domain and frequency domain measurements.
- Bandwidth (BW) is tied to the rise time (t_r) of the signal
- Dynamic range, noise floor, sensitivity is the difference between the max and min signals that can be measured

	VNA	TDR
Bandwidth	< 1 GHz < 6 GHz < 20 GHz < 40 GHz	20 GHz t_r=15-30 ps
Dynamic range/ noise floor	90-140 dB	mV-V
Cost	50.000-200.000 $	30.000 $

cost →

SIEMENS | Communications

Outline

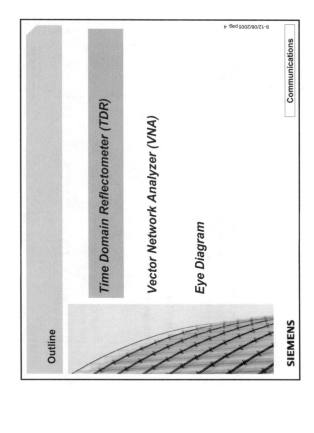

Time Domain Reflectometer (TDR)

Vector Network Analyzer (VNA)

Eye Diagram

SIEMENS | Communications

Trade offs

	VNA	TDR
Capabilities	Measure in frequency domain	Measure in time domain
Space & time resolution	**Can not** resolve time & space from measurements	Can resolve time & space from measurement $\Delta t = \Delta x / v$
Modeling	Good for determining component values *(by using resonant frequencies)*	Good for developing parasitic models Bad for determining component values

SIEMENS | Communications

The echo technique

The echo technique reveals at a glance the position and the nature (resistive, inductive or capacitive) of each discontinuity along the line in terms of bumps and dips.

Incident Step: very fast (20 - 40ps)

Wide spectrum: about 20GHz

A bump indicates an higher-impedance event (e.g. open or reduction in line-width).

A dip indicates a lower-impedance event (e.g. short or increase in line-width).

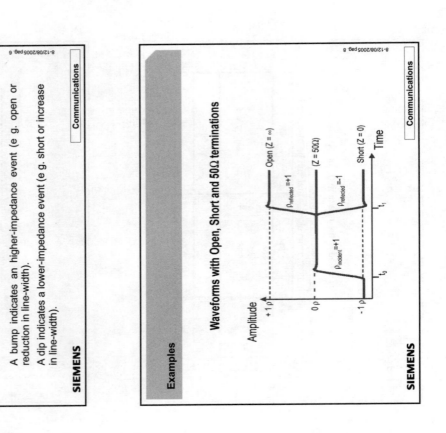

SIEMENS

Communications

8-12/08/2005 pag. 6

Examples

Waveforms with Open, Short and 50Ω terminations

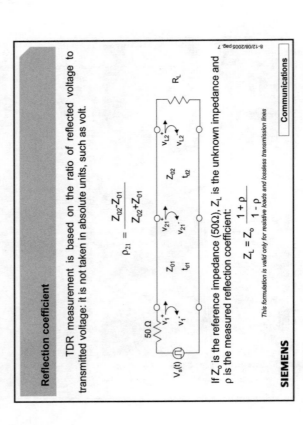

SIEMENS

Communications

8-12/08/2005 pag. 8

'Closed-loop radar' system

TDR employs a system described as 'closed-loop radar'

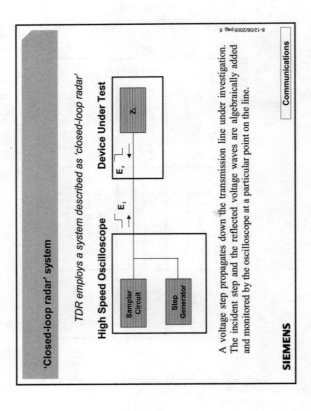

A voltage step propagates down the transmission line under investigation. The incident step and the reflected voltage waves are algebraically added and monitored by the oscilloscope at a particular point on the line.

SIEMENS

Communications

8-12/08/2005 pag. 5

Reflection coefficient

TDR measurement is based on the ratio of reflected voltage to transmitted voltage: it is not taken in absolute units, such as volt.

$$\rho_{21} = \frac{Z_{02}-Z_{01}}{Z_{02}+Z_{01}}$$

If Z_o is the reference impedance (50Ω), Z_L is the unknown impedance and ρ is the measured reflection coefficient:

$$Z_L = Z_o \ \frac{1+\rho}{1-\rho}$$

This formulation is valid only for resistive loads and lossless transmission lines

SIEMENS

Communications

8-12/08/2005 pag. 7

Basic TDR Equivalent Circuit

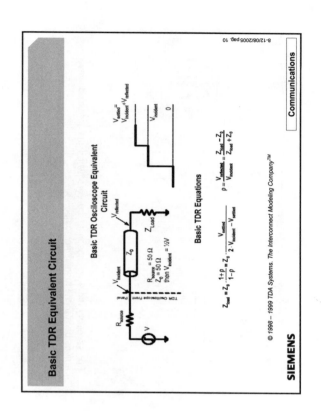

Basic TDR Oscilloscope Equivalent Circuit

$R_{source} = 50\ \Omega$
$Z_0 = 50\ \Omega$
then $V_{incident} = \frac{1}{2}V$

Basic TDR Equations

$$Z_{load} = Z_0\,\frac{1+\rho}{1-\rho} = Z_0\cdot\frac{V_{settled}}{2\,V_{incident} - V_{settled}}$$

$$\rho = \frac{V_{reflected}}{V_{incident}} = \frac{Z_{load} - Z_0}{Z_{load} + Z_0}$$

$V_{settled} = V_{incident} + V_{reflected}$

© 1998 – 1999 TDA Systems. The Interconnect Modeling Company™

SIEMENS — Communications

8-12/08/2005 pag. 10

TDR Interconnect Modeling Quick Guide

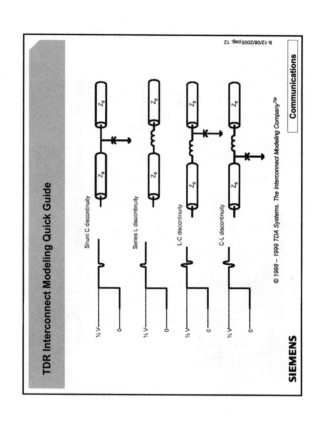

Shunt C discontinuity

Series L discontinuity

L-C discontinuity

C-L discontinuity

© 1998 – 1999 TDA Systems. The Interconnect Modeling Company™

SIEMENS — Communications

8-12/08/2005 pag. 12

Examples

T = t₁ – t₀ = the time from the TDR to the mismatch and back again, as measured on the instrument

v_p = velocity of propagation

D = distance to the fault

It is:

$$D = \frac{v_p\,T}{2}$$

SIEMENS — Communications

8-12/08/2005 pag. 9

TDR Interconnect Modeling Quick Guide

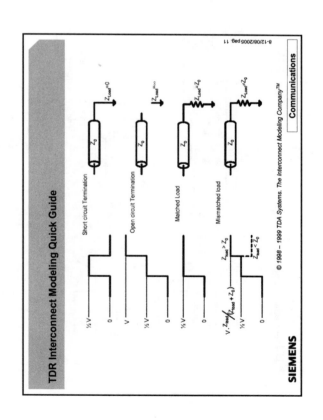

Short circuit Termination — $Z_{load} = 0$

Open circuit Termination — $Z_{load} = \infty$

Matched Load — $Z_{Load} = Z_0$

Mismatched load — $Z_{Load} \neq Z_0$

© 1998 – 1999 TDA Systems. The Interconnect Modeling Company™

SIEMENS — Communications

8-12/08/2005 pag. 11

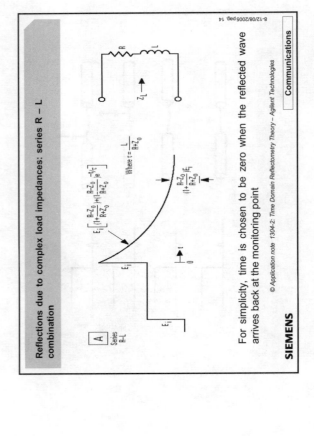

Reflections due to complex load impedances: series R – L combination

A — Series R-L

$$E_i\left[\left(1+\frac{R-Z_0}{R+Z_0}\right)+\frac{R-Z_0}{R+Z_0}\,e^{-t/\tau}\right]$$

$$\left(1+\frac{R-Z_0}{R+Z_0}\right)E_i$$

Where $\tau=\dfrac{L}{R+Z_0}$

For simplicity, time is chosen to be zero when the reflected wave arrives back at the monitoring point

© Application note 1304-2: Time Domain Reflectometry Theory – Agilent Technologies

Communications

SIEMENS

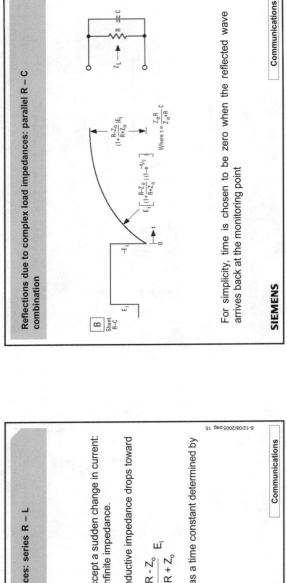

Reflections due to complex load impedances: parallel R – C combination

B — Shunt R-C

$$E_i\left[\left(1+\frac{R-Z_0}{R+Z_0}\right)\left(1-e^{-t/\tau}\right)\right]$$

$$\left(1+\frac{R-Z_0}{R+Z_0}\right)|E_i|$$

Where $\tau=\dfrac{Z_0 R}{Z_0+R}\,C$

For simplicity, time is chosen to be zero when the reflected wave arrives back at the monitoring point

Communications

SIEMENS

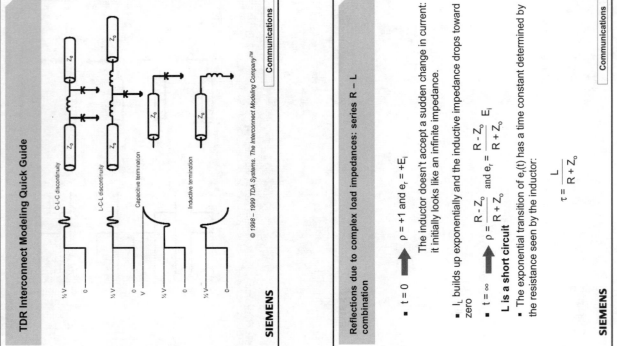

TDR Interconnect Modeling Quick Guide

C-L-C discontinuity

L-C-L discontinuity

Capacitive termination

Inductive termination

© 1998 – 1999 TDA Systems. The Interconnect Modeling Company™

Communications

Reflections due to complex load impedances: series R – L combination

- $t = 0$ $\rho = +1$ and $e_r = +E_i$

  The inductor doesn't accept a sudden change in current: it initially looks like an infinite impedance.

- I_L builds up exponentially and the inductive impedance drops toward zero

- $t = \infty$ $\rho = \dfrac{R - Z_0}{R + Z_0}$ and $e_r = \dfrac{R - Z_0}{R + Z_0}\,E_i$

  L is a short circuit

- The exponential transition of $e_r(t)$ has a time constant determined by the resistance seen by the inductor:

$$\tau = \frac{L}{R + Z_0}$$

Communications

SIEMENS

Reflections due to complex load impedances: examples

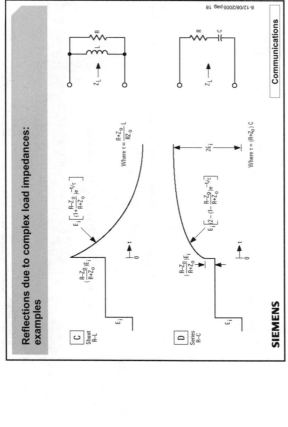

SIEMENS — Communications

Self inductance computation

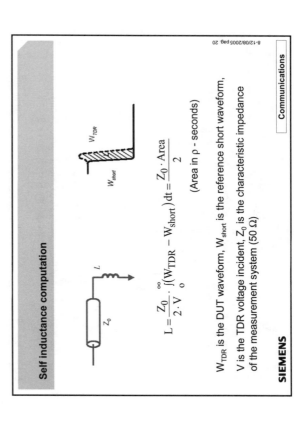

$$L = \frac{Z_0}{2 \cdot V} \cdot \int_0^\infty \left(W_{TDR} - W_{short}\right) dt = \frac{Z_0 \cdot Area}{2}$$

(Area in ρ - seconds)

W_{TDR} is the DUT waveform, W_{short} is the reference short waveform,

V is the TDR voltage incident, Z_0 is the characteristic impedance of the measurement system (50 Ω)

SIEMENS — Communications

Reflections due to complex load impedances: parallel R – C combination

- t = 0 $\rho = -1$ and $e_r = -E_i$

  The capacitor doesn't accept a sudden change in voltage: it initially looks like a short circuit.

- V_C builds up exponentially and the capacitive impedance rises

- t = ∞ $\rho = \dfrac{R - Z_o}{R + Z_o}$ and $e_r = \dfrac{R - Z_o}{R + Z_o} E_i$

  C is an open circuit

- The exponential transition of $e_r(t)$ has a time constant determined by the resistance seen by the capacitor:

$$\tau = \frac{R Z_0}{R + Z_0} C$$

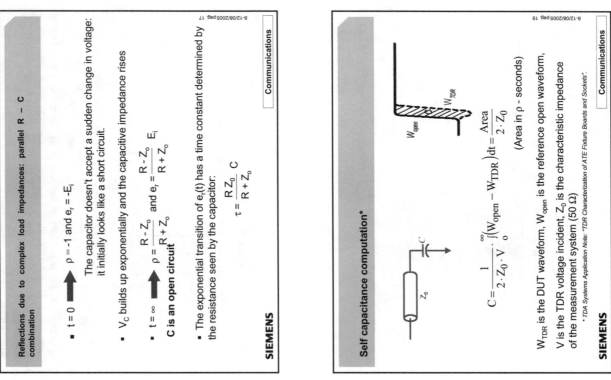

SIEMENS — Communications

Self capacitance computation*

$$C = \frac{1}{2 \cdot Z_0 \cdot V} \cdot \int_0^\infty \left(W_{open} - W_{TDR}\right) dt = \frac{Area}{2 \cdot Z_0}$$

(Area in ρ - seconds)

W_{TDR} is the DUT waveform, W_{open} is the reference open waveform,

V is the TDR voltage incident, Z_0 is the characteristic impedance of the measurement system (50 Ω)

*TDA Systems Application Note: "TDR Characterization of ATE Fixture Boards and Sockets".

SIEMENS — Communications

Evaluating cable losses: series losses

Input impedance of a lossy line infinitely long:

$$Z_{in} = Z_0 = \sqrt{\frac{R + j\omega L}{G + j\omega C}}$$

- If series losses predominate (G << ωC), it is:

$$Z_{in} = \sqrt{\frac{R + j\omega L}{j\omega C}} = \sqrt{\frac{L}{C}}\left(1 + \frac{R}{j\omega L}\right)^{1/2}$$

recalling $(1+x)^a \approx (1+ax)$ for x<1, we obtain:

$$Z_{in} = \sqrt{\frac{L}{C}}\left(1 + \frac{R}{j2\omega L}\right), \text{ when } R < \omega L$$

The leading edge of the incident step consists almost entirely of high frequency components, consequently R < ωL for t = 0+

SIEMENS

Evaluating cable losses: shunt losses

Input admittance of a lossy line infinitely long:

$$Y_{in} = \sqrt{\frac{G + j\omega C}{R + j\omega L}}$$

- If shunt losses predominate (R << ωL), it is:

$$Y_{in} = \sqrt{\frac{G + j\omega C}{j\omega L}} = \sqrt{\frac{C}{L}}\left(1 + \frac{G}{j\omega C}\right)^{1/2}$$

recalling $(1+x)^a \approx (1+ax)$ for x<1, we obtain:

$$Y_{in} = \sqrt{\frac{C}{L}}\left(1 + \frac{G}{j2\omega C}\right), \text{ when } G < \omega C$$

SIEMENS

Shunt C and series L discontinuities

Shunt Capacitance Discontinuity

Series Inductance Discontinuity

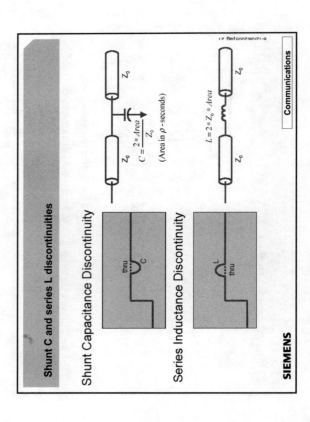

SIEMENS

Evaluating cable losses: series losses

Model valid at t = 0+ for a line with series losses

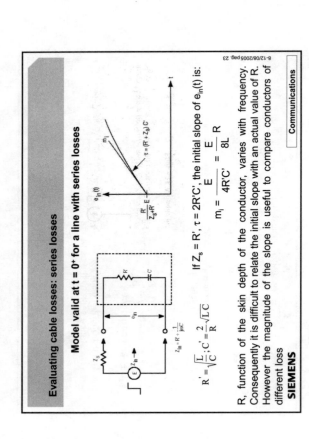

If $Z_s = R'$, $\tau = 2R'C'$, the initial slope of $e_{in}(t)$ is:

$$m_I = \frac{E}{4R'C'} = \frac{E}{8L} R$$

R, function of the skin depth of the conductor, varies with frequency. Consequently it is difficult to relate the initial slope with an actual value of R. However the magnitude of the slope is useful to compare conductors of different loss

SIEMENS

TDR resolution*

Two narrowly spaced discontinuities may be indistinguishable to the measurement instrument if they are separated by less than half the system rise time:

$$TDR_{resolution} \geq T_{r\,(system)}/2$$

The system rise time is characterized by the fall or rise time of the reflected edge from an ideal short or open at the probe tip.

$$T_{r_{system}} = \sqrt{(T_{step\ generator})^2 + (T_{sampler})^2 + (T_{probe})^2}$$

* Tektronix Application Note : "TDR Impedance Measurements: a Foundation for Signal Integrity"

8-12/08/2005 pag. 26

Communications

SIEMENS

TDR accuracy factors

Many factors contribute to the accuracy of a TDR measurement.

These include the TDR system's step response, interconnect reflections and DUT losses, step amplitude accuracy, accuracy of the reference impedance used in the measurements.

All these factors have to be kept under control.

8-12/08/2005 pag. 28

Communications

SIEMENS

Evaluating cable losses: shunt losses

Model valid at t = 0⁺ for a line with shunt losses

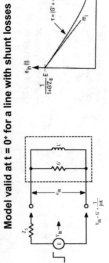

If $G' = 1/Z_s$, $\tau = 2G'L'$, the initial slope of $e_{in}(t)$ is:

$$m_i = \frac{E}{4G'L'} = \frac{E}{8C}\,G$$

G varies with frequency, but relative loss can be estimated from the value of m_i

8-12/08/2005 pag. 25

Communications

SIEMENS

TDR aberrations*

Aberrations that occur prior to the main incident step can be particularly troublesome because they arrive at a discontinuity and begin generating reflections before the main step arrives. These reflections reduce resolution by obscuring closely-spaced discontinuities.

Aberrations, e. g. ringing, that occur after the incident step will cause corresponding aberrations in the reflections. They will be difficult to distinguish from the reflections due to the DUT discontinuities.

* Tektronix Application Note : "TDR Impedance Measurements: a Foundation for Signal Integrity"

8-12/08/2005 pag. 27

Communications

SIEMENS

Outline

Time Domain Reflectometer (TDR)

Vector Network Analyzer (VNA)

Eye Diagram

SIEMENS

Vector Network Analyzer (VNA)

Network analyzers are mainly used to measure the amplitude and phase relationships between two signals: S-parameters

➢ Scalar network analyzers: for amplitude measurements

➢ Vector network analyzers: both amplitude and phase measurements

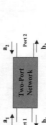

VNA ANRITSU 37247C 40 MHz – 20 GHz

SIEMENS

Two-port Network: Z parameters

$$V_1 = Z_{11} \cdot I_1 + Z_{12} \cdot I_2$$
$$V_2 = Z_{21} \cdot I_1 + Z_{22} \cdot I_2$$

$$Z_{11} = \left.\frac{V_1}{I_1}\right|_{I_2=0} \; ; Z_{12} = \left.\frac{V_1}{I_2}\right|_{I_1=0} \; ; Z_{21} = \left.\frac{V_2}{I_1}\right|_{I_2=0} \; ; Z_{22} = \left.\frac{V_2}{I_2}\right|_{I_1=0}$$

At high frequencies, when parasitic capacitances and inductances have considerable effects, short and open circuits can be obtained using stubs which carry short and open conditions at the input ports.

SIEMENS

Two-port Network: S parameters

$$b_1 = S_{11} \cdot a_1 + S_{12} \cdot a_2$$
$$b_2 = S_{21} \cdot a_1 + S_{22} \cdot a_2$$

$$S_{11} = \left.\frac{b_1}{a_1}\right|_{a_2=0} \; ; S_{12} = \left.\frac{b_1}{a_2}\right|_{a_1=0} \; ; S_{21} = \left.\frac{b_2}{a_1}\right|_{a_2=0} \; ; S_{22} = \left.\frac{b_2}{a_2}\right|_{a_1=0} \; ;$$

a_i = waves traveling towards port i (incident waves)

b_i = waves propagating away from the port i (reflected waves)

If V^+ is the incident voltage wave at port i, V^- is the reflected voltage wave and the characteristic impedance of the transmission line connected at port i is 50 Ω:

$$a = \frac{V^+}{\sqrt{50}}; b = \frac{V^-}{\sqrt{50}}$$

SIEMENS

S-parameters: advantages

VNAs commercially available covering the range from 300 KHz to 100 GHz.

General purpose electromagnetic simulators usually produce their results in the form of S-parameters.

S-parameters can easily be converted into Z, Y and ABCD parameters. For example:

$$Z = Z_0 (I + S) (I - S)^{-1}$$

where **Z** is the impedance matrix, **S** is the S-parameter matrix, **I** is the identity matrix and **Z_0** is the reference impedance (characteristic impedance of the transmission lines driving the ports)

SIEMENS

Communications

8-12/08/2005 pag. 33

Calibration and error correction

S-parameter calibration :

1. to determine the systematic artifacts of the measurement system by measuring a number of known standards (such as thru lines, transmission lines, loads, shorts and opens).

2. the various calibration algorithms mainly differ in what standards they use and each combination has its advantages under certain conditions.

Error correction:

1. the error model consists of error boxes into which all the instrument's non-idealities can be lumped.

2. the parameters corresponding to these boxes, found during calibration, can be mathematically removed.

SIEMENS

Communications

8-12/08/2005 pag. 34

Types of calibration

The purpose of the calibration is to quantify each systematic error term through measurement of standards.

Coaxial environment: Short-Open-Load-Thru (SOLT) calibration.

Non-coaxial environment: Thru-Reflect-Line (TRL) calibration.

SIEMENS

Communications

8-12/08/2005 pag. 35

Reference planes and SOLT calibration

Reference planes: the positions (relative to each port) where 0 phase is defined.

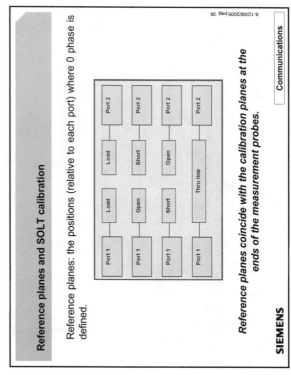

Reference planes coincide with the calibration planes at the ends of the measurement probes.

SIEMENS

Communications

8-12/08/2005 pag. 36

De-embedding*

Sometimes there may be a test fixture between the coaxial calibration planes and the DUT.

To remove the effects of these fixture we can use de-embedding techniques.

De-embedding:

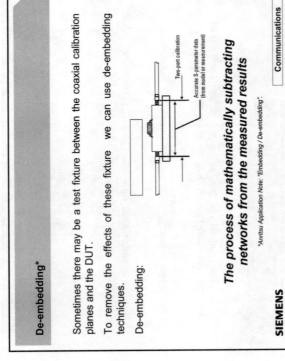

Two-port calibration

Accurate S-parameter data (from model or measurement)

The process of mathematically subtracting networks from the measured results

*Anritsu Application Note:"Embedding / De-embedding".

SIEMENS Communications 8-12/08/2005 pag. 37

Port extension

Shorts (or opens if the capacitance is small enough) can be placed at the actual DUT planes and an 'auto reference plane' extension function can be used to calculate the distance required to put the reference planes exactly where the artifact was placed.

The fixture in port extension procedure is considered an ideal matched transmission line (no mismatch, no attenuation) that generates only a phase shift (time delay).

open   thru

short   load

SIEMENS Communications 8-12/08/2005 pag. 39

Port extension

If one can treat the fixture as a simple length of 50 ohm transmission line, the problem reduces to one of shifting the reference planes: *port extension*.

This assumes that launch parasitics are small enough and usually that the frequencies involved are not too high: a frequency dependent phase shift is all that is required.

Two-port calibration

Mathematically extend reference plane

SIEMENS Communications 8-12/08/2005 pag. 38

Outline

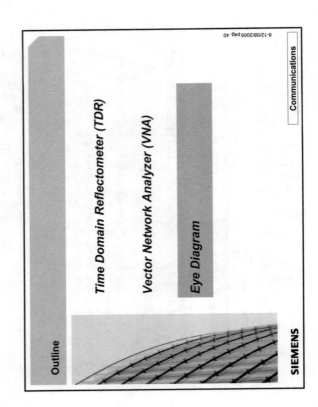

Time Domain Reflectometer (TDR)

Vector Network Analyzer (VNA)

Eye Diagram

SIEMENS Communications 8-12/08/2005 pag. 40

Formation of an eye pattern by superposition

SIEMENS

Eye pattern: example

Input: PRBS pattern (NRZ 2^{15}-1 @ 2.5 Gbps;)

Output: end of the microstrip (W = 160 µm; L = 70 cm; Z_0 = 50 Ω). Dielectric: 'IS 620

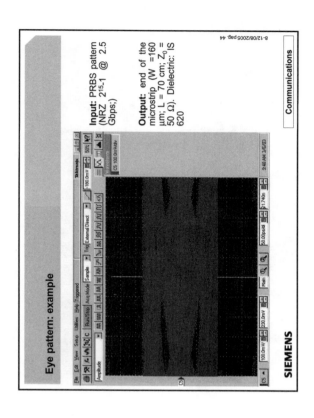

SIEMENS

Eye pattern

A very effective method of measuring time distortion thru a data transmission system is based on the eye pattern, displayed on an oscilloscope.

The eye pattern is simply the superposition - over one unit interval – of all the Zero-to-One and One-to-Zero transitions, each preceded and followed by various combinations of One and Zero, and also constant One and Zero levels.

The data sequence can be generated by a pseudo-random sequence generator (PRSG), which is a digital shift register with feedback connected to produce a max length sequence.

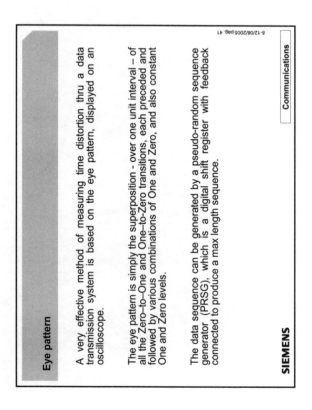

SIEMENS

NRZ data eye pattern

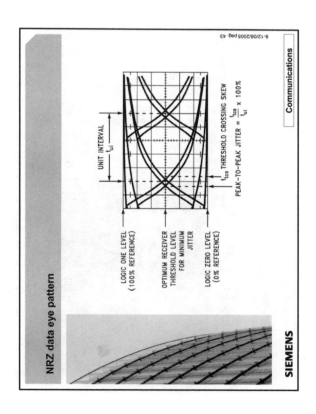

SIEMENS

Eye pattern: example

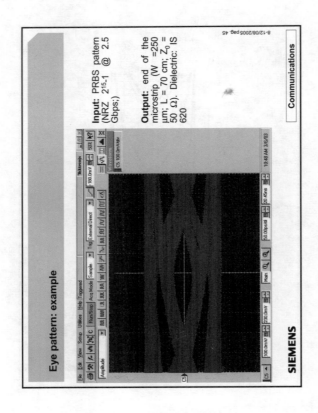

Input: PRBS pattern (NRZ 2^{15}-1 @ 2.5 Gbps;)

Output: end of the microstrip (W =250 µm; L = 70 cm; Z_0 = 50 Ω). Dielectric: IS 620

Communications

What is SPICE and IBIS?

- **SPICE** (*Simulation Program with Integrated Circuit Emphasis*) - general-purpose circuit simulation program for nonlinear dc/transient, and linear signal analysis.

- **IBIS** (*Input/Output Buffer Information Specification*) - standard describing analog behavior for buffers of digital logic using plain ASCII text formatted data.

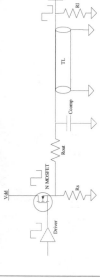

Basics in
SPICE & IBIS Modeling of IC

J.Ted DiBene II – Intel Corporation

Giuseppe Selli – UMR EMC Laboratory

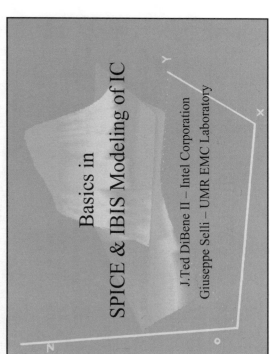

IBIS vs. SPICE

- IBIS handles large numbers of I/O circuit cells for understanding complex interaction of signal timing and interaction.

  - Usually computationally fast
  - Circuit models typically fairly simple – behavioral
  - Good for complex digital signal circuit analysis

SPICE vs. IBIS

- SPICE allows analysis of complex circuit elements for signal integrity – very versatile

  - Usually very accurate
  - Very common
  - Portable – virtually every platform

Why IBIS ?

- PCB and Device level Signal Integrity
  - SI issues gaining more attention in past decade pushing IC vendors and users to understand complex device and PCB level signal interactions in shorter and shorter timeframes.

"Keep proprietary information residing in the IC recipes"

When IBIS? -- When SPICE?

	IBIS	SPICE
Computational Efficiency	Good	From good to poor
Model Complexity	Usually fairly simple	Complex depending upon the needs
Accuracy	From good to poor	Typically good
Applications	Signal Integrity	Signal and power integrity
Programs	Small number	Large number
I/O Circuit Cells	Very large	Limited

Simple I/O Circuit Example

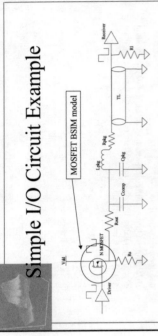

MOSFET BSIM model

- Non-inverting MOSFET circuit configuration with the output connected to a 50 Ω TL through a 50 Ω load.
- Generic driver - 50 Ω load terminates the 50 Ω TL.
- The MOSFET 'driver' - source-follower with Drain connected to a DC voltage source of (typically 3.3 V) Source connected to ground through a 150 Ω load.

Why IBIS ?

- SPICE typically not very suitable for large circuit path board level design.
- The detailed equations in SPICE transistor and I/O models often contain proprietary information on geometry and materials which is intellectual property.
- IBIS model is typically considered a 'behavioral model', in contrast SPICE is typically a 'structured model'.
- The interests of several EDA tool vendors in a common modeling format initiated the IBIS Open Forum (ANSI/EIA-656-A, http://www.eigroup.org/ibis/ibis.htm) and the first IBIS specifications were written in 1993.

SPICE Model

- The SPICE model:
  - Mere translation of each circuit component, i.e., MOSFET driver, resistors, transmission line, etc., into a line of code representing the element itself between two or more voltage nodes.

- For this example:
  - Generic Driver has no output impedance, while the generic Receiver has infinite input impedance.

- The choice of the MOSFET parameters, such as V_{TO}, K_P, l and w, is intended to achieve low output impedance – *but still be practical!*

Basic Transistor Circuit Models

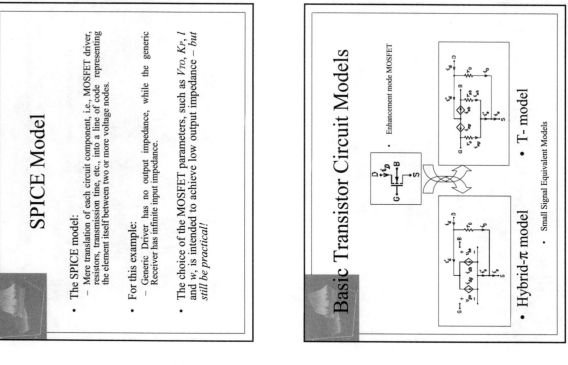

- Enhancement mode MOSFET

- **Hybrid-π model**
- **T- model**

- Small Signal Equivalent Models

Typical SPICE Model for Source-Follower Circuit

- MOSFET Model

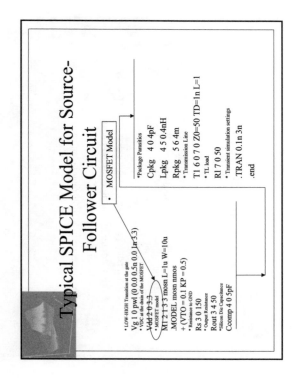

* LOW-HIGH Transition at the gate
Vg 1 0 pwl (0 0 0.5n 0.0 .1n 3.3)
* VDC at the drain of the MOSFET
Vdd 2 0 3.3
* MOSFET model
MT 2 1 3 3 mosn L=1u W=10u
.MODEL mosn nmos
+ (VTO = 0.1 KP = 0.5)
* Resistance to GND
Rs 3 0 150
* Output Resistance
Rout 3 4 50
* Silicon Die Capacitance
Ccomp 4 0 5pF

* Package Parasitics
Cpkg   4 0 4pF
Lpkg   4 5 0.4nH
Rpkg   5 6 4m
* Transmission Line
T1 6 0 7 0 Z0=50 TD=1n L=1
* TL load
R1 7 0 50
* Transient simulation settings
.TRAN 0.1n 3n
.end

Where did SPICE deck come from?

- Device is probed on wafer or package
- Characteristics of device are plotted
- Curve-fitting of device characteristics
- SPICE model generated

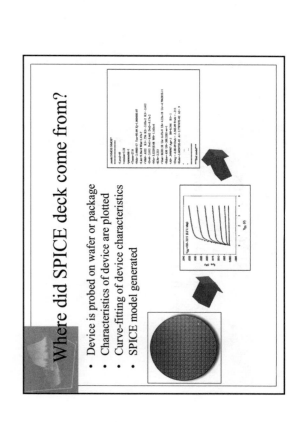

247

Transistor level

- Transistor level parameter effects
- Variations in geometry and materials prediction

- Key parameters which may vary in process variability may often need to be considered in extraction process for accuracy

---

SPICE to IBIS Translation: Step 1

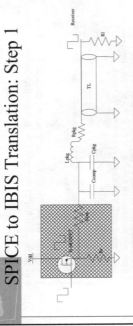

- Locate the device(s) to be "behaviorally" modeled, i.e., provide tables of currents values as a function of voltage values enforced at the available pins of the device under test.
- In this example, circuit to be behaviorally modeled consists N-channel-MOSFET in source follower configuration with series Rout resistance.

SPICE deck

- equivalent parameters in simple deck
- equations from BSIM 3 model.

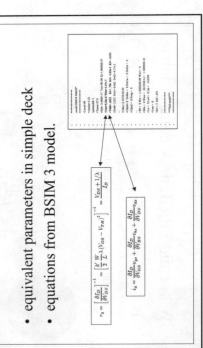

$$r_0 = \left[\frac{\partial I_D}{\partial V_{DS}}\right]^{-1} = \left[\frac{k'}{2}\frac{W}{L}\lambda(V_{GS}-V_{TH})^2\right]^{-1} = \frac{V_{DS}+1/\lambda}{I_D}$$

$$i_d = \frac{\partial I_D}{\partial V_{GS}}v_{gs} + \frac{\partial I_D}{\partial V_{BS}}v_{bs} + \frac{\partial I_D}{\partial V_{DS}}v_{ds}$$

SPICE model Outputs

- Need IBIS?
  - If need multiple I/O circuits – translate to IBIS
  - Generate table of voltages/currents from SPICE for input to IBIS.
- When to Translate
  - Circuit path quantities become extensive (typically > 20)
  - Critical circuit interactions are on multiple paths
  - Simulation time is crucial
  - Convergence in SPICE may be an issue

Example Waveform Table(s)

Time	Voltage	Time	Voltage
0.	0.	0.	1.528e+00
1.0000e-10	7.994e-02	1.0000e-10	1.410e+00
2.0000e-10	2.661e-01	2.0000e-10	1.203e+00
3.0000e-10	5.210e-01	3.0000e-10	9.484e-01
4.0000e-10	8.233e-01	4.0000e-10	6.950e-01
5.0000e-10	1.125e+00	5.0000e-10	4.415e-01
6.0000e-10	1.334e+00	6.0000e-10	2.826e-01
7.0000e-10	1.420e+00	7.0000e-10	1.793e-01
8.0000e-10	1.505e+00	8.0000e-10	1.141e-01
9.0000e-10	1.516e+00	9.0000e-10	4.892e-02
1.0000e-09	1.521e+00	1.0000e-09	3.195e-02
1.1000e-09	1.525e+00	1.1000e-09	2.185e-02
1.2000e-09	1.528e+00	1.2000e-09	1.311e-02
1.3000e-09	1.528e+00	1.3000e-09	6.032e-03
1.4000e-09	1.528e+00	1.4000e-09	3.934e-03
1.5000e-09	1.528e+00	1.5000e-09	1.836e-03

The IBIS model of the Open Source Buffer has the keyword [Rising Waveform] or [Falling Waveform] followed by the parameters R_fixture = 50, V_fixture = 0.0 and the tables consisting of the values of the time and the corresponding voltages observed at the output.

Example IBIS Model: T & V

[Model]   driver   Model name assignment (Required)
Model_type Open_source Model type assignment (Required)
Polarity   Non-Inverting   Polarity (Optional)
C_comp 5.pF NA NA   Silicon die capacitance (Required [1])
[Temperature Range] 27 NA NA   T (Celsius) (Required [1])
[Voltage Range] 3.0 NA NA   Vdd tolerance (Required [1])

- Model name assignment must match "model_name" in the pin assignment
- The model_type needs to be specified, whereas the polarity is optional
- The silicon die capacitance needs to be specified in it typical, min and max values (the last two may be NA)
- The temperature range and the power supply voltage tolerance need to be given as weel in their typ, min and max values (the last two may be NA)

SPICE to IBIS: Step 2 - I/V Tables

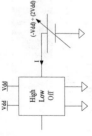

- All characteristics obtained by connecting a sweeping a DC source from minus Vdd to 2Vdd and observing current flowing at the output terminal [1].
- Current is considered positive when it flows into the device.

- The 'High-state' table is obtained by setting the device into the HIGH state (e.g. when voltages are pulled-up to Vdd rail).
- The 'Low-state' table is obtained by setting the device into the LOW state (e.g. when voltages are pulled down to GND).
- The GND Clamp and POWER Clamp are obtained by switching the device off and sweeping the DC source from –Vdd to Vdd and from Vdd to 2Vdd, respectively

---

SPICE to IBIS: Circuit Example

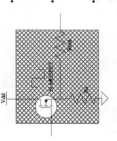

- Device under test in the circuit example needs only one of four V/I characteristics.
- Device is Open Source Buffer (note:no ESD protection) -- output sources current.
- Only High state V/I characteristics are needed.

- The input is set to the high state and a DC voltage steps swept at output from -3.3 Volts to 6.6 Volts.
- Rout is needed to keep VDS small enough, when MOSFET is reverse biased, so that the current is limited to practical values.

249

IBIS SPICE Simulation Comparison

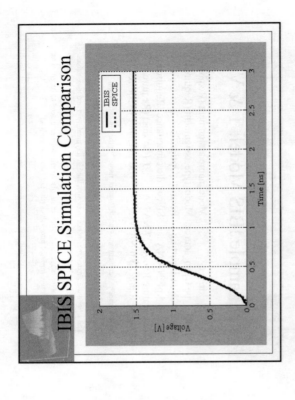

Results Again

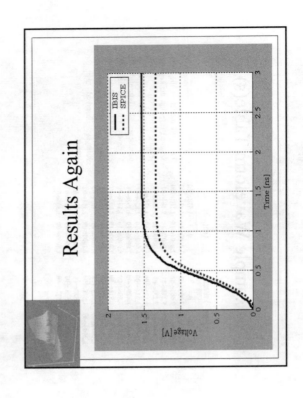

IBIS Simulation

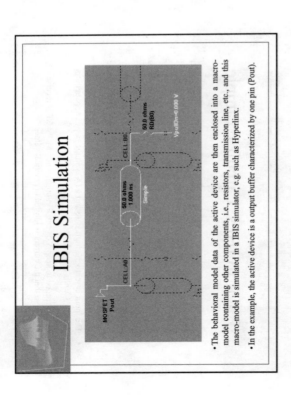

- The behavioral model data of the active device are then enclosed into a macro-model containing other components, i.e., resistors, transmission line, etc., and this macro-model is simulated in a IBIS simulator, e.g. such as Hyperlinx.
- In the example, the active device is a output buffer characterized by one pin (Pout).

So what happens when MOSFET Parameters change?

- If process variations occur how does IBIS handle?
  - Change V_{TO}, K_P, l and w

Parameter	Old value	New value?
V_{TO}	0.1V	? V
K_P	0.5 A/V²	? A/V²
l	1 um	? um
w	10 um	? um

References

[1] IBIS Specifications available at http://www.eigroup.org/ibis/specs.htm

[2] Arpad Muranji, "Introduction to IBIS models and IBIS model making", Intel Corporation, Folsom CA, November 3rd-4th 2003.

[3] Stephen Peters (IBIS Open Forum), "IBIS forum I/O buffer modeling cookbook", Revision 2.0X, 1997.

[4] Bob Roos, "IBIS present and future", 7th IEEE Workshop on Signal Propagation on Interconnects, Siena, Italy, May 11th-14th 2003

[5] Mercedes Casamayor, "A first approach to IBIS models: what they are and how are they generated", AN-715Application Note, Analog Device.

[6] "IBIS behavioral models" TN-00-07 Technical Note, Micron.

[7] "Validating and using IBIS files", Revision 1.0, National Semiconductor Corporation, Interface Product Group, January 2003.

[8] Vadym Heyfitch, " What makes a better I/O driver model", International Cadence Usergroup.

[9] Microelectronics, Millman-Grabel, McGraw-Hill, 2nd Ed. 1984

[10] MOSFET Modeling with SPICE, Foty, Prentice-Hall, 1997

Final IBIS Model: Package & Pin

[Package]   Package Parasitics (Optional)

R_pkg 2.00m NA NA   Resistance (Required)

L_pkg 0.20nH NA NA   Inductance (Required)

C_pkg 2.00pF NA NA   Capacitance (Required)

[Pin] signal_name model_name   Pin assignment (Required)

Sout Pout   driver   Output Pin (Required)

- The package parasitics are usually specified with their typical value, min and max value (the last two may be NA).

- The Pin assignment associates the model type (driver) to the specified pin (Sout) and signal name (Pout).

- When ground and power pins are present, signal_name coincides with model_name and GND or POWER names are associated with them.

Conclusion

- Use SPICE when accuracy warrants it.
- Use IBIS when complexity and circuit quantity warrants it.
- Some Do Not's
  - Do not rely on behavioral models under all circumstances.
  - Do not create modeling efforts without some understanding of expectations of results
- Some Do's
  - Understand the source of the models you have received.
  - Always verify models with test data.

Backup

Rising/Falling Waveforms Examples

- The recommended number of rising/falling waveform tables needed to build a behavioral model for a three-state buffer output is at least 4:

		Pullup	MOSFET on
Load connected to GND	LOW TO HIGH	Pullup	MOSFET off → Pullup
	HIGH TO LOW	Pullup	MOSFET on → Pullup
Load connected to Vdd	LOW TO HIGH	Pulldown	MOSFET off → Pulldown MOSFET off
	HIGH TO LOW	Pulldown MOSFET off → Pulldown MOSFET on	

- On the other hand, the number of recommended rising/falling waveform tables for an Open Source Buffer is 2:

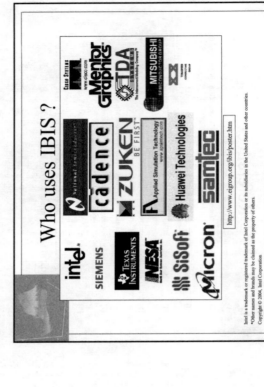

- The Comp, which is the die capacitance, needs to be considered when the V/T rising/falling waveform tables are computed.

Who uses IBIS ?

http://www.eigroup.org/ibis/poster.htm

Pullup V/I Table

Voltage	Current
-3.000V	48.730mA
-2.400V	38.120mA
-1.800V	28.060mA
-1.200V	22.500mA
-0.6V	14.980mA
0.0V	3.656mA
0.6V	-7.865mA
1.200V	-19.470mA
1.800V	-31.130mA
2.400V	-42.820mA
3.000V	-54.540mA
3.600V	-66.280mA
4.200V	-78.040mA
4.800V	-89.810mA
5.400V	-101.60mA
6.000V	-113.400mA
6.600V	-125.200mA

- IBIS model Open Source Buffer has the keyword [Pullup] followed by the table consisting of the values of the voltage and the corresponding current observed at the output.

- This table as weel as the POWER Clamp table are Vdd relative, meaning that the value of the voltages in the first column is not *Voutput*, but *Vdd – Voutput* [].

- Although this voltage range exceeds the ratings the semiconductor vendors indicate in the specifications, it is very important because it covers the region where undershoot, overshoot, and reflections could happen [].

Final IBIS Model: Header

[IBIS ver]	3.2	IBIS version (Required)
[File name]	nmos_50_ohm.ibs	File name (Required)
[File Rev]	3.0	File revision (Required)
[Date]	June, 6th 2004	Date (Optional)
[Source]	UMR EMC Laboratory	Source (Optional)
[Disclaimer]	Test Purpose	Disclaimer (Optional)
[Copyright]	UMR EMC Laboratory	Copyright (Optional)

- Several IBIS versions are public domain. [].
- Some guidelines are recommended for the File revision [].
- The character | can be used as a comment out words.

Rising/Falling Waveforms

- The shapes of the rising and the falling edge waveforms are not required, however it is usually recommended to provide this information especially when the waveforms do not exhibit a linear behavior.
- The description of the rising/falling waveform is given in V/T tables and it is required to specify the load conditions, usually R_fixture and V_fixture, although up to a maximum of 9 parameters can be specified [].
- It is common to have an IBIS model with different sets of rising/falling V/T tables, each of which characterized by different load conditions.

SPICE & IBIS

SPICE (**S**imulation **P**rogram with **I**ntegrated **C**ircuit **E**mphasis) is a general-purpose circuit simulation program for nonlinear dc, nonlinear transient, and linear ac analyses.

IBIS (**I**nput/Output **B**uffer **I**nformation **S**pecification) is a standard for describing the analog behavior of the buffers of digital devices using plain ASCII text formatted data.

Final IBIS Model: Pullup & Ramp

[Pullup]   I/V Pullup Characteristic []

Voltage	I(typ)	I(min)	I(max)

[Ramp]   Ramp specifications (Required)

	typ	min	max	
dV/dt_r	0.9/500p	NA	NA	dV/dT rising waveform
dV/dt_f	0.9/500p	NA	NA	dV/dT falling waveform

- The Ramp keyword specifies the fall and the rise time in terms of the ratio between 20% to 80% of the voltage swing divided by the time it takes to swing it.
- Although the Ramp keyword is required, this parameter cannot described the rising/falling waveforms when these do not increase/decrease linearly
- The min or max values of the I/V Pullup characteristic and the ramp specifications may be NA.

Final IBIS Model: Rising/Falling

[Rising Waveform]			Rising waveform (Optional)
R_fixture = 50.000			Fixture resistance
V_fixture = 0.000			Fixture voltage
Time	V(typ)	V(min)	V(max)
[Falling Waveform]			Falling waveform (Optional)
R_fixture = 50.000			Fixture resistance
V_fixture = 0.000			Fixture voltage
Time	V(typ)	V(min)	V(max)
[End]			End keyword (Required)

- The rising/falling waveform tables need to be specified in their typical, min and max values, although the last two may be NA.

SPICE to IBIS: Common Configuration

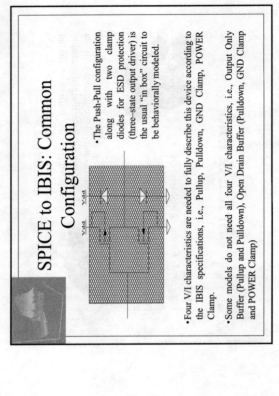

- The Push-Pull configuration along with two clamp diodes for ESD protection (three-state output driver) is the usual "in box" circuit to be behaviorally modeled.

- Four V/I characteristics are needed to fully describe this device according to the IBIS specifications, i.e., Pullup, Pulldown, GND Clamp, POWER Clamp.

- Some models do not need all four V/I characteristics, i.e., Output Only Buffer (Pullup and Pulldown), Open Drain Buffer (Pulldown, GND Clamp and POWER Clamp)

Simple I/O Circuit Example

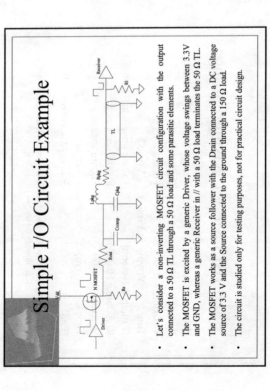

- Let's consider a non-inverting MOSFET circuit configuration with the output connected to a 50 Ω TL through a 50 Ω load and some parasitic elements.

- The MOSFET is excited by a generic Driver, whose voltage swings between 3.3V and GND, whereas a generic Receiver in // with a 50 Ω load terminates the 50 Ω TL.

- The MOSFET works as a source follower with the Drain connected to a DC voltage source of 3.3 V and the Source connected to the ground through a 150 Ω load.

- The circuit is studied only for testing purposes, not for practical circuit design.

Passive equalization

Connector/board termination

RECEIVER

Signal conditioning

Cable

Cable connector

Pre-emphasis

TRANSMITTER

Backpanel connector

Via hole

PCB interconnection

High Speed Link Design Approach

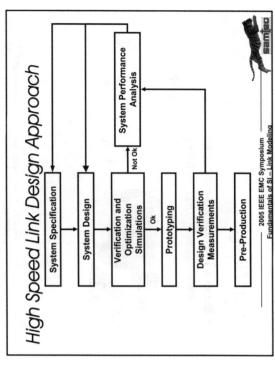

System Specification

System Design

Verification and Optimization Simulations — Not Ok → System Performance Analysis

Ok

Prototyping

Design Verification Measurements

Pre-Production

High Speed Link Design and Simulation

Jim Nadolny

2005 EMC Symposium
Fundamentals of SI Workshop

Signal Integrity in Interconnection Links - Dynamics

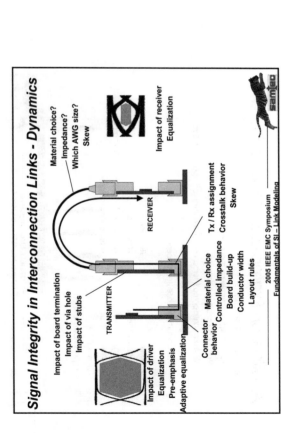

Material choice?
Impedance?
Which AWG size?
Skew

Impact of receiver Equalization

RECEIVER

Tx / Rx assignment
Crosstalk behavior
Skew

TRANSMITTER

Connector behavior
Material choice
Controlled impedance
Board build-up
Conductor width
Layout rules

Impact of board termination
Impact of via hole
Impact of stubs

Impact of driver Equalization
Pre-emphasis
Adaptive equalization

System Design

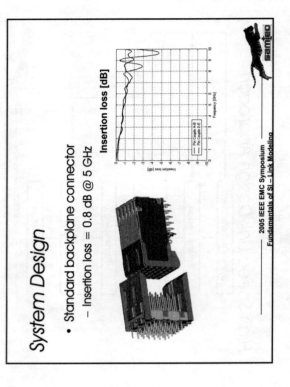

- Standard backplane connector
  - Insertion loss = 0.8 dB @ 5 GHz

Insertion loss [dB]

System Design

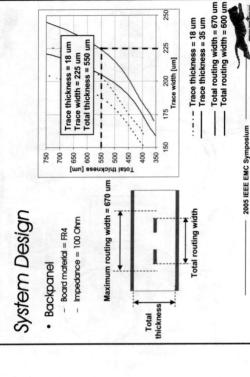

- Backpanel
  - Board material = FR4
  - Impedance = 100 Ohm

Maximum routing width = 670 um

Total thickness

Total routing width

Trace thickness = 18 um
Trace width = 225 um
Total thickness = 550 um

Trace thickness = 18 um
Trace thickness = 35 um
Total routing width = 670 um
Total routing width = 600 um

Total thickness [um]

Trace width [um]

Application Example: Backpanel Link

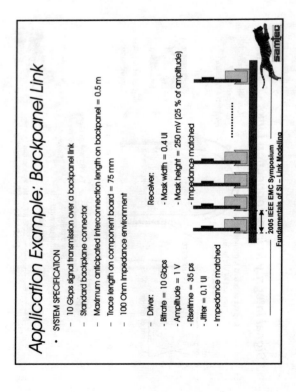

- SYSTEM SPECIFICATION
  - 10 Gbps signal transmission over a backpanel link
  - Standard backplane connector
  - Maximum anticipated interconnection length on backpanel = 0.5 m
  - Trace length on component board = 75 mm
  - 100 Ohm Impedance environment

- Driver:
  - Bitrate = 10 Gbps
  - Amplitude = 1 V
  - Risetime = 35 ps
  - Jitter = 0.1 UI
  - Impedance matched

- Receiver:
  - Mask width = 0.4 UI
  - Mask height = 250 mV (25 % of amplitude)
  - Impedance matched

System Design

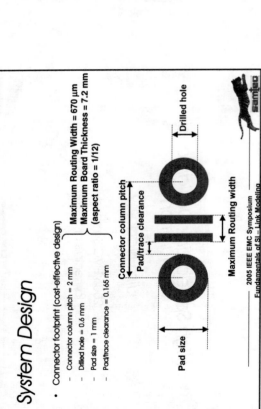

- Connector footprint (cost-effective design)
  - Connector column pitch = 2 mm
  - Drilled hole = 0.6 mm
  - Pad size = 1 mm
  - Pad/trace clearance = 0.165 mm

Maximum Routing Width = 670 µm
Maximum Board Thickness = 7.2 mm
(aspect ratio = 1/12)

Connector column pitch

Pad/trace clearance

Drilled hole

Pad size

Maximum Routing width

System design

• Backpanel via holes (cost-effective)
  – Board thickness = 6.4 mm (10 signal layers, impedance controlled)
  – Drilled hole size = 0.6 mm
  – Pad size = 1 mm
  – Anti-pad size = 1.33 mm

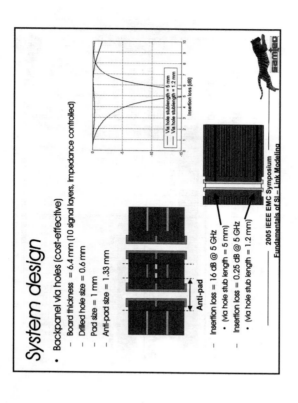

Anti-pad

  – Insertion loss = 16 dB @ 5 GHz
    • (Via hole stub length = 5 mm)
  – Insertion loss = 0.25 dB @ 5 GHz
    • (Via hole stub length = 1.2 mm)

2005 IEEE EMC Symposium
Fundamentals of SI – Link Modeling

Design Verification

FR4 Backpanel

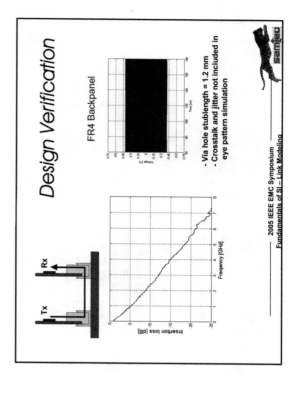

– Via hole stublength = 1.2 mm
– Crosstalk and jitter not included in eye pattern simulation

2005 IEEE EMC Symposium
Fundamentals of SI – Link Modeling

System design

• Backpanel
  – Board material = FR4
  – ε = 4, tg δ = 0.02
  – Impedance = 100 Ohm
  – Trace length = 0.5 m
  – Trace width = 225 μm
  – Trace thickness = 18 μm
    • Insertion loss =
      12.4 dB @ 5 GHz

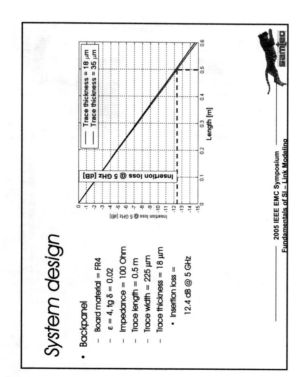

2005 IEEE EMC Symposium
Fundamentals of SI – Link Modeling

System Design

• Component board traces
  – Board material = FR4
  – ε = 4, tg δ = 0.02
  – Impedance = 100 Ohm
  – Trace length = 0.075 m (3")
  – Trace width = 150 μm
  – Trace thickness = 18 μm
    • Insertion loss = 2.0 dB @ 5 GHz

• Component board via holes
  – Board thickness = 1.6 mm
  – Drilled hole size = 0.6 mm
  – Pad size = 1 mm
  – Anti-pad size = 1.3 mm
    • Insertion loss = 0.1 dB @ 5 GHz

2005 IEEE EMC Symposium
Fundamentals of SI – Link Modeling

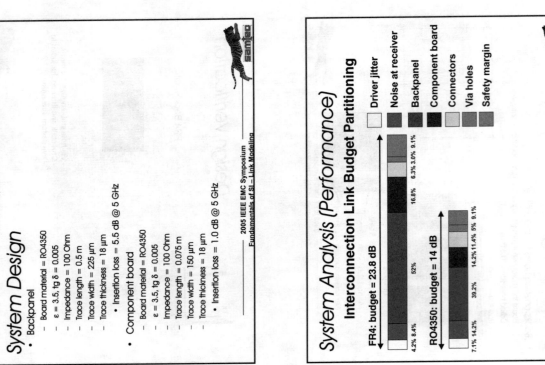

System Design

- Backpanel
  - Board material = RO4350
  - ε = 3.5, tg δ = 0.005
  - Impedance = 100 Ohm
  - Trace length = 0.5 m
  - Trace width = 225 µm
  - Trace thickness = 18 µm
    - Insertion loss = 5.5 dB @ 5 GHz
- Component board
  - Board material = RO4350
  - ε = 3.5, tg δ = 0.005
  - Impedance = 100 Ohm
  - Trace length = 0.075 m
  - Trace width = 150 µm
  - Trace thickness = 18 µm
    - Insertion loss = 1.0 dB @ 5 GHz

System Analysis (Performance)
Interconnection Link Budget Partitioning

Legend: Driver jitter, Noise at receiver, Backpanel, Component board, Connectors, Via holes, Safety margin

FR4: budget = 23.8 dB
4.2% 8.4% 52% 16.8% 6.3% 3.0% 9.1%

RO4350: budget = 14 dB
7.1% 14.2% 39.2% 14.2% 11.4% 5% 9.1%

System Analysis (Performance)
Interconnection Link Budget Partitioning

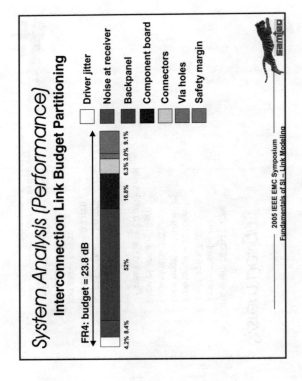

Legend: Driver jitter, Noise at receiver, Backpanel, Component board, Connectors, Via holes, Safety margin

FR4: budget = 23.8 dB
4.2% 8.4% 52% 16.8% 6.3% 3.0% 9.1%

Design Verification

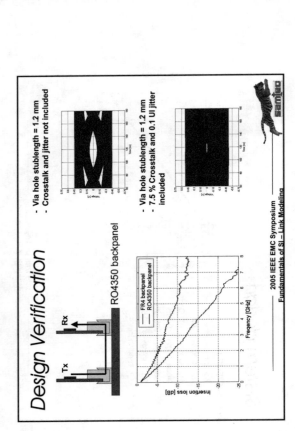

RO4350 backpanel

- Via hole stublength = 1.2 mm
- Crosstalk and jitter not included

- Via hole stublength = 1.2 mm
- 7.5 % Crosstalk and 0.1 UI jitter included

FR4 backpanel
RO4350 backpanel

Insertion loss [dB] — Frequency [GHz]

258

Definition of System Budget

- Approach
  - Definition of insertion loss for
    - Transmission without noise and jitter
  - Calculate budget loss because of
    - Jitter
    - Noise at receiver

2005 IEEE EMC Symposium
Fundamentals of SI – Link Modeling

How much insertion loss is allowed to meet the eye opening specification ?

2005 IEEE EMC Symposium
Fundamentals of SI – Link Modeling

Definition of System Budget

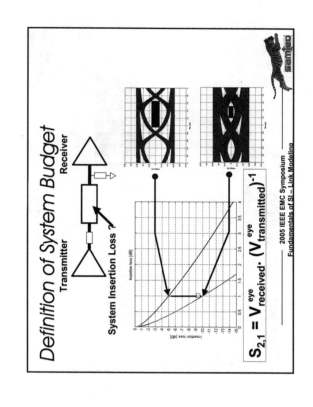

System Insertion Loss ?

$$S_{2,1} = V^{eye}_{received} \cdot (V^{eye}_{transmitted})^{-1}$$

2005 IEEE EMC Symposium
Fundamentals of SI – Link Modeling

Definition of System Budget

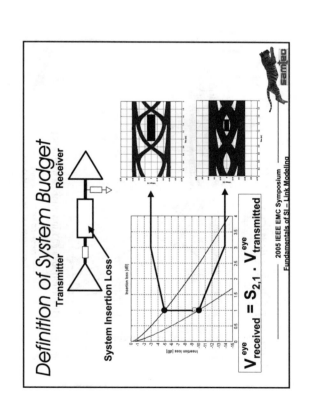

System Insertion Loss

$$V^{eye}_{received} = S_{2,1} \cdot V^{eye}_{transmitted}$$

2005 IEEE EMC Symposium
Fundamentals of SI – Link Modeling

Budget Calculation

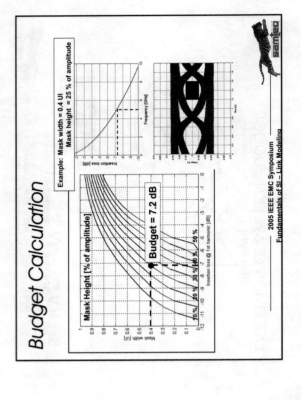

Driver Jitter

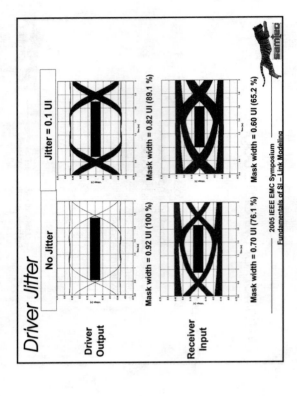

Budget Calculation

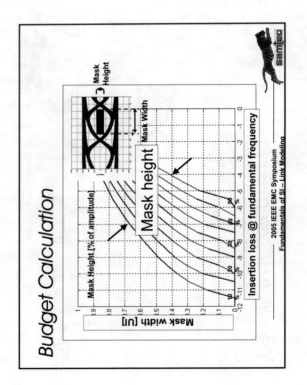

Factors That Affect System Budget

- Driver jitter

Sources of Noise

- Connectors
- Coupling between via holes
- Coupling between traces
- Coupling between traces and via holes
- Internal reflections
- Driver impedance mismatch
- Receiver impedance mismatch
- Radiation

How to Take Jitter/Loss into Account

- Perform simulations that include jitter/noise

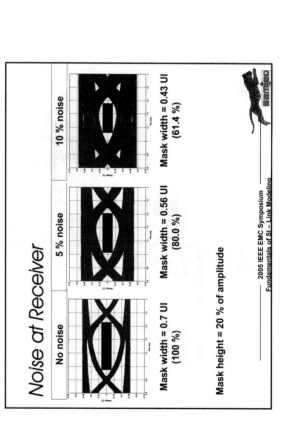

Budget

- Simulations are time and memory consuming
- Each time jitter and/or noise level changes, new simulation needs to be performed

---

Factors That Affect System Budget

- Driver jitter
- Noise at receiver

Noise at Receiver

No noise	5 % noise	10 % noise

Mask width = 0.7 UI (100 %)   Mask width = 0.56 UI (80.0 %)   Mask width = 0.43 UI (61.4 %)

Mask height = 20 % of amplitude

Impact of Jitter/Noise on Budget

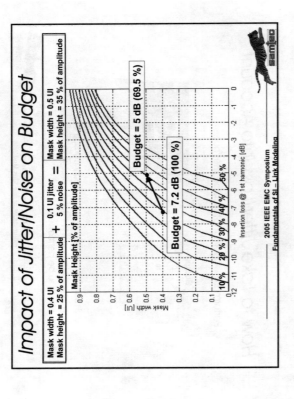

Mask width = 0.4 UI   **0.1 UI jitter**   **Mask width = 0.5 UI**
Mask height = 25 % of amplitude + **5 % noise** = **Mask height = 35 % of amplitude**

Budget = 5 dB (69.5 %)

Budget = 7.2 dB (100 %)

How to Take Jitter/Loss into Account

- Perform simulations without jitter/noise
- Increase receiver mask to compensate for jitter/noise

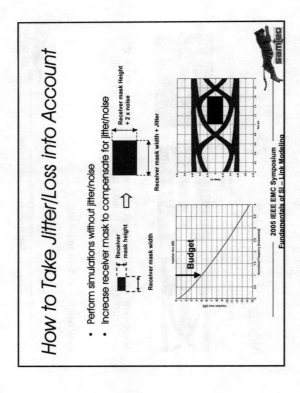

How Do We Design a System That Works?

- Improve system performance
  - Board materials with lower loss
  - Higher performing connector
  - Better via holes and connector board termination (SMT)
  - Less noise
  - Less jitter

System Analysis (Performance)
Interconnection Link Budget Partitioning

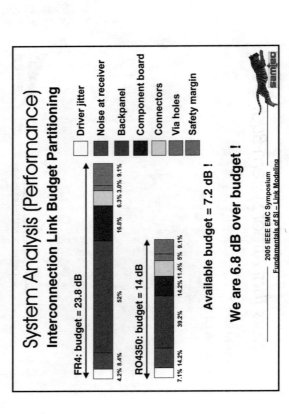

FR4: budget = 23.8 dB

RO4350: budget = 14 dB

Available budget = 7.2 dB !

We are 6.8 dB over budget !

262

How Do We Design a System That Works?

- Increase of budget
  - Receiver sensitivity
  - Signal conditioning
    - Pre-emphasis
    - Active equalization
    - Multi-level signalling
    - ...

Pre-emphasis

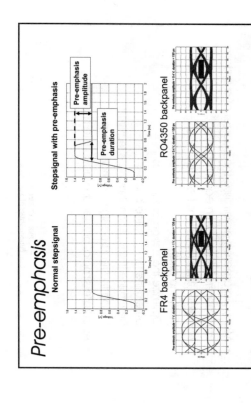

Normal stepsignal

Stepsignal with pre-emphasis

FR4 backpanel

RO4350 backpanel

Improve System Performance

- Assumptions
  - Perfect impedance controlled connector - no crosstalk, SMT
    - Insertion loss = 0.1 dB
  - Best material available for backpanel and component boards
    - tg δ = 0.001
    - Insertion loss backpanel = 3.8 dB
    - Insertion loss component board = 0.6 dB
  - Via holes
    - Component board: 0.1 dB
    - Backpanel: 0.1 dB
  - Jitter
    - 0.1 UI = 1 dB
  - Noise
    - 2 % = 0.5 dB
  - Safety margin + simulation accuracy
    - 10 % = 0.7 dB

Total budget = 7.8 dB

Receiver Sensitivity

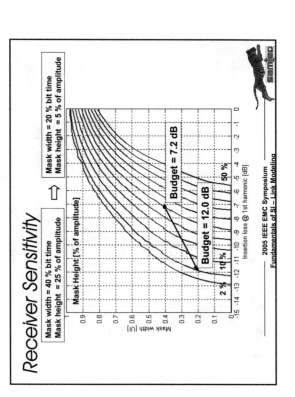

Mask width = 40 % bit time
Mask height = 25 % of amplitude

Mask width = 20 % bit time
Mask height = 5 % of amplitude

Budget = 7.2 dB

Budget = 12.0 dB

Conclusion

- Many parameters determine the budget of a system
- Parameters interact with each other
- Accurate link simulations help to
  - Verify the design
  - Optimize the design parameters
  - Determine the required budget
  - Determine if signal conditioning is required
  - Define the required signal conditioning
- Accurate simulations require accurate models

Pre-emphasis

Pre-emphasis amplitude = 1 V, Pre-emphasis duration = 135 ps

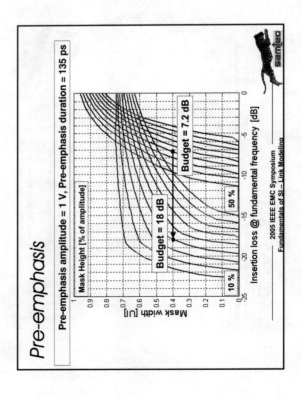

Mask Height [% of amplitude]

Mask width [UI]

Insertion loss @ fundamental frequency [dB]

Budget = 18 dB

Budget = 7.2 dB

50 %

10 %

What Will Be Discussed

- **Transmission-line basics**: propagation loss, different types of loss;
- **Loss of microstrip line**: conduction loss versus dielectric loss, reference height fixed, trace width fixed;
- **Loss of Stripline**;
- **Loss of high-speed Twin-Ax cable**;
- **Optimizing link loss by choosing the right cable impedance**

Propagation and Loss

Propagation constant: $\gamma = \sqrt{(R + j\omega L)(G + j\omega C)}$

$$= \alpha + j\beta$$

Lossless: $\quad \alpha = 0, \; \beta = \omega\sqrt{LC}, \; Z_0 = \sqrt{\dfrac{L}{C}}$

Lossy: $\quad \alpha \approx \dfrac{1}{2}\left(R\sqrt{\dfrac{C}{L}} + G\sqrt{\dfrac{L}{C}} \right), \; \beta \approx \omega\sqrt{LC}, \; Z_0 \approx \sqrt{\dfrac{L}{C}}$

$$(R \ll \omega L, \; G \ll \omega C)$$

Attenuation per unit length: $\quad 8.869\alpha$ dB/m

2005 IEEE International Symposium on Electromagnetic Compatibility

Understanding Transmission-Line Loss

Jun Fan, Kai Xiao*, James L. Knighten

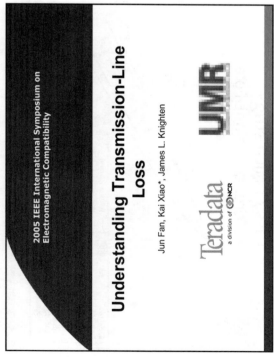

Transmission Line Basics

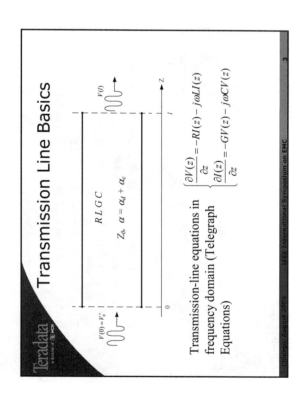

$RLGC$

$Z_0, \; \alpha = \alpha_d + \alpha_c$

$V(0) = V_0^+$

$V(l)$

Transmission-line equations in frequency domain (Telegraph Equations)

$$\frac{\partial V(z)}{\partial z} = -RI(z) - j\omega L I(z)$$

$$\frac{\partial I(z)}{\partial z} = -GV(z) - j\omega C V(z)$$

Different Types of Loss

- Conduction Loss: dominant at low frequencies
  - DC loss: conductivity of the conductor and cross-sectional area
  - Skin-effect loss: current concentrated toward outer surface; the depth where current is concentrated (skin depth) decreases with increase of frequency; this type of loss is approx. proportional to the square root of frequency
- Dielectric Loss: dominant at high frequencies
  - DC loss: due to finite conductivity, usually negligible
  - Frequency-dependent loss: due to heating effect, proportional to frequency
- Since loss increases with frequency, a lossy transmission line acts like a low pass filter.

Loss of Microstrip

- Conduction attenuation constant: $\alpha_c = \dfrac{\sqrt{\omega \mu_0 / 2\sigma}}{Z_0 W}$

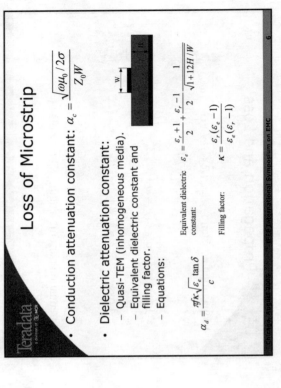

- Dielectric attenuation constant:
  - Quasi-TEM (inhomogeneous media).
  - Equivalent dielectric constant and filling factor.
  - Equations:

$$\alpha_d = \frac{\pi f \kappa \sqrt{\varepsilon_e} \tan \delta}{c}$$

Equivalent dielectric constant:

$$\varepsilon_e = \frac{\varepsilon_r + 1}{2} + \frac{\varepsilon_r - 1}{2} \cdot \frac{1}{\sqrt{1 + 12H/W}}$$

Filling factor:

$$\kappa = \frac{\varepsilon_r (\varepsilon_e - 1)}{\varepsilon_e (\varepsilon_r - 1)}$$

Loss of Microstrip – Reference Height Fixed

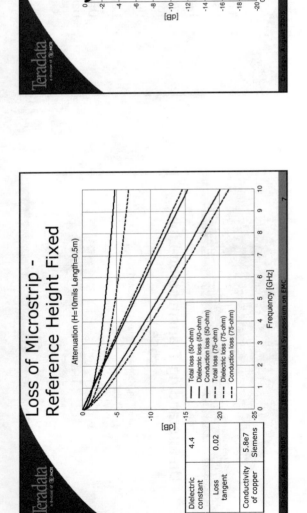

Dielectric constant	4.4
Loss tangent	0.02
Conductivity of copper	5.8e7 Siemens

Loss of Microstrip – Trace Width Fixed

Attenuation (W=20mils Length=0.5m)

Remarks on Loss of Microstrip

- **Reference height fixed: a trace with a higher Z_0 usually has more loss.** Smaller trace width results in higher conduction loss but lower dielectric loss. In general difference in dielectric loss is smaller; thus a narrower trace (higher Z_0) usually has higher total loss.

- **Trace width fixed: a trace with a lower Z_0 always has more loss.** Smaller dielectric thickness (lower Z_0) results in higher dielectric loss. It also forces return current on the reference plane to be more concentrated under the trace, causing higher conduction loss.

Loss of Stripline

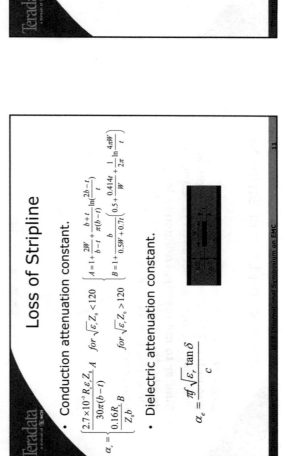

Loss of Microstrip (Z_0=50)

Loss of Stripline

- Conduction attenuation constant.

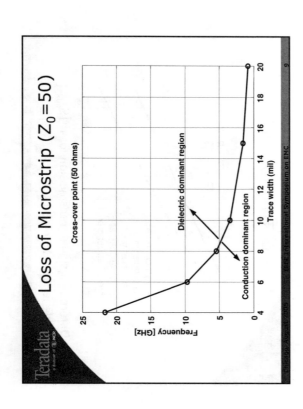

- Dielectric attenuation constant.

$$\alpha_e = \frac{\pi f \sqrt{\varepsilon_r} \tan \delta}{c}$$

High-Speed Twin-Ax Cable

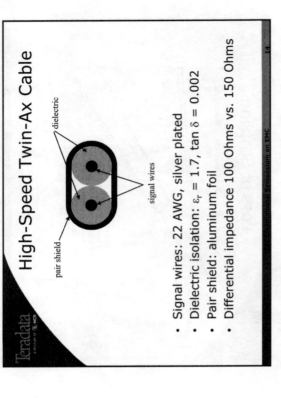

dielectric

pair shield

signal wires

- Signal wires: 22 AWG, silver plated
- Dielectric isolation: $\varepsilon_r = 1.7$, tan $\delta = 0.002$
- Pair shield: aluminum foil
- Differential impedance 100 Ohms vs. 150 Ohms

Choose Right Cable Impedance

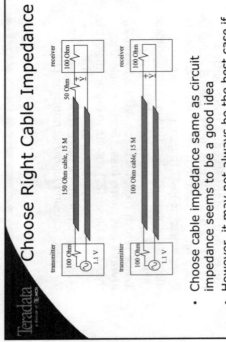

- Choose cable impedance same as circuit impedance seems to be a good idea
- However, it may not always be the best case if signal needs to be transmitted through a long cable

---

Remarks on Loss of Stripline

- **Dielectric loss is independent of geometry.** The differences in trace width and dielectric thickness do not affect dielectric loss.
- **Similar to microstrip, conduction loss dominates at low frequencies, while dielectric loss dominates at high frequencies.**

Loss of Twin-Ax Cable

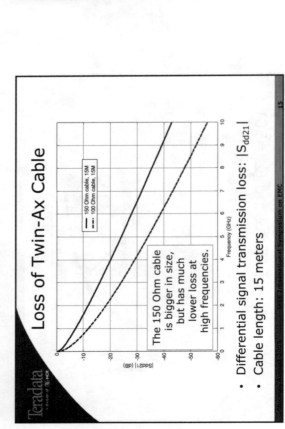

The 150 Ohm cable is bigger in size, but has much lower loss at high frequencies.

- Differential signal transmission loss: $|S_{dd21}|$
- Cable length: 15 meters

Summary

- Dielectric loss dominates at high frequencies while conduction loss dominates at low

- **For a microstrip,** when reference height is fixed, a trace with a higher Z_0 usually has more loss. However, when trace width is fixed, a trace with a lower Z_0 always has more loss.

- **For a stripline,** dielectric loss is independent of trace geometry.

- **For a cable,** when the conductor gauge size is fixed, higher Z_0 means lower loss.

- Cable loss dominates the link loss when the cable is long and data speed is high. Choosing a higher-impedance cable may help when insertion loss is critical

Choose Right Cable Impedance

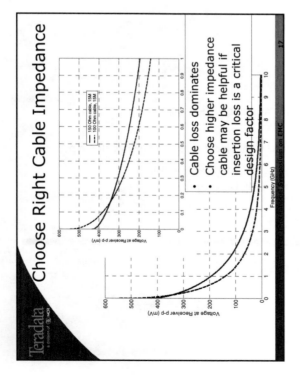

- Cable loss dominates

- Choose higher impedance cable may be helpful if insertion loss is a critical design factor

WORKSHOP: EMC DIRECTIVE IN EUROPE (MO-PM-WS-11)

Gary Fenical

Laid Technologies

This session will discuss the NEW EU EMC Directive. Topics will include in-depth explanations of the changes and implications of those changes. A detailed timeline of the implementation of the Directive will be presented. Several major changes will affect manufacturers and third party agencies (Conformity assessment Bodies and Competent Bodies).

Presenters will come from both industry and government from the European Union as well as a presenter on behalf of the US CAB's. As of the submission of this advanced information, the list of presenters is being compiled.

Attendees should include manufacturers of any electrical or electronic apparatus being sent to the European Union, Conformity Assessment Bodies, Competent Bodies dealing with the EMC Directive, Notified Bodies dealing with the EMC Directive, government regulatory personnel dealing with the EMC Directive, and EMC laboratories

Presentations (not available for publication):

(1) Revision of the EMC Directive from a CAB's Point of View
Donald L. Sweeney

(2) EMC Directive Ed. 2 - Its Application to Fixed Installations - and the Items They are Made From
Keith Armstrong

(3) Revision of the EMC Directive
Thierry Brefort

(4) Clarifying Scope and Definitions
Doede Bakker

(5) Essential Requirements and Harmonised Standards
Christian M. Verholt

(6) Conformity Assessment Procedure for Apparatus
Per Döfnäs

(7) The Role of the Notified Bodies
Dave Imeson

(8) Facilitating Market Surveillance: Information, Documentation and Marking
Lars Ström

(9) Practical Application of the EMC Directive to Broadband Cable Networks - A Technical Perspective
Dirk Jaeger

(10) Ensuring a High Level of Protection: Enforcement of the EMCD
Jan Coenraads

NOTES

Slide 1

The EMC Directive, from the Brussels Meeting Edited and Modified by Donald L. Sweeney

Improving the regulatory environment for electrical, electronic and telecommunication products

Revision of the EMC Directive

from a

CAB's Point of View

EMC Directive revision Brussels, 3/02/2005
These slides have been modified by Don Sweeney.
Page 1

Slide 2

Donald L Sweeney

- **DONALD L. SWEENEY**

Donald Sweeney, Senior EMC Engineer (NARTE Certificate Numbers EMC-001209-NE & EMC-001210-NT), is president of D.L.S. Electronic Systems, Inc. He is a graduate of the department of electrical engineering, University of Illinois at Urbana and has over 30 years experience in the electrical engineering field. Most of his time has been devoted to solving problems in electromagnetic engineering and closely related disciplines. He has worked for Extel Corporation, Teletype Corporation, Gates Radio, and Collins Radio prior to forming D.L.S. Electronic Systems, Inc.; a Wheeling, Illinois based company. He specializes in EMC, RFI, & EMI consulting and testing. Don has taught at Oakton College & the University of Wisconsin (at both the Madison and Milwaukee Campuses), and consults nation-wide on electromagnetic compatibility. His company offers a class on EMC design developed over 20 years and he has taught these to more than 2500 engineers. He has served as a special consultant to Lawrence Livermore National Laboratory and the Nuclear Regulatory Commission. He is the founding chairman of the U.S. Council of EMC Laboratories and a NARTE certified EMC Engineer. He also was the Chicago area Chairman of the IEEE EMC Society and now serves on the board of directors and the Standards Development Committee of the IEEE EMC Society. On a personal note he takes travel videos, edits them and shares them with those who might not have the opportunity to travel.

EMC Directive revision Brussels, 3/02/2005
These slides have been modified by Don Sweeney.
Page 2

Slide 3

The Goal of this Presentation is to give you a feel and Insight into the "New" EMC Directive and the Role of the USCAB's

- First let me define USCAB, United States Conformity Assessment Body. It is an organization recognized by NIST, to have the same status and authority as a Competent or Notified Body in the European Union.
- The New Directive makes changes to 89/336/EEC.
- Please read it and consider how it affects you and your company.
- You can get a copy of the Directive from www.dlsemc.com. This is the latest copy with the correct dates as published.

EMC Directive revision Brussels, 3/02/2005
These slides have been modified by Don Sweeney.
Page 3

Slide 4

The EMC Directive

- **This material was originally generated by the following people before I edited it. I have made changes by comments, deletions and a lot of additions in an attempt make it clearer and also explain the role of U.S. CAB's as I see it. No liability is assumed by any of the authors nor myself. Note, I have never gotten anyone in trouble with my interpretation in the past!   Donald L Sweeney**

- Thierry Brefort, EMC Directive Manager, DG ENTR/H5
- Doede Bakker, Chairman ORGALIME TCC
- Christian M. Verholt, Danish Standards, Chairman TC 210
- Per Döfnäs, Issue Manager for "New Approach", EICTA
- Dave Imeson, Chairman ECACB
- Lars Ström, Swedish National Electrical Safety Board
- Marc Cumps, AGORIA, EMC issue manager ORGALIME

EMC Directive revision Brussels, 3/02/2005
These slides have been modified by Don Sweeney.
Page 4

Info Day EMC Directive Revision Brussels 3
Febuary 2005

Attended by about 200 interested parties

- Four were Americans

DLS ELECTRONIC SYSTEMS, INC.

The EMC Directive, Why?

- Objectives of the EMC Directive
  - To ensure the functioning of the Internal European Market.
  - To ensure an adequate level of Electromagnetic Compatibility.
- The Impact :
  - The EMC Directive potentially affects 800 Million products placed into the European market per year.
  - The costs of compliance with the 89/336 EMC Directive was estimated from 1% to 5% of product price.
  - 60% of the products are from small & medium size enterprises.

DLS ELECTRONIC SYSTEMS, INC.

The EMC Directive: Key Concepts

- The Directive is part of **Community legislation**. It needs to be transposed by each Member State into its national regulatory system.
- **Decentralized enforcement** by Member States
  - Member States ensure correct application and will take enforcement measures, if necessary
  - Member States designate Competent Bodies/CAB's (Now), Notified Bodies/CAB's (Future) and monitor their activities

The EMC Directive: Key Concepts

- EU Commission ensures a **coherent application** of the system
  - In cases of incorrect transpositions and application
  - Guidelines to ensure uniform application
  - Coordination of various activities

The EMC Directive: Key Elements

- It is a New approach Directive:
  - Essential requirements (non-technical)
  - Based on harmonized standards
- Compliance with HS Compliance with ER (Essential Requirements)
- Conformity assessment procedure required Is proportionate to the risk envolved
- Consistent application of safeguards
- Information and marking: DoC, Technical File and Labeling

Background

- Existing Directive:
  - EMC Directive - 89/336/EEC of 03/05/1989
  - Applicable since 01/01/1992, but delayed
  - Mandatory since 01/01/1996
  - Amended by 91/263/EEC, 92/31/EEC and 93/68/EEC
  - 89/336/EEC Directive is based on the concepts of the new approach
- A Guideline was issued in 1997 to clarify issues and ensure homogeneous application

What were the Basic Problem of 89/336?

- We had:
  - About 40 CB's in Europe
  - 12 countries in Europe
  - The European commission
  - About 50 – 60 U.S. laboratories
  - NIST
  - FCC
  - Other World Countries
- Everyone had their own interpretations!

Other Problems with 89/336

- There was a guideline issued (1997) but it never had any official status.
- I thought the British were very clever as they issued a number of procedures which became defacto "official ways to do some things".

  e.g. "How to do a TCF"

Moving Towards 2004/108/EC: Why?

- December 1998 : Conclusion of a panel of experts was to revise the EMC Directive
  - main aspects of concern:
    - ✓ Basic principles
    - ✓ treatment of installations
    - ✓ conformity assessment procedure and application of standards
    - ✓ consideration of the solutions provided in the guide
  - The Conclusion was endorsed by the Commission

Some of the Basic Problems

- Everyone seemed to have a vested interest.
- I personally feel that between the public meeting in Brussels and the Guideline issued, I rarely ever felt there was any issues that were of a real concern.
- But there were various interpretations of what was required.

USCEL

- USCEL was formed in February 1996.
- I remember asking during our first meeting, "Why are you here?"
- The common answer was, "I have asked two or more CB's in Europe a question and I get two or more **different** answers".
- The goal of USCEL was to develop a "consensus" answer to each question submitted.

So What was the Problem?

- I have always felt the briefing in Brussels should have been given official status. Minutes of that meeting should have been issued. Most of the questions ever asked, were answered way back then.
- I also believe the Guide to the EMC Directive should have been given official status.

Trying to Solve the Problems with 89/336?

- When the 89/336/EEC was issued there were no Competent Bodies in the U.S.
  - Many U.S. laboratories wanted to help their customers meet the CE requirements but had difficulty getting a straight answer to their questions.
  - There was an informative meeting in Brussels in 1991, but there were only a handful (about 5 of us) from the United States present.
  - ECACB was formed in Europe for the European CB's to answer European's questions.
  - USCEL was formed for the U.S. laboratories, many of who later became U.S. CAB's.

USCEL

- Developed about 20 TGNs (Technical Guidance Notes), over the course of about 8 years.
- The total number of negative votes was about 6, with a couple of abstentions. Basically a "consensus" on every concern!
- As I think back I would say that 80% of the TGN's were straight forward, and would simply reiterate the Standard.

Moving Towards 2004/108/EC

- Objective
  - Improve legal status through a clearer and more precise text and giving an answer to divergent interpretations of the 89/336/EEC.

Moving Towards 2004/108/EC

- Means
  - Clarification of the scope and definitions
  - Better definition of the essential requirements
    - ✓ Protection requirements
    - ✓ Specific requirements for apparatus and fixed installations
  - Better information and documentation requirements

What is the Time Table?

Publication : T- 20 days (31 Dec 2004)	• Starting point
Entry into force : T (20 Jan 2005)	• All national provisions incompatible with the act become inapplicable **89/336/EEC still in force**
Deadline for transposition T+24 months (20 Jan 2007)	• Transposition must be performed **89/336/EEC still in force** • New directive cannot be applied even if transposed
Date of application : T +30 months (20 July 2007)	• Pivot date • 89/336/EEC is repealed • New directive can be applied from that date
End of transitional period T+54 months (20 July 2009)	• New directive is of mandatory application • Apparatus compliant with 89/336/ cannot be put on the market anymore

---

Definitions: Apparatus

- Any finished appliance
- Any combination of finished appliances made commercially available as a single functional unit
- Intended for the end user
- Liable to generate electromagnetic disturbance, or
- The performance of which is liable to be affected by such disturbance

Definitions: Component / Subassembly

• Also a component or subassembly

  – intended for incorporation into an apparatus by the end user

  – liable to generate or transmit electromagnetic disturbance when connected to it

  is an apparatus

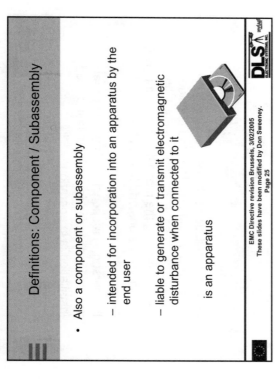

Definitions: Passive Equipment

• **Emission**

  – Equipment incapable of generating or contributing EMC emissions

• **Immunity**

  – Equipment that can operate without unacceptable degradation as consequent to its intended use

Definitions: Mobile Installation

• A mobile installation

  – Combination of apparatus

  – Intended to be moved and operated in a range of locations

  Is an apparatus

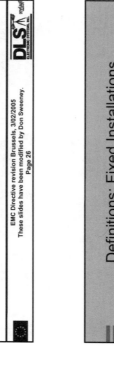

Definitions: Fixed Installations

Fixed installation means

  – Particular combination of several apparatus or other devices

  – Assembled, installed and intended to be used permanently at a predefined location

  – Note it does not imply that large machines are fixed installations

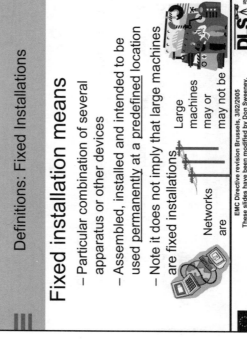

Networks are   Large machines may or may not be

Slide 1 (top-left)

Fixed Installation
Specific to Apparatus

Apparatus

- Intended for incorporation into a given fixed installation and otherwise not commercially available

- It is not required to have CE marking on the apparatus

Slide 2 (top-right)

Not Applicable to the EMC Directive

- **R&TTE**
  - (1999/5/EC)
- **Aeronautical products**
  - (Regulation 1592/2002)
- **Radio amateur equipment**
  - ITU Radio Regulations

- **Art 1.4 Specificity clause:**
  - IF EMC **more specifically** laid down by other directives it is not covered by the EMC Directive (e.g. Medical Devices Directive)

Slide 3 (bottom-left)

Fixed Installation
Essential Requirements

- Protection requirements
  - Emission
  - Immunity

- Specific requirements
  - Documented good engineering practices

Slide 4 (bottom-right)

New Directive has Specific Requirements for Fixed Installations

- A fixed installation shall be installed applying good engineering practices and considering the intended use of its components, with a view to meeting the protection requirements of both Emissions and Immunity.

- Practices shall be documented and held by the person(s) responsible, at the disposal of national authorities for as long as the fixed installation is in operation.

Role of harmonized Standard

- Is to specify, in technical terms, the requirements which ensure for all practical purposes that non-compatibility between equipment and installations is unlikely to happen in typical environments

- Gives a **"Presumption of Conformity"**

- To provide a standardized, repeatable and accepted method for the assessment of equipment

- 'Harmonized standard' means a technical specification adopted by a recognized standardization body under a mandate from the Commission

EMC Directive revision Brussels, 3/02/2005
These slides have been modified by Don Sweeney.
Page 33

Harmonized Standards

- **Gives a "Level Playing Field"**
- **Is considered the preferred method**
- Compliance with a 'harmonized standard' is not required but it is recommended
- **Should give a "better day in court"** - if challenged, market surveillance authorities must prove that the apparatus does not meet the essential requirements

EMC Directive revision Brussels, 3/02/2005
These slides have been modified by Don Sweeney.
Page 35

Harmonized Standards

The compliance of equipment with the relevant harmonized standards published in the Official Journal shall raise a presumption, on the part of the Member States, of conformity with the essential requirements referred to in Annex I, to which such standards relate.

Note, this presumption is limited to the scope of the harmonized standard(s) applied, and the relevant essential requirements covered by such harmonized standard(s).

EMC Directive revision Brussels, 3/02/2005
These slides have been modified by Don Sweeney.
Page 34

Why Would You Choose a CAB?

- Much of the preceding requires EMC expertise.
- All of the following requires EMC experts.
  I will refer to CAB but remember CAB = NB
- It is not required to use a **CAB/NB**.
- Choose a **CAB**/NB to give you the piece of mind of knowing you have used an expert!
- When you use a **CAB**/NB, you can be confident that someone has reviewed **their** EMC competence and issued a positive opinion!

EMC Directive revision Brussels, 3/02/2005
These slides have been modified by Don Sweeney.
Page 36

279

EMC Assessment

- To do an EMC Assessment requires someone who is an expert in EMC.
- As we go through the next few slides consider who will make these decisions for you.
- The manufacturer is allowed to make the decisions, but do they have the EMC expertise to make those decisions correctly?

EMC Directive revision Brussels, 3/02/2005
These slides have been modified by Don Sweeney.
Page 37

Conformity Assessment

- **Full responsibility is placed on the manufacturer for all aspects of the conformity assessment.**
- New in 2004/108: No mandatory 3rd party (**CAB**/NB) involvement is required even when harmonized standards are not used. This was not the case with 89/336/EEC.
- More details of conformity assessment process is expected to be given in the EMC Guide (later this year 2005)

EMC Directive revision Brussels, 3/02/2005
These slides have been modified by Don Sweeney.
Page 38

EMC Assessment

- An EMC assessment must be performed, on the basis of the relevant phenomena, to ensure that the protection requirements are met
- This can be done by:
  - Using harmonized standards
  - Using other methods
  - Or a combination of these

EMC Directive revision Brussels, 3/02/2005
These slides have been modified by Don Sweeney.
Page 39

EMC Assessment

- What is the intended area of use?
  - Residential area
    - ✓ Close distance between disturbing and disturbed apparatus
    - ✓ "Controlled" environment
  - Non-residential area
    - ✓ Longer distance between apparatus
    - ✓ "Uncontrolled" environment

EMC Directive revision Brussels, 3/02/2005
These slides have been modified by Don Sweeney.
Page 40

EMC Assessment

- If you use harmonized standards
  - Advantage: Presumption of conformity with the essential requirement(s) covered by the standard
    - ✓ **"Better day in court"**

EMC Assessment

- Use of harmonized standards
  - The correct application of all the relevant harmonized standards is equivalent to making an EMC assessment
    - ✓ Product or Product Family standards can be presumed to have taken into account all relevant phenomena
    - ✓ If Generic standards are used, it is advised to check that they cover the anticipated phenomena for the apparatus in question

---

EMC Assessment

- Use of harmonized standards
  - "Correct application"
    - ✓ Ensure compliance with all applicable requirements in the standard
    - ✓ Follow the prescribed test procedures in the standard (or test standards)
    - ✓ "Ensuring compliance" does not always mean testing, in particular when only a small revision has been made of the apparatus

---

EMC Assessment

- Use of other methods
  - A thorough investigation of which EMC phenomena relevant to the apparatus must be done
    - ✓ Intended use and location of use to be considered
    - ✓ A list, short description and relevance of immunity phenomena having standardized test methods is given in EN 61000-4-1 (see next two slides)

Example of Phenomena per Apparatus Port

Table 2 – Applicability of immunity tests based on EUT ports

Basic standard	Description	Applicability [1] AC power	DC power	En-closure	Signal data	Earth
61000-4-2	ESD	—3	g.n.a.	g.a.	g.n.a.	g.n.a.
61000-4-3	Radiated electromagnetic field	g.a.	g.a.	g.a.	g.n.a.	g.n.a.
61000-4-4	EFT/Burst	g.a.	g.a.	—	g.a.	g.a.
61000-4-5	Surge	g.a.	may	—	may	may
61000-4-6	Conducted disturbances by RF fields	g.a.	g.a.	—	g.a.	g.a.
61000-4-7	General guide on harmonics and interharmonics measurements and instrumentation	n.i.s.	n.i.s.	n.i.s.	n.i.s.	n.i.s.
61000-4-8	50/60 Hz magnetic field	—	—	may	—	—
61000-4-9	Pulse magnetic field	—	—	may	—	—
61000-4-10	Oscillatory magnetic field	g.a.	—	may	—	—
61000-4-11	Oscillatory waves 100 kHz and 1 kHz	may	g.n.a.	—	may	g.n.a.
61000-4-12	Oscillatory waves "ring wave"	may	may	—	may	may
61000-4-13	Harmonics, interharmonics, mains	may	—	—	may	may

[1] Applicability explanation:
n.i.s. = not an immunity standard
g.a. = generally applicable except in special cases

g.n.a. = generally not applicable except in special cases
may = may be applicable in certain circumstances
(-) means not applicable.

EMC Assessment

- Use of other methods
  - Establish acceptable limits for compliance for the applicable phenomena
    - ✓ For emissions, distances to other apparatus that can be disturbed (in most cases radio apparatus) must be considered
    - ✓ For immunity, the likely levels occurring and the resulting performance (permissible reduction of performance) during or after the phenomena is present, must be considered

---

Example of Phenomena per Location

Table 1 – Applicability of immunity tests based on location (environment)

Basic standard	Description	Applicability [1] Residential, commercial and light industrial	Industrial area	Special (e.g. power plant)
61000-4-2	ESD	g.a.	g.a.	g.a.
61000-4-3	Radiated electromagnetic field	g.a.	g.a.	g.a.
61000-4-4	EFT/Burst	g.a.	g.a.	g.a.
61000-4-5	Surge	g.a.	g.a.	g.a.
61000-4-6	Conducted disturbances by RF fields	g.a.	g.a.	g.a.
61000-4-7	General guide on harmonics and interharmonics measurements and instrumentation	n.i.s.	n.i.s.	n.i.s.
61000-4-8	50/60 Hz magnetic field	may	may	g.a.
61000-4-9	Pulse magnetic field	g.n.a.	g.n.a.	g.a.
61000-4-10	Oscillatory magnetic field	g.a.	g.a.	g.a.
61000-4-11	Voltage dips and interruption	g.a.	g.a.	g.a.
61000-4-12	Oscillatory waves "ring wave"	may	may	may

[1] Applicability explanation:
n.i.s. = not an immunity standard
g.a. = generally applicable except in special cases

g.n.a. = generally not applicable except in special cases
may = may be applicable in certain circumstances
(-) means not applicable.

EMC Assessment

- Use of other methods
  - Establish acceptable limits for compliance for the applicable phenomena
    - ✓ Guidance can be taken from existing harmonized standards for related apparatus types and areas of use (these will form the basis of an opinion regarding appropriate compatibility levels in your different circumstance

Configurations to Test and Evaluate

- EMC assessment shall take into account all normal intended operating conditions
- EMC assessment shall confirm that the apparatus meets the protection requirements in all its representative configurations

EMC Directive revision Brussels, 3/02/2005
These slides have been modified by Don Sweeney.
Page 50

Configurations to Test and Evaluate

- "Normal intended operating conditions"
  - Specified by the manufacturer, e.g. in the manual
  - What can be expected for the type of apparatus ("anticipated use")
  - During testing, exercise the apparatus in its main modes of operation unless one "worst normal mode" can be identified

EMC Directive revision Brussels, 3/02/2005
These slides have been modified by Don Sweeney.
Page 51

Configurations to Test and Evaluate

- Representative configurations
  - Foreseeable by the manufacturer
  - May be one of similar models, or different configurations of one model
  - Choose the "**worst case**" of these
    - √ Causing maximum disturbance
    - √ Most susceptible to disturbances
  - **Remember worst case configuration may differ for different phenomena's**

EMC Directive revision Brussels, 3/02/2005
These slides have been modified by Don Sweeney.
Page 52

What is a Notified Body/USCAB?

- **CAB**/NB's can carry out the tasks pertaining to the conformity assessment procedures referred to in the directive.
- There are major differences in the types of Notified Bodies specified by New Approach directives, for example
  - LVD   CAB/NB's are final arbiters but rarely used
  - MDD   Use of CAB/NB's mandatory for some apparatus
  - RTTE   CAB/NB's used in Annex III, IV and V
  - EMCD   Optional use

EMC Directive revision Brussels, 3/02/2005
These slides have been modified by Don Sweeney.
Page 53

Why use a Notified Body or CAB?

- A manufacturer may wish to use a Notified Body/**CAB** because:
  - There is no in-house EMC expert
  - There is an in-house EMC expert but a third-party opinion is desired
  - There are no relevant harmonized standards
  - The manufacturer chooses to apply the standard in part or not at all
  - The manufacturer chooses to use a non-harmonized standard

EMC Directive revision Brussels, 3/02/2005
These slides have been modified by Don Sweeney.
Page 54

Conflicting Roles

- 2004/108 does not require the use of a **CAB**/NB for the assessment of apparatus or even for Fixed Installations.
- There may be EMC problems for which the manufacturer will require technical expertise.
- The Directive does not prohibit the use of a **CAB**/NB in these situations, but the **CAB**/NB will not be acting as a **CAB**/NB but as an EMC expert.
- I believe the use of a **CAB**/NB should be encouraged when EMC expertise is needed and missing in the company.
- Please note, my company is a CAB but I honestly feel a CAB's involvement can avoid a lot of problems and help minimize a manufacturer's risk.

EMC Directive revision Brussels, 3/02/2005
These slides have been modified by Don Sweeney.
Page 55

The Use of CAB/NB

- It is up to the manufacturer to specify to the **CAB**/NB what parts of the essential requirements they want assessed.
- The **CAB**/NB then must take into consideration whether it is technically feasible to make an assessment based on the limited information provided.
- If a **CAB**/NB is used to provide a statement to only a portion of the essential requirements, consideration will need to be given as to how the **CAB**/NB involvement should be reflected in the DoC and the Technical File, which we will discuss later.

EMC Directive revision Brussels, 3/02/2005
These slides have been modified by Don Sweeney.
Page 56

What is the Difference Between Competent Bodies and **CAB**/NB's?

- 2004/108 does not have a TCF route as we had under 89/336, but it does define a limited role for **CAB**/NB's

- A **CAB**/NB in Directive 2004/108 performs the same functions as a Competent Body did in 89/336, except that the role is not mandatory.

- The **CAB**/NB's will continue to provide an essential service as we begin to use 2004/108.

Information Requirements

Marking requirements

- Each apparatus shall be identified in terms of

  - type

  - batch

  - serial number

Technical Rationale to Show Compliance

- The manufacturers must show justification that the apparatus complies with the essential requirements of 2004/108.

- The simplest method is to base the rationale on testing even if the test is not using a harmonized standard.

Additional Directions Introduced in 2004/108 To Facilitate Market Surveillance

Information requirements expanded

  - Markings

  - Traceability

  - Precautions

  - Residential/Industrial

  - Instructions

Information Requirements

Traceability requirements
- Name and address of
  - manufacturer
  - authorized representative
  - person responsible for placing on the market

Information Requirements

Precautions
- Information on specific precautions when
  - assembling
  - installing
  - maintaining
  - using

Information Requirements

Use, Residential/Industrial
- Clear indication of restriction of use
  - accompanied with the apparatus
  - on the packaging

Information Requirements

Instructions
- Information enabling use with the intended purpose

DoC

Declaration of Conformity (DoC)

- reference to the directive(s)
- identification of the apparatus
- name and address of the manufacturer
- reference to specifications
- date of declaration
- identification and signature

Concluding Remarks

- The new Directive does not remove the Assessment requirements.
- **You are still required to assess the apparatus and or installation!**
- The revised EMC directive specifically places the EMC assessment in the hands of the manufacturer.
- Use of harmonized standards simplifies this assessment.

"Technical File"
The Assessment Documentation, not TCF

- When you test, describe the details
  - Test set-up along with similarities and deviations from "harmonized standard tests"
  - Instrumentation used
  - Calculated uncertainties
  - Rationale for choice of parameters and limits

Technical Documentation

Technical documentation
- description of the apparatus
- evidence of compliance
  - ✓ evidence of compliance with harmonized standards or,
  - ✓ description of EMC assessment carried out or,
  - ✓ description of EMC assessment carried out and a statement from Notified body.

Additional Information

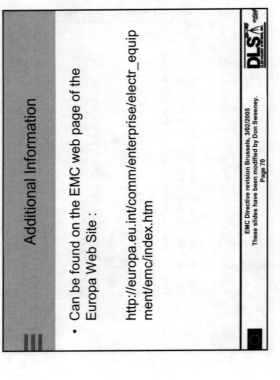

- Can be found on the EMC web page of the Europa Web Site :

  http://europa.eu.int/comm/enterprise/electr_equip ment/emc/index.htm

EMC Directive revision Brussels, 3/02/2005
These slides have been modified by Don Sweeney.
Page 70

For Now

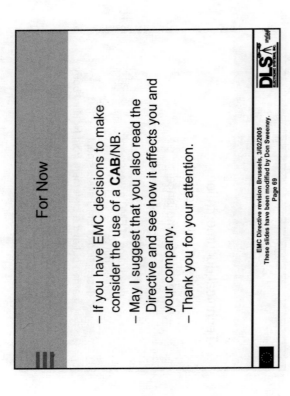

- If you have EMC decisions to make consider the use of a **CAB**/NB.
- May I suggest that you also read the Directive and see how it affects you and your company.
- Thank you for your attention.

EMC Directive revision Brussels, 3/02/2005
These slides have been modified by Don Sweeney.
Page 69

CCC

EMC Directive Ed. 2
— its application to Fixed Installations —

and the items they are made from

Cherry Clough
Consultants

www.cherryclough.com

Eur Ing Keith Armstrong   CEng MIEE MIEEE
phone: +44 (0)1457 871 605   fax: +44 (0)1457 820 145
keith.armstrong@cherryclough.com

emc2c

CCC

Contents

- Introduction to the problem of installations
- Requirements for "Fixed Installations"
- Discussion of *fixed installations*
- Requirements for "Items" incorporated into a *fixed installation*
- Discussion of *items*
- Discussion of EMC expertise
- Summaries

emc2c

CCC

Introduction

- There has always been confusion about how 89/336 applies to custom-made (bespoke) equipment, and to systems and installations
  - dispelling this confusion was a main aim of the EC's 1997 Guidelines on the EMC Directive...
    ◆ but this did not change the EMC Directive, or the national implementing legislation in the member states
- Dealing with this is one of the main issues in 2004/108
    ◆ and its requirements are described in the following slides...

emc2c

CCC

The 2004/108 applies to "equipment" that is "placed on the market" or "put into service"

- And its definition of *equipment* includes both "apparatus" and "fixed installations"
- But 2004/108 treats *fixed installations* very differently from *apparatus*
  - (mobile installations are considered to be *apparatus*)

emc2c

Fixed installations
must comply with 2004/108's "Protection Requirements"

emc2c

"Equipment shall be so designed and manufactured, having regard to the state of the art, as to ensure that:

(a) the electromagnetic disturbance generated does not exceed the level above which radio and telecommunication equipment or other equipment cannot operate as intended;

(b) it has a level of immunity to the electromagnetic disturbance to be expected in its intended use which allows it to operate without unacceptable degradation of its intended use."

Unlike apparatus, fixed installations are not required to have...

emc2c

- an electromagnetic compatibility assessment

- a conformity assessment

- an EC declaration of conformity

- the CE marking affixed

■ But 2004/108 does have some compliance requirements for fixed installations

  ◆ described in the next few slides...

"Fixed Installations"

emc2c

■ A fixed installation consists of apparatus and other devices...

  – intended for permanent use at a predefined location

    ◆ e.g. a factory, plant, warehouse, shop, office, cinema, restaurant, airport, school, telephone exchange, etc....

  – a fixed installation is never placed on the market

    ◆ in other words it is never:
    made commercially available to an end user... as a single functional product...

Changes from the protection requirements of 89/336

emc2c

■ The wording of the emissions and immunity requirements have been clarified

  ◆ without changing their intended meaning

■ But, most importantly, the requirement to have regard to the state of the art is new in 2004/108

  – this could have very significant implications for fixed installations

emc2c

Fixed installations shall be installed by applying "good engineering practices"

- The *good engineering practices* employed shall be documented...
  - and the documents held ready for inspection by the national authorities by the *responsible person*
    - ◆ for as long as the *fixed installation* is in operation
- But the documentation of a *fixed installation* is <u>not</u> the same as is required for an *apparatus*

---

emc2c

If the EMC of the *fixed installation* is suspect...

- ...or if complaints of interference are received...
  - the national EMC authorities may request evidence of compliance...
    - ◆ or initiate an investigation
- Where non-compliance is established...
  - the authorities may impose measures to bring it into compliance with the *protection requirements*

---

emc2c

A "Responsible Person" shall be identified for each fixed installation

- He or she is responsible for ensuring that the *fixed installation* complies with the *protection requirements*
  - and also for keeping the compliance documentation at the disposal of the national authorities
- It is up to each member state to decide on the rules they will apply for identifying the *responsible person*

---

emc2c

Fixed installations shall also be installed by...

- ...respecting the information on the intended use of the 'items' incorporated into them
  - described later
- Note: at the present time there are no standards for *fixed installations* listed under the 89/336

Discussion continued...

If modern good EMC engineering practices are indeed required by 2004/108...

- then this is a problem for the majority of installation owners, system integrators, panel builders, custom engineers, installers, contract electricians, etc,
  - ◆ most of them still think that all that is required is single-point earthing (grounding)...
  - ◆ plus terminating cable screens at one end, and grounding filters, using any length of green/yellow insulated wire
- is it really likely that they will all learn to do EMC engineering properly?

emc2c

Discussion continued...

2004/108 says nothing specific about modifications to a fixed installation

- Some modifications or additions can cost more than the original installation
  - ◆ and completely alter its EM characteristics
- so should "putting into service" only apply the very first time a fixed installation is used by its end user?
  - ◆ i.e. a fixed installation need not comply after modification
- or should a fixed installation comply throughout its entire operational life, even if it is modified?

emc2c

Discussion

Good engineering practices are not defined in 2004/108...

- Should we assume that the use of good modern EMC engineering practices is required?
  - ◆ e.g. as described by modern standards such as IEC 61000-5-2 and other recent guides on EMC for systems and installations (having regard to the state of the art)
- after all, using non-EMC good engineering practices (e.g. complying with the IEE's Wiring Regulations) will not help ensure that the fixed installation complies with the protection requirements...

emc2c

Discussion continued...

Documentation for fixed installations

- The Directive only requires documenting the good engineering practices that were employed
- but retaining the EMC assembly and installation instructions for the incorporated items...
  - ◆ and showing how they were actually followed...
- is a good documentation practice when trying to show the steps taken to comply...
- so should we assume that this information should also be included in the documentation?

emc2c

292

Items intended for incorporation into a *fixed installation*

emc2c

(the word "*item*" is used in this presentation to mean something incorporated into a *fixed installation*)

- These *items* could be systems (of <u>any</u> size) or any other *apparatus*, sub-systems or devices

- If *items* are products that are *placed on the market* for distribution or final use...
  - ◆ e.g. PCs, Ethernet devices, power supplies, motor drives, instrumentation and control modules, generators, etc.
  - – they must comply with <u>all</u> of 2004/108's provisions
    - ◆ plus have an EC declaration of conformity and the CE mark

---

All such *items* <u>*must*</u> be provided to their end user with documents that...

emc2c

- – identify the *fixed installation* the *item* is intended for
  - ◆ and identify the *EMC characteristics* of the *fixed installation*

- – indicate the precautions to be taken for incorporating the item into the *fixed installation* so as not to compromise the installation's conformity

- – uniquely identify the *item* (e.g. its serial number)

- – give its manufacturer's name and address (or that of its agent or importer)

Discussion continued....

The compliance of *fixed installations* that predate 89/336 might be unknown

emc2c

- So each time they are modified, should they...
  - ◆ be allowed to continue not to comply?
  - ◆ ensure that the modified area complies?
  - ◆ ensure that the whole *fixed installation* complies?

- Should the *protection requirements* cover:
  - – possible interference with radio, telecommunications or other equipment that might reasonably be used nearby at some future time?

But where an item is intended for a specified *fixed installation*...

emc2c

- – and is *not* otherwise commercially available to an end-user as a single functional unit...

- 2004/108 still applies, but *does not* require it to...
  - a) comply with the *protection requirements*
  - b) or undergo a *conformity assessment procedure*
  - c) or carry the *CE marking*

Discussion continued...

How should an *item's* supplier...

(of an *item* that is "not otherwise commercially available")

...indicate the precautions to be taken during incorporation not to compromise the compliance of the *fixed installation* ?

- is it enough to simply list EM mitigation measures (such as shielding, filtering, power conditioning) ?
  - ◆ and let someone else worry about what to do in practice
- or does 2004/108 require the application of proper EMC engineering to the *item* ?
  - ◆ so the installer has clear and detailed instructions to follow

emc2c — CCC

Discussion on EMC expertise

It seems reasonable to assume that 2004/108 requires a *fixed installation* to employ someone who has (or has access to) *state of the art*....

- ...knowledge of EMC standards and guides
- ...skills in assessing EM environments
- ...skills in EM good practices for assembly, installation, and remedial measures (EM fixes)

- it also seems reasonable to assume this person has access to EM measuring equipment, plus...
  - ◆ has the necessary authority over suppliers
  - ◆ compiles the documentation on good engineering practices

emc2c — CCC

Discussion

The accompanying documents

(for an *item* that is "not otherwise commercially available")

■ To create these, the suppliers of the *items* need to know the fixed installation's EM environment

- but does 2004/108 require a full assessment of the EM environment to be conducted ?
  - ◆ as would be needed to do EMC engineering properly
- or is it enough to classify a *fixed installation* as "Domestic, commercial or light-industrial" or as "Industrial" ?
  - ◆ according to the generic standards (EN 61000-6 series)

emc2c — CCC

Discussion continued...

Instructions for installing *items* that <u>are</u> *placed on the market*

■ 2004/108 requires such *items* to have EMC installation instructions

- but they are unlikely to maintain the compliance of every *fixed installation* they might be used in

■ So, on behalf of the *fixed installation*...

- someone needs to specify the additional shielding, filtering or other suppression that may be needed
  - ◆ when incorporating such standard products

emc2c — CCC

Summary for fixed installations

- **Must comply with the protection requirements having regard to the state of the art**

- **Do not have to undergo conformity assessment, have a declaration of conformity, or CE marking**
  - but must use *good engineering practices* and "respect" the information on the intended use of the items incorporated into it...
    - and document the good engineering practices

- **For each fixed installation, someone will be identified as being responsible for the above**

Summary of discussions

- **Should a *fixed installation* use good modern EMC engineering practices ?**

- **Should all of a modified *fixed installation* comply ?**
  - or, if it originally predates 89/336, just the modified part ?

- **What level of detail of the *fixed installation*'s EM environment should the *item* suppliers know ?**
  - and how should their EMC precautions be documented ?

- **Should a *fixed installation* employ an EMC expert ?**
  - and is there a great need for training in 2004/108 ?

Discussion on EMC expertise
continued...

- It seems that during the next 4½ years, many installation owners, system integrators, panel builders, custom engineers, installers, contract electricians, etc, should follow a learning curve on 2004/108 compliance

- **Many currently use the 'CE + CE = CE' approach**
  - which requires no EMC skills or testing so is low-cost

- **But this has no technical or legal basis and was never sufficient for 89/336**
  - and clearly won't meet 2004/108's requirements for *fixed installations* and their incorporated *items*

Summary for the items to be incorporated into a fixed installation

- **These can be systems of any size, apparatus, sub-systems or other devices**
  - if made for a specified fixed installation they do not need to undergo a conformity assessment, or have an EC declaration of conformity, or be CE marked
    - but documentation must identify which fixed installation they are intended for, and the EMC characteristics of that installation
    - and they must be supplied with documentation that identifies the precautions to be taken when installing them, so that they do not compromise the EMC compliance of the fixed installation

emc2c

EMC Directive Ed. 2

– its application to Fixed Installations –

and the items they are made from

the end

Cherry Clough

C o n s u l t a n t s

www.cherryclough.com
Eur Ing Keith Armstrong CEng MIEE MIEEE
phone: +44 (0)1457 871 605 fax: +44 (0)1457 820 145
keith.armstrong@cherryclough.com

CCC

Info Day EMC Directive Revision Brussels 3 February 2005

Improving the regulatory environment for electrical, electronic and telecommunication products

Revision of the EMC Directive

Thierry Brefort
EMC Directive Manager
DG ENTR/H5

European Commission
DG Enterprise & Industry

EMC Directive revision
Brussels, 3/02/2005
Page 1

The EMC Directive : Objectives

- Objective
  - Ensure the functioning of the Internal Market,
  - Ensure an adequate level of Electromagnetic
  - Compatibility.
- Impact :
  - The EMC Directive potentially affects 800 Million products placed onto the EEA market per year.
  - The costs of compliance with the current EMC Directive ranges from 1% to 5% of product price.
  - 60% of the products are from small & medium size enterprises.

European Commission
DG Enterprise & Industry

EMC Directive revision
Brussels, 3/02/2005
Page 2

The EMC Directive : Key concepts

- Directive is part of **Community legislation**. It needs to be transposed by each Member State into its national regulatory system.
- **Decentralized enforcement** by Member States
  - Member States ensure correct application and take enforcement measures, if necessary
  - Member States designate Competent / Notified Bodies and monitor continuously their activities
- EU Commission ensures **coherent application** of the system
  - Infringement procedures in cases of incorrect transpositions, applications
  - Guidelines to ensure uniform application
  - Coordination of various activities
  - Instruction of safeguard clauses

European Commission
DG Enterprise & Industry

EMC Directive revision
Brussels, 3/02/2005
Page 3

The EMC Directive: Key elements

- New approach Directive:
  - Essential requirements (non technical)
  - Based on harmonised standards
- Compliance with HS  Compliance with ER
- Conformity assessment procedure : proportionate to the risk
- Consistent application : Safeguards.
- Information and marking

European Commission
DG Enterprise & Industry

EMC Directive revision
Brussels, 3/02/2005
Page 4

Towards 2004/108/EC: Background

- Existing framework :
  - EMC Directive - 89/336/EEC of 03/05/1989
  - Applicable since 01/01/1992
  - Mandatory application since 01/01/96
  - Amended by 91/263/EEC, 92/31/EEC and 93/68/EEC
  - EMC Directive is based on the concepts of the new approach
- Guide issued in 1997 to clarify issues and ensure homogeneous application

European Commission
DG Enterprise & Industry

EMC Directive revision
Brussels, 3/02/2005
Page 5

Towards 2004/108/EC : Why ? (1)

- March 1998 : EMC Directive included in the 3rd phase of the SLIM programme (SEC (98) 559)
- December 1998 : conclusion of the panel of experts : to revise the EMC Directive
  - main aspects :
    - ✓ Basic principles,
    - ✓ treatment of installations,
    - ✓ conformity assessment procedure, application of standards,
    - ✓ consideration of the solutions provided in the guide
  - endorsed by the Commission (COM(1999)88)

European Commission
DG Enterprise & Industry

EMC Directive revision
Brussels, 3/02/2005
Page 6

Towards 2004/108/EC : What ?

- Objective
  - Improve legal security through a clearer and more precise text giving an answer to divergent interpretations of the 89/336/EEC directive.
- Means
  - Clarification of the scope and definitions
  - Better definition of the essential requirements
    - ✓ Protection requirements
    - ✓ Specific requirements for apparatus and for fixed installations
  - Unique conformity assessment procedure for apparatus
  - Better information and documentation requirements
  - Particular regime for fixed installations

European Commission
DG Enterprise & Industry

EMC Directive revision
Brussels, 3/02/2005
Page 7

How ?
The public process

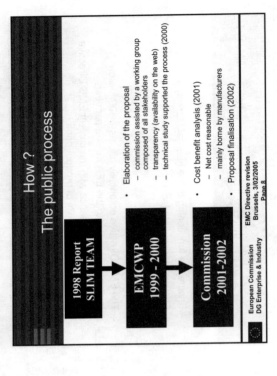

- Elaboration of the proposal
  - commission assisted by a working group composed of all stakeholders
  - transparency (availability on the web)
  - technical study supported the process (2000)
- Cost benefit analysis (2001)
  - Net cost reasonable
  - mainly borne by manufacturers
- Proposal finalisation (2002)

European Commission
DG Enterprise & Industry

EMC Directive revision
Brussels, 3/02/2005
Page 8

How ?
The interinstitutional process

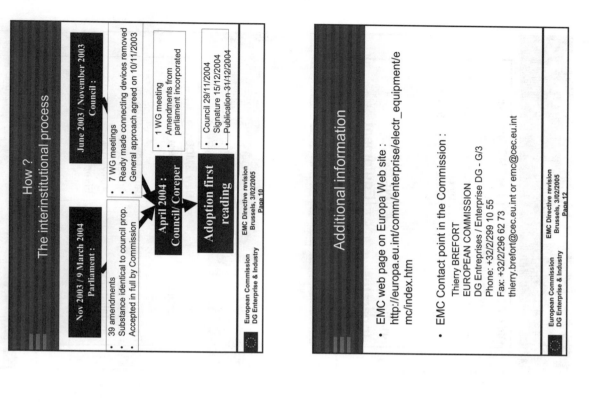

Nov 2003 / 9 March 2004 Parliament :
- 39 amendments
- Substance identical to council prop.
- Accepted in full by Commission

June 2003 / November 2003 Council :
- 7 WG meetings
- Ready made connecting devices removed
- General approach agreed on 10/11/2003

April 2004 : Council / Coreper
- 1 WG meeting
- Amendments from parliament incorporated

Adoption first reading
- Council 29/11/2004
- Signature 15/12/2004
- Publication 31/12/2004

Cost benefit analysis - outcomes

- Analysis performed by an independent consultant
- All concerned parties consulted (manufacturers, installers, competent/notified bodies, end users, network operators, public authorities)
- Main outcomes:
  - Recognition basis to already existing procedures, based on the guide to the application of the directive 89/336/EEC
  - Expected reduction of the electromagnetic interference
  - Global cost estimated to less than 0.1% of the revenues generated in the sector, weighted over 8 years
  - Costs borne at 90% by the manufacturers

Additional information

- EMC web page on Europa Web site :
  http://europa.eu.int/comm/enterprise/electr_equipment/emc/index.htm

- EMC Contact point in the Commission :
  Thierry BREFORT
  EUROPEAN COMMISSION
  DG Entreprises / Enterprise DG - G/3
  Phone : +32/2/299 10 55
  Fax : +32/2/296 62 73
  thierry.brefort@cec.eu.int or emc@cec.eu.int

What next ?

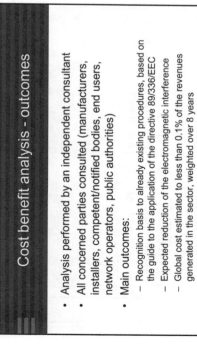

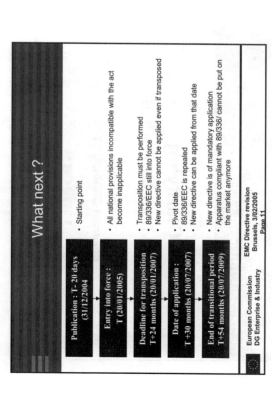

Publication : T- 20 days (31/12/2004)
- Starting point

Entry into force : T (20/01/2005)
- All national provisions incompatible with the act become inapplicable

Deadline for transposition T+24 months (20/01/2007)
- Transposition must be performed
- 89/336/EEC still into force
- New directive cannot be applied even if transposed

Date of application : T +30 months (20/07/2007)
- Pivot date
- 89/336/EEC is repealed
- New directive can be applied from that date

End of transitional period T+54 months (20/07/2009)
- New directive is of mandatory application
- Apparatus compliant with 89/336/ cannot be put on the market anymore

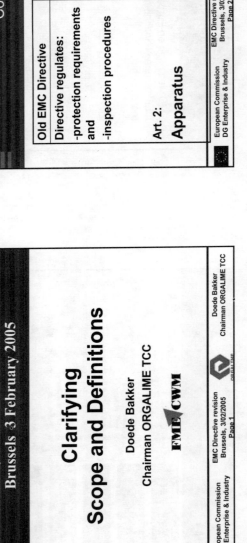

Info Day EMC Directive Revision
Brussels 3 February 2005

Clarifying
Scope and Definitions

Doede Bakker
Chairman ORGALIME TCC

European Commission
DG Enterprise & Industry

EMC Directive revision
Brussels, 3/02/2005
Page 1

Doede Bakker
Chairman ORGALIME TCC

Concept

Old EMC Directive	New EMC Directive
Directive regulates: -protection requirements and -inspection procedures	Total concept: Directive regulates EMC by ensuring the functioning of the IM.
Art. 2: **Apparatus**	Art. 1: **Equipment**

European Commission
DG Enterprise & Industry

EMC Directive revision
Brussels, 3/02/2005
Page 2

Doede Bakker
Chairman ORGALIME TCC

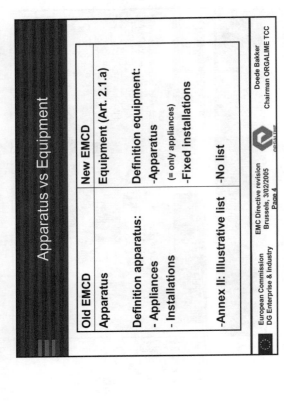

Apparatus vs Equipment

Old EMCD	New EMCD
Apparatus	Equipment (Art. 2.1.a)
Definition apparatus: - Appliances - Installations	Definition equipment: -Apparatus (= only appliances) -Fixed installations
-Annex II: Illustrative list	-No list

European Commission
DG Enterprise & Industry

EMC Directive revision
Brussels, 3/02/2005
Page 4

Doede Bakker
Chairman ORGALIME TCC

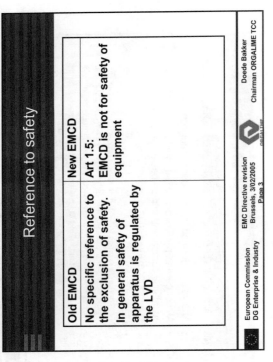

Reference to safety

Old EMCD	New EMCD
No specific reference to the exclusion of safety. In general safety of apparatus is regulated by the LVD	Art 1.5: EMCD is not for safety of equipment

European Commission
DG Enterprise & Industry

EMC Directive revision
Brussels, 3/02/2005
Page 3

Doede Bakker
Chairman ORGALIME TCC

Apparatus

Definition (Art. 2.1.b)

- **Apparatus means**
  - Any finished appliance or combination
  - Made commercially available
  - As a single functional unit
  - Intended for the end user
  - Liable to cause or to be affected by EM disturbance

Fixed installations

Definition (Art. 2.1.c)

- **Fixed installation means**
  - Particular combination of several apparatus or other devices
  - Assembled, installed and intended to be used permanently at a predefined location

---

Fixed installations

Mobile installations (Art. 2.2.b)

- **Definition**
  - Combination of apparatus and other devices, intended to be moved and operated in a wide range of locations

---

Fixed installations

- **Large machines (Preamble 18)**
  - Production streets for cars or for carpet

- **Networks (Preamble 18)**
  - National telecom network

- **Except editorial unchanged:**
  - Electromagnetic compatibility
  - Electromagnetic disturbance
  - Immunity

European Commission
DG Enterprise & Industry

EMC Directive revision
Brussels, 3/02/2005
Page 10

Doede Bakker
Chairman ORGALIME TCC

- **R&TTED**
  - (1999/5/EC)
- **Aeronautical products**
  - (Regulation 1592/2002)
- **Radio amateur equipment**
  - ITU Radio Regulations

- **Art 1.4 Specificity clause:**
  - EMC more specifically laid down by other directives (e.g. Medical Devices Directive)

European Commission
DG Enterprise & Industry

EMC Directive revision
Brussels, 3/02/2005
Page 12

Doede Bakker
Chairman ORGALIME TCC

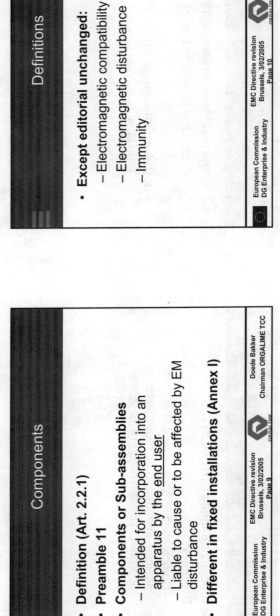

- **Definition (Art. 2.2.1)**
- **Preamble 11**
- **Components or Sub-assemblies**
  - Intended for incorporation into an apparatus by the end user
  - Liable to cause or to be affected by EM disturbance
- **Different in fixed installations (Annex I)**

European Commission
DG Enterprise & Industry

EMC Directive revision
Brussels, 3/02/2005
Page 9

Doede Bakker
Chairman ORGALIME TCC

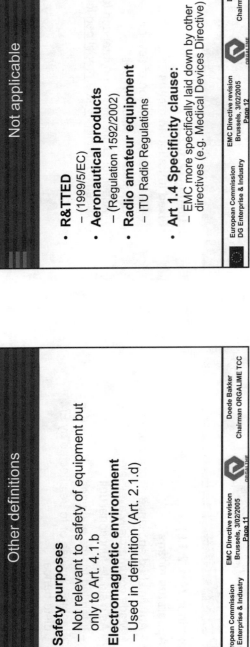

- **Safety purposes**
  - Not relevant to safety of equipment but only to Art. 4.1.b
- **Electromagnetic environment**
  - Used in definition (Art. 2.1.d)

European Commission
DG Enterprise & Industry

EMC Directive revision
Brussels, 3/02/2005
Page 11

Doede Bakker
Chairman ORGALIME TCC

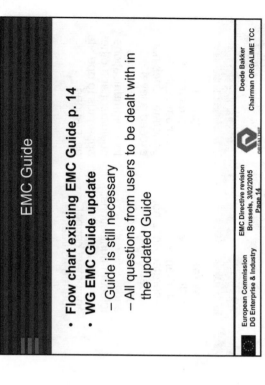

EMC Guide

- **Flow chart existing EMC Guide p. 14**
- **WG EMC Guide update**
  - Guide is still necessary
  - All questions from users to be dealt with in the updated Guide

European Commission
DG Enterprise & Industry

EMC Directive revision
Brussels, 3/02/2005
Page 14

Doede Bakker
Chairman ORGALIME TCC

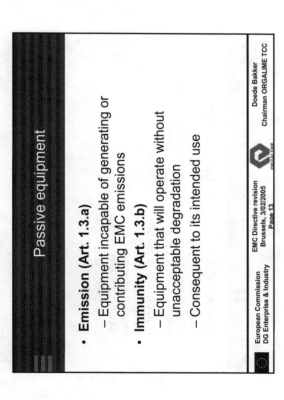

Passive equipment

- **Emission (Art. 1.3.a)**
  - Equipment incapable of generating or contributing EMC emissions
- **Immunity (Art. 1.3.b)**
  - Equipment that will operate without unacceptable degradation
  - Consequent to its intended use

European Commission
DG Enterprise & Industry

EMC Directive revision
Brussels, 3/02/2005
Page 13

Doede Bakker
Chairman ORGALIME TCC

Thank you for your attention!

European Commission
DG Enterprise & Industry

EMC Directive revision
Brussels, 3/02/2005
Page 15

Doede Bakker
Chairman ORGALIME TCC

Slide 1

Info Day EMC Directive Revision
Brussels 3 February 2005

Essential requirements and harmonised standards

Christian M. Verholt

Danish Standards

Chairman CENELEC TC 210

Slide 2

Directive Clauses addressing Essential requirements

- **New:** Article 5
- Essential requirements
- The equipment referred to in Article 1 shall meet the essential requirements set out in Annex I.

- **Old:** Article 4 includes essential requirements

Slide 3

Protection requirements

- **New** ANNEX I
- Essential requirements referred to in Article 5
- Equipment shall be so designed and manufactured, having regard to the state of the art, as to ensure that:

- **Old:** Article 4
- The apparatus referred to in Article 2 shall be so constructed that:

Slide 4

Protection requirements

- **NEW (a)** The electromagnetic disturbance generated does not exceed the level above which radio and telecommunications equipment or other equipment cannot operate as intended;

- **OLD (a)** The electromagnetic disturbance it generates does not exceed a level allowing radio and telecommunications equipment and other apparatus to operate as intended

New directive only
2. Specific requirements for fixed installations
Installation and intended use of components

- A fixed installation shall be installed applying good engineering practices and respecting the information on the intended use of its components, with a view to meeting the protection requirements set out in Point 1. Those good engineering practices shall be documented and the documentation shall be held by the person(s) responsible at the disposal of the relevant national authorities for inspection purposes for as long as the fixed installation is in operation.

European Commission
DG Enterprise & Industry

EMC Directive revision
Brussels, 3/02/2005
Page 6

Article 6
Harmonised standards

- 1. 'Harmonised standard' means a technical specification adopted by a recognised European standardisation body under a mandate from the Commission in conformity with the procedures laid down in Directive 98/34/EC for the purpose of establishing a European requirement. Compliance with a 'harmonised standard' is not compulsory.

European Commission
DG Enterprise & Industry

EMC Directive revision
Brussels, 3/02/2005
Page 8

Protection requirements

- **NEW (b)** It has a level of immunity to the electromagnetic disturbance to be expected in its intended use which allows it to operate as without unacceptable degradation of its intended use.

- **OLD (b)** The apparatus has an adequate level of intrinsic immunity to electromagnetic disturbance to enable it to operate as intended

- The principal protection requirements are set out in Annex III

European Commission
DG Enterprise & Industry

EMC Directive revision
Brussels, 3/02/2005
Page 5

Role of harmonised standard

- To specify - in technical terms -requirements which ensure that practical occurrances of non-compatibility between equipment(s) and installations is unlikely to happen in typical environments

- "Presumption of conformity"

- To provide a standardised, repeatable, accurate and accepted method for the assessment of equipment

European Commission
DG Enterprise & Industry

EMC Directive revision
Brussels, 3/02/2005
Page 7

Other marks and information

3. The manufacturer shall provide information on any specific precautions that must be taken when the apparatus is assembled, installed, maintained or used, in order to ensure that, when put into service, the apparatus is in conformity with the protection requirements set out in Annex I, point 1.

European Commission
DG Enterprise & Industry

EMC Directive revision
Brussels, 3/02/2005
Page 10

Annex IV1. Technical documentation

- where the manufacturer has not applied harmonised standards, or has applied them only in part, a description and explanation of the steps taken to meet the essential requirements of the Directive, including a description of the electromagnetic compatibility assessment set out in Annex II, point 1, results of design calculations made, examinations carried out, test reports, etc.;
- a statement from the notified body, when the procedure referred to in Annex III has been followed.

European Commission
DG Enterprise & Industry

EMC Directive revision
Brussels, 3/02/2005
Page 12

Article 6
Harmonised standards

2. The compliance of equipment with the relevant harmonised standards whose references have been published in the Official Journal of the European Union shall raise a presumption, on the part of the Member States, of conformity with the essential requirements referred to in Annex I to which such standards relate. This presumption of conformity is limited to the scope of the harmonised standard(s) applied and the relevant essential requirements covered by such harmonised standard(s).

European Commission
DG Enterprise & Industry

EMC Directive revision
Brussels, 3/02/2005
Page 9

Annex IV1. Technical documentation

- The technical documentation must enable the conformity of the apparatus with the essential requirements to be assessed. It must cover the design and manufacture of the apparatus, in particular:
  - a general description of the apparatus;
  - evidence of compliance with the harmonised standards, if any, applied in full or in part;

European Commission
DG Enterprise & Industry

EMC Directive revision
Brussels, 3/02/2005
Page 11

Harmonised standards are

- A "Level Playing Field"
- Agreed through a democratic process
- Generally accepted as the preferred method

DS

New areas for standardisation

- Standards for the assessment of fixed installations
- New ANNEX ZZ states the relation between the content of a standard and the essential requirements

DS

EMC Assessment

- Use of harmonised standards
  - Definition of harmonised standard
    - ✓ Mandate from the Commission
    - ✓ Prepared by a "recognised European standardisation body" (CEN, CENELEC or ETSI), published as European Standard
  - When referenced in the *Official Journal of the European Union* it gives presumption of conformity

European Commission
DG Enterprise & Industry

EMC Directive revision
Brussels, 3/02/2005
Page 6

Per Döfnäs, Issue manager for
"New Approach", EICTA

EMC Assessment

- Use of harmonised standards (cont)
  - The correct application of all the relevant harmonised standards is equivalent to making an EMC assessment
    - ✓ Product or Product Family standards can be presumed to have taken all relevant phenomena into account
    - ✓ If Generic standards are used, it is advised to check that they sufficiently cover the anticipated phenomena for the apparatus in question

European Commission
DG Enterprise & Industry

EMC Directive revision
Brussels, 3/02/2005
Page 8

Per Döfnäs, Issue manager for
"New Approach", EICTA

EMC Assessment

- What is the intended area of use?
  - Residential area
    - ✓ Close distance between disturbing and disturbed apparatus
    - ✓ "Controlled" environment
  - Non-residential area
    - ✓ Longer distance between apparatus
    - ✓ "Uncontrolled" environment

European Commission
DG Enterprise & Industry

EMC Directive revision
Brussels, 3/02/2005
Page 5

Per Döfnäs, Issue manager for
"New Approach", EICTA

EMC Assessment

- Use of harmonised standards (cont)
  - Advantage: Presumption of conformity with the essential requirement(s) covered by the standard
    - ✓ "Better day in court" - if challenged, market surveillance authorities must prove that the apparatus does not meet the essential requirements

European Commission
DG Enterprise & Industry

EMC Directive revision
Brussels, 3/02/2005
Page 7

Per Döfnäs, Issue manager for
"New Approach", EICTA

EMC Assessment

- Use of harmonised standards (cont)
  - "Correct application"
    - ✓ Ensure compliance with all applicable requirements in the standard
    - ✓ Follow the prescribed test procedures in the standard (or a test standard being referenced)
    - ✓ "Ensuring compliance" does not always mean testing, in particular when only a small revision has been made of the apparatus

European Commission
DG Enterprise & Industry

EMC Directive revision
Brussels, 3/02/2005
Page 9

Per Döfnäs, Issue manager for "New Approach", EICTA

EMC Assessment

- Use of harmonised standards (cont)
  - If apparatus is intended to be "placed on the EU market" after date of cessation of presumption of conformity of the used harmonised standard(s)
    - ✓ Ensure full compliance with the new applicable harmonised standard, or
    - ✓ Continue with the old, perform an EMC assessment regarding the changes in the standard, however no "presumption" anymore

European Commission
DG Enterprise & Industry

EMC Directive revision
Brussels, 3/02/2005
Page 10

Per Döfnäs, Issue manager for "New Approach", EICTA

EMC Assessment

- Use of other methods
  - A thorough investigation of which EMC phenomena are relevant to the apparatus must be done
    - ✓ Intended use and location of use to be considered
    - ✓ A list, short description and relevance of immunity phenomena having standardised test methods is given in EN 61000-4-1 (see next two slides)

European Commission
DG Enterprise & Industry

EMC Directive revision
Brussels, 3/02/2005
Page 11

Per Döfnäs, Issue manager for "New Approach", EICTA

Example of phenomena per location

Table 1 – Applicability of immunity tests based on location (environment)

Basic standard	Description	Residential, commercial and light industrial	Industrial area	Special (e.g. power plant)
61000-4-2	ESD	g.a.	g.a.	g.a.
61000-4-3	Radiated electromagnetic field	g.a.	g.a.	g.a.
61000-4-4	EFT/Burst	g.a.	g.a.	g.a.
61000-4-5	Surge	g.a.	g.a.	g.a.
61000-4-6	Conducted disturbances by RF fields	g.a.	g.a.	g.a.
61000-4-7	General guide on harmonics and interharmonics measurements and instrumentation	n.i.s.	n.i.s.	n.i.s.
61000-4-8	50/60 Hz magnetic field	may	may	g.a.
61000-4-9	Pulse magnetic field	g.n.a.	g.n.a.	g.a.
61000-4-10	Oscillatory magnetic field	g.n.a.	g.n.a.	g.a.
61000-4-11	Voltage dips and interruption	g.a.	g.a.	g.a.
61000-4-12	Oscillatory waves "ring wave"	may	may	may

[1] Applicability explanation:
n.i.s. = not an immunity standard
g.a. = generally applicable except in special cases
g.n.a. = generally not applicable except in special cases
may = may be applicable in certain circumstances.
(–) means not applicable.

European Commission
DG Enterprise & Industry

EMC Directive revision
Brussels, 3/02/2005
Page 12

Per Döfnäs, Issue manager for "New Approach", EICTA

EMC Assessment

- Use of other methods (cont)
  - Establish acceptable limits for compliance for the applicable phenomena
    - ✓ Guidance can be taken from existing harmonised standards for related apparatus types and areas of use (these will inevitably form the basis of opinion regarding appropriate compatibility levels in different circumstances

---

EMC Assessment

- Use of other methods (cont)
  - Ensuring compliance: Tests, simulations, calculations
    - ✓ Test where relevant, according to a test plan
    - ✓ In some cases, simulations or calculations may be sufficient to establish compliance

---

Example of phenomena per apparatus port

Table 2 – Applicability of immunity tests based on EUT ports

Basic standard	Description	Applicability [1]				
		AC power	DC power	En-closure	Signal data	Earth
61000-4-2	ESD	— [3]	g.n.a.	g.a.	g.n.a.	g.n.a.
61000-4-3	Radiated electromagnetic field	g.n.a.	g.n.a.	g.a.	g.n.a.	g.n.a.
61000-4-4	EFT/Burst	g.a.	g.a.	—	g.a.	g.a.
61000-4-5	Surge	g.a.	may	—	may	may
61000-4-6	Conducted disturbances by RF fields	g.a.	may	—	g.a.	g.a.
61000-4-7	General guide on harmonics and interharmonics measurements and instrumentation	n.i.s.	n.i.s.	n.i.s.	n.i.s.	n.i.s.
61000-4-8	50/60 Hz magnetic field	—	—	may	—	—
61000-4-9	Pulse magnetic field	—	—	may	—	—
61000-4-10	Oscillatory magnetic field	—	—	may	—	—
61000-4-11	Voltage dips and interruption	g.a.	—	—	—	—
61000-4-12	Oscillatory waves "ring wave"	may	g.n.a.	—	may	g.n.a.
61000-4-12	Oscillatory waves 100 kHz and 1 MHz	may	may	—	may	may
61000-4-13	Harmonics, interharmonics, mains	may				

1 Applicability explanation:
n.i.s. = not an immunity standard
g.a. = generally applicable except in special cases

g.n.a = generally not applicable except in special cases
may = may be applicable in certain circumstances
(—) means not applicable

EMC Assessment

- Use of other methods (cont)
  - Establish acceptable limits for compliance for the applicable phenomena (cont)
    - ✓ For emission, distances to other apparatus that can be disturbed (in most cases radio apparatus) must be considered
    - ✓ For immunity the likely levels occurring, and the resulting performance (permissible reduction of performance) during or after the phenomena is present must be considered

Slide 1 (Page 17)

Configurations to test and evaluate

- EMC assessment shall take into account all normal intended operating conditions

- EMC assessment shall confirm that the apparatus meets the protection requirements in all its representative configurations

European Commission
DG Enterprise & Industry

EMC Directive revision
Brussels, 3/02/2005
Page 17

Per Döfnäs, Issue manager for "New Approach", EICTA

Slide 2 (Page 18)

Configurations to test and evaluate

- "Normal intended operating conditions"
  - Specified by the manufacturer, e.g. in the manual
  - What can be expected for the type of apparatus ("anticipated use")
  - During testing, exercise the apparatus in its main modes of operation unless one "worst normal mode" can be identified

European Commission
DG Enterprise & Industry

EMC Directive revision
Brussels, 3/02/2005
Page 18

Per Döfnäs, Issue manager for "New Approach", EICTA

Slide 3 (Page 19)

Configurations to test and evaluate

- Representative configurations
  - Foreseeable by the manufacturer
  - May be one of similar models, or different configurations of one model
  - Choose the "worst case" of these
    - ✓ Causing maximum disturbance
    - ✓ Most susceptible to disturbances
  - Worst case configuration may differ for different immunity phenomena

European Commission
DG Enterprise & Industry

EMC Directive revision
Brussels, 3/02/2005
Page 19

Per Döfnäs, Issue manager for "New Approach", EICTA

Slide 4 (Page 20)

"Technical construction file"

- Where harmonised standards are not used, more detailed proof of compliance must be documented – a "technical construction file"

- More detailed description of the apparatus as a whole
  - Design drawings
  - Layout of EMC critical components, etc

European Commission
DG Enterprise & Industry

EMC Directive revision
Brussels, 3/02/2005
Page 20

Per Döfnäs, Issue manager for "New Approach", EICTA

Concluding remarks

- In conclusion
  - The revised EMC directive more visibly places the initiative for EMC assessment in the hands of the manufacturer
  - Use of harmonised standards simplifies the assessment

European Commission
DG Enterprise & Industry

EMC Directive revision
Brussels, 3/02/2005
Page 22

Per Döfnäs, Issue manager for
"New Approach", EICTA

"Technical construction file"

- If testing, describe details
  - Test set-up (e.g. similarities and deviations from "harmonised standard tests")
  - Instrumentation used
  - Calculated uncertainties
  - Rationale for choice of parameters and limits

European Commission
DG Enterprise & Industry

EMC Directive revision
Brussels, 3/02/2005
Page 21

Per Döfnäs, Issue manager for
"New Approach", EICTA

Thank you for your attention!

European Commission
DG Enterprise & Industry

EMC Directive revision
Brussels, 3/02/2005
Page 23

Per Döfnäs, Issue manager for
"New Approach", EICTA

The Role of the Notified Body

This paper will consider:

- What is the role of the Notified Body in the context of this specific directive?
- How the NBs will fulfil that role?
- What are the obligations of the NB?
- What are the obligations of the Manufacturer?
- What is the future for the NBs?

European Commission
DG Enterprise & Industry

EMC Directive revision
Brussels, 3/02/2005
Page 2

Dave Imeson

Compliance Europe ltd

CBs versus NBs

- The duties of a Competent Body were not defined in Directive 89/336.
- Equally the duties of a Notified Body are not defined in directive 2004/108 except in Article III.
- In both cases the end product is a Statement or Certificate that the manufacturer may use to support the Declaration of Conformity.

European Commission
DG Enterprise & Industry

EMC Directive revision
Brussels, 3/02/2005
Page 4

Dave Imeson

Compliance Europe ltd

Info Day EMC Directive Revision
Brussels 3 February 2005

The Role of the Notified Bodies

Dave Imeson

Chairman ECACB

Compliance Europe Ltd

European Commission
DG Enterprise & Industry

EMC Directive revision
Brussels, 3/02/2005
Page 1

Dave Imeson

Compliance Europe ltd

Notified Bodies in 2004/108

- 89/336 had Notified Bodies only for Article 10.5 Type Approval – made obsolete by the R&TTE Directive.
- 89/336 had Competent Bodies as a mandatory requirement for Article 10.2 – the Technical Construction File, TCF
- 2004/108 has Notified Bodies as an option in Article 7 detailed in Annex III.

European Commission
DG Enterprise & Industry

EMC Directive revision
Brussels, 3/02/2005
Page 3

Dave Imeson

Compliance Europe ltd

What is a Notified Body

- NBs carry out the tasks pertaining to the conformity assessment procedures referred to in the directive.
- There are major differences in the types of Notified Bodies specified by New Approach directives, for example
  - LVD – NBs are final arbiters but rarely used.
  - MDD – Use of NBs mandatory for some apparatus
  - RTTE – NBs used in Annex III,IV and V
  - EMCD – Optional use

European Commission
DG Enterprise & Industry
EMC Directive revision
Brussels, 3/02/2005
Page 6
Dave Imeson
Compliance Europe ltd

Why use a Notified Body?

- A manufacturer may wish to use a Notified Body because:-
  - There is no in-house EMC expertise
  - There is in-house EMC expertise but a third-party opinion is required
  - There are no relevant harmonised standards
  - The manufacturer chooses to apply the standard in part or not at all
  - The manufacturer chooses to use a non-harmonised standard.

European Commission
DG Enterprise & Industry
EMC Directive revision
Brussels, 3/02/2005
Page 8
Dave Imeson
Compliance Europe ltd

Annex III

"The notified body shall review the technical documentation and assess whether the technical documentation properly demonstrates that the requirements of the Directive that it is to assess have been met.

If the compliance of the apparatus is confirmed, the notified body shall issue a statement to the manufacturer confirming the compliance of the apparatus.

That statement shall be limited to those aspects of the essential requirements which have been assessed by the notified body."

European Commission
DG Enterprise & Industry
EMC Directive revision
Brussels, 3/02/2005
Page 5
Dave Imeson
Compliance Europe ltd

Obligations of a Notified Body

- Maintain commercial confidentiality
- Process the file in an expeditious manner.
- If the data presented by the manufacturer shows that the apparatus conforms to the essential requirements then a NB statement will be issued.
- If the above statement is not the case then no statement will be issued.

European Commission
DG Enterprise & Industry
EMC Directive revision
Brussels, 3/02/2005
Page 7
Dave Imeson
Compliance Europe ltd

Conflict of Roles

- EMCD 2004/108 does not require the intervention of a NB for the application of Article 13 – Fixed Installations
- There may still be EMC problems with Fixed Installations for which the manufacturer will require technical expertise.
- The Directive does not prohibit the use of a NB in this situation but it will nor be acting as an NB.

European Commission
DG Enterprise & Industry

EMC Directive revision
Brussels, 3/02/2005
Page 10

Dave Imeson

Compliance
Europe ltd

Documentation

- The technical documentation required is, in effect, what was required under Article 10.2 of 89/336.
- The essential documentation that the manufacturer must submit are:
  - Technical Description
  - Technical Rationale

European Commission
DG Enterprise & Industry

EMC Directive revision
Brussels, 3/02/2005
Page 12

Dave Imeson

Compliance
Europe ltd

Conflict of Roles?

- Most Notified Bodies are also test laboratories.
- The NB may not insist on testing in its own test lab, however it is permissible for the NB to perform both functions.
- The division of responsibilities for a given product must be clearly defined

European Commission
DG Enterprise & Industry

EMC Directive revision
Brussels, 3/02/2005
Page 9

Dave Imeson

Compliance
Europe ltd

The use of NBs

- Whilst it is up to the manufacturer to specify to the NB what parts of the essential requirements are to assessed there must be a consideration as to whether it is technically feasible to make an assessment on the limited information provided.
- If a NB is used to provide a statement in regard to only a part of the essential requirements consideration will need to be given as to how his should be reflected in the DoC

European Commission
DG Enterprise & Industry

EMC Directive revision
Brussels, 3/02/2005
Page 11

Dave Imeson

Compliance
Europe ltd

Identification of the Apparatus

- Unique Brand Name and Model(s) Number
- Must include the name and address of the original manufacturer
- If not unique, model number and adequate description of apparatus and variants
- Preferably with photographs
- A brief summary of the purpose and operation of the equipment

European Commission
DG Enterprise & Industry

EMC Directive revision
Brussels, 3/02/2005
Page 14

Dave Imeson

Compliance Europe ltd

Assessment of File

- EMC is not an exact science, there can be no 'check list' but…some items might be:-
- Assess the technical rationale, does it fulfil the requirements?
- If test results, how close to the standards?
- Risk Assessment?
- Check all the paperwork.

European Commission
DG Enterprise & Industry

EMC Directive revision
Brussels, 3/02/2005
Page 16

Dave Imeson

Compliance Europe ltd

Technical Description

- Needs only to clearly define what apparatus is the subject of this file.
- Could range from a page to several volumes and might contain:-
  - Block Diagrams
  - Circuit Diagrams
  - Component Listings
  - Interfaces
  - Installation instructions/ Manuals

European Commission
DG Enterprise & Industry

EMC Directive revision
Brussels, 3/02/2005
Page 13

Dave Imeson

Compliance Europe ltd

Technical Rationale

- **The most important part!**
- The Manufacturer's justification that the apparatus will comply with the essential requirements of 2004/108.
- The simplest method is to base the rationale on testing even if the test is not using a harmonised standard.

European Commission
DG Enterprise & Industry

EMC Directive revision
Brussels, 3/02/2005
Page 15

Dave Imeson

Compliance Europe ltd

What is the difference between Competent Bodies and NBs

- Competent Bodies were appointed under directive 89/336 to enable Art 10.2 – the Technical Construction File.
- Directive 2004/108 does not have a TCF route but it does define Notified Bodies.
- The role of the Notified Bodies is defined in Directive 2004/108 Article 7 and Annex III

European Commission
DG Enterprise & Industry

EMC Directive revision
Brussels, 3/02/2005
Page 18

Dave Imeson

Compliance Europe ltd

Notified Body Certificate

- An assessment that the procedures used to demonstrate conformity have been correctly performed and documented including any limitations or reservations.
- The name, address and identity number of the Notified Body
- The signature of the engineer responsible for the assessment
- The signature of the manager of the NB

European Commission
DG Enterprise & Industry

EMC Directive revision
Brussels, 3/02/2005
Page 17

Dave Imeson

Compliance Europe ltd

Conclusion

- A NB in directive 2004/108 performs the same functions as a CB in 89/336 except that the role is not mandatory.
- The NBs will continue to provide an essential service.
- "What's in a name? That which we call a rose by any other name would smell as sweet" William Shakespeare

European Commission
DG Enterprise & Industry

EMC Directive revision
Brussels, 3/02/2005
Page 19

Dave Imeson

Compliance Europe ltd

Slide 1

Info Day EMC Directive Revision
Brussels 3 February 2005

Facilitating Market Surveillance

Information, Documentation and Marking

Lars Ström

Swedish National Electrical Safety Board

Slide 2

Facilitating Market Surveillance

- Information requirements in the new EMC directive

- Requirements and content of
  - EC Declaration of Conformity
  - Technical documentation

European Commission
DG Enterprise & Industry

EMC Directive revision
Brussels, 3/02/2005
Page 2

Lars Ström
Swedish National Electrical Safety Board

Slide 3

Introduction

Information requirements
- Markings
- Traceability
- Precautions
- Residential/Industrial
- Instructions

European Commission
DG Enterprise & Industry

EMC Directive revision
Brussels, 3/02/2005
Page 3

Lars Ström
Swedish National Electrical Safety Board

Slide 4

Information requirements

Markings
- Each apparatus shall be identified in terms of
  - type
  - batch
  - serial number

European Commission
DG Enterprise & Industry

EMC Directive revision
Brussels, 3/02/2005
Page 4

Lars Ström
Swedish National Electrical Safety Board

Information requirements

Traceability

- Name and address of
  - manufacturer
  - authorised representative
  - person responsible for placing on the market

European Commission
DG Enterprise & Industry

EMC Directive revision
Brussels, 3/02/2005
Page 5

Lars Ström
Swedish National Electrical Safety Board

Information requirements

Precautions

- Information on specific precautions when
  - assembling
  - installing
  - maintaining
  - using

European Commission
DG Enterprise & Industry

EMC Directive revision
Brussels, 3/02/2005
Page 6

Lars Ström
Swedish National Electrical Safety Board

Information requirements

Residential/Industrial

- Clear indication of restriction of use
  - accompanied with the apparatus
  - on the packaging

European Commission
DG Enterprise & Industry

EMC Directive revision
Brussels, 3/02/2005
Page 7

Lars Ström
Swedish National Electrical Safety Board

Information requirements

Instructions

- Information enabling use with the intended purpose

European Commission
DG Enterprise & Industry

EMC Directive revision
Brussels, 3/02/2005
Page 8

Lars Ström
Swedish National Electrical Safety Board

Introduction

Requirements and content of

- EC Declaration of conformity, DoC
- Technical documentation

European Commission
DG Enterprise & Industry

EMC Directive revision
Brussels, 3/02/2005
Page 9

Lars Ström
Swedish National Electrical Safety Board

DoC and Technical doc.

EC Declaration of Conformity, DoC

- reference to the directive
- identification of the apparatus
- name and address of the manufacturer
- reference to specifications
- date of declaration
- identification and signature

European Commission
DG Enterprise & Industry

EMC Directive revision
Brussels, 3/02/2005
Page 10

Lars Ström
Swedish National Electrical Safety Board

DoC and Technical doc.

Technical documentation

- description of the apparatus
- evidence of compliance
  - ✓ evidence of compliance with harmonised standards or,
  - ✓ description of EMC assessment carried out or,
  - ✓ description of EMC assessment carried out and a statement from Notified body.

European Commission
DG Enterprise & Industry

EMC Directive revision
Brussels, 3/02/2005
Page 11

Lars Ström
Swedish National Electrical Safety Board

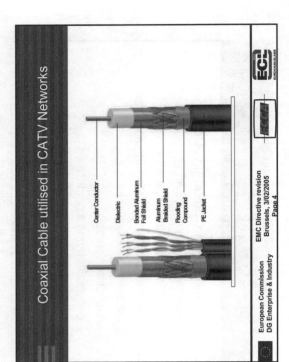

Table of Contents

- Introduction
- Network configuration
- Standardisation and technology issues for broadband cable networks
- Good engineering practice
- Network ownership
- Conclusions

European Commission
DG Enterprise & Industry

EMC Directive revision
Brussels, 3/02/2005
Page 2

Coaxial Cable utilised in CATV Networks

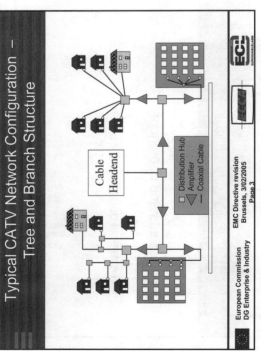

Center Conductor
Dielectric
Bonded Aluminum Foil Shield
Aluminum Braided Shield
Flooding Compound
PE Jacket

European Commission
DG Enterprise & Industry

EMC Directive revision
Brussels, 3/02/2005
Page 4

Info Day EMC Directive Revision Brussels 3 February 2005

Practical application of the EMC Directive to broadband cable networks – a technical perspective

Dr. Dirk Jaeger
European Cable Communications Association – ECCA
EuroCableLabs

European Commission
DG Enterprise & Industry

EMC Directive revision
Brussels, 3/02/2005
Page 1

Typical CATV Network Configuration – Tree and Branch Structure

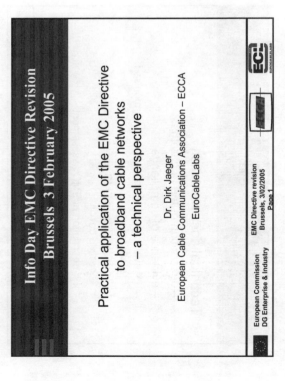

Cable Headend

☐ Distribution Hub
▽ Amplifier
— Coaxial Cable

European Commission
DG Enterprise & Industry

EMC Directive revision
Brussels, 3/02/2005
Page 3

Typical CATV Frequency Usage

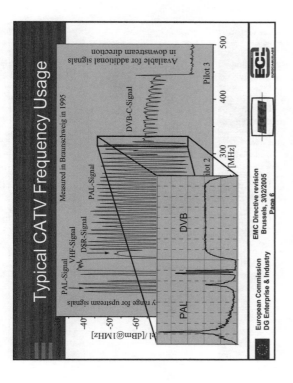

Essential Requirements - General

- Conformity with Directive's Essential Requirements facilitated by standards which address:
  - Low network egress (radiation) — helps coexistence with radiocommunications and other ECNs
  - Low network ingress (immunity) – helps the provision of high quality services to customers

Structure of a Modern HFC Network

HFC - Hybrid Fibre Coax

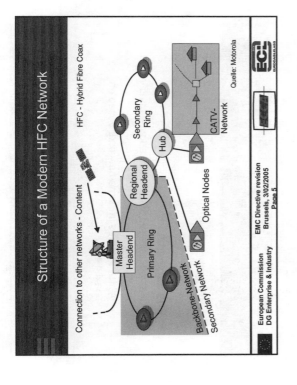

Quelle: Motorola

Table of Contents

- Introduction
- Network configuration
- Standardisation and technology issues for broadband cable networks
- Good engineering practice
- Network ownership
- Conclusions

EMC Standardisation for Cable by CENELEC

- EN 55022 – harmonised standard for IT equipment
  - Used as a reference by the IT sector
  - Provides presumption of conformity
- EN 50083-2 – harmonised standard for cable network apparatus
  - Used as reference by the cable industry
  - Provides presumption of conformity
  - Provides greater protection for radiocommunications services

European Commission
DG Enterprise & Industry

EMC Directive revision
Brussels, 3/02/2005
Page 9

Standardisation (cont.)

BUT … that's not all !

- The cable industry has developed a voluntary network standard EN 50083-8
  - Also used as reference by the cable industry
  - Covers immunity as well as radiation aspects
  - Limits similar to those in the U.S.

European Commission
DG Enterprise & Industry

EMC Directive revision
Brussels, 3/02/2005
Page 10

Standardisation (contd.)

- AND furthermore …

- The cable industry:
  - Has encouraged installers to adopt a quality regime,
  - Which includes in-home networks based on coaxial cables

European Commission
DG Enterprise & Industry

EMC Directive revision
Brussels, 3/02/2005
Page 11

Technology

- Digitisation brings advantages
- The absence of vision, sound and colour sub-carriers reduces the possibility of disturbance
- High level digital modulation methods spreads energy across a broad bandwidth

European Commission
DG Enterprise & Industry

EMC Directive revision
Brussels, 3/02/2005
Page 12

Table of Contents

- Introduction
- Network configuration
- Standardisation and technology issues for broadband cable networks
- Good engineering practice
- Network ownership
- Conclusions

European Commission
DG Enterprise & Industry

EMC Directive revision
Brussels, 3/02/2005
Page 14

Network Build/Modification

- Quality of material
  - In compliance with EN 50083-2
- Quality of installation
  - In compliance with EN 50083-8
- Applies to all networks including in-home

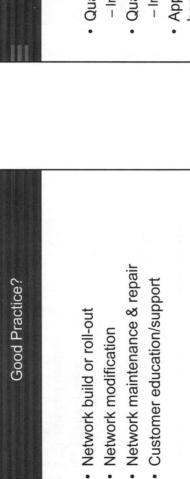

European Commission
DG Enterprise & Industry

EMC Directive revision
Brussels, 3/02/2005
Page 16

Technology (contd.)

- Frequencies in guided media not radio and therefore not protected from radio services
- There maybe a limit to practicable immunity improvement especially for in-home networks
- Broadband cable provides competition
- General objective is maximising 'on-air' frequency usage – i.e. increasing spectrum usage and radio penetration
- Should frequency usage on cable, at least, be a (minor) factor considered in the planning of radio systems?

European Commission
DG Enterprise & Industry

EMC Directive revision
Brussels, 3/02/2005
Page 13

Good Practice?

- Network build or roll-out
- Network modification
- Network maintenance & repair
- Customer education/support

European Commission
DG Enterprise & Industry

EMC Directive revision
Brussels, 3/02/2005
Page 15

Portable Equipment

- Portable unit for finding individual leaks - example

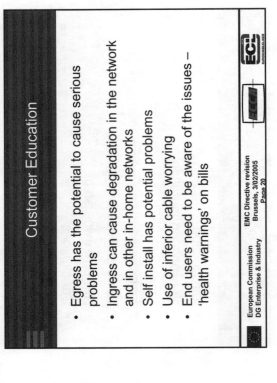

Trilithic Leakage Detector – Ingress Locator

European Commission
DG Enterprise & Industry

EMC Directive revision
Brussels, 3/02/2005
Page 18

Customer Education

- Egress has the potential to cause serious problems
- Ingress can cause degradation in the network and in other in-home networks
- Self install has potential problems
- Use of inferior cable worrying
- End users need to be aware of the issues – 'health warnings' on bills

European Commission
DG Enterprise & Industry

EMC Directive revision
Brussels, 3/02/2005
Page 20

Network Maintenance & Repair

- Network monitoring – several methods
  - Continuous monitoring:
    - ✓ Return path measurements of ingress likely to indicate egress and lack of immunity
  - Samples:
    - ✓ Equipping maintenance staff with monitors to identify egress
- Efficient call centres
- Speedy response to fault situations

European Commission
DG Enterprise & Industry

EMC Directive revision
Brussels, 3/02/2005
Page 17

Measuring Equipment

- Equipment can be installed in an aircraft or ground vehicle
- Flyover to measure measurement or continuous monitoring purposes! Very cost intensive Not suitable GPS positional information

European Commission
DG Enterprise & Industry

EMC Directive revision
Brussels, 3/02/2005
Page 19

Table of Contents

- Introduction
- Network configuration
- Standardisation and technology issues for broadband cable networks
- Good engineering practice
- Network ownership
- Conclusions

European Commission
DG Enterprise & Industry

EMC Directive revision
Brussels, 3/02/2005
Page 21

ECL
EUROCABLELABS

Network Ownership

- Consequences
  - Poor in-home networks can lead to excessive egress (and ingress)
  - Effect can be cumulative
  - Public are not EMC aware
  - Network owners subject to regulatory process after transposition
  - Resolution?

European Commission
DG Enterprise & Industry

EMC Directive revision
Brussels, 3/02/2005
Page 23

ECL
EUROCABLELABS

Network Ownership

- Cable operator's network responsibility ends at some point where network ownership changes hands i.e. in customers' homes

- In-home networks are generally under the control of the property owner
  - Operator has little influence on the quality of the installation and material used

European Commission
DG Enterprise & Industry

EMC Directive revision
Brussels, 3/02/2005
Page 22

ECL
EUROCABLELABS

Table of Contents

- Introduction
- Network configuration
- Standardisation and technology issues for broadband cable networks
- Good engineering practice
- Network ownership
- Conclusions

European Commission
DG Enterprise & Industry

EMC Directive revision
Brussels, 3/02/2005
Page 24

ECL
EUROCABLELABS

Info Day EMC Directive Revision
Brussels 3 February 2005

Thank You

European Commission
DG Enterprise & Industry

EMC Directive revision
Brussels, 3/02/2005
Page 26

Conclusions

- Broadband cable networks
  - Internet, TV, and telephone services
  - Installation according to good engineering practice
  - Maintenance regime to facilitate low radiation and high immunity
  - Ownership situation may cause problems for trouble shooting at customer premises

- New EMC Directive supported by the cable industry

European Commission
DG Enterprise & Industry

EMC Directive revision
Brussels, 3/02/2005
Page 25

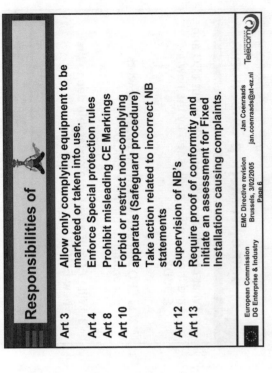

Responsibilities of

Art 3	Allow only complying equipment to be marketed or taken into use.
Art 4	Enforce Special protection rules
Art 8	Prohibit misleading CE Markings
Art 10	Forbid or restrict non-complying apparatus (Safeguard procedure)
	Take action related to incorrect NB statements
Art 12	Supervision of NB's
Art 13	Require proof of conformity and initiate an assessment for Fixed Installations causing complaints.

European Commission
DG Enterprise & Industry

EMC Directive revision
Brussels, 3/02/2005
Page 6

Jan Coenraads
jan.coenraads@at-ez.nl

Telecom

Market Surveillance Purpose

That: Regardless of product origin:

"Compliance is ensured across the EEA."

- All users entitled to equivalent level of protection,
- Eliminate unfair competition.

European Commission
DG Enterprise & Industry

EMC Directive revision
Brussels, 3/02/2005
Page 8

Jan Coenraads
jan.coenraads@at-ez.nl

Telecom

Where can you meet

Apparatus	1.	Market Surveillance. (incl. EU border control)
Equipment	2.	Interference complaints.
Equipment	3.	Trade fairs & demonstrations.
Equipment	4.	Special protection situations.
Apparatus	5.	NB surveillance.
Equipment	6.	Fixed Installations.

European Commission
DG Enterprise & Industry

EMC Directive revision
Brussels, 3/02/2005
Page 5

Jan Coenraads
jan.coenraads@at-ez.nl

Telecom

Task 1

Market Surveillance

European Commission
DG Enterprise & Industry

EMC Directive revision
Brussels, 3/02/2005
Page 7

Jan Coenraads
jan.coenraads@at-ez.nl

Telecom

330

General concept of Market Surveillance

Essential tool for EMCD enforcement

- Requires from LEO to:
  - Take appropriate measures to ensure Market Surveillance obligations;
  - check that products meet the EMCD;
  - bring non-compliant products into compliance, and apply sanctions when necessary.

European Commission
DG Enterprise & Industry | EMC Directive revision
Brussels, 3/02/2005
Page 9 | Jan Coenraads
jan.coenraads@at-ez.nl | Telecom

NEW Market Surveillance Tasks for the EMCD (1)

Monitoring products placed on the market and verification of:

- o NEW: Identification of the <u>apparatus</u>; (on it?)
- o NEW: Name/address manufacturer/representative/importing person
- o NEW: Validity of any Notified Body Statement;

European Commission
DG Enterprise & Industry | EMC Directive revision
Brussels, 3/02/2005
Page 10 | Jan Coenraads
jan.coenraads@at-ez.nl | Telecom

NEW Market Surveillance Tasks for the EMCD (2)

Verification of availability & content of the Technical Doc & other information, such as related to:

FOR FIXED INSTALLATIONS extra rules:
o NEW identifying the FI and its EMC characteristics and indicate the precautions to be taken for the incorporation of the apparatus into the FI;
o NEW identification of person(s) responsible for the compliance of the FI.

European Commission
DG Enterprise & Industry | EMC Directive revision
Brussels, 3/02/2005
Page 11 | Jan Coenraads
jan.coenraads@at-ez.nl | Telecom

Note that:

Market surveillance does not take place during design and production, but:

 may check on the <u>production premises</u> (based on a non-compliance discovered) to:

- verify whether a constant error can be established and/or
- prevent the further placing on the market of non-compliant products.

European Commission
DG Enterprise & Industry | EMC Directive revision
Brussels, 3/02/2005
Page 12 | Jan Coenraads
jan.coenraads@at-ez.nl | Telecom

Internet-Market Surveillance – Future work structure

Internet-market surveillance, also called "desktop market surveillance" = electronic market surveillance of market parties that trade or show products via Internet.

It is expected that desktop market surveillance:

- makes LEO more efficient;
- provides LEO with a faster insight into new product developments, and;
- allows LEO to respond more quickly to equipment developments.

European Commission
DG Enterprise & Industry

EMC Directive revision
Brussels, 3/02/2005
Page 14

Jan Coenraads
jan.coenraads@at-ez.nl

Telecom

Follow up situations

Safeguard Clause

Remember that LEO will:

- Withdrawn from the market;
- Prohibit placing on the market or putting into service;
- Restrict the free movement:

Of <u>CE</u> marked apparatus that does not comply

European Commission
DG Enterprise & Industry

EMC Directive revision
Brussels, 3/02/2005
Page 16

Jan Coenraads
jan.coenraads@at-ez.nl

Telecom

Note also that:

No products shall be excluded from market surveillance operations!

Including those subject to:

– any (voluntary) certification scheme or other voluntary initiatives,

– an assessment involving a Notified Body.

Question: Is there any added value in these voluntary schemes?

European Commission
DG Enterprise & Industry

EMC Directive revision
Brussels, 3/02/2005
Page 13

Jan Coenraads
jan.coenraads@at-ez.nl

Telecom

Some Workshop Questions

1. Has LEO sofar performed market surveillance adequately?

2. Is the new EMCD improving LEO's capabilities?

3. Are there unclear situations that need an explanation text in the new Guide?

4. Are there too many differences between actions of LEO's in different MS?

European Commission
DG Enterprise & Industry

EMC Directive revision
Brussels, 3/02/2005
Page 15

Jan Coenraads
jan.coenraads@at-ez.nl

Telecom

Note that:

The safeguard procedure does not apply in the following cases:

- *Apparatus without CE marking*
- *CE marking applied without necessary assessment. (illegal CE marking)*
- *Fixed installations.*

European Commission
DG Enterprise & Industry

EMC Directive revision
Brussels, 3/02/2005
Page 18

Jan Coenraads
jan.coenraads@at-ez.nl

Telecom

Task 2

Solving Interference complaints

European Commission
DG Enterprise & Industry

EMC Directive revision
Brussels, 3/02/2005
Page 20

Jan Coenraads
jan.coenraads@at-ez.nl

Telecom

Safeguard Clause Art 10.

Only for "not Note: Safeguard procedure apparatus. is not for FI's!

It can relate to particular 3 situations:
1. incorrect application of Harmonised Standards; or
2. failure in the HS; or
3. non compliance with essential requirements (when not complying with HS)

European Commission
DG Enterprise & Industry

EMC Directive revision
Brussels, 3/02/2005
Page 17

Jan Coenraads
jan.coenraads@at-ez.nl

Telecom

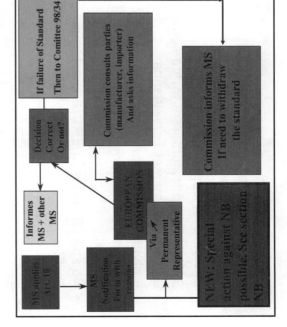

Key-issues for complaint solving actions

- Determine priorities;
- Allocating enforcement recourses;
- Develop/use risk calculation system
- Come to a conclusion/solution;
- Coordinate and synchronise enforcement decisions at an EU level.

European Commission
DG Enterprise & Industry

EMC Directive revision
Brussels, 3/02/2005
Page 22

Jan Coenraads
jan.coenraads@at-ez.nl

Telecom

Trade fairs, Exhibitions & Demonstrations

"Exception to principle that market surveillance only takes place after the manufacturer has taken formal responsibility for the products."

- Will monitor that the obligations are respected;
- Can take appropriate measures when this obligation is not followed.
- This may include:
  - stopping any demonstration;
  - having the product being removed from the event.
  - issuing warnings.

European Commission
DG Enterprise & Industry

EMC Directive revision
Brussels, 3/02/2005
Page 24

Jan Coenraads
jan.coenraads@at-ez.nl

Telecom

Interference complaints

- Different for apparatus and FI's.
- Some authorities different for complaint solving and market surveillance.
- Individual direct action, not necessarily a direct link to market surveillance, unless...
- No specific rules in EMCD, apart from for FI's

European Commission
DG Enterprise & Industry

EMC Directive revision
Brussels, 3/02/2005
Page 21

Jan Coenraads
jan.coenraads@at-ez.nl

Telecom

Task 3

Trade fairs, exhibitions, Demonstrations

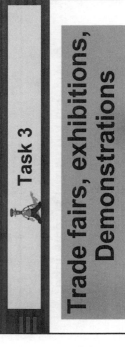

European Commission
DG Enterprise & Industry

EMC Directive revision
Brussels, 3/02/2005
Page 23

Jan Coenraads
jan.coenraads@at-ez.nl

Telecom

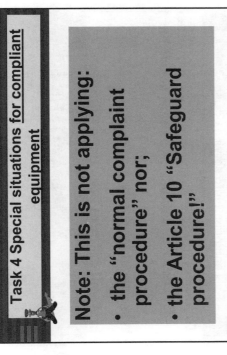

Task 4 Special situations for compliant equipment

Note: This is not applying:

- the "normal complaint procedure" nor;
- the Article 10 "Safeguard procedure!"

European Commission
DG Enterprise & Industry

EMC Directive revision
Brussels, 3/02/2005
Page 26

Jan Coenraads
jan.coenraads@at-ez.nl

Telecom

Probably due to:

Could:

- convince parties to voluntary apply precautionary measures, and
- provide adequate practical suggestions.

without the need to formally enter the Article 4 procedures!

European Commission
DG Enterprise & Industry

EMC Directive revision
Brussels, 3/02/2005
Page 28

Jan Coenraads
jan.coenraads@at-ez.nl

Telecom

Obligations for Trade fairs, exhibitions, etc. NEW

Equipment not yet complying with the Directive may be displayed & demonstrated (= operated) provided that:

- Indication: "Equipment may <u>not</u> be placed on the market or put into service, unless......."
- Adequate measures to avoid interference have been taken.

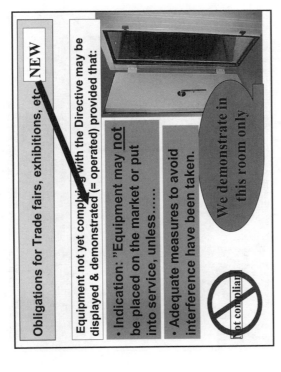

We demonstrate in this room only

Not compliant

European Commission
DG Enterprise & Industry

EMC Directive revision
Brussels, 3/02/2005
Page 27

Jan Coenraads
jan.coenraads@at-ez.nl

Art 4.2 Special situations

- Provides a tool for MS to handle special <u>exceptional situations</u>.
- Enables MS to set-up customised regulations.

Indication of exceptional character:

"Art. 6 current EMCD = similar *but <u>has never been used by any MS</u>.*"

European Commission
DG Enterprise & Industry

EMC Directive revision
Brussels, 3/02/2005
Page 27

Jan Coenraads
jan.coenraads@at-ez.nl

Telecom

An example

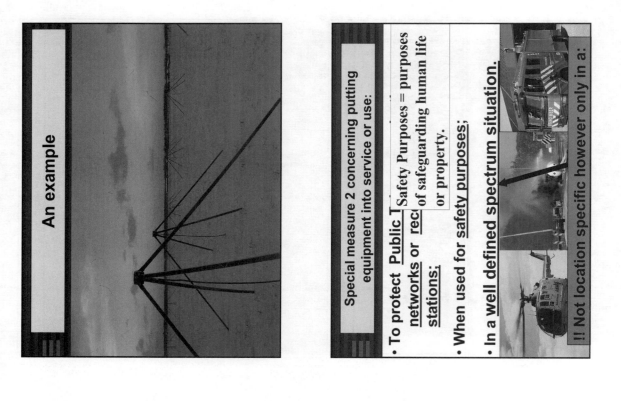

Special measure 2 concerning putting equipment into service or use:

- To protect Public Safety Purposes = purposes networks or reco of safeguarding human life stations; or property.

- When used for safety purposes;

- In a well defined spectrum situation.

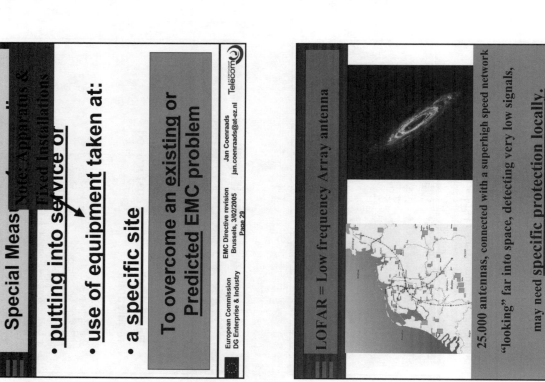

!! Not location specific however only in a:

Special Meas   Notes: Apparatus &
                Fixed Installations

- putting into service or

- use of equipment taken at:

- a specific site

To overcome an existing or
Predicted EMC problem

European Commission   EMC Directive revision   Jan Coenrrads
DG Enterprise & Industry   Brussels, 3/02/2005   jan.coenrraads@at-ez.nl
                             Page 29

LOFAR = Low frequency Array antenna

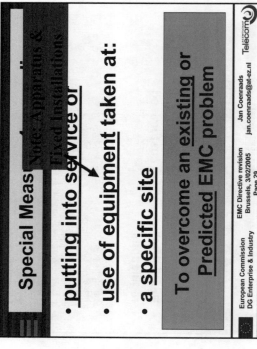

25.000 antennas, connected with a superhigh speed network

"looking" far into space, detecting very low signals,

may need specific protection locally.

Task 5

NB Surveillance

European Commission
DG Enterprise & Industry

EMC Directive revision
Brussels, 3/02/2005
Page 34

Jan Coenraads
jan.coenraads@at-ez.nl

NEW - Actions against the author of an incorrect NB Statement (1)

EMC Analyses or Harmonised Standard is used.

Non-compliant apparatus

Positive NB Statement on relevant essential requirement

- take appropriate action against author;
- inform the Commission & MS;
- free to choose sanctions against the author, (EMCD states no penalty).

European Commission
DG Enterprise & Industry

EMC Directive revision
Brussels, 3/02/2005
Page 36

Jan Coenraads
jan.coenraads@at-ez.nl

Some Workshop Questions

1. Are the rules for special situations adequate?

2. Do you foresee any real practical use?

3. Or is it all very much theory?

European Commission
DG Enterprise & Industry

EMC Directive revision
Brussels, 3/02/2005
Page 33

Jan Coenraads
jan.coenraads@at-ez.nl

NB Surveillance

Use of an NB is totally voluntary, but an NB:

- acts in areas of public interest = answerable to LEO
- is under surveillance by LEO at regular intervals,

   responsible to ensure that NB maintain competence and performs its work correctly.

- will choose means and methods (national deviation).
- will act when in doubt about the competence of the NB, based on:
  – market surveillance activities on (non-compliant) products,
  – complaints received regarding the operation of the NB,
  – any other indication that the NB no longer meets the criteria of the EMCD.

European Commission
DG Enterprise & Industry

EMC Directive revision
Brussels, 3/02/2005
Page 35

Jan Coenraads
jan.coenraads@at-ez.nl

Some Workshop questions

1. If the NB issues an incorrect statement should the penalty be withdrawal of NB status?

2. Is the NB liable in respect of the manufacturer suffering damage as a result of an error in the statement?

3. Are there not to many NB's and should they be limited to those who are actually doing real NB work?

4. Should the local LEO be informed about the amount of projects that the NB carries out?

European Commission
DG Enterprise & Industry

EMC Directive revision
Brussels, 3/02/2005
Page 38

Jan Coenraads
jan.coenraads@at-ez.nl

Telecom

What is new for FI's?

FI's were covered by the 1997 EMC Guide, nothing new now in EMCD except:

1. Resonsible person to be indicated;
2. Rules for incorporated apparatus;
3. Specific rules to apply when indication of non-compliance = complaints.

For LEO it is in practice not really new but :

- Similar to dealing with apparatus
- now only legally formulated stricter!

European Commission
DG Enterprise & Industry

EMC Directive revision
Brussels, 3/02/2005
Page 40

Jan Coenraads
jan.coenraads@at-ez.nl

Telecom

Actions against the NB (2)

Any NB Status withdrawal does not affect any (other) statements issued by that NB:

Unless it is clear that those statements are also incorrect and should be withdrawn.

European Commission
DG Enterprise & Industry

EMC Directive revision
Brussels, 3/02/2005
Page 37

Jan Coenraads
jan.coenraads@at-ez.nl

Telecom

Task 6

Fixed Installations

European Commission
DG Enterprise & Industry

EMC Directive revision
Brussels, 3/02/2005
Page 39

Jan Coenraads
jan.coenraads@at-ez.nl

Telecom

End of presentation

Thank you for your attention

Any Questions?

European Commission
DG Enterprise & Industry

EMC Directive revision
Brussels, 3/02/2005
Page 42

Jan Coenraads
jan.coenraads@at-ez.nl

Telecom

Some Workshop questions

1. In what manner should the evidence of compliance be presented to LEO?

2. When an assessment is initiated should LEO or the FI responsible person bear the costs involved?

3. Can LEO apply all measures including, if necessary, stopping the operation of the FI?

European Commission
DG Enterprise & Industry

EMC Directive revision
Brussels, 3/02/2005
Page 41

Jan Coenraads
jan.coenraads@at-ez.nl

Telecom

TUTORIAL: BASIC EMC MEASUREMENTS (FR-AM-WS-13)
Donald Heirman
Don Heirman Consultants

This workshop will be an introduction to basic EMC measurements with primary focus on emission testing. While intended for those new to these disciplines, the latest activity in national and international standards related to EMC measurements will be presented. A special focus will be on measurements and associated issues above 1 GHz as well as measurement uncertainty. An open discussion will follow the presentations.

Presentations:

(1) Emission Measurements for Tabletop Equipment
   Robert A. Oglesbee

(2) Emission Measurements for Floor-Standing Equipment
   H. R. (Bob) Hofmann

(3) IEC Transient-Immunity Testing Overview
   Thomas E. Braxton

(4) Immunity to Continuous RF Disturbances
   John Maas

(5) Basic Measurement Sites, Methods, and Associated Errors
   Don Heirman

(6) Selecting a Quality EMC Lab
   Daniel D. Hoolihan

(7) Uncertainty Considerations in Stating Pass/Fail
   Don Heirman

NOTES

Emission Measurements
for
Tabletop Equipment

Robert A. Oglesbee
Lexmark International, Inc.
Lexington, KY
(859) 232-7292
roglesbe@lexmark.com

Session FR-AM-WS-13

Topics

- Basic Tabletop EUT Configuration
- Interface Cabling
- Radiated Emissions Measurements
- Conducted Emissions Measurements
- Discussion will Pertain to Tabletop Equipment and ANSI C63.4-2003

Basic EUT Configuration

- Minimum Tabletop EUT Configuration for a PC or PC Peripheral or Accessory (Sec. 11.2)
  - Personal Computer
  - Keyboard
  - VDU (Monitor)
  - If host PC is the EUT, cables attached to each functional I/O port
  - If host PC is not EUT, parallel & serial ports shall be connected. If not available, substitute a different I/O e.g. IEEE 1394 or USB
  - Dedicated special-purpose ports of the EUT or minimum system (e.g. mouse) must be populated

---

Basic EUT Configuration

- For multiple ports of same type on EUT, add cables until less than 2dB variation in emissions
- EUT Placement (Sec. 11.2.1 - 11.2.3)
  - Non-conducting table, 80 cm height, 1.5 m x 1 m preferred but can be larger or smaller if required
  - See Figure 13 for arrangement of tabletop equipment
  - For tabletop systems, EUT centered laterally (left to right), flush with rear of table. If Host PC is used, it should be centered laterally
  - Standalone EUT placed in center of tabletop
  - Monitor on top of host, centered and flush with front of host
  - If not possible to place on top of host, locate monitor 10 cm to left or right of host

Basic EUT Configuration

- Placement of Power Accessories (Sec. 6.2.1.2)
  - If accessory is not the EUT but connects to EUT
    - Place on tabletop if line cord < 80 cm
    - If line cord ≥ 80 cm, place on floor under EUT
    - If accessory plugs directly into wall outlet, plug into power source directly on top of ground plane under EUT
  - If accessory is the EUT
    - Place on table if line cord ≥ 80 cm
    - If line cord < 80 cm, place at a height such that power cord is fully extended vertically
    - If accessory plugs directly into wall outlet, place on table top with extension cord providing power

Basic EUT Configuration

- EUT Placement (cont)
  - Keyboard centered in front of monitor, flush with front of table
  - Peripherals on each side of host with 10 cm separation
  - If only one peripheral used, locate to left of EUT
  - Mouse or joystick located 10 cm to right of keyboard, flush with back of keyboard
  - Keyboard & mouse cabling routed along side of CPU to maximize coupling
  - Do not stack devices unless inherent with design
- Various Modes of Operation of EUT Must be Examined
  - Video or print modes, processor speeds, etc.

Radiated Emissions Measurements

- Follow Figure 11a of C63.4 for Test Arrangement
- Power Cords Draped to Floor and Routed to Outlet
- Measurement Distance is From Center of Antenna to Closest Periphery of the EUT (Front-to-Back Center for LPDA)
  - 3 meter distance for limits in FCC Part 15 Rules (Class B)
  - 10 meter distance for limits in CISPR 22
- Emissions Must be Maximized
  - EUT rotated 0 to 360 degrees
  - Antenna height scanned from 1 to 4 meters
  - Both horizontal and vertical polarization
- Record 6 Highest Emissions Relative to Limit
- Include Diagrams or Photos of Test Setup

Interface Cabling

- Excess Length Draped Over Back Edge of Table
- No Cables Closer Than 40 cm to Groundplane
  - Bundle excess in serpentine fashion using 30-40 cm bundles
  - Overall length of bundled cable shall not exceed 1 m
- Do Not Place Cables Under or on Top of System Components Unless Inherent by Design
- Cables Must be Manipulated During Exploratory Testing to Determine Maximum Emission Configuration
  - Manipulated only within range of likely arrangement
  - Record cable positions for final testing
  - Maximize only the highest emission in final testing

342

Conducted Emissions Measurements

- Follow Figure 10a of C63.4 for Test Arrangement
- LISN Located at Least 80 cm from EUT
  - 1 LISN for EUT, 1 or more for support equipment
  - Outlet strip can be used for non-EUT devices; only allowed for EUT if provided by manufacturer
  - Any adapters or extension cords to EUT must be included in LISN calibration
  - LISN bonded to floor
  - Unused measurement ports terminated in 50Ω
  - Rear of Table Located 40 cm From Vertical Conducting Plane
    - Plane at least 2 m x 2 m in size
    - Plane not required but measurements with plane take precedence

---

Radiated Emissions Measurements

- Frequency Range of Measurement
  - For unintentional radiator, upper limit based upon maximum operating frequency generated or used in device (See FCC Part 15.33):

Highest Operating Frequency (MHz)	Upper Measurement Frequency (MHz)
< 1,705	30
1,705 - 108	1,000
108 - 500	2,000
500 - 1,000	5,000
> 1,000	5th harmonic of highest frequency or 40 GHz, whichever is lower

---

Conducted Emissions Measurements

- Excess Length of EUT Power Cord is Bundled
- Record 6 Highest Emissions Relative to Limit
- Include Diagrams or Photos of Test Setup
- Frequency Range of Measurement
  - See FCC Part 15.37(j)
  - As of July 11, 2005, all products manufactured or imported must be measured over 150 kHz - 30 MHz range

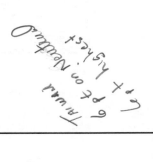

343

Emission Measurements for Floor-standing Equipment

by

H. R. (Bob) Hofmann

Hofmann EMC Engineering

hrhofmann@att.net

FR-AM-WS13

Hofmann EMC Engineering 2005

HRH-1

Basic Emission Measurements for Floor-standing Equipment

- Must Use FCC Part 15.107/CISPR-22 Clause 5 Conducted Emission Limits
- New FCC Rules Require Measuring 150 kHz to 30 MH Conducted
- Can Use Either FCC Part 15.109 or CISPR-22 Clause 6 Radiated Emission Limits
- Must Test Up To Highest Frequency Following The FCC Rules
- Must Use C63.4 Measurement Procedures
- Can Use CISPR Measurement Distances With Linear Extrapolation To FCC Measurement Distances
- New Requirements Took Effect July 10, 2004 For All New Designs

HRH-2

Basic Emission Measurements for Floor-standing Equipment

- Small Floor-Standing Systems Use ANSI C63.4 - 2003 Directly - Use The Text & Figures (Clauses 6, 7, & 8 & Figs 10b, 11b, 12a, 12b & 14)
- Large Computer, Communications Or Other Large Systems That May Be Larger Than Available Turntables Require Special Consideration
- Frame / Cabinet Arrangement Must Be Representative Of Actual Installations
- At Least One Of Every Type Of Circuit Must Be Included In the Equipment Configuration -Minimum Representative System (MRS)
- A Full PC Must Be Included If Normally Used As Part Of The EUT
- Cabling Must Be Representative Of Actual Installations

HRH-3

Basic Emission Measurements for Floor-standing Equipment

- System Must Be Capable Of Actually Running Its Normal Processes
- Special Software May Be Needed. If So, Archive The Software
- Accessories Should Have Normal Spacing, 10 cm Recommended If Variable Arrangements Are Possible. Justify Spacing In The Test Report
- Cables Are Not Manipulated Where Wiring/Cabling Layouts Are Normally Fixed
- Cables Should Be Manipulated Over Range Of Possible Variations If Every Installation Is Different
- Combinations Of Table-Top And Floor-Mounted Equipment May Be Tested Together
- Do **NOT** Use Atypical Configurations Or Arrangements

HRH-4

[handwritten notes: Test photos / Justify Testing / Envelope Terminology / Exposures]

Basic Emission Measurements for Floor-standing Equipment

- Want To Follow ANSI C63.4 As Closely As Possible To Minimize Any Doubts About Results

- Must Have A Defendable Position On Any Deviations From ANSI C63.4

- If System Overhangs Turntable Slightly, Mount System On Flooring That Overhangs The Turntable, Must Provide An Electrically Equivalent Ground Plane In Some Manner, Otherwise Must Use Fixed Position Installation And Move Antenna Around Periphery

- If Multiple Cabinet Types Are Used, One Of Every Cabinet Type Must Be Measured

- Document The Actual Procedures Used And Any Deviations in Minute Detail To Allow Consistent Retesting If Necessary, Do **Not** Just Say "Followed ANSI C63.4"

HRH-6

Basic Emission Measurements for Floor-standing Equipment

- Current Probes Are Very Useful For Finding "Hot" Cables

- Photograph The Test Arrangement With Rulers Visible Where Cabinet Spacing Is Critical, Show Cabling Details, "Polaroids" Are Usually Not Clear Enough

- Simulators Can Be Used To Exercise The System, But Beware Of Noise from Simulators, Ferrite Beads Are Very Useful With Simulators

- Cables Between Cabinets Are To Be Run Bundled In Center If Longer Than Direct Route Distance, Use Serpentine If Bundling Not Possible

- Overhead Cables Should Be Installed As Normally Installed

- C63.4-200? Allows Mounting Floor-Standing Equipment Up To 34 Cm Above The Reference Groundplane To Simulate A Raised Floor Site

HRH-8

Basic Emission Measurements for Floor-standing Equipment

- On-Site vs OATS - Need To Evaluate Total Weight Capability Of Turntable vs System Weight

- On-Site vs OATS - Power And LISN Availability

- On-Site vs OATS - Effects of Ambient Noise On Both Radiated And Conducted Measurements

- On-Site vs OATS - Need Room To Place Antenna For Radiated Emission Measurements, Must Move Antenna Around Periphery At No Greater Than 22.5 Degree Spacing. This May Be Outside Of The Building/Installation Site. (Should Run A Radial At Point Of Max Signal)

- On-Site Permitted Only If First Three Installations Are Similar. All Three Sites Must Be Measured. If The First Three Typical Sites Meet FCC Requirements, All Similar Sites May Be Considered Acceptable. However This Procedure Is **NOT** Acceptable Outside Of The US

HRH-5

Basic Emission Measurements for Floor-standing Equipment

- When Types Of Circuit Packs / Plug-Ins Exceeds Available Socket Spaces, Must Rotate Circuit Packs / Plug-Ins While Performing Complete Testing For Each Group Of Plug-Ins, Or Expand Plug-In Slots To Accommodate Enough Packs/Plug-Ins

- Cables Must Be Attached To All Different Types Of Ports, Must Be Correctly (RF) Terminated, And Must Carry Actual Signals

- Effects Of Multiple Circuit Packs / Plug-Ins And Cables Must Be Investigated By Adding More Packs / Plug-Ins And Cables Until Emissions Do Not Go Up By More Than 2dB, Must Still Meet Limits At That Point

HRH-7

Basic Emission Measurements for Floor-standing Equipment

- Cabinets Normally Mounted In Contact With A Grounded Metal Floor/Grid Should be Placed Directly On the Reference Ground Plane. Where The EUT Is Normally Installed Not In Contact With A Metal Floor/Grid, Insulating Material Up to 12 mm Shall Be Placed Under The EUT. Should Simulate Normal Installation If Possible

- C63.4-2003 Figures Are Now In Close Agreement With CISPR-22 Figs

- Where There Are Separate AC Mains Power Cords, Measure One Cord At A Time With Remaining Power Cords Connected To A Separate LISN. If A Common Manufacturer-Supplied AC Power Cord Is Used To Feed A Power Strip, Only The Common Cord Needs To Be Measured

- A Voltage Probe May Be Used If LISN Is Impractical (Excessive Current Demands Or Hard-Wired Power Mains Connections)

HRH-9

H. Robert (Bob) Hofmann

Telephone – USA-630-355-2440,   Cell - USA -630-664-9448,   Fax – USA-630-355-2440,   E-mail - hrhofmann@att.net

Bob Hofmann retired from Bell Laboratories/Lucent Technologies after 44 years of service. At Bell Labs, he was a Distinguished Member of Technical Staff based in Naperville, Illinois. Bob has a BSEE degree from the University of Florida and an MSEE degree from New York University. He joined Bell Laboratories in 1957 and has been concerned with electromagnetic compatibility issues since 1968. He served as chairman of the Lucent Corporate EMC committee for 19 years prior to his retirement. In that role, he acted to coordinate EMC efforts across the many Lucent locations throughout the world.

He is currently working as an EMC consultant to the University of Wisconsin - Madison on electromagnetic compatibility issues for the South Pole Ice Cube Neutrino Detector project.

Bob is a past President of the IEEE EMC Society and is currently serving as treasurer of the 2005 IEEE EMC Symposium committee. He is a Life Member of the IEEE EMC Society and a Senior Member of the IEEE. He received the Laurence G. Cumming award from the IEEE EMC Society in 1994 and has received numerous other awards.

Bob represented Lucent and served as chairman of the Information Technologies Industries Council (formerly CBEMA-Computer and Business Equipment Manufacturers Association) TC-5 EMC Committee from 1990 to 1999. He also represented Lucent and served as vice-chairman of the ECMA (formerly European Computer Manufacturers Association) TC-20 EMC Committee. He is a NARTE registered engineer.

Bob represented Lucent on the ANSI C63 EMC Committee and continues to serve as a member of several ANSI C63 subcommittees and working groups. He led the 1987 and 1999 revisions of ANSI/IEEE C63.12 on Electromagnetic Compatibility Limits, and was an active member of the editing committee for the 1991, 1992, 2001, and 2003 revisions of C63.4 on Methods of Measurement of Emissions. He has authored and presented a number of papers on EMC standards and testing in the United States, Europe, and Japan, and has chaired several sessions on International EMC standards and EMC testing at various EMC symposia. His work on EMC standards has concentrated on developing standards that are easy to implement, and that have wording that is unambiguous to the reader. Bob has taught a number of courses on EMC measurements and is one of the reviewers of papers submitted for presentation at the IEEE EMC Symposia. He is also a reviewer of questions used in NARTE engineer and technician certification.

For a change from EMC, Bob likes to climb 14,000 foot mountains in Colorado, ski the sides of the same mountains in winter, bike the flat land of Illinois, and run 10 kilometer races.

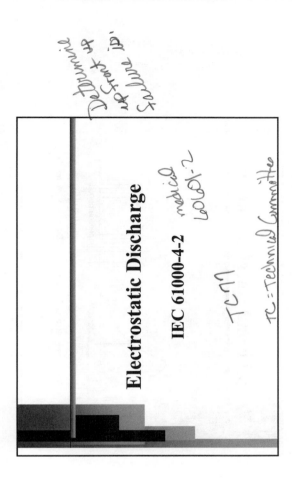

Electrostatic Discharge

IEC 61000-4-2

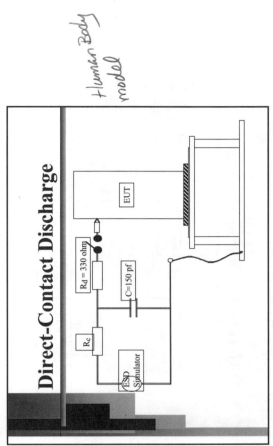

Direct-Contact Discharge

Rd = 330 ohm

C=150 pf

Rc

ESD
Simulator

EUT

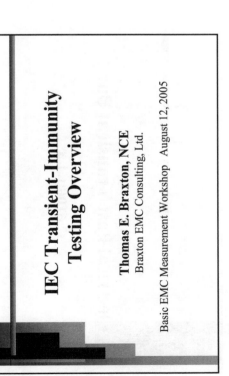

IEC Transient-Immunity
Testing Overview

Thomas E. Braxton, NCE
Braxton EMC Consulting, Ltd.

Basic EMC Measurement Workshop   August 12, 2005

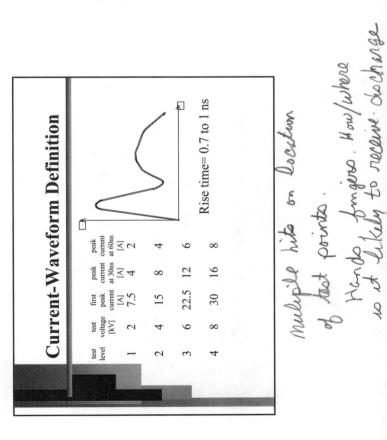

Current-Waveform Definition

test level	test voltage [kV]	first peak current [A]	peak current at 30ns [A]	peak current at 60ns [A]
1	2	7.5	4	2
2	4	15	8	4
3	6	22.5	12	6
4	8	30	16	8

Rise time= 0.7 to 1 ns

Different Discharge Methods

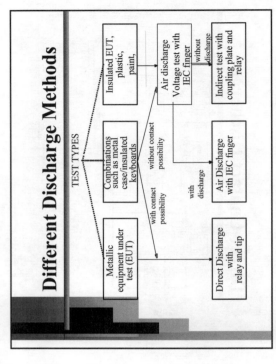

TEST TYPES

- Metallic equipment under test (EUT)
- Combinations such as metal case/insulated keyboards
- Insulated EUT, plastic, paint,

with contact possibility

without contact possibility

with discharge

without discharge

Air discharge Voltage test with IEC finger

Direct Discharge with relay and tip

Air Discharge with IEC finger

Indirect test with coupling plate and relay

Spike and Burst Definition

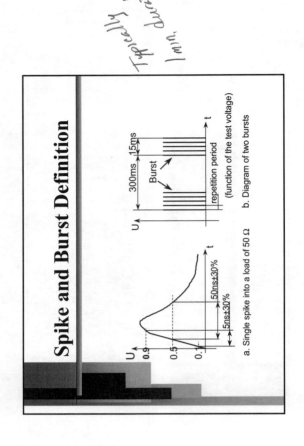

a. Single spike into a load of 50 Ω

5ns±30%
50ns±30%

b. Diagram of two bursts

Burst

300ms   15ms

repetition period
(function of the test voltage)

Indirect Contact Discharge

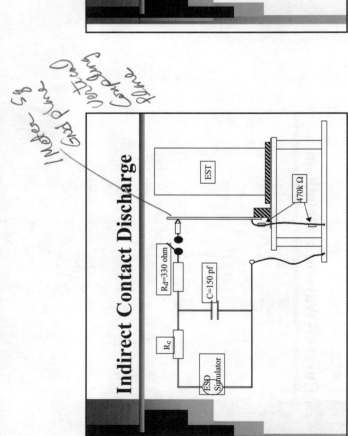

ESD Simulator

Rc

Rd=330 ohm

C=150 pf

EST

470k Ω

Typically 1min. duration

Meter 1 End plane (Coupling plate)

Electrical Fast Transient Burst

IEC 61000-4-4

348

Lightning & Switching Surges

IEC 61000-4-5

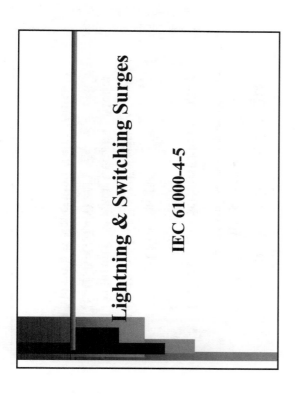

Single Phase Mains and DC Differential Mode

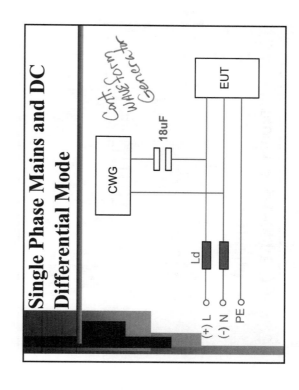

Coupling and Test Setup

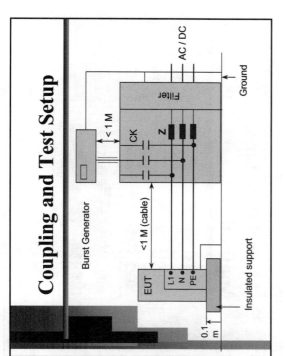

Surge Tests For:

- **Single-Phase Mains and DC Power**
- **Three-Phase Mains**
- **Telecommunications**
- **Data Lines**

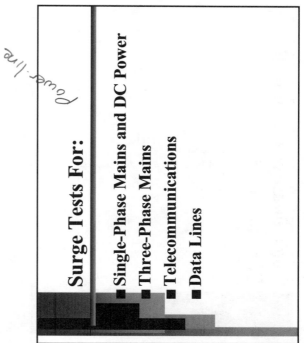

IEC 1000-4-5 Telecom Application

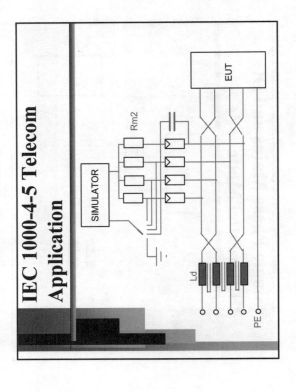

Single Phase Mains and DC Common Mode

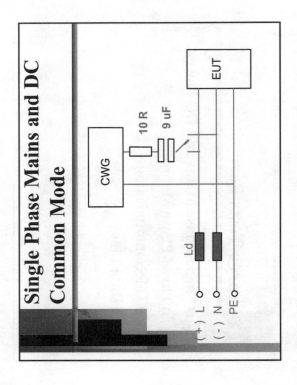

Typical Number of Surges on AC Lines

- **Performed At Selected Phase Angles (0°, 90°, 180°, 270°)**
- **At Least Five Surges**
- **Performed At Each Polarity**
- **Performed At Each Coupling Mode: (L-G, N-G, L-N)**
- **Maximum Repetition Rate: 1/minute**

Shielded Data Line Application

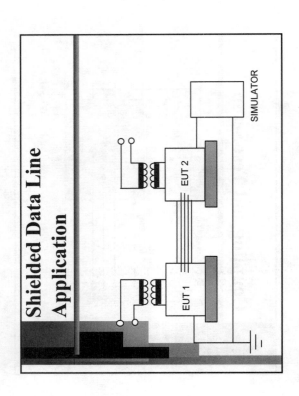

Thomas E. Braxton, NCE – Biographical Information

Tom Braxton has worked in the EMC industry for over 25 years. He was a Member of the Technical Staff at Lucent Technologies (previously AT&T Bell Laboratories) for over 20 years, and is currently President of Braxton EMC Consulting, Ltd., an independent EMC consulting company. He is a member of the IEEE EMC Society, and is General Chair of the 2005 International EMC Symposium in Chicago. Tom has authored a wide range of EMC-related papers published at international symposia and has taught numerous seminars and workshops. He is a NARTE-certified EMC Engineer and a NARTE-Certified Electrostatic Discharge (ESD) Engineer. A graduate of Purdue University (AAS-EET, BS-EET) and of the Illinois Institute of Technology (MSEE), Tom is also a licensed radio amateur (WB9VRW).

Slide 1

Immunity to
Continuous RF Disturbances

John Maas
IBM Corporation
Rochester, Minnesota USA

August 12, 2005

1

Slide 2

Continuous RF Disturbances

Two tests intended to gauge a product's immunity to radiated electromagnetic fields and the conducted disturbances induced by them

- Sources are intended RF transmitters
  - Radio & TV transmission
  - Digital radio telephones
  - Radar installations
  - Wireless WANs, LANs
  - Broadband communications over power lines
  - RFID systems

2

Slide 3

Two Tests

Conducted disturbances induced by RF fields
- IEC 61000-4-6
- 150 kHz to 80 MHz
- At lower frequencies, the primary coupling is through external interconnection cables
- Uniform fields harder to achieve in practical labs

Radiated RF fields
- IEC 61000-4-3
- 80 MHz to 2 GHz (CISPR 24: 80 – 1000 MHz)
- At higher frequencies, the primary coupling is direct radiation into the device
- Generating uniform fields is more reasonable

3

Slide 4

Standards

IEC 61000-4-3 & 61000-4-6 are the basic standards for these tests
- Basic test methodologies, set ups & procedures
- Test equipment
- Do not include limits or specific performance criteria
- Only become required when picked up in a product standard or by a country regulation

Product & national standards reference basic standards and add specific details for test limits, performance criteria, frequency ranges, etc
- Latest level of IEC basic standard not automatically picked up by product/national standards

4

352

Immunity to Conducted Disturbances

IEC 61000-4-6

Test Equipment
- Test Generator
  - Coupling Devices
  - Decoupling Devices

Test Set Up
- Selecting Injection Method
  - CDN Injection
  - Clamp Injection
  - Direct Injection

Test Procedure
- Setting test generator
- Applying disturbance to EUT

Analyzing Test Results

5

Test Equipment

Test Equipment
- Test Generator provides modulated signal and amplification needed to drive coupling devices to test levels/limits
  - 150 kHz – 80 MHz
  - 80% AM with 1 kHz sine wave
- Coupling Devices
  - CDNs, EM clamp, current clamp, direct injection
- Decoupling Devices
  - 150 ohm impedance to provide isolation
  - CDNs & other devices may be used
  - Used on cable under test and untested cables attached to EUT or AE

6

Test Set Up

Procedure for selecting injection method
- Use CDNs if suitable
- Use direct injection on shielded cables
- Use clamp injection on unshielded cables if CDN not suitable
  - Procedure varies depending on whether common mode impedance specification is met

Test intended to be applied with minimum number of cables attached
- Can pose challenges for EUTs with many cables attached
- Updated edition of 61000-4-6 addresses this

7

Test Set Up

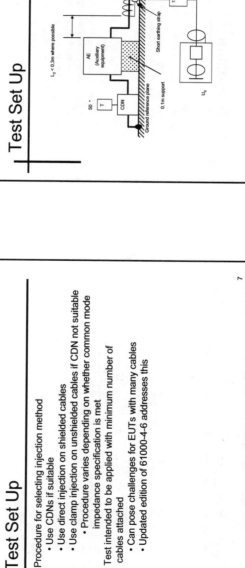

8

Test Procedure

Set generator output for each coupling device

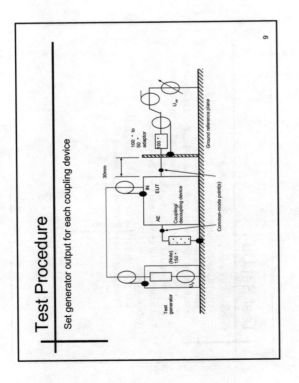

Test Procedure

Apply disturbance to each port individually
- All other coupling devices terminated in 50 ohms

All EUT operating modes should be evaluated
- All at once, sequentially, worst case only????

Frequency step size 1% of preceding frequency
- Dwell time long enough for EUT to be exercised and respond

Analyze results
- Basic standard provides basic criteria
  - Normal operation
  - Self-recoverable temporary degradation
  - Temporary degradation requiring operating intervention
  - Unrecoverable loss of function, damage
- Product standards give more specific, detailed performance
  - criteria for specific product types
  - Still room for interpretation

10

Immunity to Radiated Disturbances

IEC 61000-4-3

Test Equipment
- Test Generator
- Test facility
- Antennas

Test Set Up
- High-level basic details
- Floor-standing EUT
- Table-top EUT

Test Procedure
- Setting test generator
- Applying disturbance to EUT

Analyzing Test Results

11

Test Equipment

Test Equipment
- Test generator provides modulated signal and amplification needed to drive transmitting antenna to test level
- Test facility
  - Specialized lab is needed to contain radiated RF energy and provide suitable test area
  - Absorber-lined, semi-anechoic chamber
  - Primary specification is uniform field area (UFA)
    - -0/+6 dB variation over UFA plane
    - Up to 25% of points allowed to be out of tolerance
    - Preferred size is 1.5 X 1.5 m
    - Located 0.8 m above floor
  - Calibration of uniformity required
  - Field sensor critical element in UFA calibration
    - No single method defined for calibrating sensor
    - Potential source of lab-to-lab variation
  - Linearly polarized antennas with sufficient beamwidth to illuminate UFA or EUT

Verification

12

Test Facility

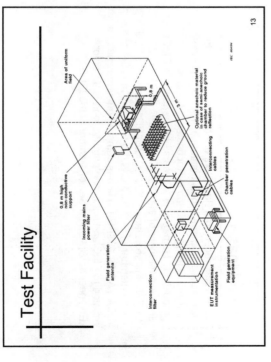

Area of uniform field

0.8 m

0.8 m high non-conductive support

Incoming mains power filter

Field generation antenna

Optional anechoic material in case of semi-anechoic chamber to reduce ground reflection

Interconnecting cables

Chamber penetration cables

Interconnection filter

EUT measurement instrumentation

Field generation equipment

IEC ...

13

Test Set Up for Floor-Standing EUT

Shielded connection through chamber wall

Power cable filter

Shielded power cable

Shielded signal cable

Cable length 1 m

Absorbing ferrite or EMI filter

Chamber wall

Non-conducting table

Non-conducting support

Area of uniform field

0.1 m

0.8 m

Optional anechoic material in case of semi-anechoic chamber to reduce floor reflections

IEC 807764

14

Test Procedure

Test Procedure

- Verify operation of test equipment
  - Often done using field sensor to check field strength before EUT is placed in chamber
- Set field strength
  - Utilize data from calibration to determine power to be applied to transmitting antenna at each frequency
  - Power meter in line for direct indication of applied power
  - If no power meter, set signal source output; power amplifier gain must be known at each frequency
- Apply disturbance to EUT
  - Generally 4 faces tested, one at a time
  - 1% frequency step sizes
  - Dwell time long enough for EUT to exercise and respond
  - 80% AM with 1kHz sine wave
  - Horizontal and vertical polarities
  - 3 m test distance preferred

Spot Check
Very Quick

15

Analyzing Test Results

One of the most basic issues is what is a failure
- Basic standard provides basic criteria
  - Normal operation
  - Self-recoverable temporary degradation
  - Temporary degradation requiring operating intervention
  - Unrecoverable loss of function, damage
  - Product standards give more specific, detailed performance criteria for specific product types
    - Often room for interpretation

Define failure up front.

16

Measurement Uncertainty

Not required by basic standards, but may be required for lab accreditation or other reasons
- Expression of the possible error in the estimated values of the quantity measured
- Useful for improving accuracy of test results

Status of IEC TC77 activity
- Being explored for possible inclusion in basic standards
- Each standard progressing individually
- Immunity: Focus on interference signal
  - Should tolerance of field uniformity be included?

18

Key Elements

UFA Calibration
- Set up critical to performance
- Set up for test must match calibration set up
- Calibrations and use of field sensor

Capacity of power amplifier
- Calibration done without modulation
- Peak power at 80% AM is 5.1 dB greater than unmodulated signal used for calibration

EUT face greater than UFA
- Larger UFA possible?
- Partial illumination
- Windowing at frequencies greater than 1 GHz

Dwell time and exercising of EUT
- How long is long enough?

17

John Maas

John Maas received a Bachelors of Science degree with high honors from the Illinois Institute of Technology in 1981 and joined IBM's EMC lab in Rochester, MN, upon graduation. He has over 20 years of experience in EMC. John is a member of the USA TAG for IEC SC77A and SC77B, the secretary of IEC SC77B/WG10 and SC77B/MT12 and a member of SC77B/WG11, as well as a member of the USA TAG for CISPR/I. He has authored numerous papers related to EMC and holds one patent. John is a Senior Engineer at IBM and a Senior Member of the IEEE.

19

Basic Measurement Sites, Methods, and Associated Errors

Don Heirman

Don HEIRMAN Consultants
d.heirman@ieee.org
www.DonHEIRMAN.com

Test Facility Objective
(for radiated measurements)

- Create an environment providing for repeatable measurements of parameters which constitute a true representation of radio noise emitted from or received by equipment under test (EUT)

General Requirements for EMC Test Facilities

- Meet the test need
- Technically feasible
- Economically feasible
- Provides reproducible results
- Accepted by regulatory authority

¿ Customer

Typical Test Facilities

Fully Absorber Lined Room

FAR

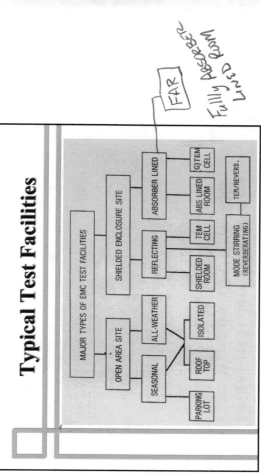

Gigahertz Transverse Electromagnetic Waveguide (IEC 61000-4-20)

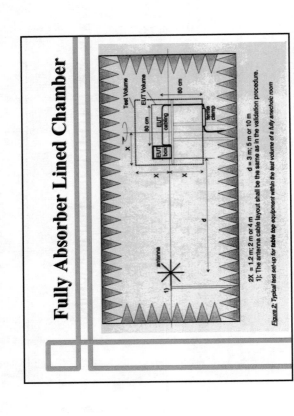

Fully Absorber Lined Chamber

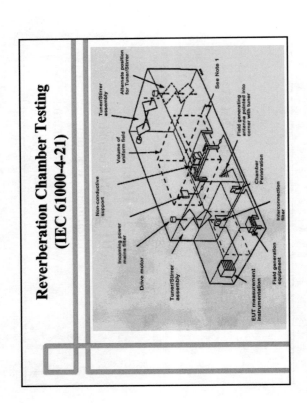

$2X = 1.2 \, m; 2 \, m \, or \, 4 \, m$ $d = 3 \, m; 5 \, m \, or \, 10 \, m$

1): The antenna cable layout shall be the same as in the validation procedure.

Figure 2: Typical test set-up for table top equipment within the test volume of a fully anechoic room

Technical Aspects of Radiated Test Facility Selection

- ■ RF Ambients
- ■ Wave scattering
- ■ Test volume limitations
- ■ Frequency limitations
- ■ Correlation with alternate facilities or independent test
- ■ Measurement uncertainties

Reverberation Chamber Testing (IEC 61000-4-21)

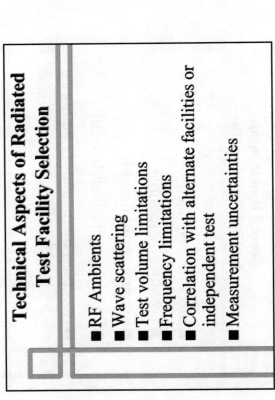

358

Uniform Test Set-ups
(Tabletop products)

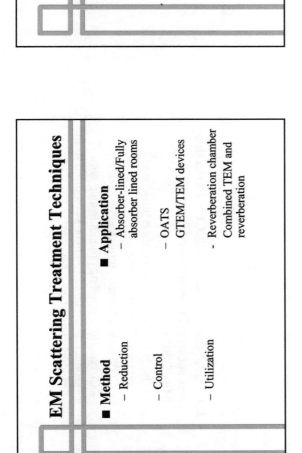

Uniform Test Set-up
(Field Calibration)

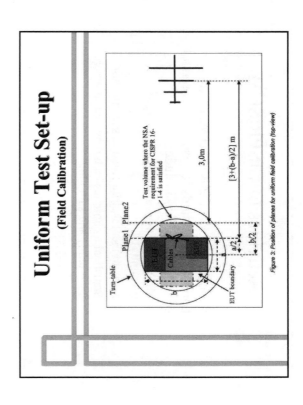

EM Scattering Treatment Techniques

- **Method**
  - Reduction

  - Control

  - Utilization

- **Application**
  - Absorber-lined/Fully absorber lined rooms

  - OATS

    GTEM/TEM devices

  - Reverberation chamber

    Combined TEM and reverberation

Uniform Test Set-up
(Floor standing products)

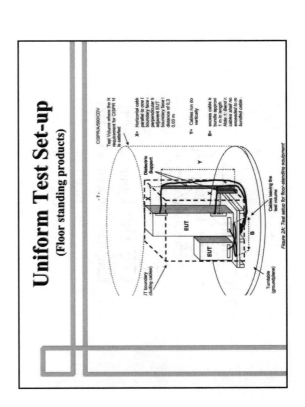

Activities of CISPR SC A

- Subcommittee A deals provides basic horizontal standards for use by the product committees. They include:
  - Methods of measurement (emission and immunity)
  - Measurement instrumentation specifications
  - Statistical techniques including measurement uncertainty and sampling

---

Pub 16-1-4

- CIS/A/531/CD & A/550/CC: Site validation > 1 GHz:
  - Uses VSWR method of comparing maximum deviations for several antenna geometries
  - Suitable antennas becoming available for 1-18 GHz range
  - Transmit antenna specifications to be stated
  - Receive antenna repositioned to illuminate volume sides
  - Possible to include validation for both polarizations; FARs would have only one selected.
  - VSWR of +/- 3.5 dB in 6th CD (increased to 5 dB in CDV)
  - Proposal to use omnidirectional probe in test volume; transmit antenna at receive antenna site
  - CDV undergoing French Translation-available near July 2005

EMC International Standards Update

CISPR SC A and I Activity (emphasis on above 1 GHz)

Don Heirman

Don HEIRMAN Consultants

Pub 16-1-4

- CIS/A/565/CDV & A/548/CC: Turntable, test setup table and tower (vote closed in May 2005)
  - Use NSA measurements; short broadband antenna 30 to 1000 MHz
  - CDV covers "raised" turntables
  - Covers floor-standing product testing with product raised up to 15 cm or as required by the product committee

CISPR A 16-1-4 Site validation above 1 GHz

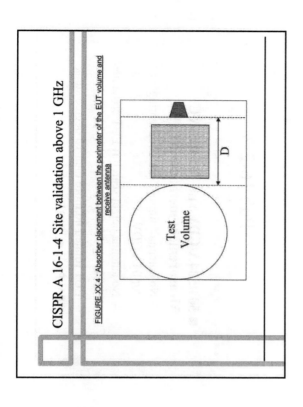

FIGURE XX.4 : Absorber placement between the perimeter of the EUT volume and receive antenna

CISPR A 16-1-4 Site validation above 1 GHz

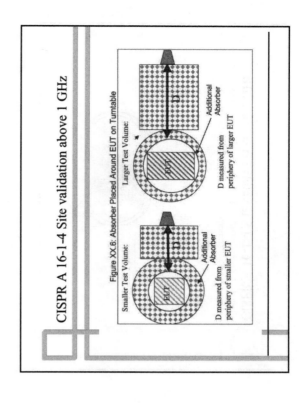

Figure XX.6: Absorber Placed Around EUT on Turntable

CISPR A 16-1-4 Site validation above 1 GHz

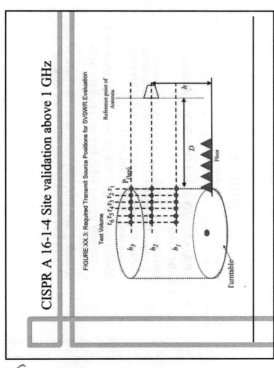

FIGURE XX.3: Required Transmit Source Positions for SVSWR Evaluation

CISPR A 16-1-4 Site validation above 1 GHz

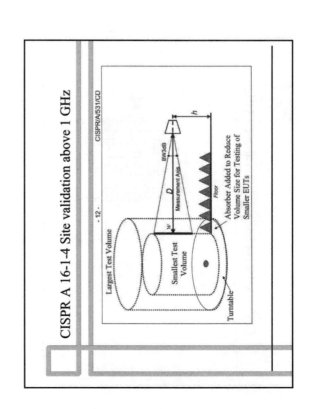

CISPR A 16-1-4 Site validation above 1 GHz

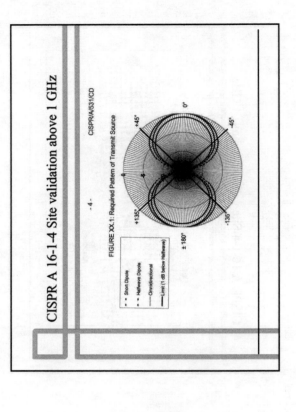

CISPR A 16-1-4 Site validation above 1 GHz

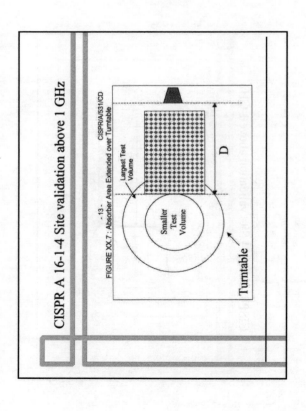

Pub 16-2-3

- **504/504A/CDV and A/545/RVC: Measurement method > 1 GHz:**
  - No antenna "aiming" or "boresighting" in A/504A/CDV
  - No antenna height search if EUT contained in receiving antenna beamwidth
  - EUT rotated no more than 15 degree steps
- **CDV Passed; FDIS next**

Pub 16-1-5

- **CISPR/A/454/Q and A/476/RQ: Antenna Calibration**
  - Questionnaire results indicated that National Committees preferred that E-field measurement forms the basis for compliance using properly calibrated common antennas
  - Maintenance project will be launched to implement
    » Initially up to 1 GHz, but has application over 1 GHz
  - Awaiting first CD; may have to set this back to stage zero and restart project due to not making 5 year publication schedule

CISPR 22

4 dB More Restrictive from 1-3GHz

CISPR A 16-2-3 Measurements above 1 GHz

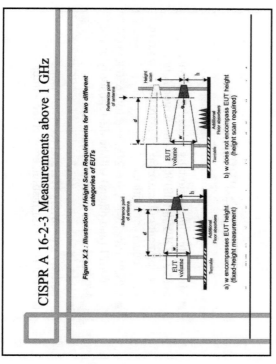

Figure X.1:
Illustration of Terms used in Measurement Method Above 1GHz
Receive Antenna in Vertical Polarization

Where (definitions refer to Figure X.1):

CISPR A 16-2-3 Measurements above 1 GHz

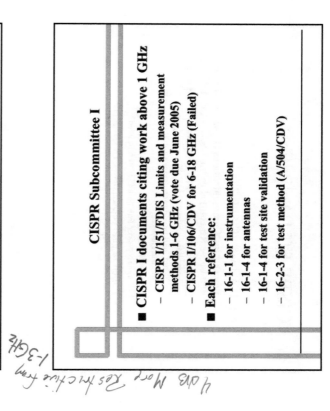

Figure X.2 : Illustration of Height Scan Requirements for two different categories of EUTs

a) w encompasses EUT height (fixed-height measurement)

b) w does not encompass EUT height (height scan required)

CISPR Subcommittee I

- CISPR I documents citing work above 1 GHz
  - CISPR I/151/FDIS Limits and measurement methods 1-6 GHz (vote due June 2005)
  - CISPR I/106/CDV for 6-18 GHz (Failed)
- Each reference:
  - 16-1-1 for instrumentation
  - 16-1-4 for antennas
  - 16-1-4 for test site validation
  - 16-2-3 for test method (A/504/CDV)

Proposed Use of Spectrum Analyzers

- *"Spectrum analyzers may be used for performing compliance measurements to this standard providing the precautions cited in CISPR 16-1-1 on the use of spectrum analyzers are adhered to and that the broadband emissions from the product being tested have a repetition frequency greater than 20 Hz."*

CISPR SC I Activities

- ITE Activity (CISPR 22)
  - **Power Line Communications (Broadband Access and home RF control in the USA)—CIS/I/89/CD**
    » Should only conducted emission measurements be used for compliance below 30 MHz?
    » What load impedance device should be used in the measurement?
    » Can the Longitudinal Conversion Loss (LCL) be quantified as this power line "load" is unbalanced?
  - Failed to gain consensus—CIS/I/145/NP

CISPR SC I Activities

- ITE Activity
  - **Test Setup Improvements** (I/136/FDIS-passed)
  - **Improvement of telecom port measurements (I/114/FDIS)**
    » Clarified test methods (flow chart added)
  - **Measurement uncertainty in test reports (CISPR 22, Fifth Edition)**
    » Follows CISPR 16-4-2 except for pass/fail application and in-situ site effects
  - **Definition of ITE with radio transmitter and/or reception function (I/115/CDV)**
    » Failed ballot

Summary

- Much work internationally related to activity above 1 GHz in CISPR Subcommittee A in its development of horizontal standards to be used by the product committees.
- CISPR Pub 16-1-X, 16-2-X, and IEC 61000-4-20 and 4-21 (and others) will be the repository of this work
- Work in Subcommittee I makes use of SC A activity and covers ITE and receiver issues
- For further information, contact the author

CISPR SC I Activities

- **ITE and other product activity**
  - **Immunity work for CISPR 24**
    » Radiated immunity up to 6 GHz
    » Application to multimedia products
    » Performance degradation for printing, scanning and copying proposed
  - **Immunity work for new CISPR 29**
    » Immunity testing for TV receivers—Objective picture assessment

Typical Sources of Radiated Emission Errors

- RF Ambient for OATS and now in-situ testing
  - Aperiodic
  - Continuous
- Test site anomalies
- Measurement procedure not fully specified
- Inadequate test instrumentation calibration
- Product (EUT) arrangement, configuration, and mode of operation not maximized
- EUT exercise software not well defined
- EUT manufacturing variability

Errors Using Alternate Measurement Sites

- Emission pattern changes (caused by test site)
- Receiving antenna pattern/gain changes
- Limited antenna height search
- Absorber ineffectiveness at low frequencies
- "Compression" of EUT arrangement
- Test setup changes between exploratory and final testing
- Correlation with open area test sites if required

Immunity vs Emission Radiated Testing

- Immunity testing not necessarily reciprocal of radiated emission testing (not even common test setups, although that is being worked in CISPR)
- Immunity testing
  - More time consuming
  - More difficult to instrument and contain fields
  - Possible EUT damage
- Similar to emission testing in:
  - I/O and power cables act as "antennas"
  - System test ultimate receptor/radiator
  - Subassembly testing helpful

Traditional OATS Measurement

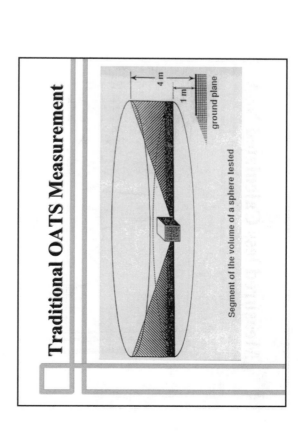

Segment of the volume of a sphere tested

365

Antenna Use Differences

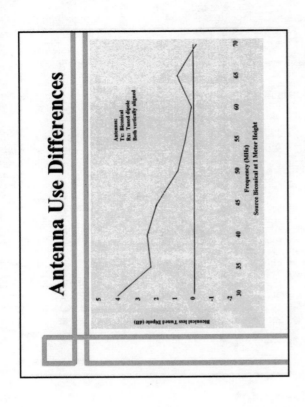

Influence of Table Tops

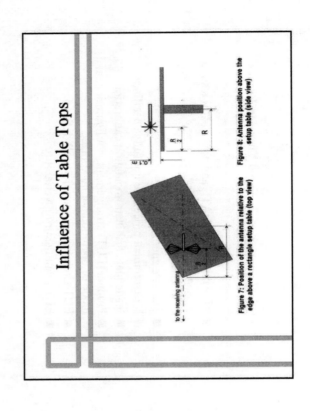

Figure 7: Position of the antenna relative to the edge above a rectangle setup table (top view)

Figure 8: Antenna position above the setup table (side view)

Measured less Calculated NSA

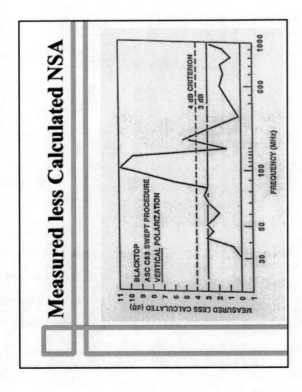

Turntable/ground plane Discontinuity
(Biconical Tx @ 1 m; dipole Rx with 25 cm clearance at 30 MHz)

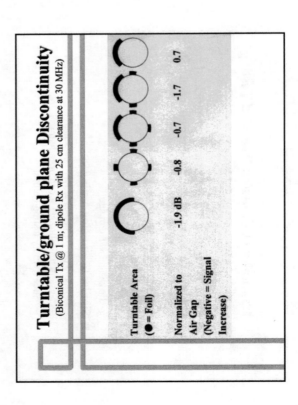

Turntable Area
(● = Foil)

Normalized to   -1.9 dB   -0.8   -0.7   -1.7   0.7
Air Gap

(Negative = Signal
Increase)

Accommodating Errors

Condition

- Margin Exceeds uncertainty

- Margin and uncertainty comparable

- Margin negative

Action

- Recommended goal (long term cost effective)

- Action necessary to increase margin

- Few choices and significant cost involved

Don Heirman Biography

- Donald Heirman is president of Don HEIRMAN Consultants, a training, standards, and educational electromagnetic compatibility (EMC) consultation corporation. Previously he was with Bell Laboratories for over 30 years in many EMC roles including Manager of Lucent Technologies (Bell Labs) Global Product Compliance Laboratory where he was in charge of the Corporation's major EMC and regulatory test facility and its participation in ANSI and international EMC standardization. He chairs, or is a principal contributor to, US and international EMC standards organizations including ANSI ASC C63 (committee vice chairman and subcommittee chair) and the International Electrotechnical Commission's (IEC) Special International Committee on Radio Interference (CISPR) where he is its subcommittee chairman responsible for CISPR Publication 16. Mr. Heirman is a Fellow of the IEEE and a member of its EMC Society Board of Directors (and its Vice President for Standards). He is past president of the National Cooperation for Laboratory Accreditation (NACLA). He is also president of the IEEE Standards Association (SA) and presently member of the SA Board of Governors. As SA president, he servers on the IEEE Board of Directors and its Executive Committee. He is a member of the IEC's Advisory Committee on EMC (ACEC) and the Technical Management Committee of the US National Committee of the IEC. Mr. Heirman is also an adjunct professor/senior research scientist at the University of Oklahoma and is the Associate Director for Wireless EMC at the University's Center for the Study of Wireless EMC. He is a retired commander in the US Navy Reserves.

Immunity Errors

- Field calibration technique
- Interactions among EUT, transmit antenna, and test chamber (fully or partially lined)
- Appropriate performance degradation criteria
- Unperturbed telemetry
- Repeatability
- Maximization of EUT response
- Impact of variable test setups in different test chambers
- Correlation among different test chambers
- Measurement uncertainty

Error Correction

- Repeat test and EUT maximization response
- Check instrumentation calibration
- Improve standard details
- Take into account measurement uncertainty in terms of adequate margin
- Determine if test facilities and instrumentation need improvement
- Participate in inter-laboratory comparisons and/or proficiency training

SELECTING A QUALITY EMC LAB

2005

Daniel D. Hoolihan
Hoolihan EMC Consulting
32515 Nottingham Court PO Box 367
Lindstrom, MN 55045
651-213-0966
hoolihan@emcxpert.com

Selecting a Quality EMC Lab

- How do you determine the quality of an EMC laboratory?
- Quality EMC labs can be accredited and Quality EMC labs can be non-accredited
- Accreditation can be a minimum or a maximum - depending on the lab

Introduction

- EMC Labs can be accredited to a limited scope of tests or a wide-ranging scope of tests
- Lab Accreditation should give the user confidence in the capability of the lab
- Lab Accreditation helps Qualify EMC labs for a customer

Introduction

- Accreditation allows a lab to test products for a Declaration of Conformity under the United States FCC Rules
- Declaration of Conformity covers devices such as Class B Personal Computers and Peripherals, CB receivers, TV interface devices, and Consumer ISM equipment.

MRA RE ABRE
Mutual Rec Agree

What is scope of test

Accreditation Criteria

- International Requirements
  - ISO/IEC 17025
  - International Standard
  - "General Requirements for the Competence of Testing and Calibration Laboratories"
  - First Edition
  - Published 15 December 1999

ISO/IEC 17025

- ISO/IEC 17025 supersedes both ISO/IEC Guide 25 and European Norm 45001
- ISO/IEC 17025 is the next generation of Guide 25
- ISO/IEC 17025 has been adopted by many countries around the world

ISO/IEC 17025

- CONTENTS
  - 1 - SCOPE
  - 2 - NORMATIVE REFERENCES
  - 3 - TERMS AND DEFINITIONS
  - 4 - MANAGEMENT REQUIREMENTS
  - 5 - TECHNICAL REQUIREMENTS

ISO/IEC 17025

- ALSO INCLUDES TWO ANNEXES:
  - Annex A - Nominal Cross References to ISO 9001:1994 and ISO 9002:1994
  - Annex B - Guidelines for Establishing Applications for Specific Fields

9001:2000

ISO/IEC 17025

- 17025 separates the Management Requirements (ISO 9000 requirements) and the Technical Requirements
- The Technical Requirements section is what differentiates 17025 from ISO 9000
- If you comply with 17025, you comply with ISO 9000

ISO/IEC 17025

- Management Requirements *Systems*
  - Organization
  - Quality System
  - Document Control
  - Review of Requests, Tenders, and Contracts
  - Subcontracting of Tests and Calibrations

ISO/IEC 17025

- Management Requirements (Cont.)
  - Purchasing Services and Supplies
  - Service to the Client *Customers*
  - Complaints
  - Control of Nonconforming Testing and/or Calibration Work
  - Corrective Action

ISO/IEC 17025

- Management Requirements (Cont.)
  - Preventive Action
  - Control of Records
  - Internal Audits
  - Management Review

ISO/IEC 17025

- Technical Requirements (continued)
  - Measurement Traceability
  - Sampling
  - Handling of Test and Calibration Items
  - Assuring the Quality of Test and Calibration Results
  - Reporting the Results

ISO/IEC 17025

- 5.9 Assuring the Quality of Test Results
  - The lab shall have quality control procedures
  - The resulting data shall be recorded in such a way that trends are detectable
  - This monitoring shall be planned and reviewed and may include...participation in interlaboratory comparison or proficiency-testing programs

ISO/IEC 17025

- Technical Requirements
  - General
  - Personnel
  - Accommodation and Environmental Conditions
  - Test and Calibration Methods and Method Validation
  - Equipment

ISO/IEC 17025

- 5.6 - Measurement Traceability
  - Includes Measurement Uncertainty for testing laboratories
  - Requirements for Measurement Uncertainty is one of the major differences between Guide 25 and ISO/IEC 17025

SUMMARY

- Qualified EMC Labs may or may not be accredited
- In general, however, Qualified EMC labs are accredited to ISO/IEC 17025 these days
- Two EMC accreditors in the United States - NIST/NVLAP, and A2LA
- Other accreditors outside the USA

ISO/IEC 17025

- Accreditation to 17025 does not necessarily guarantee a Qualified EMC Laboratory – people, equipment and procedures can all change since the last accreditation assessment!
- You must check the SCOPE of accreditation of the EMC Lab to assure that the lab is qualified for those specific tests you want performed on your product

Daniel D. Hoolihan's Biography

- Daniel D. Hoolihan is currently President of Hoolihan EMC Consulting, 32515 Nottingham Court-Box 367, Lindstrom, Minnesota, 55045.
- Hoolihan has been consulting in EMC Engineering since January of 2000. He specializes in EMC-Laboratory evaluations, EMC standards, and EMC Education. Previous to consulting, he worked as Vice-President of Minnesota Operations for TUV Product Service from 1994 to 2000. From 1984 to 1994, he was the Co-Founder and Chief Operating Officer of AMADOR Corporation; a small business specializing in EMC testing of electronic products ranging in size from pacemakers to supercomputers. His first employment out of graduate school (in 1969) was with Control Data Corporation in their internal EMC lab.
- Dan has been on the Board of Directors of the EMC Society of the IEEE since 1987. He is the past-president of the EMCS (1998-1999) and has held many positions with the EMCS board in his years of service. He most recently served as the Chair of the 2002 IEEE International Symposium on EMC which was held in Minneapolis in August of 2002. He helped found the EMC chapter of the Minnesota-Twin Cities Section in 1985 and has been active in the local chapter since that time.
- He has been actively involved with ANSI-Accredited Standards Committee C63 on EMC since 1985. He is presently on the Steering Committee of C63 as well as chairing Subcommittee 6 (SC-6 - Lab Accreditation) and Subcommittee 8 (SC-8 - EMC and Medical Devices).
- Hoolihan is also an active member of the United States Technical Advisory Group on CISPR B; Industrial, Scientific and Medical Equipment.
- His formal education includes a Bachelors Degree in Physics from Saint John's University (Minnesota), a Masters Degree in Physics from Louisiana Sate University (Baton Rouge), and a Masters in Business Administration from the University of Minnesota (Minneapolis).

Uncertainty Considerations in Stating Pass/Fail

Don Heirman

Don HEIRMAN Consultants
d.heirman@ieee.org
www.DonHEIRMAN.com

CISPR Uncertainty Approach

- Protect the radio spectrum
- Encourage lower measurement uncertainty
- Make margin greater than uncertainty
- First international standard published as CISPR 16, Part 4-2 and is normative
- Second international uncertainty activity:
  - CISPR 16, Part 4-1 on Uncertainties in Standardized EMC Tests

Radiated Emission Uncertainty Drivers

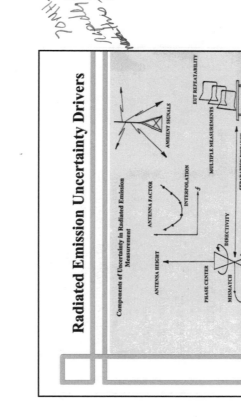

CISPR Approach to Uncertainty

(handwritten) Instrumentation

- CISPR sets values for uncertainty Ux; presently this is for the measurement instrumentation uncertainty
- If Ulab < or = Ux, product accepted or rejected on the basis of Mr (measured value) alone (present view)
- If Ulab > Ux, product accepted or rejected on the basis of Mr + (Ulab – Ux) alone where Ulab is the test lab measurement uncertainty
- Test laboratory reports Mr and Ulab

First Application of Ucispr

INTERNATIONAL ELECTROTECHNICAL COMMISSION

CISPR 22
Fifth edition
2005-04

Information technology equipment –
Radio disturbance characteristics –
Limits and methods of measurement

CISPR Values for Ux

- Conducted Emissions:
  - 9 kHz to 150 kHz   **4.0 dB**
  - 150 kHz to 30 MHz   **3.6 dB**
- Radiated Disturbance
  - 30 to 1000 MHz   **5.2 dB**
- Not addressing immunity at this time
- Applies to measurement instrumentation only
- *CISPR approach is contained in CISPR 16-4-2*

ISO/IEC 17025-1999

- Clause 5.4.6 Estimation of Uncertainty of Measurement
  - 5.4.6.1 "…**shall have and shall apply** a procedure to estimate the uncertainty…"
  - 5.4.6.2 "…test method may preclude rigorous, metrological and statistically valid calculations…attempt to identify components and make reasonable estimation…" This can be based on "performance of the method…previous experience, and validation data…"

First Application of Ucispr

- Results of emissions shall reference CISPR 16-4-2
- Uncertainty of measurement instrumentation chain shall be calculated and shall appear in the test report
- Compliance determined by measurement result, not using uncertainty *(for the time being)*
- In-situ measurement site uncertainty contribution excluded from calculation

ISO/IEC 17025-1999

- Clause 5.4.6.2 (continued) Estimation of Uncertainty of Measurement
  - Rigor depends on
    - » Test method requirement
    - » Client requirement
    - » Existence of narrow limits on which decisions on conformance to a specification are based
  - If the test method states limits of uncertainty, then lab satisfies uncertainty considerations if it follows test method and reporting instructions
  - (Note that ESD standard does this, for example)

ISO/IEC 17025-1999

- 5.4.6.3 All uncertainty components which are of importance shall be taken into account using appropriate methods of analysis
  - Sources: reference standards, methods and equipment used, environmental conditions, properties and condition of the test item, operator…
  - Predicted long term behavior of testing item is not normally taken into account when estimating uncertainty
  - See ISO 5725 or the "GUM" *Guide for Uncertainty of Measurement*

ISO/IEC 17025-1999

- 5.10 Reporting the Results
  - 5.10.1 General
    - » The results shall include …information…normally required by…5.10.3 (Test Reports) which contains the application of measurement uncertainty in the test report

ISO/IEC 17025-1999

- 5.10 Reporting the Results
  - 5.10.3 Test Reports: "Where applicable, a statement on the estimated uncertainty of measurement; information on uncertainty is needed in test reports when it is relevant to the validity or application of the test results, when a client's instructions so requires, or when the uncertainty affects compliance to a specification limit"
  - Note: No specific statement is made for stating "pass/fail" based on the application of measurement uncertainty in testing.

375

One Application to Pass/Fail

- Pass/fail must be stated unequivocally for UKAS

Handwritten annotations: 95% CI, PASS, PASS/FAIL, FAIL/PASS, FAIL

Test Lab Concerns with Uncertainty

- Varying approaches by accrediting bodies:
  - "where relevant"
  - "adversely affect compliance" – when can pass/fail be stated?
  - "client requests" (shared risk?)
- No obvious common procedure for calculation
  - Major components left out
  - Competitive disadvantage if all do not use same components
  - Continued training of lab personnel as well as auditors needed to catch inconsistencies and to be consistent

---

Changing Requirement Summary

- Measurement uncertainty must be:
  - Applied consistently and appropriately
  - Not be a competitive disadvantage
  - Assessed fairly by accreditation bodies
  - Agreed to by customer and regulator alike
- NVLAP and A2LA fully implemented ISO/IEC 17025 which requires that measurement uncertainty is addressed
  - Some issues still unresolved when to use uncertainty

WORKSHOP: THE SHIELDING EFFECTIVENESS OF ENCLOSURES: THEORY AND MEASUREMENT TECHNIQUES (FR-AM-WS-14)

Prof. Maria Sabrina Sarto *(co-chair)*
Univ. of Rome "La Sapienza"
Prof. Johan Catrysse *(co-chair)*
Katholieke Hogeschool Brugge Oostende - KHBO

The wide-spreading use of innovative lightweight materials like advanced composites and metal coated plastics in several fields of applications has pushed toward an increasing interest in the characterization of the shielding performances of test specimen and enclosures. Moreover, the increasing working frequencies of digital components and electronic devices require electromagnetic testing of metallic and composite housings in a wider frequency range, up to a few tens of gigahertz.

An existing standard for the complete characterization of the shielding performances of test specimen is the ASTM 4935/89, which is limited to the characterization of flat samples of material in the frequency-range up to 1.5 GHz. A standard method for the measurement of the shielding effectiveness of enclosures is reported in the IEEE Std.299-1997, which addresses to "large" enclosures having minimum dimension greater than 2 m in the frequency range from 9 kHz to 18 GHz. A revision of this standard was completed in August 2004.

An emerging technique for the SE measurement of test specimen and enclosure makes use of reverberating chamber, as described in the standard IEC 61000-4-21.

However, all the existing standards for the SE measurements leave some open questions. One of the most important concerns the testing of "small" enclosures, i.e. enclosures having minimum dimension less than 2 m like racks for telecommunication apparatus, boxes for avionics and electronic equipments, enclosures for PCBs. A new IEEE working group on a guideline for the SE measurement of small enclosure is under constitution.

The scope of the workshop is to present the latest version of the IEEE Std. 299, by highlighting the new features included in the Aug. 2004 revision and the open issues, like the uncertainty study. Moreover, an overview on the most commonly used techniques for the measurement of the SE of "small" enclosure will be provided, with reference to the different possible applications, size and material of the box under test.

Finally, the use of reverberation chambers for the SE measurement of enclosures will be discussed.

Presentations ((3) not available for publication):

(1) Shielding Effectiveness of Enclosures: An Introduction
Maria Sabrina Sarto

(2) Shielding Characterisation of Small Enclosures: Actual Status and IEEE P299-2 Proposal
Johan Catrysse

(3) The Benefits of Using IEEE Std 299 for Shielding Effectiveness Testing—Update *(not published)*
Dale Svetanoff

(4) Suggested Definitions of Shielding for Enclosures at Microwave Frequencies
Andy Marvin and Yong Cui

(5) Nested Reverberation Chamber Measurements for the Shielding Effectiveness of Advanced Materials
C. L. Holloway

(6) The Shielding Effectiveness of Enclosures: Theory and Measurement Techniques
Maria Sabrina Sarto and Johan Catrysse

NOTES

2005 IEEE International Symposium on EMC
Chicago (CA), Aug.8-12, 2005

Workshop on:

"Shielding effectiveness of enclosures: theory and measurement techniques"

"Shielding effectiveness of enclosures: An introduction"

Maria Sabrina Sarto

Univ. of Rome "La Sapienza"
Department of Electrical Engineering

OUTLINE

1. Shielding performances of conducting panels: sensitivity analysis

2. Shielding performances of panels with apertures: 3D-FDTD analysis

3. Shielding performances of enclosures

4. Transient electromagnetic field penetration inside shielded enclosures

---

The shielding performances of enclosures are strongly affected by:

· The material realizing the enclosure;
· The geometry and dimensions of the enclosure;
· The presence of apertures;
· The characteristics of the incident EM field.

The distribution of the EM field inside an enclosure can be highly non uniform.

SHIELDING PERFORMANCES OF CONDUCTING PANELS: SENSITIVITY ANALYSIS

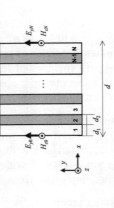

Multilayered shielding panel illuminated by a plane wave

Hp: Infinite planar shield

The EM field propagation through the shield is calculated by applying the equivalent 1D transmission line model

The SE can be computed analytically:

$$SE = 20\log\left\{0.5\left[\Phi_{tot}(1,1) + \Phi_{tot}(2,2) + \eta_0\Phi_{tot}(2,1) + \eta_0^{-1}\Phi_{tot}(1,2)\right]\right\}$$

$\Phi_{tot}(1,1), \Phi_{tot}(1,2), \Phi_{tot}(2,1), \Phi_{tot}(2,2)$ are the coefficients of the Transmission matrix of the N-layer shield:

$$[\Phi_{tot}] = \prod_{i=1}^{N}[\Phi_i]$$

SE of infinite panels

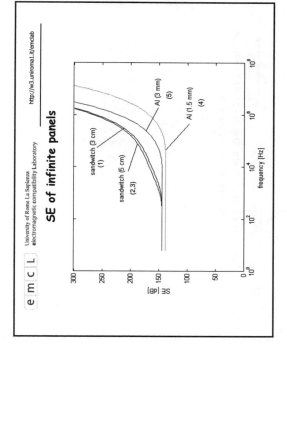

Shielding effectiveness against the electric field:

$$SE = 20\log\frac{E^i}{E^t}$$

E^i : electric field without the shield

E^t : electric field with the shield

The shielding effectiveness SE against the electric field is coincident with the one against the magnetic field in the plane wave assumption and in the case of infinite panel.

Predition of the SE of infinite panels of aluminum with single layer or sandwitch structure

no.	layers	conductivity [S/m]	relative permittivity	thickness [mm]
1	Al/foam/Al	$2.8 \cdot 10^7$ / 0 / $2.8 \cdot 10^7$	1 / 4 / 1	1.5 / 30 / 1.5
2	Al/foam/Al	$2.8 \cdot 10^7$ / 0 / $2.8 \cdot 10^7$	1 / 4 / 1	1.5 / 50 / 1.5
3	Al/foam/Al	$2.8 \cdot 10^7$ / 0 / $2.8 \cdot 10^7$	1 / 1 / 1	1.5 / 50 / 1.5
4	Al	$2.8 \cdot 10^7$	1	1.5
5	Al	$2.8 \cdot 10^7$	1	3

SE$_0$ as a function of the shield thickness for different values of electrical conductivity

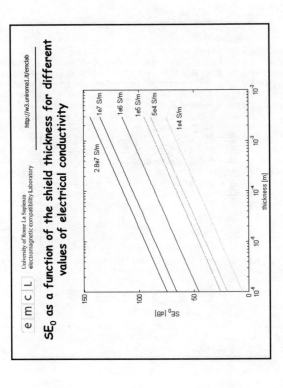

Carbon fiber reinforced composites (σ = 5e4 S/m)

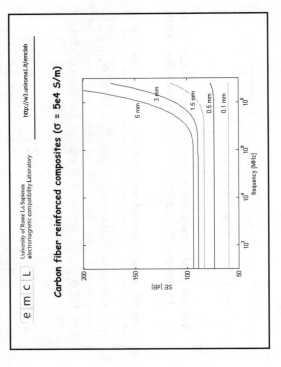

The low-frequency asymptotic value of the SE of multilayered infinite panels against a plane wave is:

$$SE_0 = \lim_{f \to 0} SE = 45.5 + \sum_{i=1}^{N} 20\log(\sigma_i d_i)$$

SE$_0$ is affected only by the conducting layers of the shielding panel.

At higher frequencies, above 10 - 100 kHz, the SE increases exponentially due to the attenuation lossess inside the shielding material.

Sensitivity analysis of SE against variation of the shield thickness

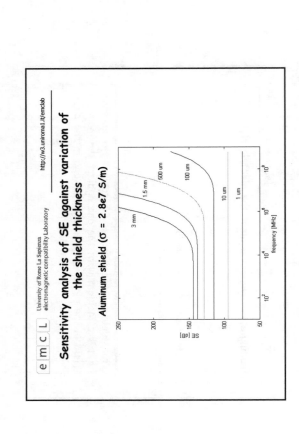

Aluminum shield (σ = 2.8e7 S/m)

Slide 1

e m c L University of Rome La Sapienza
electromagnetic compatibility Laboratory
http://w3.uniroma1.it/emclab

The SE spectrum begins to increase exponentially at the frequency f*, which is inversely proportional to the thickness and electrical conductivity of the shielding panel.

... IN THE CASE OF A SHIELDING ENCLOSURE ...

The shielding effectiveness against the electric field is different from the one against the magnetic field, in general.

Slide 2

e m c L University of Rome La Sapienza
electromagnetic compatibility Laboratory
http://w3.uniroma1.it/emclab

The SE of an enclosure against the magnetic field starts to increase is correlated to the penetration depth of the conducting material realizing the shield:

$$\delta = \frac{1}{\sqrt{\mu_0 \pi f \sigma}}$$

At frequencies such that the thickness d of the panel satisfies the condition $d > 3\delta$ the absorption phenomenon cannot be neglected any more and it results $SE > SE_0$.

Slide 3

e m c L University of Rome La Sapienza
electromagnetic compatibility Laboratory
http://w3.uniroma1.it/emclab

The shielding effectiveness of conducting enclosures without apertures agaisnt the electric field is mainly produced by reflection.

The shielding effectiveness of conducting enclosures without apertures against the magnetic field is strongly affected by the diffusion phenomenon.

THE SHIELDING ENCLOSURES BEHAVE AS "LOW-PASS FILTERS" AS REGARDS THE MAGNETIC FIELD

Slide 4

e m c L University of Rome La Sapienza
electromagnetic compatibility Laboratory
http://w3.uniroma1.it/emclab

Penetration depth for different values of the electrical conductivity

1e4 S/m
1e5 S/m
1e6 S/m
1e7 S/m
2.8e7 S/m

frequency [Hz]
skin depth [m]

SHIELDING PERFORMANCES OF PANELS WITH APERTURES: 3D-FDTD ANALYSIS

Aperture dimensions:
175 cm × 140 cm
The aperture is loaded with a conducting panel

The SE is computed in the middle of the aperture in different positions.

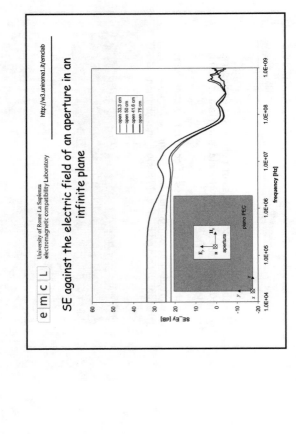

piano PEC

no.	material	Consductivity [S/m]	thickness [μm]
1	Stagno / Nickel	$9.0 \cdot 10^6$ / $1.56 \cdot 10^7$	5 / 0.05
2	Al	$2.8 \cdot 10^7$	1000

SE against the electric field of an aperture in an infinite plane

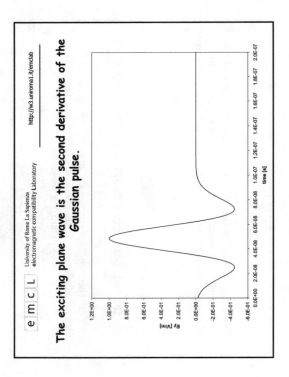

open 33.3 cm
open 50 cm
open 41.6 cm
open 75 cm

Frequencies such that the thickness d of the panel satisfies the condition d=3δ

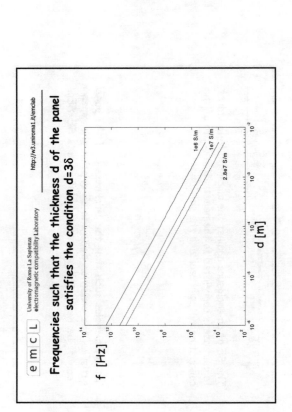

1e6 S/m
1e7 S/m
2.8e7 S/m

The exciting plane wave is the second derivative of the Gaussian pulse.

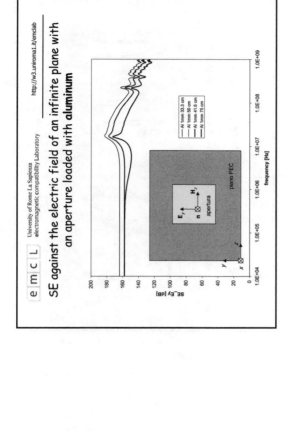

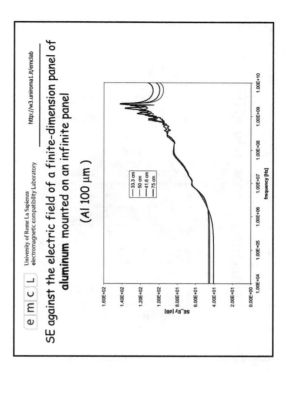

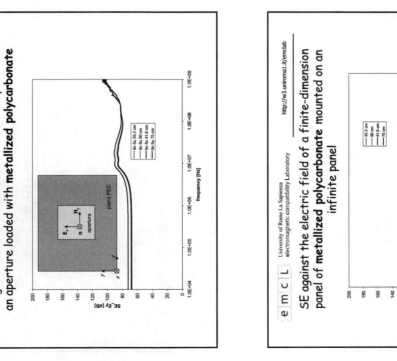

383

SHIELDING PERFORMANCES OF ENCLOSURES

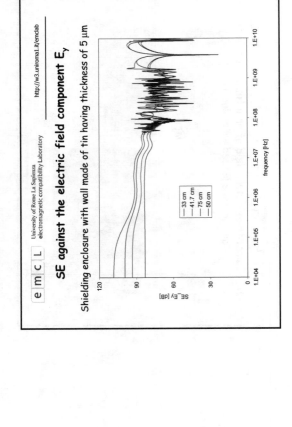

- box dimensions: 2m × 2m × 3.5 m
- aperture dimensions 175 cm × 125 cm

EM plane wave with normal incidence

SE against the electric field component E_y

Shielding enclosure with wall made of tin having thickness of 5 µm

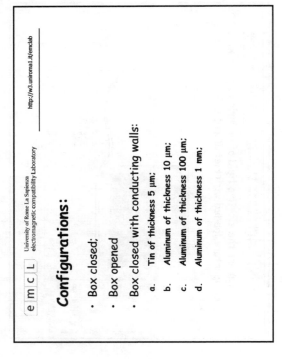

Legend: 33 cm; 41.7 cm; 75 cm; 50 cm

SE against the electric field of a finite-dimension panel of aluminum mounted on an infinite panel

(Al 1 mm)

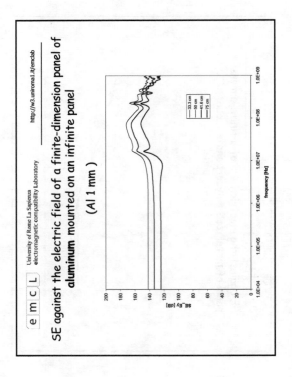

Legend: 33.3 cm; 50 cm; 41.6 cm; 75 cm

Configurations:

- Box closed;
- Box opened
- Box closed with conducting walls:
  a. Tin of thickness 5 µm;
  b. Aluminum of thickness 10 µm;
  c. Aluminum of thickness 100 µm;
  d. Aluminum of thickness 1 mm;

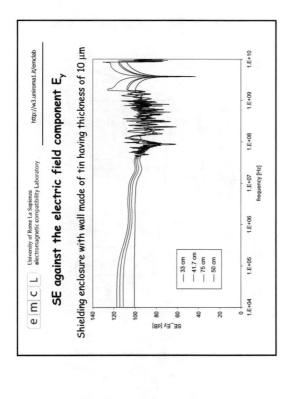

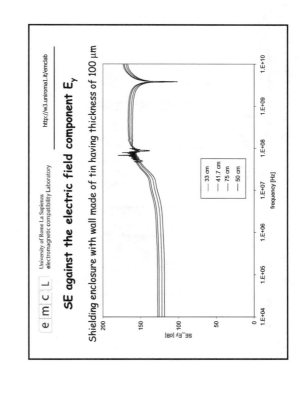

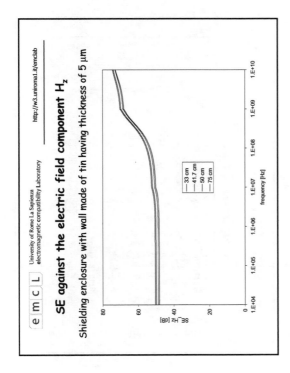

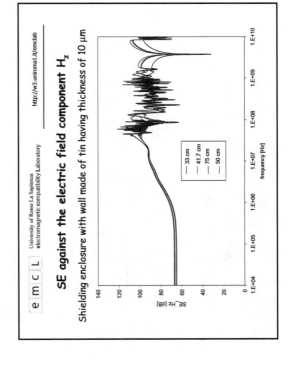

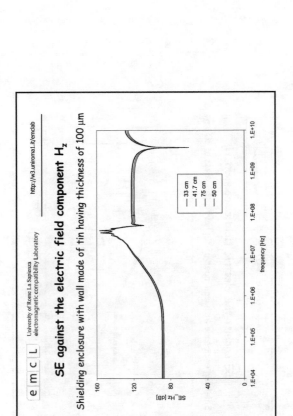

Impulsive EM field

carbon fiber composite panel

0.1 cm

0°/90°/0°

Experimental analysis

Bounded-wave EMP simulator

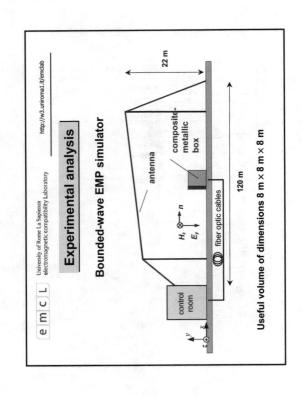

Useful volume of dimensions 8 m × 8 m × 8 m

SE against the electric field component H_z

Shielding enclosure with wall made of tin having thickness of 100 μm

33 cm
41.7 cm
75 cm
50 cm

3D-FDTD analysis

- **Carbon fiber composite panel:**

  $\varepsilon_{rr} = 4$, $\varepsilon_{rr} = 2$, $\sigma_f = 5$ kS/m , $\rho_f = 20\% - 32\%$

- **Incident EMP plane wave:**

  $E_y^i(t) = \hat{E}_y^i \left[\exp(-t/\tau_2) - \exp(-t/\tau_1) \right]$

  $\hat{E}_y^i = 50$ kV/m , $\tau_1 = 5$ ns , $\tau_2 = 200$ ns

- **FDTD grid:**

  $\Delta x = \Delta y = \Delta z = 5$ cm , $\Delta t = 0.083$ ns

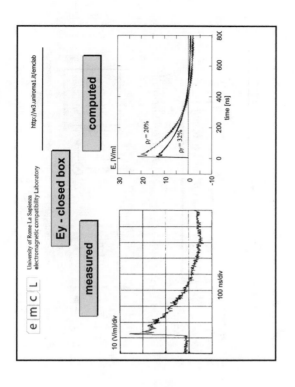

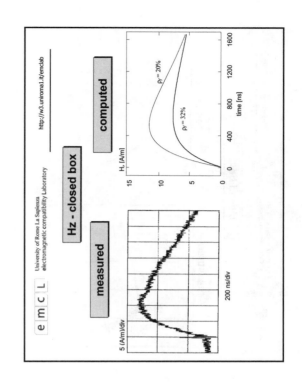

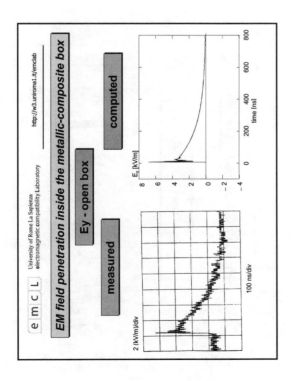

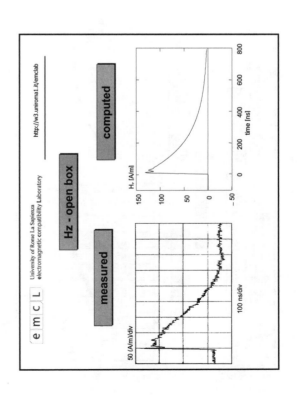

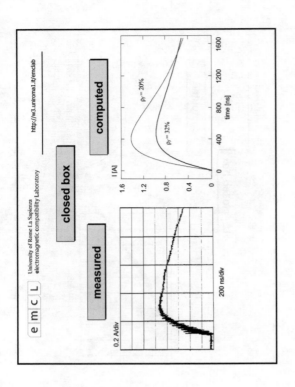

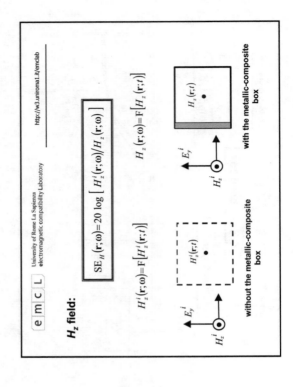

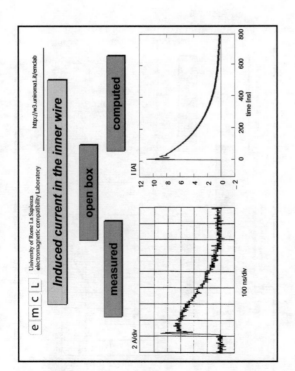

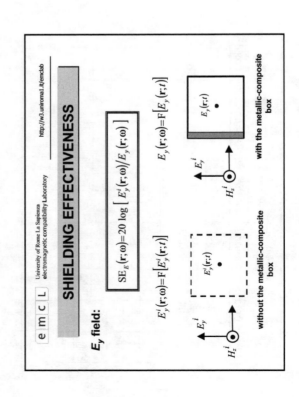

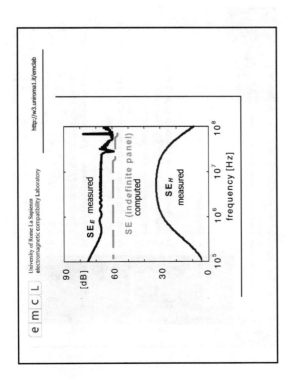

Electronics Department

Lab for EMC

IEEE 299-2

Shielding characterisation of small enclosures

actual status and IEEE P299-2 proposal

Johan Catrysse

Chicago, 2005

IEEE/EMC Symposium

Master in de Industriële Wetenschappen - Bachelor in de technologie

KHBO

Electronics Department

Lab for EMC

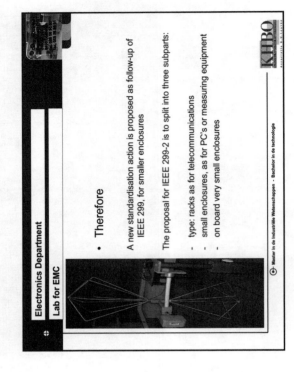

- **Problem**

  - "Old" standard for shielding characterisation of (large) enclosures was only MIL STD 285

  - "New" version, actually under revision, is IEEE 299

  - Applicable only for large enclosures, with a minimum size of 2 m, so that antenna's can be put in the inner space of the enclosure

Master in de Industriële Wetenschappen - Bachelor in de technologie

---

Electronics Department

Lab for EMC

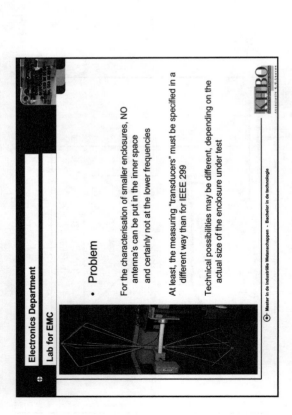

- **Therefore**

  A new standardisation action is proposed as follow-up of IEEE 299, for smaller enclosures

  The proposal for IEEE 299-2 is to split into three subparts:

  - type: racks as for telecommunications

  - small enclosures, as for PC's or measuring equipment

  - on board very small enclosures

Master in de Industriële Wetenschappen - Bachelor in de technologie

---

Electronics Department

Lab for EMC

- **Problem**

  For the characterisation of smaller enclosures, NO antenna's can be put in the inner space and certainly not at the lower frequencies

  At least, the measuring "transducers" must be specified in a different way than for IEEE 299

  Technical possibilities may be different, depending on the actual size of the enclosure under test

Master in de Industriële Wetenschappen - Bachelor in de technologie

Electronics Department

Lab for EMC

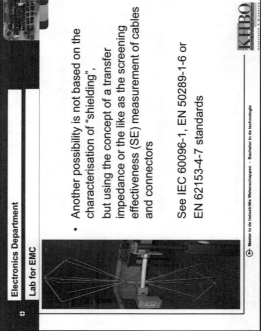

- Subpart 2 – small enclosures
  Known measuring techniques:

  - TEM/GTEM cells with an internal transducer:
    * monopole/dipole for electric field
    * loop antenna for magnetic field

  - (semi) anechoic chamber with an external antenna and an internal transducer

  - noise source inside the enclosure

  - Other ???

Electronics Department

Lab for EMC

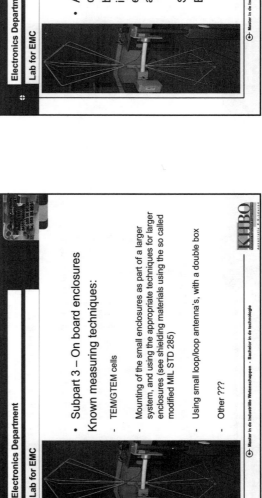

- Another possibility is not based on the characterisation of "shielding", but using the concept of a transfer impedance or the like as the screening effectiveness (SE) measurement of cables and connectors

  See IEC 60096-1, EN 50289-1-6 or EN 62153-4-7 standards

Electronics Department

Lab for EMC

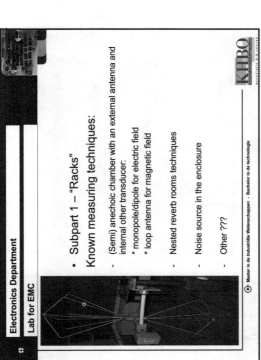

- Subpart 1 – "Racks"
  Known measuring techniques:

  - (Semi) anechoic chamber with an external antenna and internal other transducer:
    * monopole/dipole for electric field
    * loop antenna for magnetic field

  - Nested reverb rooms techniques

  - Noise source in the enclosure

  - Other ???

Electronics Department

Lab for EMC

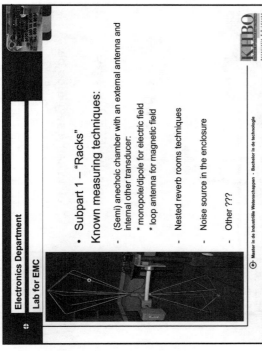

- Subpart 3 – On board enclosures
  Known measuring techniques:

  - TEM/GTEM cells

  - Mounting of the small enclosures as part of a larger system, and using the appropriate techniques for larger enclosures (see shielding materials using the so called modified MIL STD 285)

  - Using small loop/loop antenna's, with a double box

  - Other ???

Electronics Department

Lab for EMC

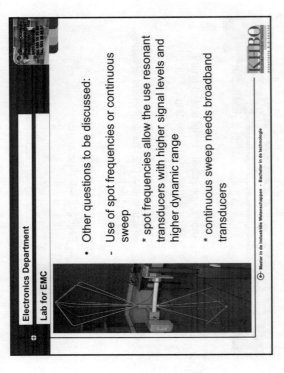

- Other questions to be discussed:

  - Effect of the loading of an enclosure (ie. the effect of PCB's – ref. Univ. of York)

  - Frequency range and the related type of transducer to be used

  - Reference position of the transducers

  - Influence of polarisation, joints, holes

Electronics Department

Lab for EMC

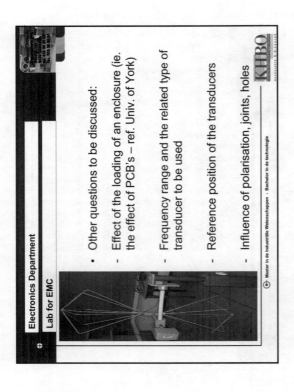

- Other questions to be discussed:

  - Use of spot frequencies or continuous sweep

  * spot frequencies allow the use resonant transducers with higher signal levels and higher dynamic range

  * continuous sweep needs broadband transducers

Electronics Department

Lab for EMC

Interested ?

Join the IEEE 299-2 WG

johan.catrysse@khbo.be

Slide 1

"Suggested Definitions of Shielding for Enclosures at Microwave Frequencies"

Prof Andy Marvin & Yong Cui

Department of Electronics

THE UNIVERSITY *of York*

1

Slide 2

Why a new definition of Shielding?

Definition of SE from IEEE dictionary:

For a given external source, the ratio of electric field strength at a point before and after placement of the shield in question, is given in equation below where Eo is the field without the shield and Es is the field with the shield present:

$$SE = 20 \cdot \log_{10} \frac{E_o}{E_s}$$

2

Slide 3

Why a new definition of Shielding?

Shortcoming of the SE definition for the measurement of shielding

- Does not account for the spatial variation of the fields around the enclosure.

- Does not consider the source position inside. Different positions of the energy source within the enclosure mean various excitation of the radiating apertures.

- Does not consider the effect of enclosure contents. The type and distribution of the contents inside an enclosure also have effects on the aperture radiation.

3

Slide 4

Measurement Setup: Configuration of EUT

- The enclosure used in the experimental work described here was a copper cuboid of dimensions 480*480*120mm. This represents a typical 19" equipment enclosure.

- The PCB to represent the contents inside, on which the energy source was mounted, was 300*240mm.

- Energy source: Comb Generator Emitter CGE02 from York EMC Services Ltd.

- A variety of apertures are placed in one wall to simulate apertures in real enclosures.

4

The Emission source CEG02 and the Test Enclosure

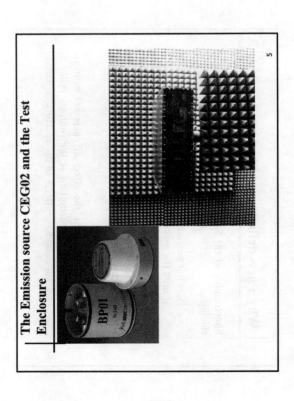

Measurement Setup: Measurement procedure

- To measure the variation of the field outside the enclosure, two different kinds of scan were performed.

  - Cylindrical scan: The enclosure-under-test (EUT) was repeatedly rotated for each different receiving antenna height over a certain height range.

  - Planar scan: The EUT was fixed and the receiving antenna was repeatedly moved horizontally at different heights.

Circuit card source positions

- Six different source positions on the PCB were chosen.

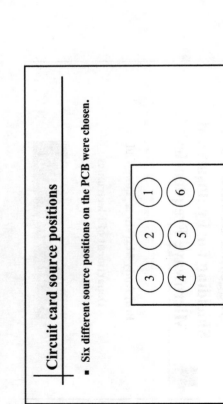

Different emission source positions on the PCB

Measurement setup: sketch of cylindrical scan

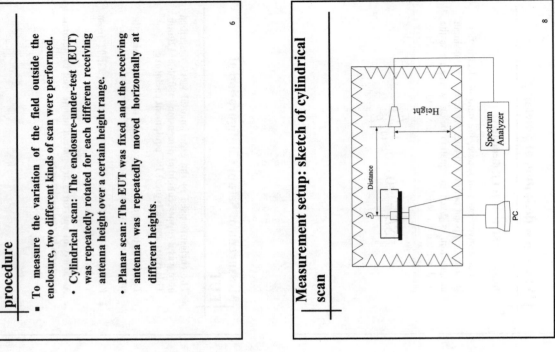

cylindrical scan (−45° ~ + 45°, Height: −45~+45 cm)

- For different source positions the emission pattern is different

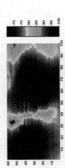

Cylindrical scan with enclosure, source position: 4, frequency: 5 GHz

Cylindrical scan without enclosure, source position: 4, frequency: 5 GHz

9

Examples of the emission patterns of cylindrical scan

- The shielding performance of the enclosure

Cylindrical scan, source position: 3, frequency: 6 GHz; enclosure included.

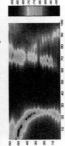

Cylindrical scan, source position: 3, frequency: 6 GHz; enclosure excluded.

10

Proposed definition 1

- The first definition of Shielding S_I is defined as the ratio of the power measured when the enclosure is absent to the power measured when the enclosure is present:

$$S_I = 10\lg\left(\frac{P_O}{P_S}\right) = 10\lg\left(\frac{\sum p_o^i}{\sum p_i^i}\right)$$

11

Proposed definition 1

Where:

p_o^i : the enclosure is absent, the power measured at the 'i'th test point

p_I^i : the enclosure is present, the power measured at the 'i'th test point

P_O : the enclosure is absent, the sum of power measured at all the test points

P_I : the enclosure is present, the sum of power measured at all the test points

12

Proposed definition 2

- Definition S_{II} consists of two parameters S_{II}^{max}

  And S_{II}^{min}. Where:

$$S_{II}^{max} = MAX\left\{10\lg\left(\frac{P_O^i}{P_I^i}\right)\right\} = MAX\left\{P_O^i(dBm) - P_I^i(dBm)\right\}$$

$$S_{II}^{min} = MIN\left\{10\lg\left(\frac{P_O^i}{P_I^i}\right)\right\} = MIN\left\{P_O^i(dBm) - P_I^i(dBm)\right\}$$

13

Calculation results for S_I

Table I: S_I at different frequencies and source positions

Source Position	1GHz	2GHz	3GHz	4GHz	5GHz	6GHz
Position 1	22.6	22.1	16.8	-0.8	-1.5	-4.6
Position 2	20.6	19.0	6.3	1.2	3.1	1.4
Position 3	21.5	21.8	8.0	6.1	5.8	9.2
Position 4	25.3	21.9	3.6	2.8	3.1	20.1
Position 5	28.1	18.5	16.5	7.7	-1.8	4.0
Position 6	23.7	19.1	8.7	-0.1	-3.5	8.7

14

Interesting result!

- If we arrange the power measured without/with enclosure in ascending order, we get two sequences:

  Sequence 1: $P_0(1)$, $P_0(2)$, $P_0(3)$,..... $P_0(i)$.... $P_0(m)$, (m=the number of test points)

  Sequence 2: $P_I(1)$, $P_I(2)$, $P_I(3)$,..... $P_I(i)$.... $P_I(m)$

  Then over the range up to 'm':
  $P_0(i)/P_I(i) = P_0(i+1)/P_I(i+1) = ... = ... = P_0(m)/P_I(m)$

15

An example to illustrate the phenomenon

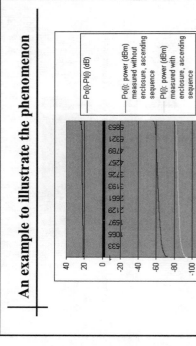

Data measured at 1GHz, source position 1.

16

A second example to illustrate the phenomenon

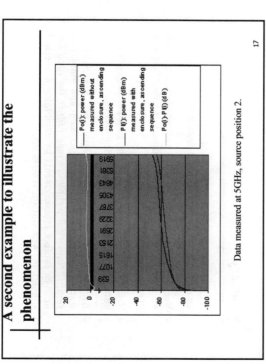

Legend:
- Po(f): power (dBm) measured without enclosure, ascending sequence
- P(f): power (dBm) measured with enclosure, ascending sequence
- Po(f)-P(f) (dB)

Data measured at 5GHz, source position 2.

17

Data reduction by different methods

A practical measurement of the different definitions of shielding as described is highly time consuming and therefore undesirable. Both statistical methods and numerical modelling are under development to reduce the measurement work.

18

Data reduction: Statistical method

- **The PDF of the power measured: Rayleigh distribution**

Example of the PDF of the power measured without/ with enclosure, cylindrical scan, 1GHz, source position 3

- **Can the new measure of Shielding defined by the PDF?**

19

Data reduction: Numerical modelling

- Numerical simulations based on the transmission-line matrix modeling method are employed.

- So far numerical modeling is not expected to predict the emission pattern accurately at frequencies higher than 1GHz.

- Numerical modeling can be expected to predict the relative values of the experiment results, such as the uncertainty due to limited sample points.

20

Data reduction: Future work

- **Why does the PDF look like a Rayleigh distribution? What is the mechanism? Can we define the Shielding by the PDF?**

- **Try to reduce the experiment points both outside and inside the enclosure by the application of some other statistical methods, such as correlation analysis and regression.**

22

Data reduction: Numerical modelling

■Comparison between statistics of experiment and statistics of simulation

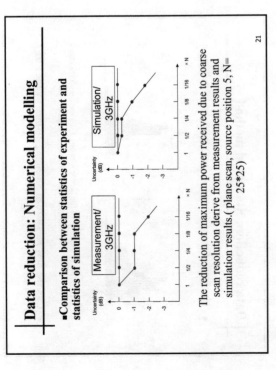

The reduction of maximum power received due to coarse scan resolution derive from measurement results and simulation results.(plane scan, source position 5, N= 25*25)

21

Summary

- It is not suitable to evaluate the shielding performance of an enclosure with the traditional definition of SE.

- Because of the complexity of the radiated fields, it seems hard to find a simple rule to estimate the shielding of a practical enclosure.

- Several new measures of Shielding based on the emission pattern are proposed here to elicit comment.

- By resorting to TLM technique, we can achieve statistical agreement between experiment and simulation results. Numerical techniques may reduce the need for or even replace measurements by combining numerical simulations with statistical methods.

23

Nested Reverberation Chamber Measurements for the Shielding Effectiveness of Advanced Materials

C.L. Holloway
National Institute of Standards and Technology (NIST)
Boulder, CO 80305, USA
303-497-6184
holloway@boulder.nist.gov

2005 IEEEE International Symposium on Electromagnetic Compatibility,
August 8-12, 2005, Chicago, IL, USA

Conventional Methods of Measuring Shielding

Normal Incident Plane-Wave

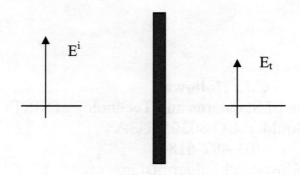

$$SE = -10 Log_{10} \left(\frac{P_t}{P_i} \right)$$

Coaxial TEM Fixture: ASTM Standards Methods

However, these approaches determine SE for only a very limited set of incident wave conditions.

Realistic Environment

In most applications, ACMs are exposed to complex electromagnetic environments where fields are incident on the material with various polarizations and angles of incidence.

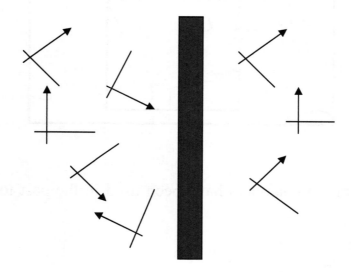

Therefore, a test methodology that better represents this type of environment would be beneficial.

Nested Reverberation Chamber

A reverberation-chamber SE test offers such an environment.

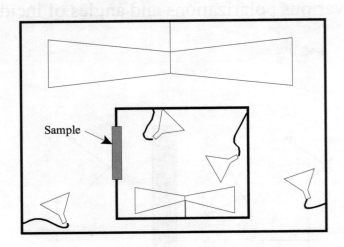

Nested reverberation chambers have been used in the past to determine the SE of material

$$SE_1 = -10 Log_{10}\left(\frac{P_{ic,s}}{P_{oc,s}}\right)$$

where $P_{ic,s}$ is the power received inside the inner chamber with a sample, and $P_{oc,s}$ is the power received in the outer chamber with a sample in the aperture and source in the outer chamber.

The received powers and power densities are actually ensemble averages that are obtained from a large number of stirrer (tuner) positions, where stirrers are located in both the inner and outer chamber.

Nested Reverberation Chambers

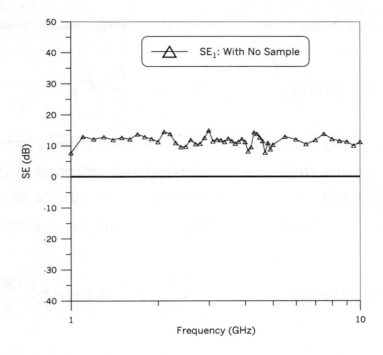

There appears to be shielding with no sample in the aperture.

The power that couples into the inner chamber is a function of aperture, cavity-size, and chamber loading effects.

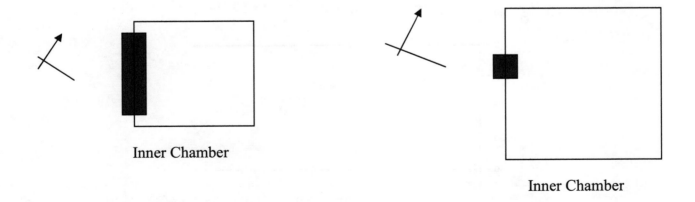

Inner Chamber

Inner Chamber

Thus, corrections are needed to accurately account for aperture, cavity-size, and chamber loading effects.

Proposed IEC 61000-4-21 Corrections

IEC 61000-4-21: EMC, Part 4: Testing and measurement techniques; Section 21: Reverberation chamber test methods, International Electrotechnical Commission

$$SE_2 = -10Log_{10}\left(\frac{P_{ic,s}}{P_{oc,s}}\right) + 10Log_{10}\left(\frac{P_{rQ,in,s}}{P_{tx,in,s}}\right),$$

where $P_{rQ,in,s}$ is the measured power in the inner chamber with a sample in the aperture for a transmitting antenna located in the inner chamber with an output power $P_{tx,in,s}$. It can be shown that the ratio $P_{rQ,in,s}/P_{tx,in,s}$ is directly proportional to the inner chamber quality factor Q:

$$SE_2 = -10Log_{10}\left(\frac{P_{ic,s}}{P_{oc,s}}\right) + Log_{10}(Q) - 10Log_{10}\left(\frac{16\pi^2 V}{\lambda^3}\right)$$

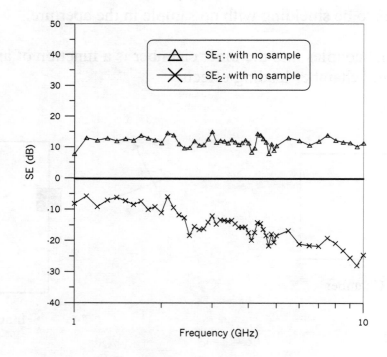

We have gain!

New Approach

Start with:

$$SE_3 = -10 Log_{10} \left(\frac{P_{t,s} / S_s^{inc}}{P_{t,ns} / S_{ns}^{inc}} \right)$$

where $P_{t,s}$ is the power transmitted through an aperture with a sample, $P_{t,ns}$ is the power transmitted through the same aperture with no sample (i.e., open aperture), and S_s^{inc} and S_{ns}^{inc} are respectively the power densities incident onto the aperture with and without the sample.

Defined in this way, all the environmental effects have been removed or normalized out and only the effects of the materials in the aperture are accounted for.

The powers transmitted through the aperture can be expressed in terms of an effective cross section, where

$$P_{t,s} = \sigma_{t,s} \, S_s^{inc}$$
$$P_{t,ns} = \sigma_{t,ns} \, S_{ns}^{inc}$$

In this expression, $\sigma_{t,s}$ and $\sigma_{t,ns}$ are the respective effective cross sections of the aperture with and without a sample.

Thus,

$$SE_3 = -10 Log_{10} \left(\frac{\sigma_{t,s}}{\sigma_{t,ns}} \right)$$

This expression states that the SE is just the ratio of the effective cross section of the aperture with and without a sample in the aperture.

This definition of SE is now basically a function of only the material under test.

New Approach

These effective cross sections can be expressed as

$$\sigma_{t,s} = \frac{S_{in,s}}{S_{o,s}} \frac{2\pi V}{\lambda Q_{in,s}}$$

$$\sigma_{t,ns} = \frac{S_{in,ns}}{S_{o,ns}} \frac{2\pi V}{\lambda Q_{in,ns}}$$

where $S_{in,s}$ and $S_{in,ns}$ are respectively the power densities in the inner chamber with and without the sample, $S_{o,s}$ and $S_{o,ns}$ are respectively the power densities in the outer chamber with and without the sample, $Q_{in,s}$ and $Q_{in,ns}$ are respectively the quality factors of the inner chamber with and without a sample, V is the volume of the inner chamber, and λ is the wavelength.

Each of the power densities S can be expressed in terms of the measured power P through an effective area ($\lambda^2/(8\pi)$) of the receiving antenna by the following

$$S = \frac{8\pi}{\lambda^2} P$$

With this expression we have

$$SE_3 = -10 Log_{10}\left(\frac{P_{r,in,s}}{P_{r,in,ns}} \frac{P_{r,o,ns}}{P_{r,o,s}} \frac{Q_{in,ns}}{Q_{in,s}} \right)$$

From this expression for SE, it is shown that the SE is a function of the ratio of two Qs of the inner chamber (with and without a sample), and not just in terms of a single Q of the inner chamber with a sample covering the aperture (as suggested in the proposed IEC approach).

New Approach

It is shown that the quality factors $Q_{in,s}$ and $Q_{in,ns}$ can be expressed as

$$Q_{in,s} = \frac{16\pi^2 \, V}{\lambda^3} \frac{P_{rQ,in,s}}{P_{tx,in,s}}$$

$$Q_{in,ns} = \frac{16\pi^2 \, V}{\lambda^3} \frac{P_{rQ,in,ns}}{P_{tx,in,ns}}$$

Thus,

$$SE_3 = -10 Log_{10} \left(\frac{P_{r,in,s}}{P_{r,in,ns}} \frac{P_{r,o,ns}}{P_{r,o,s}} \frac{P_{rQ,in,ns}}{P_{rQ,in,s}} \frac{P_{tx,in,s}}{P_{tx,in,ns}} \right)$$

Here again, it is readily seen in this equation that all four ratios are equal to 1 when no sample is in place and that the SE reduces to zero.

This expression can be thought of as a first-order measurement of the SE. A zeroth-order SE can be obtained by assuming that the wall loss is dominant in both cavities. Under this condition

$$\frac{P_{r,o,ns}}{P_{r,o,s}} \approx 1 \quad \& \quad \frac{Q_{in,ns}}{Q_{in,s}} \approx 1$$

and

$$SE_4 = -10 Log_{10} \left(\frac{P_{r,in,s}}{P_{r,in,ns}} \right)$$

By zeroth-order, we mean that changes in chamber loading and Q are neglected. The first-order result includes such effects, but does not include the possible effects of multiple interactions between the two chambers.

No Sample

It is readily seen in this equation that this ratio is 1 for no sample and that the SE reduces to zero, as it should.

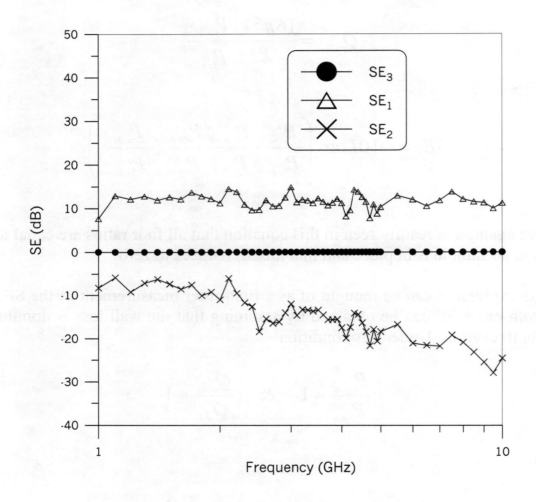

Measured Shielding Effectiveness of Different ACM

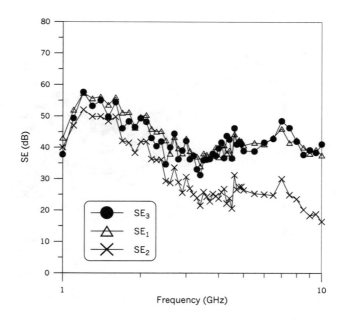

SE obtained from the three approaches with Material 1 in the aperture.

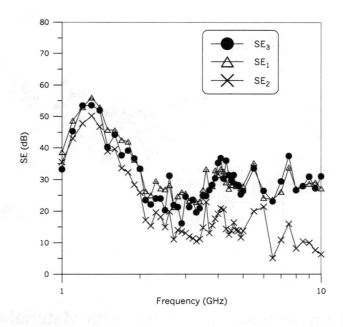

SE obtained from the three approaches with Material 2 in the aperture.

Measured Shielding Effectiveness of Different ACM

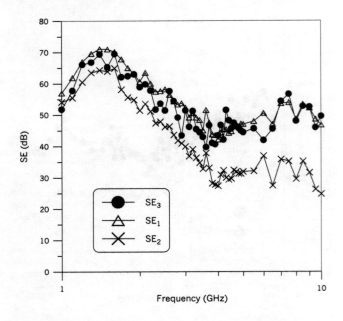

SE obtained from the three approaches with Material 3 in the aperture.

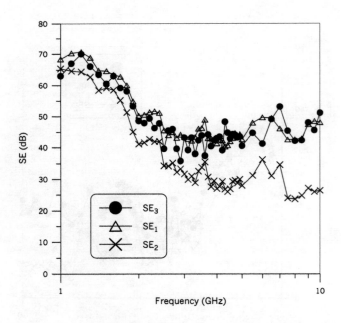

SE obtained from the three approaches with Material 4 in the aperture.

Comparison of All four Materials

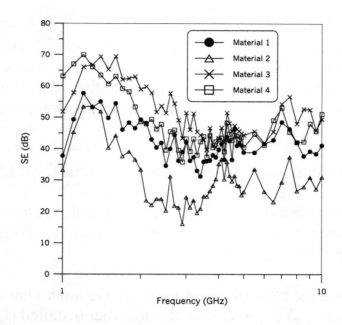

A comparison of the SE for the four different materials obtained using SE_3.

Description of the composites materials used in this study.

Material #	Type	Thickness
Material 1	Carbon fiber	1mm
Material 2	Sandwich: external fiber glass with inside carbon fiber	4 mm
Material 3	Carbon fiber	1.5 mm
Material 4	Carbon fabric with external rubber coating	0.5 mm

This comparison shows that Material 3 offers the best shielding, while Material 2 has the worst shielding.

Aperture and Chamber Size Effects

If the SE measurement correctly accounts for cavity and aperture size effects, then the same SE results should be obtained if one or both of the cavity size or aperture size is varied. To confirm that this is indeed the situation, the SE for the four different materials were measured in two different chambers.

Unfortunately, we only had one inner chamber with a fixed aperture size.

Therefore, to simulate a different inner chamber, electromagnetic absorbing material was placed in the inner chamber. This had the effect of altering the inner chamber, by lowering its Q.

This Figure shows the ratio of the in the Q of the inner chamber without the absorber installed (Q_{na}) to the Q with the absorber installed (Q_a).

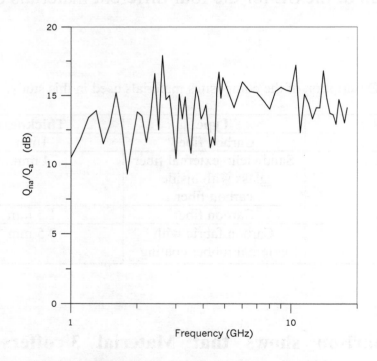

Notice that the ratio has changed by 10 to 15 dB over the frequency range.

Aperture and Chamber Size Effects

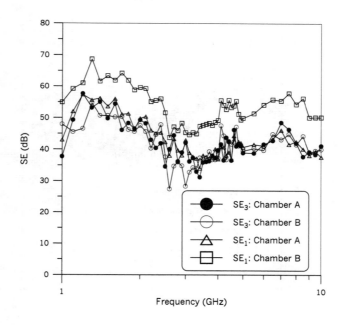

A comparison of SE for the two different chambers with Material 1 in the aperture.

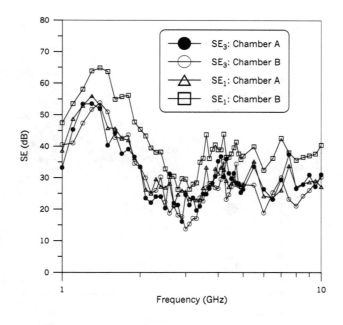

A comparison of SE for the two different chambers with Material 2 in the aperture.

Aperture and Chamber Size Effects

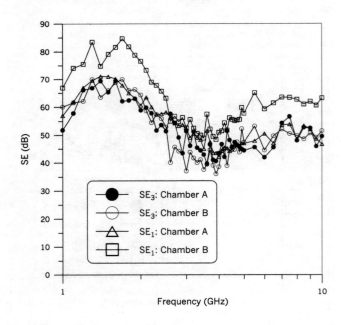

A comparison of SE for the two different chambers with Material 3 in the aperture.

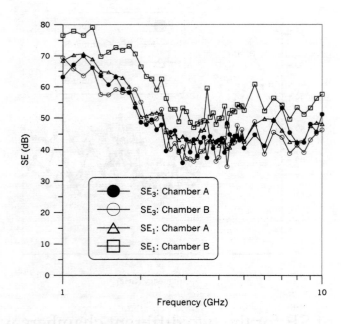

A comparison of SE for the two different chambers with Material 4 in the aperture.

Aperture and Chamber Size Effects

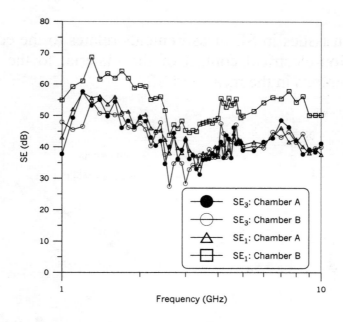

A comparison of SE for the two different chambers with Material 1 in the aperture.

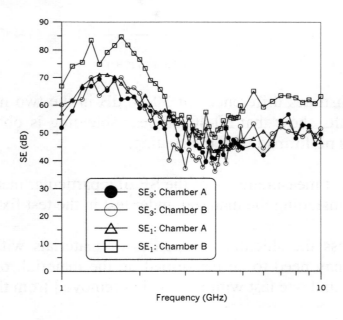

A comparison of SE for the two different chambers with Material 3 in the aperture.

Edge Treatment Effects

One of the main issues in SE measurements relates to the edge treatment of the material. Non-electrical contact of the material to the test fixture can cause large variations in the measured SE.

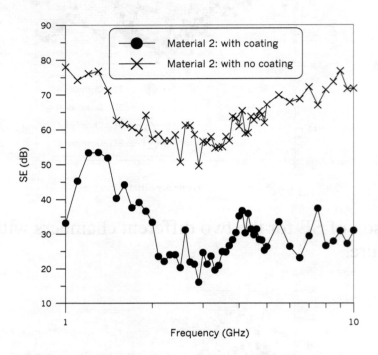

This Figure illustrates differences of 30-40 dB in the two measurements of SE. These results show that 30-40 dB less shielding is obtained when the measurement is performed with the coating.

To ensure correct measurements of the SE of a particular material, care must be taken when installing the material under test in the test fixture.

In fact, to assess the shielding properties of materials with coatings, two separate tests may need to be performed on the material: one test with the coating present and one test with the coating removed from the edges.

Edge Treatment Effects

We also investigated the effects of tightness of the sample within the test fixture.

The Figure shows results of Material 4 for various values of torque pressure (i.e., the tightness of the cover plate in the test fixture).

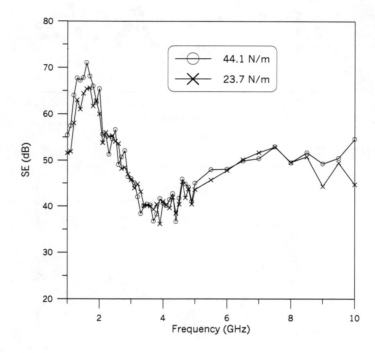

The SE of this sample is affected little by the tightness of the aperture cover.

Edge Treatment Effects

COATINGS

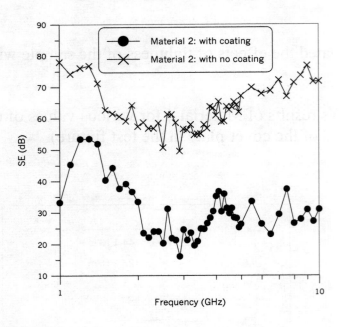

TORQUE PRESSURE

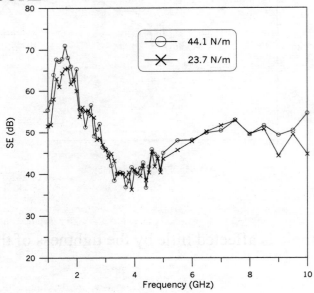

To ensure correct measurements of the SE of a particular material, care must be taken when installing the material under test in the test fixture.

In fact, to assess the shielding properties of materials with coatings, two separate tests may need to be performed on the material: one test with the coating present and one test with the coating removed from the edges.

Summary

1) We review existing techniques for measuring shielding effectiveness of materials.

2) We discussed limitations of existing approaches.

3) We presented a new technique for determining the shielding effectiveness of materials from nested reverberation-chamber measurements.

4) The new approach accounts for aperture, cavity-size, and chamber loading effects.

5) Various examples are presented to illustrate the utility of the new approach.

6) We discussed edge treatments of the materials in a given test fixture.

OBJECTIVES

A standard method for the measurement of the shielding effectiveness of enclosures is reported in the IEEE Std.299-1997, which addresses to "large" enclosures having minimum dimension greater than 2 m in the frequency range from 9 kHz to 18 GHz. A revision of this standard was completed in August 2004.

The scope of the workshop is to present the latest version of the IEEE Std. 299, by highlighting the new features included in the Aug. 2004 revision and the open issues.

OUTLINE

"Shielding effectiveness of enclosures: an introduction"
Maria Sabrina Sarto, Univ. of Rome "La Sapienza"

"The Benefits of Using IEEE Std 299 for Shielding Effectiveness Testing - Update"
Dale Swetanoff, D.L.S. Electronic Systems

2005 IEEE International Symposium on EMC
Chicago (CA), Aug.8-12, 2005

Workshop organized by WG IEEE Std.299

The shielding effectiveness of enclosures: theory and measurement techniques

organized by:

Maria Sabrina Sarto
Univ. of Rome "La Sapienza"
Department of Electrical
Engineering

Johan Catrysse
Department of Industrial and
Technological Sciences

Katholieke Hogeschool Brugge
Oostende - KHBO

The new project on the definition of a guideline for the measurement of the SE of "small" enclosure, with reference to the different possible applications, size and material of the box under test, is presented.

The use of reverberation chambers for the SE measurement of enclosures, according to the standard IEC 61000-4-21 is also discussed.

"Shielding characterisation of small enclosures: actual status and IEEE P299-2 proposal"

Johan Catrysse, KHBO, Oostende, Belgium

"Suggested Definitions of Shielding for Enclosures at Microwave Frequencies"

Andy Marvin, Univ. of York, UK

"Nested Reverberation Chamber Measurements for the Shielding Effectiveness of Advanced Materials"

Chris Holloway, NIST, Boulder, CO

WORKSHOP: PRODUCT SAFETY (FR-AM-WS-15)
Richard Georgerian

The Product Safety Workshop is intended to provide a practical overview of several key product safety areas. Each presentation provides an overview of current requirements and up-coming changes, then focus on areas of interest, based on technical complexity or regulatory changes.

The final element of the workshop will be a dialog covering areas of particular interest, there will be a panel discussion open to all topics.

In the past, the Product Safety Workshop has attracted a wide audience ranging from product safety experts looking for an exchange of information to EMC engineers wishing to get background in product safety and up-coming regulations. The workshop is a good opportunity to compare notes and see more of the forest after focusing on the trees. It is an opportunity to meet and hear some of the leaders in the respective fields.

Presentations:

(1) Risk of Fire: Enclosure Design & Internal Plastics
Bill Bisenius

(2) Alternative Method for Determining Minimum Clearances
Dave Lorusso

(3) How EMI Can Cause Functional Safety Problems
Keith Armstrong

NOTES

ED&D

Presented by
Bill Bisenius – President, NCE/NCT
billb@productsafeT.com

Educated Design & Development, Inc.
2200-215 Gateway Centre Blvd., Morrisville, NC
Tel: 919-469-9434; Fax: 919-469-5743
www.productsafeT.com

Product Safety Consulting, Test Equipment &
Training Services
from
People Who Know Product Safety

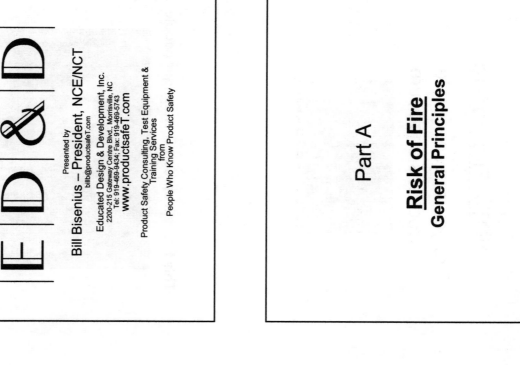

Part A

Risk of Fire
General Principles

Risk of Fire

Enclosure Design

&

Internal Plastics

Don't let this be your product

NOT a Fire Hazard

Smoke coming from the product

NOT a Fire Hazard

Fire you can see inside the product's enclosure

Fire Hazard Definition

Fire is only considered a "hazard" if it spreads beyond the product's enclosure

This fire will spread & endanger people

Risk of Fire - Requirements

1) Construct to contain fires,
2) Space & insulate to limit fires and,
3) Test to verify no fires

Flammability of Materials

- PWB's   min. V-1
- Wiring   VW-1
- Plastic Enclosure
  : products up to 40 lbs   min. V-2
  : products over 40 lbs   min. 5V

Part B

Risk of Fire - Prevention
The Requirements

Fire Containment

- Limit temperatures on flammable materials = temperature testing
- Limit flammability of combustible materials = flame ratings
- Properly size & position vents

Fire Containment - Vents

Prevent igniting the support surface

➡️

NO flaming particles through vents

Flame Rating System

HB or HBF = Most Flammable

V-2   =

V-1   =

V-0   =

5V   = Least Flammable

Enclosure Side Openings

Position and size vents
and internal flammable materials
to prevent particles from falling
through vents

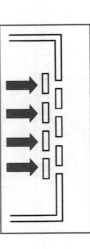

Enclosure Vent Openings

- Top Openings = shock hazard only
- Side Openings = 5° drip concern
- Bottom Openings = AVOID

Enclosure Bottom Openings

- Best advice is to avoid
- NEVER have openings under component side of PWB
- Sometimes ok under wires/motors
- Sometimes ok if very small openings
- Other option is to baffle openings

Enclosure Side Openings

Fire can drip from flammable materials and drift by up to 5° from vertical

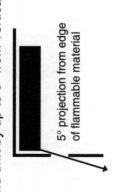

5° projection from edge of flammable material

Risk of Fire - Tests

Tissue Paper = under product
Cheese Cloth = draped over product

Risk of Fire - Tests

Verify no fire outside of the enclosure under single fault and abnormal operating conditions

Part C

Risk of Fire - Protection
Design Guidelines

Selecting Plastic Materials

- Is the material certified?
- What is the flammability rating at the thickness & color used?
- Within temperature ratings of material?
- Any conductive coatings? Certified for application to this specific material?
- Are other physical properties needed? (i.e. HWI, HAI, CTI, etc.)

Risk of Fire – Test Indicators

Discoloration of tissue paper or cheese cloth = Fire outside of enclosure

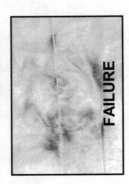

FAILURE

Enclosure Design

- No bottom openings
- No flammable materials within 5° of side openings
  : Vertical side openings = bad
  : Horizontal side openings = good
  : With horizontal vents, by adjusting vent height and material thickness, you can eliminate 5° concern = mount closer to vent

Risk of Fire
Enclosure Design & Internal Plastics
CONCLUSION

Risk of Fire - Summary

1) Construct to contain fires,
2) Space & insulate to limit fires and,
3) Test to verify no fires

E D & D

William S. Bisenius (Bill)

- 21+ years of Product Safety experience
- NCE/NCT
- BSEE from SJSU (IEEE student chapter President)
- President/Co-Founder of E.D.& D.
- Former Engineering Group Leader for UL = ITE, Lab, Lasers, Appliances, Seminars
- Develops Product Safety Test Equipment
- Consultant/Seminar Leader in ITE, Lab, Medical, Lasers, IP Codes, Appliances

Alternative Method for Determining Minimum Clearances

Dave Lorusso

DELL Inc

Overview

- Insulation Coordination
- Determination of Clearance per IEC product standards
- How to use the www.creepage.com tool
- Alternative method procedure summary
- Alternative method - Details
- Wrap up

Insulation Coordination

- Insulation coordination concepts are documented in IEC 60664
- Addresses the dynamics between:
  - How and where the equipment is used, and
  - How the equipment is designed

Installation Category → IV

Clearance and Creepage

- Clearance (1.2.10.1)
  - The shortest distance between 2 conductive parts measured through air.
  - Also called "through-air spacing"
  - Uses Peak Voltage
- Creepage (1.2.10.2)
  - The shortest path between 2 conductive parts measured along the surface of the insulation.
  - Also called "over-surface spacing"
  - Uses rms Voltage

From IEC 60950-1

Table 2H – Minimum clearances for insulation in primary circuits, and between primary and secondary circuits

---

From IEC 60950-1

Table 2K – Minimum clearances in secondary circuits

Insulation Coordination Factors

- Working Voltage (Peak or rms)
- Nominal Mains Supply Voltage (120, 240, …)
  - Transient Voltage (800 V, 1500 V, 2500 V)
- Installation Category (I, II, III, IV)
- Insulation Type (F, B, S, D, R)
- Pollution Degree (1, 2, 3)
- Material Group (I, II, IIIa or IIIb)
- Electric Strength Value (across insulation)

From IEC 60950-1

Table 2J – Additional clearances for insulation in primary circuits with peak working voltage exceeding the peak value of the nominal a.c. mains supply voltage

Clearance

- To determine, need to know…
  - Peak voltage
  - Nominal mains supply voltage
  - Transient Voltage (800 V, 1500 V, 2500 V)
  - Installation category
  - Pollution degree
  - Insulation Type

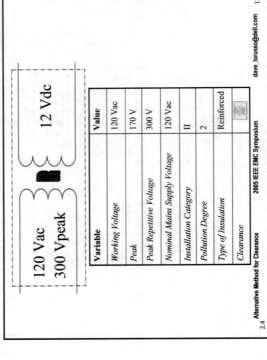

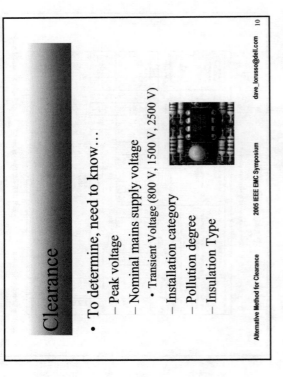

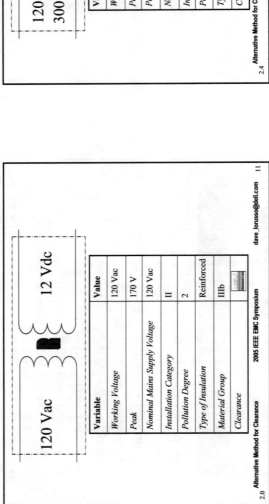

120 Vac
300 Vpeak

12 Vdc

Variable	Value
Working Voltage	120 Vac
Peak	170 V
Peak Repetitive Voltage	300 V
Nominal Mains Supply Voltage	120 Vac
Installation Category	II
Pollution Degree	2
Type of Insulation	Reinforced
Clearance	

2.4

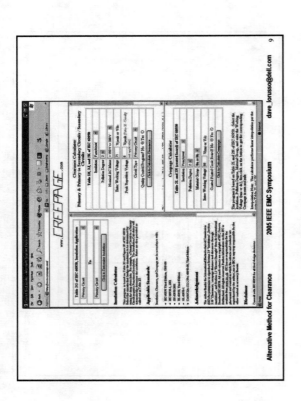

120 Vac

12 Vdc

Variable	Value
Working Voltage	120 Vac
Peak	170 V
Nominal Mains Supply Voltage	120 Vac
Installation Category	II
Pollution Degree	2
Type of Insulation	Reinforced
Material Group	IIIb
Clearance	

2.0

Procedure Summary

- Minimum clearances depend on the REQUIRED WITHSTAND VOLTAGE

- REQUIRED WITHSTAND VOLTAGE depends on the combined effect of the normal operating voltage (including repetitive peaks) and non-repetitive overvoltages from external transients

Alternative Method for Clearance   2005 IEEE EMC Symposium   dave_lorusso@dell.com   13

From IEC 60950-1, Annex G

Table G.2 – Minimum clearances up to 2 000 m above sea level

REQUIRED WITHSTAND VOLTAGE V peak or d.c.	Minimum CLEARANCES in air		CLEARANCES in millimetres
	FUNCTIONAL INSULATION (0.1)	BASIC INSULATION and SUPPLEMENTARY INSULATION (0.1)	REINFORCED INSULATION (0.2)
Up to 400	0,1	0,2	0,4
800	0,1	0,2	0,4
1 000	0,2	0,3	0,6
1 200	0,3	0,4	0,8
1 500	0,5 (0,5)	0,8 (0,5)	1,6 (1)
2 000	1 (1)	1,3 (1)	2,6 (2)
2 500	1,5 (1,5)	2 (1,5)	4 (3)
3 000	2 (2)	2,6 (2)	5,2 (4)
4 000	3 (3)	4 (3)	6
6 000	5,5	7,5	11
8 000	8	11	16
10 000	11	15	22
12 000	14	19	28
15 000	18	24	36
25 000	33	44	66
40 000	60	80	120
50 000	75	100	150
60 000	90	120	180
80 000	130	173	260

Alternative Method for Clearance   2005 IEEE EMC Symposium   dave_lorusso@dell.com   14

Determining minimum value for Clearance - Equipment not connected to a TELECOMMUNICATION NETWORK

1. Measure the PEAK WORKING VOLTAGE across the CLEARANCE
2a. Determine MAINS TRANSIENT VOLTAGE (G.2)
2b. For AC MAINS SUPPLY equipment, calculate the peak value of the nominal AC MAINS SUPPLY voltage
3. Determine REQUIRED WITHSTAND VOLTAGE using rules in item a) of G.4 and the above voltage values – covers:
   - PRIMARY CIRCUIT receiving unattenuated mains transient;
   - SECONDARY CIRCUIT whose PRIMARY CIRCUIT receives unattenuated mains transient;
   - PRIMARY and SECONDARY CIRCUIT not receiving unattenuated mains transient;
   - SECONDARY CIRCUIT supplied by d.c. source with capacitive filtering
7. Use the REQUIRED WITHSTAND VOLTAGE to determine the minimum CLEARANCE (G.6)

Alternative Method for Clearance   2005 IEEE EMC Symposium   dave_lorusso@dell.com   15

Determine MAINS TRANSIENT VOLTAGE

1. Measure the PEAK WORKING VOLTAGE across the CLEARANCE in question
2a. Determine MAINS TRANSIENT VOLTAGE (G.2)

Table G.1 – Mains transient voltages

Nominal AC MAINS SUPPLY voltage line-to-neutral up to and including V r.m.s.	MAINS TRANSIENT VOLTAGE V_{peak}			
	Overvoltage category			
	I	II	III	IV
50	330	500	800	1 500
100	500	800	1 500	2 500
150 [1]	800	1 500	2 500	4 000
300 [2]	1 500	2 500	4 000	6 000
600 [3]	2 500	4 000	6 000	8 000

1) Including 120/208 or 120/240 V.
2) Including 230/400 or 277/480 V.
3) Including 400/690 V.

Alternative Method for Clearance   2005 IEEE EMC Symposium   dave_lorusso@dell.com   16

Slide 17

Determine REQUIRED WITHSTAND VOLTAGE

3. Use the rules in item a) of G.4 and:
   - PEAK WORKING VOLTAGE across the CLEARANCE in question
   - MAINS TRANSIENT VOLTAGE
   - peak value of the nominal AC MAINS SUPPLY voltage (for AC MAINS SUPPLY Equipment)

- Rule 1 and 2 of item a) of G.4
   - Assume PRIMARY CIRCUIT receives unattenuated mains transients
   - ignore effect of transients from a TELECOMMUNICATION NETWORK

Slide 18

REQUIRED WITHSTAND VOLTAGE for PRIMARY CIRCUIT receiving the unattenuated mains transient

- Rule 1: if U_{pw} < peak value of the nominal AC MAINS SUPPLY voltage:

$$U_{required\ withstand} = U_{mains\ transient}$$

- Rule 2: if U_{pw} > peak value of the nominal AC MAINS SUPPLY voltage:

$$U_{required\ withstand} = U_{mains\ transient} + U_{pw} - U_{mains\ peak}$$

7. Use the REQUIRED WITHSTAND VOLTAGE to determine the minimum CLEARANCE (G.6)

Slide 19

REQUIRED WITHSTAND VOLTAGE for SECONDARY CIRCUIT whose PRIMARY CIRCUIT receives the unattenuated mains transient

- Apply Rules 1 and 2 above
- Replace the MAINS TRANSIENT VOLTAGE with a voltage one step smaller than:
   - 330, 500, 800, 1 500, 2 500, 4 000, 6 000 and 8 000 Vpeak
- Reduction is only permitted for a floating SECONDARY CIRCUIT in equipment with a main protective earthing terminal and is separated from its PRIMARY CIRCUIT by an earthed metal screen connected to protective earth per 2.6 of 60950
- Alternatively, Rules 1 and 2 are applied, but the voltage determined by measurement (item a) of G.5) is taken as the MAINS TRANSIENT VOLTAGE

Slide 20

REQUIRED WITHSTAND VOLTAGE for SECONDARY CIRCUIT Supplied by a d.c. source having capacitive filtering

- In any earthed SECONDARY CIRCUIT supplied by a d.c. source with capacitive filtering, the REQUIRED WITHSTAND VOLTAGE shall be taken as equal to the DC VOLTAGE

Slide 21

REQUIRED WITHSTAND VOLTAGE for PRIMARY and SECONDARY CIRCUITS not receiving the unattenuated mains transient

- Apply Rules 1 and 2 above
- Reduced level of transient voltage is determined by measuring the voltage across the CLEARANCE in question using the impulse test generator reference 2 of table N.1 (1.2/50 uS)
  - U_c is equal to the MAINS TRANSIENT VOLTAGE determined in G.2
  - 3 to 6 impulses of alternating polarity, with 1 S intervals, are applied between each:
    - line-to-line;
    - all line conductors conductively joined together and neutral;
    - all line conductors conductively joined together and earth;
    - neutral and protective earth

Slide 22

Determining minimum value for Clearance - Equipment connected to a TELECOMMUNICATION NETWORK

1. Measure the PEAK WORKING VOLTAGE across the CLEARANCE
2a. Determine MAINS TRANSIENT VOLTAGE (G.2)
2b. For AC MAINS SUPPLY equipment, calculate the peak value of the nominal AC MAINS SUPPLY voltage
3. Determine REQUIRED WITHSTAND VOLTAGE using rules in item a) of G.4 and the above voltage values
4. Determine the TELECOMMUNICATIONS NETWORK TRANSIENT VOLTAGE (G.3)
   - if not known: 1500 V_{peak} for TNV-1 and TNV-3;
   - 800 V_{peak} for TNV-2

Slide 23

Determining minimum value for Clearance - Equipment connected to a TELECOMMUNICATION NETWORK

5a. Determine the REQUIRED WITHSTAND VOLTAGE using the rules in item b) of G.4 and the TELECOMMUNICATIONS NETWORK TRANSIENT VOLTAGE above
   - REQUIRED WITHSTAND VOLTAGE is 1500 V_{peak} or 800 V_{peak} unless a lower level is measured when tested according to item b) of Clause G.5 (next slide)
5b. If no mains or internal transients, go to step 7
6. Determine the REQUIRED WITHSTAND VOLTAGE using the rules in item c) of G.4:
   If Mains and/or Internal transients and Telecommunication Network transients are involved, the REQUIRED WITHSTAND VOLTAGE is the larger of the two voltages. The two values shall not be added together.
7. Use the REQUIRED WITHSTAND VOLTAGE to determine the minimum CLEARANCE (G.6).

Slide 24

REQUIRED WITHSTAND VOLTAGE for Transients due to TELECOMMUNICATION NETWORK TRANSIENT VOLTAGES

- Reduced level of transient voltage is determined by measuring the voltage across the CLEARANCE in question using the impulse test generator reference 1 of table N.1 (10/700 uS)
  - U_c is equal to the TELECOMMUNICATION NETWORK TRANSIENT VOLTAGE determined in G.3
  - 3 to 6 impulses of alternating polarity, with 1 S intervals, are applied between:
    - each pair of terminals (for example, A and B or tip and ring) in an interface;
    - all terminals of a single interface type joined together and earth

Slide 25

N.2 IEC 60065 impulse test generator

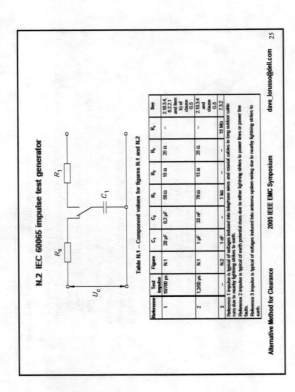

Table N.1 – Component values for figures N.1 and N.2

Reference	Test impulse	Figure	C_1	C_2	C_3	R_1	R_2	R_3	R_4	See
1	10/700 µs	N.1	20 µF	0.2 µF	50 Ω	15 Ω	25 Ω	—	2,10.3.4, 6.2.2.1 and item b) of clause G.5
2	1.2/50 µs	N.1	1 µF	1 µF	76 Ω	13 Ω	25 Ω	—	2,10.3.4 and clause G.5
3	—	N.2	1 nF	—	1 kΩ	—	—	15 MΩ	7.3.2

Reference 1 impulse is typical of voltages induced into telephone wires and coaxial cables in long outdoor cable runs due to nearby lightning strikes to earth.

Reference 2 impulse is typical of earth potential rises due to either lightning strikes to power lines or power line faults.

Reference 3 impulse is typical of voltages induced into antenna system wiring due to nearby lightning strikes to earth.

Slide 26

Wrap Up

- Insulation Coordination
- Determination of Clearance per IEC product standards
- How to use the **www.creepage.com** tool
- Alternative method procedure summary
- Alternative method - Details
- Additional material can be found at:

  www.creepage.com

Slide 27

Wrap Up

- Thank you for your participation
- References
  - UL 60950-1 "Information Technology Equipment – Safety – Part 1: General Requirements, First Edition, April 1, 2003
  - Lorusso, Dave, 2004 IEEE EMC Symposium, FR-AM-WS-13: TC-8 Product Safety Workshop, "Creepage and Clearance Tutorial"
- Resources:
  - **www.creepage.com**
  - **www.lorusso.com** or call me at 512-695-5871

Slide 28

About Dave Lorusso

Dave Lorusso has worked in the field of Compliance Engineering his entire career, 25 years. Dave started his career as an Approvals Engineer for Factory Mutual Research Corporation, Norwood, MA, a Nationally Recognized Testing Laboratory (NRTL). He worked for eight other companies as a Compliance Engineer, Compliance Manager, and Product Integrity Director, prior to starting Lorusso Technologies LLC (www.lorusso.com), a consulting firm specializing in regulatory compliance.

Dave is currently working full-time for Dell Inc., Austin, TX, as a Senior Regulatory Consultant, ensuring that Dell's products meet worldwide regulatory requirements prior to shipment. Dave can be reached at:

» dave_lorusso@dell.com
» dave@lorusso.com
» 512-695-5871

Natural sources of EM threats (disturbances)

- **Electrostatic discharge (ESD)**
  - from people, furniture, and machinery

- **Lightning**
  - direct strikes only to exposed equipment or conductors
  - but its indirect effects can cause surges (overvoltages) in power distribution networks
  - and in any long cables (e.g. telephone, signal, control)

Personnel ESD waveform — kV, ns

EM threats from electrical power distribution continued...

- **Transient over-voltages** (e.g. due to thunderstorms and reactive load switching such as large motors or capacitor banks)

  - example of unidirectional surge — kV, kA, µs - ms

  - example of 'oscillatory wave' — kV, kA, µs - ms

  - example of 'ring wave' — kV, kA, ns - ms

How EMI can cause functional safety problems

Eur Ing Keith Armstrong

Cherry Clough Consultants
Denshaw, U.K.

tel: +44 (0)1457 871 605
keith.armstrong@cherryclough.com

EM threats (disturbances) associated with electrical power distribution

- **AC waveform distortion** (example is from Israel) — %, 50Hz - 2kHz

- **Continuous radio frequency** (RF voltages and currents) — V, kHz - GHz

EM threats (disturbances) caused by electrical power use

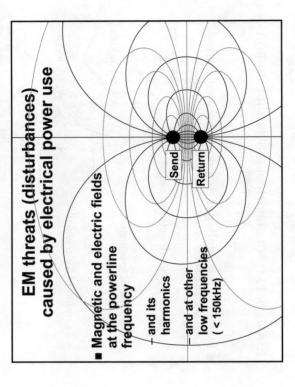

Send | Return

- Magnetic and electric fields at the powerline frequency
  – and its harmonics
  – and at other low frequencies (<150kHz)

EM threats (disturbances) from intentional radiators

- Radio and TV broadcast transmitters, civilian and military radars (fixed and mobile)
  - aircraft spec's went from 1 to 6000 V/m over 15 years
- Plastics welders, induction furnaces, microwave ovens and dryers, etc.
- Cellphones, walkie-talkies, wireless LANs
  - even low-power cellphones have strong fields nearby

EM threats from electrical power distribution   continued...

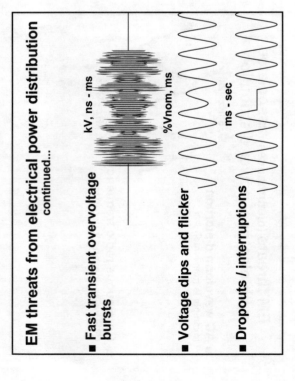

- Fast transient overvoltage bursts   kV, ns - ms
- Voltage dips and flicker   %Vnom, ms
- Dropouts / interruptions   ms - sec

EM threats (disturbances) caused by electrical power use   continued...

- Broadband random noise emissions (0 - 400GHz) from all arcs and sparks
  – from switches, relays, motor commutators, slip-rings, bad connections, arc-welding, insulation breakdown, earth-faults, etc.

What distance from a 'hand-held' is equivalent to the immunity test levels under EMC and Medical Device Directives?

Most immunity standards only test up to 1GHz, so don't cover...

V/m, GHz

- 1.8GHz GSM, 2GHz 3G cellphones

- Microwave ovens, industrial heaters and dryers (usually 2.45 GHz, but can be 0.6 - 5GHz)

- Wireless LANs (1.8, 1.9, 2.45 and 5 GHz)

- Radar (airports and aircraft, harbours, ships, intelligent cruise control on cars) up to 77GHz

- Microwave communications (up to 60GHz) use narrow beams and low power – not usually a threat when off the beam's line

EM threats (disturbances) from *unintentional* radiators

- Everything which uses electricity or electronics always 'leaks' and so emits some EM disturbances

  – the higher the rate of change of voltage or current, the worse the emissions tend to be

- Power and signals in devices, printed circuit board (PCB) traces, wires and cables leak EM waves

- Shielded enclosures leak EM waves from apertures, gaps and joints

Typical type of transmitter or radiator	For 3V/m Domestic, commercial and light industrial generic, and most medical equipment	For 10V/m Industrial generic, and medical life support equipment
Cellphone in strong signal area, 'intrinsically safe' walkie-talkie RF power = 0.8 Watts	1.7 metres (5½ feet)	0.5 metres (1½ feet)
Cellphone in weak signal area and standby mode RF power = 2 Watts	2.5 metres (8 feet)	0.76 metres (2½ feet)
Walkie-talkie handset RF power = 4 watts (emergency services can be 10W)	3.7 metres (12 feet)	1.1 metres (3½ feet)
Vehicle mobile (e.g. taxicab), Electro-Surgery RF power = 100 Watts (some ES are 400W or more)	18 metres (59 feet)	5.5 metres (18 feet)
Multiply distances by √2 for one constructive reflection from a metal surface, by √3 for two reflections, etc.		

Most immunity standards only test with unidirectional surges up to ±2kV and 100J

- Where surge protection not fitted, supply overvoltages will reach at least ±6kV, up to 300 times / year
  - ◆ depends on geography and whether the power lines are overhead or underground
- Superconducting magnet field collapse can create surges of up to 4 million Joules
- Oscillatory surges can occur, and these cause more stress

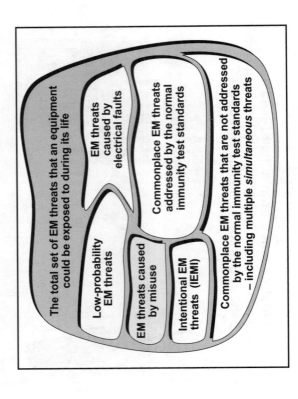

The total set of EM threats that an equipment could be exposed to during its life

Low-probability EM threats

EM threats caused by electrical faults

EM threats caused by misuse

Intentional EM threats (IEMI)

Commonplace EM threats addressed by the normal immunity test standards

Commonplace EM threats that are not addressed by the normal immunity test standards – including multiple *simultaneous* threats

Most immunity standards only test down to 150kHz (and at 50 or 60Hz) so don't cover…

V/m, Hz - kHz

- Emissions from thyristor power control; motor drives (and other switch-mode or PWM power converters)
  - ◆ typically create strong disturbances 100Hz - 200kHz
- Article surveillance systems in shop doorways
  - ◆ can create very strong fields from 200Hz to 10MHz
- Emissions at harmonics of the mains supply

Most immunity standards only test ESD with 0.7-1ns risetimes, up to ±8kV

kV

ns

- Personnel ESD can be *much* faster than 0.7ns
  - – or can exceed ±24kV, when relative humidity falls below 25%
- ESD from processing machinery can be much faster, or have a much higher voltage, and can have also have much higher energy than personnel ESD
  - – e.g. due to tribocharging from webs of material

Foreseeable interference with *analogue* devices and circuits

- Errors usually increase in proportion to the square of the magnitude of the EM threat
  - ◆ so a 6V/m RF field can cause four times the error of 3V/m
  - — full-scale errors are not unusual when measuring physical parameters
    - ◆ causing problems for measurement and control of: physiological parameters; chemical reactions; temperature; pressure; weight; mass; flow; velocity; movement; level; etc.

Foreseeable interference with *digital devices, circuits and software*

A Programmable Logic Controller (PLC) from Mitsubishi

- Functional performance errors tend only to occur when the EMI's magnitude passes a threshold
  - — but then a variety of malfunctions can occur…

Foreseeable interference with *power semiconductors*

A module-type 'stack' from Eupec

- Permanent damage can be caused by overvoltages
  - ◆ surges, fast transients, ESD
  - — and also by overcurrents
- Control terminals could be triggered at the wrong time
  - — causing malfunction, and/or actuation of protective devices, and/or damage

---

Foreseeable interference with *analogue* devices and circuits   continued…

- EMI errors are most likely in low-level signals, e.g. millivolt-output transducers
  - ◆ a common problem for microphones, strain gauge sensors, and especially for temperature sensors
- Analogue devices are easily destroyed by overvoltages from surges, fast transients, and ESD
  - — and very high-power RF (mostly a military or security issue)

Foreseeable interference with *digital devices, circuits and software* continued...

■ **Stopped operation**
(often called a 'freeze' or 'crash')

– but this can cause the control outputs to assume random combinations of states

◆ including those which can have undesirable or unsafe results for whatever is being controlled

Foreseeable interference with *electromechanical devices*

Some 'contactor relays' from Moeller

■ **'Hard-wired' circuits use electromechanical devices**

– which many designers seem to assume are totally immune to all EM threats

Foreseeable interference with *digital devices, circuits and software*

■ **False key-presses, errors in communications, data and control**

– possibly changing operational mode

■ **Incorrect software operation, e.g...**

– continually repeating an inappropriate activity

– changing operational mode (e.g. from crawl to full speed)

Foreseeable interference with *digital devices, circuits and software* continued...

■ **All digital devices can easily be destroyed by overvoltages from surges, fast transients, and ESD**

– and high-power RF (mostly a military and security issue)

◆ with powerful microprocessors and their memory chips being the most vulnerable

■ **But some programmers forget that *all* software runs on physical devices**

– and when those devices are crashed or destroyed by high levels of EMI: *software techniques cannot work*

Foreseeable interference with *electromechanical devices* continued...

- Overvoltages due to surges and fast transients can make open contacts spark-over
  - which is the same as closing them momentarily
    - ◆ applying power to circuits which should be off
- And surge currents can 'weld' contacts together
  - so that they won't open when required
    - ◆ a problem for switches, relays and contactors which don't use positively-guided or forced contacts
    - ◆ or where feedback of contact position is not used

Foreseeable interference with *electromechanical devices* continued...

- But dips and dropouts in the AC supply can cause relays, contactors and solenoids to 'drop out'
  - individually – depending on type, age, and temperature
  - and if they are held-in by a normally-open contact, or operated on a reduced 'hold-in' voltage – they may not pull back in again afterwards
- Shock and vibration can make switch contacts 'chatter', causing sparking
  - which can interfere with electronic devices

Some useful references

- *Assessing an Electromagnetic Environment*
  Keith Armstrong
  EMC Test Laboratories Association
  Technical Guidance Note, from: www.emctla.co.uk
  - also downloadable from www.cherryclough.com
  - *Note*: this document was written to help with EMC Directive compliance, not for safety purposes
- *REO booklets on EMC Testing*
  free from www.reo.co.uk
  - as well as describing how to perform tests to the IEC/EN basic EMC test methods, these booklets describe the various types of EM disturbances, where they might occur, their possible magnitudes, and what effects they might have on electrical and electronic equipment

Many electromechanical devices should now be treated as electronic devices

- An increasing proportion of electromechanical devices are employing electronic devices to add functionality
  - ◆ e.g. 'safety relays', MCCs, motors
  - but these can suffer from all the interference problems that electronics are prone to
- The electronic content of any electromechanical device should always be asked about
  - and if it contains even one diode, transistor, hall sensor or IC – it should be treated as an *electronic device*

WORKSHOP: PRODUCT EMC DESIGN STRATEGIES AND PRACTICES (FR-PM-WS-17)
Kwok Soohoo

TC1 is concerned with the development and dissemination of Best Practices and Methodologies for the successful leadership, supervision and guidance of EMC related activities.

Objectives of workshop are presentation of product EMC design strategies and practices that deal with personal computer as well as large scale computing system developments; covered topics are standards adaptation logistics, EMI/PCB modeling software applications/considerations, hardware treatment approaches (PCB, mechanical packaging etc.), components/subassemblies evaluation methods/techniques, and examples of typical problem areas requiring special attentions.

Presentations:

(1) Keeping Up with EMC Standards in Product Design
John Maas

(2) Product Design Using PCB and EMI Modeling Software
Andrew L. Drozd

(3) Personal Computer and Small Server EMC Design Logistics
Bruce Archambeault

(4) Large Computing System/Server EMC Design Logistics
Kwok M. Soohoo

NOTES

KEEPING UP WITH EMC STANDARDS IN PRODUCT DESIGN

John Maas
IBM Corporation

1

OUTLINE

INTRODUCTION

IDENTIFYING STANDARDS & REGULATIONS

DESIGN CONSIDERATIONS FOR COMPLIANCE

MEETING EVER-INCREASING SET OF STANDARDS & REGULATIONS

KEEPING UP WITH CHANGES

2

---

website slide 22 ish not published in workshop NOTES

INTRODUCTION

Regulatory compliance is a significant issue for product manufacturers
- Product Safety
- EMC
- Homologation
- Environmental/Chemical

Compliance required in many geographies

Burden includes design, test and management
- Know standards & regulations
- Design for compliance
- Test correctly to all applicable standards
- Inform designers & planners

3

EMC STANDARDS & REGULATIONS

Regulations applicable to ITE worldwide

47 CFR, Part 15 (USA)
Council Directive 89/336/EEC (EU)
  • Council Directive 2004/108/EC (EU)
AS/NZS CISPR 22 (Australia/New Zealand)
CNS 13438 (Taiwan)
ICES-003 (Canada)
GB 9254-1998 (China) — *Emmision 150K - 1GHz*
GB 17625.1-2003 (China) — *power line Harmonic*
GB 17652.2-1999 (China) — *Flicker & Voltage Fluctuation*
MIC Notice 2002-122 (Korea)
GOST 51318.22 (Russia)
VCCI** (Japan)

17625

5

EMC STANDARDS & REGULATIONS

Basic standards are developed by IEC and CISPR
- IEC 61000-3, 61000-4
- CISPR 16, CISPR 22, CISPR 24
- Basic test methodologies, set ups & procedures
- Test Equipment
- Do not include limits or specific performance criteria
- Only become required when adopted in a product, generic or country standard

Product, generic, country standards reference basic standards and add specific details for test limits, performance criteria, etc
- Latest version of basic standard not automatically picked up
- Transition dates and plans often vary between countries
- Be very careful

7

EMC STANDARDS & REGULATIONS

Four different EN 55022 editions can be applied

1994 Edition +A1:1995 +A2:1997
- Valid until 8/1/1997
1998 Edition
- Adds conducted emissions for telecom ports
- Valid until 8/1/05
1998 Edition +A1:2000
- Requires ferrites on cables leaving table top test area
- Valid until 12/1/05
1998 Edition +A1:2000 +A2:2003
- Refines definition of telecom ports, indicates operational details of multi-function equipment

Other national standards also based on CISPR 22 do not always track implementation dates in Europe

9

EMC STANDARDS & REGULATIONS

Standards applicable to ITE worldwide

CISPR 22: 1993, 1997, 2003 --- Emissions
CISPR 24 --- Immunity
EN 55022 --- European Union, Emissions
EN 55024 --- European Union, Immunity
ANSI C63.4 --- USA, Emissions Test Method
CAN/CSA-CEI/IEC CISPR 22:2002 --- Canada, Emissions
IEC/EN 61000-3-2 --- Power Line Harmonics
IEC/EN 61000-3-3 --- Flicker and Voltage Fluctuations
IEC/EN 61000-4-2 --- Electrostatic Discharge
IEC/EN 61000-4-3 --- Radiated Continuous RF Disturbances
IEC/EN 61000-4-4 --- Electrical Fast Transient/Burst
IEC/EN 61000-4-5 --- Surge
IEC/EN 61000-4-6 --- Conducted Continuous RF Disturbances
IEC/EN 61000-4-8 --- Power Frequency Magnetic Fields
IEC/EN 61000-4-11 --- Voltage Dips and Short Interruptions & Voltage Variations

6

EMC STANDARDS & REGULATIONS

Tracking versions of standards can be challenging

IEC Basic Standard	Date referenced in EN 55024	Date of current IEC version
61000-4-2	1995	2001
61000-4-3	1995	2002
61000-4-4	1995	2004
61000-4-5	1995	2001
61000-4-6	1996	2004
61000-4-8	1993	2001
61000-4-11	1994	2004

8

EMC STANDARDS & REGULATIONS

Several editions of CISPR 22 exist

Fifth edition published 2005-04
- Eliminates requirement to add ferrites on cables exiting the test area for table-top set ups
- Maintains requirement to measure conducted emissions on telecommunication cables

This is the official IEC/CISPR edition
- Previous editions still referenced by various national requirements

Several changes in recent years

Reacting to fast-paced changes in technology and some test equipment limitations learned by experience

10

DESIGN FOR COMPLIANCE

Standards must be met to market products

Lowest cost approach is to design for compliance from the earliest stages of product development

Know the requirements up front
- Do harmonic emissions need to be limited?
  - What limits apply?
- Do conducted emissions from telecom ports need to be limited?
  - How do I perform that test?
- Which editions of CISPR 22 apply in the countries where this product will be marketed?
  - What constitutes a failure

12

COMPLIANCE FOR MARKETING

What do you mean my product must be certified before Customs will release it?
- ...and it takes 6 weeks to certify???

Most regulations include technical and administrative requirements
- Both requirements are subject to change
  - New tests get added
  - Test details get updated
  - Certification replaced by Declaration of Conformity
  - Type approval yields to registration

13

DESIGN FOR COMPLIANCE

What happens when product does not comply?

- Delayed introduction to market or first shipment
- Units held in Customs until local regulation is met
- Fines issued
- Field repairs/modifications
- Product recall
- Customer complaints
- Bad press, loss of reputation
- Price of stock (value of company) falls

14

DESIGN FOR COMPLIANCE

Non-compliance found late in development cycle often results in costly design changes

- Ferrites on external cables instead of cost-free board layout or low-cost filtering/decoupling
- Enhanced shielding and extra gaskets
- Card- or chip-level shielding
- Reduced product content or limited configuration
- Long nights in the test lab testing problems out

15

HURDLES TO BE CROSSED

In EMC, it seems the only constant is that standards and regulations will change

- Advancing technology introduces new product types
  - Broadband communications on power lines
  - Test equipment technology evolves
- Standards get updated based on experience
  - Improved test methods
  - Enhanced EUT arrangements
  - Flaws discovered
- New environmental threats drive new tests

17

HURDLES TO BE CROSSED

When standards/regulations change, many areas of business are impacted

- Product designs
  - New requirements often drive design changes
  - Design changes can be significant
  - System, subsystem, component
- Test equipment
  - Upgrade or replace existing equipment
  - Add new equipment types
  - Advance planning often needed for large capital purchases
- Test facilities
  - Calibration/acceptance criteria drive facility specifications
  - Costs can be huge
- Test Process
  - Reverification of current products
  - Planning when to break in new requirements with transition dates

18

HURDLES TO BE CROSSED

Some past changes that impacted product design, test or compliance documentation:

- EN 55024 replaced EN 55082-1 and added 4 immunity test for ITE
  - Existing products had to be retested and sometimes redesigned
  - New test equipment required
  - DoCs needed to be updated or reissued
- BSMI Type Approval changed to RPC and DOC
  - Documentation needed to be refiled
- Limits added for frequencies greater than 1 GHz
  - Test in an entirely new area – new/enhanced equipment required
  - Design to meet new requirements
- Changes to definitions of harmonics classes
  - Active mitigation needed instead of lower-cost passive mitigation

19

KEEPING UP

With all the potential for changes, how does one keep up?

- Agency web sites
- Standards organizations web sites
- Daily digest, government register, official journal
- Subscription organizations
- Trade organizations
- Trade press
- Become active in standards groups, national bodies

21

KEEPING UP

Can anything be done to influence the process?

- Standards written and maintained by volunteers
  - Regulations come from governments
  - Industry input is usually part of the process
- Become active in standards groups or national bodies to help write and maintain standards
- Be active in trade organizations that input to the standards process
- Advocate positions
- Provide input and assistance to standards participants when asked

22

ANSI   TC77   61000-4
NIST   -3

Fcc.gov   access.gpo.gov/su_docs/fedreg/frcont5o.html

Bsmi.tw   Strategis.ic.gc-Ca

mic.go.kr/eng/index.jsp   bsmi.gov

Trade organization - medical

PRODUCT DESIGN USING PCB AND EMI MODELING SOFTWARE

Andrew L. Drozd, NCE

ANDRO Computational Solutions, LLC

Beeches Technical Campus

Rome, NY USA

1-877-334-1188

adrozd@androcs.com

TOPICS

- Introduction
  - EMC Modeling & Analysis
  - EMI Solution Steps
    - Defining the Problem to be Solved
    - Selecting/Applying the Appropriate Solution Technique(s)
- Brief Survey of CEM Physics Formalisms & Solution Techniques
  - Types of Techniques Available, Capabilities & Relevant Applications
  - Applications to Military and Commercial Product/System Designs
  - Some Pros/Cons on resource requirements, etc.
- Technical Issues, Potential Pitfalls & What to Expect
  - CEM Design & Analysis Environment
  - Challenging Gridding/Meshing Algorithms
  - Model Fidelity & Computational Resource Issues

TECHNICAL FOCUS / OBJECTIVES

- Raise awareness in techniques for computer modeling and simulation for analyzing the EMC of various products and complex devices (PCBs, electronic equipments, systems/subsystems).
- Provide a general guide for applying EMI/C modeling software (step-by-step modeling approach, technique based, code agnostic).
- Highlight the different type of software (techniques) available in the market and their capabilities and pertinent applications.
- Give general examples of their usage in product designs in military and commercial arenas.
- Include their pros and cons in terms of resource requirement to run them and ultimately their limitations.
- Identify potential sources of error that could detract from a code's accuracy and overall utility.

THEMES

- Assuring EMC in modern products and systems is a challenging task.
- Prior to the late 1960s, approaches for assuring EMC relied significantly on employing good EMC design rules based on 'past experience' and proven practices, in conjunction with performing fairly extensive development tests.
- Analysis was based largely on applying coarse bounding models along with selected numerical techniques rooted in *boundary element* physics.
- Since then, analysis or more specifically, computational electromagnetics (CEM), has become a key ingredient in a balanced EMC assurance program.
- The CEM discipline has come a long way to the point where we have at our disposal many powerful computer modeling and analysis tools.
- The culture is changing and leaning increasingly towards the application of CEM tools to offset expensive or premature test and evaluation programs.
- Reduce the large interference interaction sample space to a smaller, more manageable subset of possibilities that can be progressively analyzed and resolved using computer-based techniques along with limited testing.

COMPLEX SYSTEM EMC ANALYSIS (1)

- Systematic, comprehensive approach
  - Emitters
  - Receptors
  - Transfer functions

- Account for all elements of electromagnetic modeling
  - Topology
  - Structure description
  - Environment
  - Excitation
    - Functional signals
    - Extraneous energy
  - Observables
  - Solution method

- User oriented with interactive features (design/analysis tool)

POTENTIALLY MANY EM INTERACTIONS AND DEGREES OF FREEDOM (COUPLING PATHS)

MUTUAL COUPLING (PCB or System)

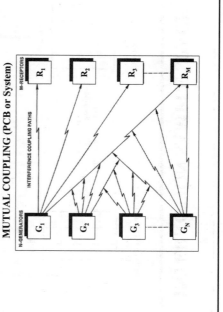

TRENDS

- The growing reliance on CEM has been influenced by:
  - The increasing complexity of electronic products and systems
  - The need for a balanced, cost-effective EMC assurance program
  - The desire for consistent, reliable digital baseline models and benchmarks to support life cycle system/product EMC
  - Technological advancements in computer hardware and the development of fast solvers, which is facilitating the use of CEM technologies for complex system/product evaluations.

- The utility, efficacy and cost-effectiveness of the approach depend on properly matching the CEM technologies to the problem to be solved.

- EMC computer modeling can help identify hardware anomalies that could lead to EMI problems and provide insights into corrective actions for interference mitigation in advance.

- Computer analysis can help focus EMC product certification and spec compliance test programs by identifying susceptible modes of operation, appropriate test frequencies, and critical test points in advance.

COMPLEX SYSTEM EMC ANALYSIS (2)

- Tailor equipment EMC specifications

- EMC waiver analysis

- Development of a system EMC database which integrates analysis output with EMC test program results

- Facilitates optimum design and equipment layout

- Extensible to multiple system-to-system EMC assessments
  - Support system/product development & deployment

INTERACTION SAMPLE SPACE

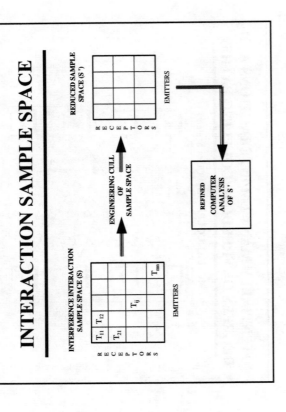

EMI SOLUTION STEPS (GENERAL)

- Brute-force application of rigorous numerical methods for a large problem space can be counter-productive
- Start with a conservative topological structure model
  - Employ canonical-type structure models
  - Define all key EM radiators in the problem
  - Perform a conservative analysis cull to isolate problems from non-problems and to reduce the EMI sample space
- Gradually enhance the accuracy of the structure problem and employ problem partitioning to reduce sample space
  - Judiciously apply frequency- and time-domain numerical methods to resolve EMI cases
  - Closely analyze "gray" areas to reduce uncertainty

ENVIRONMENT-TO-VICTIM EM EFFECTS

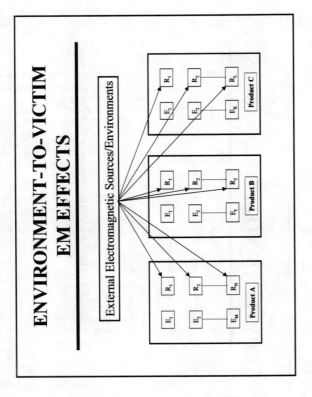

RECENT DEVELOPMENTS

- Circa 1993-1995
  - Push to build more robust, intelligent and extensible system-level computer codes to analyze various EM effects for complex systems
  - Adapt powerful EM legacy codes, identify innovative user/model capabilities
    - Frequency- and time-domain solutions
    - RF system to component modeling capability (top down, bottoms up)
    - "Monitor" signal environment and select appropriate EMI cancellation scheme(s)
  - Enabling technologies for analyzing:
    - RF communications/information/network assurance (f-hopping spread spectrum)
    - Radar cross section (RCS)
    - Co-located multi-spectral, multiple subscriber packages (COTS & military)
  - Use of framework-based expert system CEM model building and automated EMI rejection schemes to analyze complicated RF systems and environments
- 1998-Present
  - Several new CEM codes released for high performance computer use
- Present-Future
  - Development of CEM frameworks and schemes for computational efficiency

EM OBSERVABLES

Surface Currents & 3-D Antenna Patterns

Antenna Solution Current, Current Phase vs. Segment Number & Far-Field Patterns

Complex Input Impedance vs. Frequency

WHICH TECHNIQUE TO APPLY?

- Although CEM codes have their basis in Maxwell's equations of one form or another, their applicability and associated accuracies depend on:

  - The "applied" physics

  - Numerical solver approach (full or partial wave, non-matrix, etc.)

  - Mathematical basis functions (current expansion functions)

  - Canonical modeling primitives (facets, wires, patches, canonical surfaces,...)

  - Inherent modeling limitations and built-in approximations

  - Desired "observables" (current or scattered fields)

  - Other factors such as analysis frequency and time or mesh discretization further conspire to affect solution convergence and overall accuracy.

HOW DO WE BEGIN?

- If we adopt a progressive, step-by-step computer modeling and simulation (M&S) approach, then the basic steps, in order, are:

  - Defining the type of problem to be solved (PCB radiated EMI, antenna coupling, electronic assembly conducted susceptibility, etc.)

  - Determining if the problem is an exterior (surface type) or interior (volumetric) EM phenomenon, or both

  - Specifying the range of EM observables of interest (currents, fields)

  - Defining the desired level of model fidelity (low-moderate, high)

  - Specifying time constraints and any computational resource limitations.

- There are additional 'decision variables' to be considered:

  - Is the technique embodied in a selected CEM code validated against a set of canonical, standard validation or benchmark problems?

  - Does measured data exist to cross-check analytical results?

  - Other issues or concerns that may lend to or resolve uncertainty?

- The appropriate CEM techniques and codes can then be chosen.

A "VIEW" OF EM MODELING

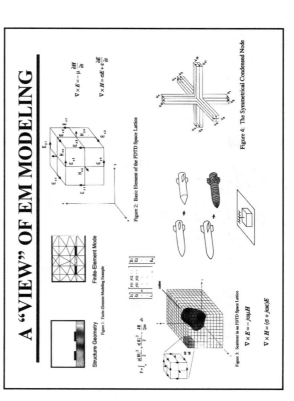

Figure 1: Finite-Element Modeling Example

Figure 2: Basic Element of the FDTD Space Lattice

Figure 3: Scatterer in an FDTD Space Lattice

Figure 4: The Symmetrical Condensed Node

Structure Geometry

Finite-Element Mode

MODELING & SIMULATION APPROACH

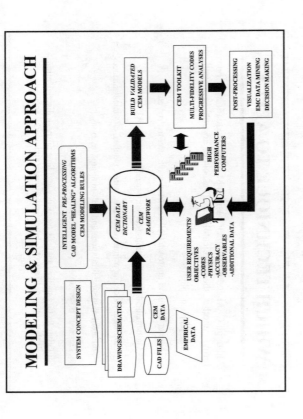

SYSTEM/ASSEMBLY EMI MODELING (1)

- Relevant EMI/EMC/RFI factors & design issues:
  - Subassembly and equipment module packaging for EMC
    - Conductor-pin isolation at cable-connector interfaces
    - Intraconnect grounding schemes
    - Crosstalk effects
  - Electrical/electronic module EMC design and specification tailoring
    - Radiated/conducted emissions and immunity (packaging, shielding)
    - Conductor/circuit isolation at I/O interfaces
    - Frequency management
    - Fundamental signal integrity schemes
    - Grounding configurations
    - Anomaly resolution
    - Power quality

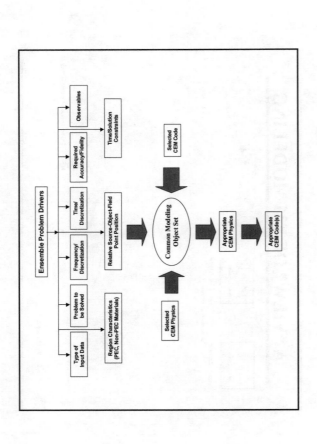

SYSTEM/EQUIPMENT/SUBASSEMBLY EMI

√ Electronics Package Geometry, Construction & Shielding
√ Analyze Radiated/Conducted Emissions/Susceptibility

SURVEY OF ELECTROMAGNETIC MODELING TECHNIQUES & TOOLS*

*Any mention of specific software codes in the following section does not constitute an endorsement of such codes by the author or by the IEEE EMC Society. These codes are named only for illustrative purposes (i.e., by way of example) and by no means is intended to be a comprehensive listing.

EXAMPLE CEM METHODS & TOOLS

- Method of Moments (MoM) (e.g., *GEMACS, NEC-MOM*)
- Uniform Theory of Diffraction (UTD) (e.g., *NEC-BSC*)
- Multi-Level Fast Multipole Algorithm (MLFMA) (e.g., *FISC*)
- Transmission Line Modeling (TLM) (e.g., *FlowEMC*)
- Finite Difference Time Domain (FDTD e.g., *CFDTD, XFDTD*)
- Finite Element Modeling/Analysis (EMAP)
- Shooting & Bouncing Rays/Physical Optics/Physical Theory of Diffraction (SBR/PO/PTD) (e.g., *XPATCH*)
- Hybrid techniques (e.g., MoM/GTD, PO/MoM, etc.) (e.g., *GEMACS, FEKO*)
- Bounded/conservative discrete analytical models (e.g., *SEMCAP*)

SYSTEM/ASSEMBLY EMI MODELING (2)

- Self-EMI/C (intrasystem/co-site interference analysis)
  - Package & component integration, equipment location and layout
  - Anomaly resolution
  - Location and characteristics of external EM sources and receptors
  - System harness interconnect routing and grounding schemes
  - Radiated/conducted emissions and immunity
  - System power quality and distribution
  - System geometry topology and shielding effectiveness (perfectly electrically conducting and other materials properties)
    - Scattering and blockage
  - Antenna, cable and equipment isolation
  - Coupling modes and mechanisms
    - RF antenna-to-antenna
    - Wire-to-wire (RF, baseband signal/control, AC/DC power, EID)
    - Equipment-to-equipment
    - External field-to-antenna, field-to-wire and field-to-equipment
  - Frequency management
  - Radar/communications transceiver compatibility

WEALTH OF CEM METHODS

- Boundary Element (Integral) Method (BEM)
- Finite Element Modeling/Analysis (FEM/A)
- Method of Moments (MoM)

- Shooting Bouncing Rays (SBR)
- Physical Optics (PO)
- Physical Theory of Diffraction (PTD)
- Geometrical Optics (GO)
- Geometrical/Uniform Theory of Diffraction (GTD/UTD)

- Transmission Line Method (TLM)
- Hybrid Lumped Circuit & Quasi-Transmission Line Method

- Finite Difference Time Domain (FDTD)
- Finite Volume Time Domain (FVTD)
- Finite Difference Frequency Domain (FDFD)
- Conjugate Gradient Method (CGM)
- Generalized Multi-pole Technique (GMT - Moment Method)

- Multiple Multi-Pole (MMP)
- Multi-Level Fast Multi-Pole Algorithm (MLFMA)

- Partial Element Equivalent Circuit Model (PEEC)
- Perfectly Matched Layers using a Partial Differential Equation Solver Method (PML/PDE)

- Adaptive Integral Method (AIM)
- Bi-Conjugate Gradient Method w/Fast Fourier Transform (BCG-FFT)
- Thin-Wire Time Domain Method (TWTD)
- Time Domain Moment Method (TDMM)
- Vector Parabolic Equation Technique (VPE)
- Pseudo-Spectral Time Domain Method (PSTD)
- Multi-Resolution Techniques (MRT)
- Finite Integration Technique (FIT)
- Recursive Green's Function Method (RGFM)

- Analytical Discrete Method(s)

- Hybrid Techniques (MoM/UTD,...)

BOUNDARY ELEMENT METHOD (BEM)

- BEM (like the FEM method) originated in the field of structural mechanics.

- It is a weighted residual technique that solves partial differential equations (PDEs) using mesh elements.

- It is essentially a MoM technique whose expansion and weighting functions are defined only on a boundary surface i.e., only the boundary of the domain of interest requires discretization.

- The computational advantages of the BEM over other methods can be considerable.

- It is particularly useful for low frequency problems i.e., mostly applicable to DC (electrostatics) and steady-state AC problems.

FINITE DIFFERENCE TIME DOMAIN (FDTD)

- Solves PDEs using a gridding technique with respect to a given boundary condition (requires the entire volume be meshed).

- In time-dependent PDEs, the FD method may be used in both space and time (i.e., FDTD) or it may be used for the spatial displacement component only for a given frequency (FDFD).

- The mesh must normally be uniform, so that the mesh density is determined by the smallest details of the problem.

- Unlike most FEM and MoM techniques, FDTD is very well suited to transient analyses.

- Time stepping is continued until a steady state solution or the desired response is obtained.

- At each time step, the equations used to update the field components are fully explicit.

- No system of linear equations must be solved and the required computer storage and running time are proportional to the electrical size of the volume modeled and the grid resolution.

- Because the basic elements are cubes, curved surfaces on a scatterer must be *staircased*.

- For configurations with sharp, acute edges, an adequately staircased approximation may require a very small grid size (0.1-0.25λ edge dimensions), which can significantly increase the computational size of the problem.

- Surface conforming FDTD techniques with non-rectangular elements can alleviate this.

- Like FEM, FDTD is very good at modeling complex inhomogeneous configurations.

- Many implementations do a better job of modeling unbounded problems than FEM codes.

ELECTROMAGNETICS CODES

- EMAP
- HFSS
- Maxwell 3-D
- NEC-BSC
- NEC-MOM
- GEMACS
- SWITCH
- APATCH
- XPATCH
- Carlos-3D
- FISC
- EIGER
- MiniNEC
- SWITCH
- AAPG 2000
- COSAM
- EMC Expert System
- :
- :

SOFTWARE/APPLICABILITY	COMPANY
MagNet - handles electrical, magnetic, and eddy current analysis	Infolytica
Maxwell 3D Engineering Software (including SI Emissary) - handles electrical, magnetic, eddy current, and microwave analysis with links to Spice CAD modeling capabilities	Ansoft Corporation
MSC/Magnetic, MSC/Magnum, and MSC/Magpie - handle electric and magnetic field analysis	MacNeal-Schwendler Corporation
Fortus - handles electric and magnetic field analysis	Princeton Electro-Technology, Inc.
WEMAP - handles electric, magnetic, thermal, and eddy current analyses	Westinghouse Electric Corporation
ANSYS - handles structural and mechanical design, and has magnetic field analysis capability	Swanson Analysis Systems, Inc.
IDEAS - handles FEM/A-based thermal, structural, electric and magnetic analyses	Structural Dynamics Research Corporation
Magnus - handles magnetic analysis	Magnus Software
TSAR - handles Finite Difference Time Domain (FDTD) electromagnetics analysis	Lawrence Livermore National Laboratory
XFDTD - handles Finite Difference Time Domain (FDTD) electric field analysis	REMCOM, Inc.
FLUX - handles electric and magnetic analyses	Magsoft Corporation
MARC/MENTAT - handles FEM/A-based electrostatic and magnetostatic problems with infinite boundaries	MARC Analysis Research Corporation
PE2D, Carmen, and Tosca - handle electric, magnetic, and eddy current analyses	Vector Fields, Inc.
Stripes - handles computer-aided engineering (CAE) and electromagnetic analysis using the 3-D Time-Domain Transmission Line Modeling (TLM) technique	KCC, Ltd.
EMFIELDS-3D, EMFIELDS-2D, EMEC, and EMIT - handle 2-D and 3-D electromagnetics	Seth Corporation
Motive, XTK, Quiet, PDQ, TLC - collectively handle the electromagnetics modeling and analyses of PC board layouts and design using boundary element, finite-domain finite element, and transmission line techniques	Quad Design
EMA3DF, EMA3D, EMA3DCYL, EMA3XT, and EMAFDM in addition to others - collectively handle electromagnetic analyses based on Finite Difference Time Domain (FDTD) methods applicable to PC boards and high frequencies or charged particles	Electromagnetic Applications, Inc.
MAFIA - handles electric and magnetic analyses based on Finite Integration Algorithm (FIA), MAFIA solves several modules suitable for static, low and high frequency applications	Computer Simulation Technology, Germany
CST MICROWAVE STUDIO offers an alternative to MAFIA in the range of high frequency applications	
High-Performance Engineering Suite including EMC Advisor and CAD Toolkit - handle PC based electromagnetic modeling and analysis based on transmission line and time-domain modeling methods	Alinta, an IBM Company
EMIT - handles EMI and radiation analyses for PC boards to antenna structures based on a general, fullwave, 3-D electromagnetic solver technique	Recal-Redac
em™ - synthesizes Spice models and handles electromagnetics analyses for lumped models of complex circuits used in PC board layouts	Sonnet Software, Inc.

FINITE ELEMENT METHOD (FEM)

- Originated in the structural mechanics engineering discipline.

- Solves PDEs for complex, nonlinear problems in magnetics and electrostatics using mesh elements.

- FEM techniques require the entire volume of the configuration to be meshed as opposed to surface integral techniques that only require the surfaces to be meshed.

- Each mesh element may have completely different material properties from those of neighboring elements.

- FEM techniques excel at modeling complex inhomogeneous configurations.

- FEM does not model unbounded radiation problems as effectively as MoM techniques.

- The method requires the discretization of the domain into a number of small homogeneous subregions or mesh cells and applying the given boundary condition resulting in field solutions using a linear system of equations.

- The model contains information about the device geometry, material constants, excitations and boundary constraints.

- The elements can be small where geometric details exist and much larger elsewhere.

- The goal of the FEM is to determine the field quantities at the nodes i.e, solving for the unknown field quantities by minimizing an energy quantity.

- Applicable to a wide range of problems and frequencies.

TRANSMISSION LINE METHOD (TLM)

- Belongs to the general class of differential time-domain numerical modeling methods and is similar to the FDTD method, where the entire region of the analysis is gridded.

- The approach is to obtain a discrete model that is then solved exactly by numerical means and where approximations are only introduced at the discretization stage.

- The discrete model is formed by conceptually filling space with a network of transmission-lines in such a way that the voltage and current give information on the electric and magnetic fields.

- The point at which the transmission-lines intersect is referred to as a node and the most commonly used node for 3-D work is the symmetrical condensed node.

- Additional elements, such as transmission-line stubs, can be added to a node so that different material properties can be represented.

- At each time step, voltage pulses are incident upon the node from each of the transmission lines.

- These pulses are then scattered to produce a new set of pulses that become incident on adjacent nodes at the next time step.

- Lossy media can be modeled by introducing loss into the TLM equations or by loading the nodes.

- Absorbing boundaries are easily constructed in TLM meshes by terminating each boundary node transmission line with its characteristic impedance.

- The advantages of using the TLM method are similar to those of the FDTD method.

- The disadvantages of the FDTD method are also shared by this technique, the primary being that voluminous problems that must use a fine grid require excessive amounts of computation.

GEOMETRICAL/UNIFORM THEORY OF DIFFRACTION (GTD/UTD)

- UTD is an extension of the GTD and GO methods (high-frequency ray tracing).

- GO applies exact ray tracing methods for light wave propagation through optical media.

- Accurate when the dimensions of objects being analyzed are electrically large i.e., relative to the wavelength of the field.

- Combines the effects of direct rays, reflection, diffraction and multi-path propagation around an EM structure comprised of canonical elements.

- Behavior of the diffracted wave at edges, corners, and surfaces are determined from an asymptotic form of the exact solution for simpler canonical problems.

- The diffraction around a sharp edge is found by considering the asymptotic form of the solution for an infinite wedge.

- Canonical problems are those comprised of simple objects e.g., right circular or elliptical cylinders with endcaps, ellipsoids, N-sided plates, frusta, etc.

- Certain formulations allow canonical geometry objects to be non-PEC type.

METHOD OF MOMENTS (MOM)

- A numerical technique based on the method of weighted residuals.

- Synonymous with "surface integral technique" even though the method of weighted residuals can be applied to differential as well as integral equations.

- Applies thin-wire mesh/grid approximations or uses perfectly electrically conducting (PEC) patch elements whose dimensions generally range between 0.1–0.25λ.

- Appropriate in analyzing electrically small-to-moderately sized unbounded radiation problems and excels at analyzing PEC configurations and homogeneous dielectrics.

- Segments can be loaded or defined as non-PEC type in certain formulations.

- EM fields are computed from wire mesh currents and patch surface current densities.

- Not well suited to analyzing complex inhomogeneous geometries.

PARTIAL ELEMENT EQUIVALENT CIRCUIT MODEL (PEEC)

- Based on the integral equation formulation.

- All structures to be modeled are divided into electrically small elements.

- An equivalent circuit describes the coupling between elements.

- Once the matrix of equivalent circuits is developed, then a circuit solver can be used to obtain a response for the system.

- It is mostly used for quasi-static partial inductance calculations to analyze PCB electromagnetic radiation problems.

- One of the main advantages in using the PEEC method is the ability to add circuit elements into an EM simulator to model lumped circuit characteristics.

PCB/ASSEMBLY EXAMPLES

Challenge Problem #98-01
(Overall View (sheet 1/3))

Techniques like FEM, PEEC, FDTD and MoM have been used to model and analyze these problems.

MODELING ISSUES

- **Model-limited errors** – Arise because of limitations associated with the geometrical elements which are used to construct CEM models.

- **Procedural errors** – Refers to the step-by-step approach used in generating and analyzing a CEM model.

- **Technique-limited errors** – Pertains to the approximations and potential errors introduced when Maxwell's equation are constrained to a particular subset of boundary conditions and modeling problems (also referred to as *quadrature error*), expressed either in differential or integral form.

- **Problem-dependent errors** – Arise when the physical problem is not fully characterized and the solution approach does not match the problem.

- **Numerical errors** – Closely tied to technique-limited error in that the physics and the numerical solvers work together to provide a total budget solution.

- **Interpretive errors** – The human's attempt to interpret the computed observables can lead to erroneous conclusions about the data and detract from the real problem solution.

FAST MULTI-POLE METHOD (FMM)

- FMM is a tree code-based method that uses two representations of the potential field referred to as the "duality principle":

  – Far field (multipole)

  – Local expansions.

- Uses a very fast calculation of the scalar potential field, which is computationally easier than dealing with the force vector (i.e., the negative of the gradient of the potential).

- The strategy of the FMM is to compute a compact expression for the potential phi (x, y, z), which can be easily evaluated along with its derivative at any point.

- It achieves this by evaluating the potential as a "multipole expansion," a kind of Taylor expansion, which is accurate when $x2+y2+z2$ is large.

MICROSTRIP PATCH ANTENNA

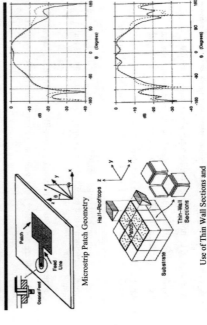

Microstrip Patch Geometry

E_θ Far Field Patterns
Measured vs. Calculated

Use of Thin Wall Sections and Rooftop Basis Functions to Model Current Density in a Structure Including the Conductive Patch
(Modeled Using FDTD, MoM, FEM and MLFMA)

MESH & CAVITY MODELING

EXTERIOR REGION

INTERIOR REGION

INTERMEDIATE REGION

MISSILE DESCRIPTION

BUILDING A CAVITY OBSTACLE

MoM Patch/Wire Model
≈80,000 Unknowns at 300 MHz at 0.1λ

Similar issues apply to PCB modeling at high frequencies!

EXAMPLE CEM MODELING RULES

- Segment lengths $\leq 0.1\lambda$
- Actual wires should be modeled using actual radii (r)
- Grid models should use $r \approx L/5$ in square mesh regions
- Grid mesh circumferences $\leq 0.5\lambda$ (large circumferences lead to loop resonances and poor results)
- Do not join segments lengths that differ by more than a factor of 2
- Unjoined segments should be separated by a segment length or more
- Wires, non-junctioned may be connected to patches, ground or plates (not cylinders or endcaps)
- Plates cannot be attached to endcaps
- Wires connected to patches must be embedded at the patch center by the wire radius
- Plate normals must be defined toward a single source
- Objects must have dimensions $\geq \lambda$ for UTD solution accuracy
- Thin wire MoM segments are connected to UTD surfaces when their segment end points are within $.001\lambda$ of the surface
- Wire segments should be located $\geq 0.25\lambda$ from plate edges

---

CONCLUSION

- A number of useful techniques and validated computer tools are available to analyze systems or products (PCBs to full systems).
- Match the tool or technique to the problem to be solved in view of other "ensemble" modeling parameters (*problem-model-data driven*).
- New tools and methods are being developed that will improve computational efficiency and accuracy.
- EMC can be analyzed in various ways and the results of simulations (i.e., *EM observables*) can be presented in meaningful ways using visualization and animation techniques.
- A comprehensive analysis will lead to reduced EMC design, retrofit, and certification test costs over the life cycle of a product and provides an effective means of assessing product EMC/performance measures.
- Simulations can be used to judiciously determine test frequencies and susceptible modes of operation.

PERFORMANCE vs. HARDWARE

Execution Time:

$$Time = \frac{245}{\#CPUs \times Speed_{GHz}} \left(\frac{N}{10,000}\right)^3 minutes$$

$$215\ minutes = \frac{245}{2 \times 2}\left(\frac{15,200}{10,000}\right)^3 (32\ bit\ max)$$

$$4\ minutes = \frac{245}{512 \times 0.4}\left(\frac{15,200}{10,000}\right)^3 (Zornig\ theoretical)$$

$$215\ minutes = \frac{245}{512 \times 0.4}\left(\frac{56,368}{10,000}\right)^3 (Zornig\ theoretical)$$

Available Memory:
2 Gigabytes ? 15,200 unknowns
384 Gigabytes ? 210,000 unknowns.

Personal Computer and Small Server EMC Design Logistics

Bruce Archambeault, Ph.D.

IBM

Research Triangle Park, NC

barch@us.ibm.com

1

Common EMC Design Process
(Unfortunately)

- EMC engineer will provide EMC rules and recommendations to product design team
- Product design engineers will largely ignore EMC 'rules'
  - Too costly
  - Too hard
  - Often unrealistic
- Product is built, tested, and fails EMC

2

Common EMC Design Process (2)
(Unfortunately)

- EMC engineers works in lab to debug/fix EMC problem
- Once fix is found, redesign cycle to build 'fixed' product
- Product is tested in EMC lab
- If fail (again), repeat as necessary

3

'OLD' vs.. 'NEW'

- The 'old' way
  - Never time to 'do it right' but always time to 'do it over'
- The 'new' way
  - Design 'up-front' to pass the first time
  - Should be accountable if not pass the first time
  - We (EMC technical community) know how to pass the first time

4

Issues

- Time-to-Market
  - Never make up for lost market share for delayed first customer ship dates
- Cost
  - Everything is cost sensitive
  - EMC 'band-aids' more costly than doing it right the first time
- Reasonableness
  - EMC can not make unreasonable demands
  - If the product does not work or cost too much, passing EMC does not matter
- Customers rarely care if product passes EMC

5

Different Levels of EMC Design Process

- Outside the product design process
  - Design Rule Development
  - Training
- During the product design process
  - Apply design rules
  - Use automated design rule checker
- During testing phase
  - Validate rules and/or create new rules

6

Outside the product design process -- Design Rule Development

- Evaluate rules from classes, books
  - Some will NOT work for *your* product family
- Use fullwave simulation tools to evaluate and understand 'gray areas
  - Different techniques for different types of problems
  - Need to Validate results
- Develop set of design rules

7

Evaluate Rules
(From Classes and Books)

- Some will NOT work for *your* product family
- Examples
  - All metal parts must be connected to earth ground
  - Every I/O connector must have a filter
  - Every I/O cable must have a 360 degree shield
  - Must have decoupling capacitor within 1/4" of all IC power pins

8

Evaluate Rules
(From Classes and Books)

- Use common sense??
- There is no 'absolute' design rule
  - Must consider engineering trade-offs
  - Must be tailored to type of product
    - Cost constraints
    - Size constraints
    - Functionality constraints
    - Other (telecom, safety, etc)

10

Evaluate Rules
for *YOUR* Products with Constraints

- Possible Approaches
  - Create physical models with variations and measure effect of variations
    - Measurements can be over shadowed by other effects
  - Create models/simulations with variations
    - Fullwave vs. quasi-static
    - Different simulation techniques for different types of problems

---

Physical Models

  - Create physical models with variations and measure effect of variations
    - Measurements can be over shadowed by other effects
      - Shielding effectiveness
      - Trace discontinuities on a PCB
      - Location/value of filter capacitor components
      - Far field effects vs. near field effects may 'hide' the true variation effects
      - Feed locations for models may dominate
      - Source impedance and load impedance can change effects
    - Must use extreme care

12

Computer Models

  - Create models/simulations with variations
    - Fullwave vs. quasi-static
      - Quasi-static much faster than fullwave
      - Requires physical dimensions to be very small vs. wavelengths
    - Different simulation techniques for different types of problems
      - Method of Moments (MoM)
      - Finite-Difference Time-Domain (FDTD)
      - Finite Element Method (FEM)
      - Transmission Line Matrix (TLM) method
      - Partial Element Equivalent Circuit (PEEC) technique

What can Modeling Do?

- Eliminate use of Out-of-Context equations and graphs
- Update Rules-of-Thumb
- Relative analysis of particular design features
  - 'What if?' analysis
- Analysis of individual problems to be eventually combined to find overall result

14

Range of Tool Levels

- Design Rules
- Automated design rule checker
- Quasi-Static Tools
  - L,C,R Extraction
- Loop current emissions
  - from PCB traces into near field locations
- Full Wave techniques
- Magic

16

EM Fullwave Modeling State-of-the-Art

- Modeling is here NOW!
  - Many papers at Symposia
- Can't do everything
  - Too much information in CAD files
- Need to break the overall problem into individual mini-problems
- GIGO applies!

13

Tool Box Approach

- There is **_NO ONE_** modeling technique that will do 'everything'
  - Vendor claims must be carefully examined
- For Real-World applications engineers need
  - Tools at various modeling levels
  - A variety of modeling techniques

15

POPULAR MODELING TECHNIQUES

17

- Don't need Ph.D. to use them
- Codes are available in many forms
  - Free from Universities
    - User beware
  - Purchase from vendors
- User should understand basic techniques and their limitations

POPULAR MODELING TECHNIQUES

18

- Each technique has areas where it *excels* and areas where *limitations* apply
- Different modeling tasks require different techniques

Mathematical Foundation

19

Electromagnetic Simulation

Analytic formulas

Integral equation methods
(Integral calculus)
MoM
PEEC

Differential equation methods
(differential calculus)
FEM
FDTD
TLM
...

Finite-Difference Time-Domain

20

- All of space must be divided into electrically small grids
  - Each grid location assigned as air, metal, dielectric, etc.
  - Usually cube or rectangular grids
  - Assume field strength constant over cell
- Time domain technique
  - Wide band of frequencies analyzed at once
  - FFT to get frequency domain information

Finite-Difference Time-Domain

- Electric and Magnetic Fields are found directly
- 'THE' Field found
  - No Near/Far field assumptions
- Very well suited to shielding problems, or problems with dielectrics, lossy materials, etc.
- Not well suited to problems with long wires

21

Method of Moments (MoM)
Boundary Element Method (BEM)

- Break all surfaces into electrically small patches
- Break all wires into electrically small segments
  - Assume RF current does not vary across a patch or segment
- Frequency domain technique
  - Model must be run for each harmonic frequency of interest

22

Method of Moments (MoM)

- RF Current on every patch and segment found
  - Due to source and currents on all other patches and segments
- Electric/Magnetic fields found at any point by summing the contribution of all currents
  - May include assumptions about far field locations

23

Method of Moments (MoM)

- Very well suited to problems with long wires
- Well suited to problems with large distances
- Not well suited to shielding problems
- Not well suited to problems with dielectrics or lossy materials

24

Finite Element Method (FEM)

- Well suited to bound problems
  - Waveguides, Resonant Cavity, etc.
- Well suited to problems with large size differences within model
- Not well suited for problems with long wires or problems with open boundaries

25

Partial Element Equivalent Circuit (PEEC)

- Break all surfaces into electrically small grids
- Find equivalent partial inductances and capacitances between all grid points
- Add lumped circuit elements
- Finds currents and voltages everywhere
  - SPICE-like solver (with delay)

26

Partial Element Equivalent Circuit (PEEC)

- Electric/Magnetic fields found at any point by summing the contribution of all currents
  - May include assumptions about far field locations
- Voltage distribution between plates easy
- Time _or_ Frequency domain technique

27

Partial Element Equivalent Circuit (PEEC)

- Very well suited to problems with long wires
- Very well suited to PCB problems
- Very well suited to problems with large numbers of lumped circuit elements
- Not well suited to shielding problems

28

Transmission Line Method (TLM)

- Time Domain Technique
  - Wide band of frequencies analyzed at once
  - FFT to get frequency domain information
- Suited for shielding problems and problems with dielectrics, etc.
- Not well suited for problems with long wires
- Same constraints as FDTD

30

Three Levels of Validation

- Technique Validation
  - This has been done by many people over the years
- Software Code Validation
  - Usually done by vendor
  - Standard problems exist to help evaluate vendor codes
- Specific Model Validation
  - GIGO applies!

32

Transmission Line Method (TLM)

- Very similar to FDTD
- All space divided into small elements
- Elements converted to Transmission Line equivalent circuits
- Voltages and currents found for 3-d transmission line circuit
- Fields found by converting voltage and currents to fields

29

Modeling Technique Summary

- Each technique has *strengths* and *weaknesses*
- Use the technique where it works well
- Do NOT try to force a square block into a round hole!
- Need a variety of techniques (Tool Box Approach) and modeling levels
- Beware of vendor claims
  - Use must decide if tool will really do what they need

31

Specific Model Validation

- Measurements
- Closed form solutions
- Intermediate results
- Known quantities
- Relative changes
- **Compare results from different simulation techniques**

33

Outside the Product Design Process --Training

- Many EMC 'experts' offering training
  - Some good
  - Some not-so-good
  - Some pretty bad
- Bottom Line
  - *NOT* 'do this because *I* tell you to do it'
  - Do what makes sense from the physics of the problem
    - This means 'good' training helps you understand the physics (without the heavy mathematics)
    - 'Good' training helps you see how to apply the information to your designs

34

How to Select an EMC 'Expert' for Training

- Evaluate course outline to see if it applies to your type product
  - Aircraft? PCB? System integration?
- Contact previous students
  - Do NOT rely on testimonials
  - Did the instructor present material in an understandable manner?
  - Was the instructor overly impressed with himself/herself?
  - Did the instructor help the students understand the physics? Or just present a bunch of his/her favorite rules?
  - Would the previous student attend this class again? 35

Different Levels of EMC Design Process

- Outside the product design process
  - Design Rule Development
  - Training
- During the product design process
  - Apply design rules
  - Use automated design rule checker
- During testing phase
  - Validate rules and/or create new rules

36

Different Levels of EMC Design Process

- Outside the product design process
  - Design Rule Development
  - Training
- During the product design process
  - Apply design rules
  - Use automated design rule checker
- During testing phase
  - Validate rules and/or create new rules

38

During The Product Design Process

- Apply rules already validated
- PCBs have too much 'stuff' for an effective review
- Use automated design rule checker
  - Must fit smoothly into existing design process
  - Help designers prioritize rule violations
  - Never expect *__all__* rules to have no violations

37

Summary

- Never time to 'do it right' but always time to 'do it over'   *Your Choice*

  ⬍

  - **Before** Product Design process
    - Create/validate design rules
  - **During** product design
    - Use automated tools to check design
  - **After** product design
    - Closed loop feedback on how effective rules were and how effectively applied

- Design 'up-front' to pass the first time

40

After the Design Process
During testing phase

- Validate rules and/or create new rules
- Closed loop feedback important
  - Was some design approach successful?
  - Is the design passing, but marginal?
  - Was extra gasket, fingerstock, ferrite required?
    - If yes…why?….where?

39

469

LARGE SYSTEM EXAMPLES

Scalar Processing System

- IBM zSeries 990 has 1024 channels, 24 processors single image, 4 x 64 GB memory, hi-speed I/O cards: 10 GB Ethernet, 2 GB FICON

Parallel Processing System

- IBM pSeries P5 595 can house up to 64 processors at 16 processors per node, 2TB Memory, 240 PCI adapters. Parallel Processing system using only P5 595 nodes can link up to 16 x 16 x 16 = 4096 processors using a max. loaded IBM 7045 switch rack.

2

LARGE COMPUTING SYSTEM CHALLENGES

- Narrow band EMI emissions: large volume of I/O adapters & cables
- Broadband EMI emissions: twice the number of noise sources (switched mode P/Ss) from redundancy design and EMI re-enforcement from internal Ethernet adapters
- Ground loop EMI susceptibilities: multi-frame systems with interconnecting cables
- Cable organizing render efficient EMI emissions due to sheer volume of I/O cables
- High I/O band-width means smaller voltage swing which leads to immunity issues
- Common Infiniband standard complicates tailored solution for each adapter type
- Raised metal floor vs. none raised floor installations
- Heat transfer vs. EMC needs (perforated sheet metal chassis)
- Determination of compliance margin needed for product upgrades

4

Large Computing System/Server EMC Design Logistics

Kwok M. Soohoo, NCE
IBM Corp.
Poughkeepsie, NY
ksoohoo@us.ibm.com

1

EMI CHARACTERISTICS

Scalar Processing System

- All processors receive clocks from a central oscillator, consequently the EMI emissions are in phase and reinforce each others. Collective emission level is more intense since multiple antennas are tied to the same source.

Parallel Processing System

- Each processor has its own oscillator and the EMI emissions therefore are asynchronous among the processors. There are some additive effects from multiple processors' emissions however it is less than 2 dB from 2X.

3

PAST PROBLEM AREAS

EXAMPLES

- Collective radiated and conducted EMI from switching mode power supplies posed emission and immunity problems
- Cables proximity to external perforated covers lead to excessive EMI emission
- Excessive EMI leakage from large light weight cover panels due to bowing resulting from gasket compression
- Collective radiated EMI from outside bound Ethernet I/O cables resulted in excessive emissions
- High density MCM compromises decoupling strategies due to real estate shortage for filtering components
- Ethernets with RJ45 connectors are especially sensitive to ESD, EFT/Burst and conducted EMI

6

EMC DESIGN STRATEGIES

RULES FOR MECHANICAL DESIGNERS

- Allowable aperture sizes for external covers, frames, logic chassis & books, tailgate openings (rivet, screw, weld spacing specification)
- Signal and power cable termination requirements
- Conductive paint and metal finishes impedance requirements
- Gasket types and shielding effectiveness
- I/O & system clock distribution using metallic connectors with good 360 degree termination

8

SPECIFIC DESIGN CHALLENGES

- Denser I/O package creates greater noise coupling
- Higher I/O speed means higher EMI emission: high speed fiber optic channels run at over 2 Gb/S and 10 Gb/S for Ethernet
- Fast optic serial and high speed I/O adapters translate into greater sensitivity to ESD and EM transients
- EMI emissions from self timing interface cables to the I/O boards carrying clock harmonic frequencies well over 5 Ghz
- High density power supplies translate into higher broad band noise level
- Ethernet links inside the power supplies raised the broad band noise floor

5

EMC DESIGN STRATEGIES

- **EMC DESIGN GROUND RULES DISSEMINATION TO KEY PLAYERS**
  - Mechanical Packaging Designers
  - Power Supply Designers
  - Electrical Packaging Designers
  - Logic/Circuit Designers
  - Power Micro-coders
  - Software Recovery Group

7

9

EMC DESIGN STRATEGIES

SHIELDING RULES FOR MECHANICAL DESIGNERS

- Conductive paint (<50 ohm/square) on frame to give > 40 dB @ 1 GHz
- Cover system: frames, external covers with EMC gaskets to provide min. 40 db @ 1 GHz
- CEC & I/O logic cages: Faraday Cage approach for the logic books
- Logic books: housed in metal container contacting adjacent book through conductive gaskets
- I/O tailgate partition to reduce aperture size
- Application of "EMC skirts" at frame bottom to provide mechanical barrier with the raised metal floor to block cable EMI emissions

---

10

EMC DESIGN STRATEGIES

Additional Mechanical Shielding Considerations

- Cover to frame gap tolerance is vital for proper EMC gasket compression to assure low impedance
- External cover latching scheme is also important to insure proper EMC gasket compression
- Perforated sheet metal too leaky at GHz especially with transmitting antennas (signal cables) or noise sources adjacent to it. Need honeycomb waveguides
- Logic gate/chassis level shielding considerations
  1. Microwave design too costly for large chassis
  2. Alternative: use logic book to form a Faraday Cage with PCB mounting stiffener

---

11

EMC DESIGN STRATEGIES

MORE MECHANICAL CONSIDERATIONS

- Understanding of gasket application for proper selection: model EMC gaskets for form and fit to avoid problems such as compression set due to over compression or gasket falling off due to shear force
- Awareness of potential cover problems due to vendor masking process for gasket contact area on covers, excessive thick phosphate coating on galvaneal surfaces
- Liquid cooling copper pipe/plumbing treatment for EMI suppression and elimination of potential ESD conduction paths
- Cover tradeoff design using honeycomb waveguide (costly) vs. 2 layers of perforated screen for external covers

---

12

EMC DESIGN STRATEGIES

RULES FOR POWER SUPPLY DESIGNERS

- Conducted emission limits at AC cords
- Radiated EMI limits for the broad band EMI emissions from power supplies and associated distribution cables
- Power surge limits
- Conducted immunity test limits
- Conducted noise compliance margin to account for vendor P/S variability
- EFT/Burst, flicker, voltage dips, power harmonic limits
- Internal filtering and clamping of the BB noise sources (MOSFETs & IGBTs)
- Shielded DC cable with good chassis termination + ferrite core on each end

EMC DESIGN STRATEGIES

GENERAL RULES FOR PCB DESIGNERS

- **Printed Circuit Board Design Techniques:**
  - Faraday cage structure for PCB using "peripheral stitching"
  - Raising PCB resonance freq. (>10GHz) by internal stitching at fixed interval
- **Use of PCB EMC Checking Software:**
  - Checks for clock module, I/O module & critical net placement violations
  - It also checks for net termination problems, differential pair mismatches, and many other features related to wiring structures

14

EMC DESIGN STRATEGIES

MORE RULES FOR LOGIC/CIRCUIT DESIGNERS

- Spread spectrum clock generation hooks in place for high current and fast switching circuits during initial design stage

- Treatment for external clock lines and critical I/O interfaces using shielded balanced differential pairs (can't afford more than 5% mismatch)

- use of built-in RJ45 differential transformer connector helped in improving both EMI emission and noise tolerance margin

16

EMC DESIGN STRATEGIES

RULES FOR ELECTRONIC PACKAGING DESIGNERS

- Layering sequence for signal, voltage and ground planes in PCB
- Shielding structure of PCB connectors
- Component placements on PCB
- Component noise decoupling schemes on PCB
- Component heatsink grounding
- PCB ESD bleed path during concurrent maintenance
- PCB grounding scheme to chassis

13

EMC DESIGN STRATEGIES

RULES FOR LOGIC/CIRCUIT DESIGNERS

- I/O interface module ESD breakdown tolerance
- I/O interface connector layouts
- I/O cable and connector shielding requirements
- Signal plane selection for distribution of oscillator and clock lines
- Spare/unused connector termination scheme
- Harmonic frequency decoupling scheme for I/O modules
- Treatment for voltage plane breaks
- I/O cable length restriction to meet electrical transient standards (ESD, power surge, EFT/Burst) due to signal degradation

15

EMC DESIGN STRATEGIES

RULES FOR POWER MICRO-CODERS

- Fault tolerance codes to accommodate transient events such as ESD, EFT/Burst etc. by re-sampling for faults after the initial interruption before taking drastic actions

RULES FOR SOFTWARE RECOVERY GROUP

- Provide adequate retries in the software codes in the event of program interrupts due to transient events (ESD etc.) and also accommodate for the misc. immunity test durations. this is especially critical for I/O adapter type with poor cable shielding (RJ45 Ethernet) and the inter-frame self timing interface cables.

17

GROUNDING CONSIDERATIONS

- Develop a grounding hierarchy for reducing ESD threats and EMI emissions at various levels using multi-point grounds
- Fiber optic transceiver module grounding to logic book chassis to reduce EMI emissions and improve ESD tolerance
- Logic board grounding to gate chassis for ESD rejection and EMI reduction
- Logic gates grounding to frame rail improves ESD rejection and reduces EMI emission
- Frame grounding to computer room ground reference grid to reduce ground loop currents on inter-frame cables between systems

18

EXTERNAL THREAT IDENTIFICATION

- ESD severity and event rates
- Radiated and conducted EMI environments
- Power line transient events (EFT/Burst)
- Lightning surge
- Are the existing IEC immunity standards sufficient?
- How to address the above threats during concurrent maintenance?
- Develop a comprehensive test plan taking all of the above factors into account

19

RAS VS. SUSCEPTIBILITY LIMITS

- Reliability (100,000 hours components)
- Availability (99%)
- Serviceability (concurrent maintenance)
- The above objectives can only be achieved with:
  - Power and logic redundancies
  - Software/microcode house keeping and recovery algorithms
  - EM susceptibility limits (ESD, RES etc.) were set during system design phase to deliver the desired RAS performances

20

POWER SUPPLY DESIGN TO HANDLE EFT/BURST AND CONDUCTED EMI

- 3 tiers power subsystem: bulk power regulator (AC to hi voltage DC), DC distribution unit and DC to DC converter

- Ferrite loaded AC distribution bus as well as DC distribution cables

- EMI filters on both AC & DC supplies for external transients as well as internal switching regulator noise suppression

21

ACHIEVING GOOD ESD PERFORMANCE

- Set min. component level ESD spec.

- Define component ESD test method to enforce the above spec.

- Definition of min. acceptable error criteria such as BER (Bit Error Rate)

- Software retry/recovery criteria

- Procedural control during concurrent maintenance (use of ESD pad during cable installation)

22

RES (RADIATED EM SUSCEPTIBILITY) PROTECTION

- Define min. SE (Shielding Effectiveness) objectives at the cable, logic cage and frame level

- Gasket se test criteria and method (Dual TEM Cell)

- Cage level SE test

- Frame level SE test

- Cable SE test

- System integration test

23

SUBASSEMBLY/COMPONENT EVALUATION

- Box level shielding effectiveness test
- Cable and connector
- Gasket shielding effectiveness test
- Component level ESD test
- P/S conducted emission test
- Power surge immunity test on P/S
- Etc.

24

VENDOR COMPONENT SPECIFICATION

- Emission limits and immunity requirements must be spelled out in subassembly design spec. in the contract. examples: fiber optic transceivers, power supplies

- Component level ESD tolerance specification is critical for sensitive components such as fiber optic receivers

- Fiber optic transceiver module grounding and shielding for EMI emission control

- Choose cable termination scheme less subjective to workmanship defects

25

CONCURRENT MAINTENANCE CONSIDERATIONS

- All immunity tests were carried out with system covers open to simulate maintenance condition.

- Mandatory use of ESD bleed pad by field service personnel for discharging of cables' ESD prior to concurrent system service

26

COMPROMISES

- Weight vs. rigidity, cover warping/bowing due to gasket resistance
- Single latching vs. double latching
- Cables overflows (10 lbs stuffs in a 5 lb bag) vs. bigger frame
- Liquid cooled vs. air cooled
- Perforated sheet metal vs. solid metal
- Conductive vs. metal gaskets
- MCM functions over decoupling
- Conductive paint vs. plating

27

SUMMARY & TEST RESULTS

- System EMC design goes from circuit chip to external covers

- Each new generation of system presents different challenges

- Many tradeoffs are made due to cost vs. efficiency

- Other EMC meaning (Everyone Must Compromise)

- With special attention paid to known problem areas, IBM z990 and p5 595 servers passed world wide compliance test requirements without difficulty despite of their sizes and complexities

28

CONCLUSION

- It is a combination of component selections and well planned RAS objectives that went into the EMC system design requirements which were ultimately responsible for successful achievement of EMC compliance and field performances of large computing systems/servers.

29

WORKSHOP: GUIDE TO ACCREDITATION OF EMC LABORATORIES IN THE US (FR-PM-WS-18)

Werner Schaefer

The workshop is planned as a true exchange of information between laboratory personnel who are either considering to seek accreditation for their laboratory or who are already accredited. The author, a lead assessor with A2LA, also manages a quality system for accredited laboratories and is actively participating in national and international EMC standards work. The presenter's extensive background knowledge about RF and microwave test instrumentation allows for an in-depth and well-rounded presentation of the material.

The workshop consists of five parts covering reasons for obtaining accreditation for an EMC laboratory, what does accreditation really mean, accrediting bodies in the US, prerequisites for an accreditation, implementation of a quality system, based on ISO 17025, plus equipment calibration requirements, measurement uncertainty requirements, test equipment and test environment suitability and other considerations for laboratory accreditation.

NOTES

Disclaimer

Cisco.com

The material presented here was prepared using the published policies and procedures of the American Association of Laboratory Accreditation (A2LA). Furthermore, references are made to currently published quality and technical standards, available from national and international standards organizations.

The views and interpretations documented in this handout and shared verbally during this workshop are those of the author **and do not represent in any way official statements of A2LA or Cisco Systems, Inc.**

All examples provided are based on the accreditation process of A2LA. Other accreditation bodies, which are recognized by NACLA, will use similar approaches. For details contact the accreditation bodies directly.

IEEE EMC Symposion 2005

Slide 2

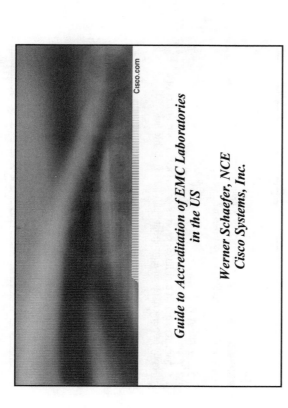

Cisco.com

Guide to Accreditation of EMC Laboratories in the US

Werner Schaefer, NCE
Cisco Systems, Inc.

IEEE EMC Symposion 2005

Workshop content - 2

Cisco.com

3) **The A2LA accreditation process**
   Application
   On-site assessment
   Accreditation decision

4) **Specific topic of interest**
   Test equipment calibration requirements
   Measurement uncertainty requirements
   Test equipment and test environment suitability

5) **Summary**

IEEE EMC Symposion 2005

Slide 4

Workshop content - 1

Cisco.com

1) **Introduction**
   What does accreditation mean?
   Reasons for obtaining accreditation
   Accreditation bodies in the US

2) **Pre-requisites for accreditation**
   Implementation of a quality system in accordance with ISO 17025
   The scope of accreditation

IEEE EMC Symposion 2005

Slide 3

Introduction

What does accreditation mean?

- Procedure by which an authoritative body gives formal recognition that a body is competent to carry out specific tasks

Or:

Procedure used to provide formal notice that a body is competent to carry out specific tasks

- More specifically: formal recognition that a testing laboratory is competent to carry out specific tests or types of tests
- Key words are: "competent" and "specific tests"

IEEE EMC Symposion 2005

Slide 5

Introduction

What does accreditation mean?

- Accreditation requires implementation of a quality system _and_ demonstrating competency in a technical field
- The quality standard to be adhered to is ISO 17025:1999
- Granted by an identified and qualified accreditation body to prescribed criteria
- For specific tests or otherwise defined by performance descriptors
- After an on-site assessment of QA management and specific capability by qualified assessors, and
- Surveillance of ongoing performance by reassessment at periodic intervals and by proficiency testing

IEEE EMC Symposion 2005

Slide 6

Introduction

What does accreditation _not_ mean?

Registration:
- Procedure by which a registration body indicates relevant characteristics of a product, process or service, or particulars of a body or person, on an appropriate publicly available list

Or:

Procedure used to give written assurance that a system conforms to specified requirements. Such systems include those established for the management of product, process or service quality, and environmental performance

- Registration is granted based on ISO 9000-2000 (or some derivatives like TL 9000)

IEEE EMC Symposion 2005

Slide 7

Introduction

What does accreditation _not_ mean?

Registration:

- ISO 9000-based quality systems are generic
- They apply to all types of organizations (hospitals, aircraft maintenance plants, grocery stores, etc.)
- The recognition of a quality system is based on a particular scope, which identifies the outputs (products/services) of the quality system
- Registration does not certify or guarantee the quality of products or services for compliance with specific technical specifications

IEEE EMC Symposion 2005

Slide 8

Introduction

Cisco.com

What does accreditation _not_ mean?

Certification:

• Procedure by which a third party gives written assurance (certificate of conformity) that a product, process or service conforms to specified requirements

Or:

Procedure used to provide written assurance that a product, process, service, or person's qualifications conform to specified requirements.

• Certification is based on a published standard specification

IEEE EMC Symposion 2005

Slide 9

Introduction

Cisco.com

What does accreditation _not_ mean?

Certification:

• Certification is a product guarantee (that it complies with a stated specification)

• Underwriters Laboratories (UL) and Technischer Überwachungsverein (TUV) certifications are examples for certification bodies

• Laboratories are not certified

IEEE EMC Symposion 2005

Slide 10

Introduction

Cisco.com

Conformity Assessment Hierarchy

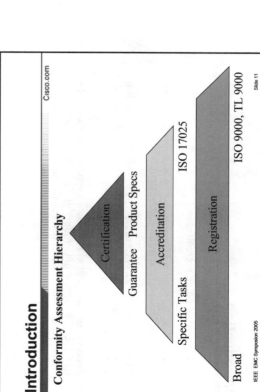

IEEE EMC Symposion 2005

Slide 11

Introduction

Cisco.com

In summary, accreditation is:

• _Not_ a guarantee (for example that test reports are free of errors)

• Not product certification

• Not just a quality system registration (quality system evaluation is only part of accreditation)

• But also an evaluation of competency (to perform specified tests or calibration activities)

IEEE EMC Symposion 2005

Slide 12

Introduction

Reasons for obtaining accreditation

- Independent verification of competency to establish confidence and trust in services (competitive advantage)

- On-going surveillance of compliance and proficiency, based on periodic assessments and proficiency testing requirements leads to higher efficiency and improved repeatability

- Access to specific product introduction approach to market place like DoC (Declaration of Conformity). This allows much faster marketing of products and is particularly important for products with a relatively short life cycle

IEEE EMC Symposion 2005

Slide 13

Introduction

Reasons for obtaining accreditation

- Provide a "level playing field" for international programs like MRAs (Mutual recognition Agreements), which are partly based on international acceptance of test reports and test data

- Accreditation is often the foundation for laboratory recognition by a group or authority responsible for a specific program. Examples are :
  - * automotive industry: AEMCLRP program
  - * mobile handset industry: CTIA program

IEEE EMC Symposion 2005

Slide 14

Introduction

Accreditation bodies in the US for EMC laboratories

A2LA: American Association for Laboratory Accreditation
NVLAP: National Voluntary Laboratory Accreditation Program
ILAC: International Laboratory Accreditation Cooperation

The two accreditation bodies mentioned are the only ones in the US which are signatories to ILAC. All others do not provide mutual recognition with other accreditation bodies, both nationally and internationally!

IEEE EMC Symposion 2005

Slide 15

Introduction

Accreditation bodies in the US for EMC laboratories

- A2LA and NVLAP (administered by NIST) are evaluated by "peers" (i.e., other international accreditation bodies); compliance with ISO Guide 58 is one criterion among others for international recognition

- Other criterion which have to be met in a satisfactory way are:
  - * Competency of staff
  - * Quality system and administration of the accreditation system
  - * Recruitment, training and monitoring of our assessors
  - * Performance of assessors via scheduled witness visits to laboratories being assessed
  - * Establishment of technical committees
  - * Decision making process for accreditation
  - * Proficiency testing and inter-laboratory comparisons
  - * Traceability and measurement uncertainty

IEEE EMC Symposion 2005

Slide 16

Introduction

Organization of accreditation systems

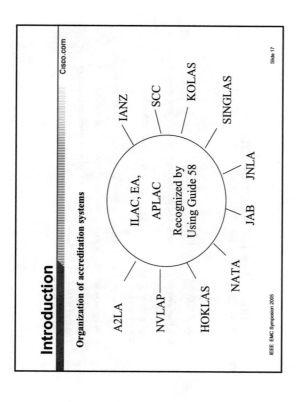

Cisco.com

A2LA

NVLAP

HOKLAS

NATA

JAB

IANZ

SCC

ILAC, EA,
APLAC
Recognized by
Using Guide 58

KOLAS

SINGLAS

JNLA

IEEE EMC Symposion 2005

Slide 17

Introduction

Organization of accreditation systems

Cisco.com

Groups that use ISO Guide 58 to recognize accrediting bodies:

- ILAC: International Laboratory Accreditation Cooperation
- EA: European Cooperation for Accreditation
- APLAC: Asia Pacific Laboratory Accreditation Conference

IEEE EMC Symposion 2005

Slide 18

Introduction

Conformity assessment - accreditation hierarchy

Cisco.com

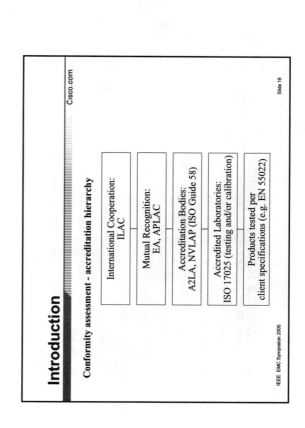

International Cooperation:
ILAC

Mutual Recognition:
EA, APLAC

Accreditation Bodies:
A2LA, NVLAP (ISO Guide 58)

Accredited Laboratories:
ISO 17025 (testing and/or calibration)

Products tested per
client specifications (e.g. EN 55022)

IEEE EMC Symposion 2005

Slide 19

Pre-requisites for Accreditation

Background of ISO/IEC 17025:1999 - ISO Guide 25

Cisco.com

- ISO Guide 25; Title: General Requirements for the Competence of Calibration and Testing Laboratories

- Called a "guide" but written as a standard, using words such as "shall" and "must", not "should" and "may"

- ISO Council Committee CASCO (Conformity Assessment Committee) is responsible for revisions and maintenance of this standard

- Associated time line:
  1999 – Approved in December
  2000 – Year of implementation
  2001 – Year of enforcement

IEEE EMC Symposion 2005

Slide 20

Slide 21

Pre-requisites for Accreditation

Cisco.com

Differences between ISO/IEC 17025:1999 and ISO Guide 25

- Broader Scope
- Formatting (Numbering, Organization, Notes, Annexes)
- Focus on Clients
- More Prescriptive
- Measurement Uncertainty
- Traceability
- ISO Guide 25 is mainly applicable to <u>routine</u> testing and calibration laboratories
- ISO 17025 includes requirements for <u>sampling and laboratory-developed methods</u>

IEEE EMC Symposion 2005

Slide 21

Slide 22

Pre-requisites for Accreditation

Cisco.com

Organization of ISO/IEC 17025:1999

- Section 1: Scope
- Section 2: Normative References
- Section 3: Terms and Definitions
- Section 4: Management Requirements
- Section 5: Technical Requirements

IEEE EMC Symposion 2005

Slide 22

Slide 23

Pre-requisites for Accreditation

Cisco.com

Scope of ISO/IEC 17025:1999

- Specifies general requirements a laboratory has to meet to be considered competent
- Applicable to all types of laboratories (i.e., testing and calibration laboratories)
- Notes are for guidance, not requirements (i.e., not part of normative text)
- Used by laboratories, clients, regulators, and accreditation bodies
- If laboratories are in compliance with ISO 17025, they will also comply with ISO 9001 – but not the other way around!

IEEE EMC Symposion 2005

Slide 23

Slide 24

Pre-requisites for Accreditation

Cisco.com

Normative references of ISO/IEC 17025:1999

- ISO/IEC Guide 2, *General terms and their definitions concerning standardization and related activities*
- VIM: 1993, *International vocabulary of basic and general terms in metrology*
- ISO 9001: 1994, Quality systems - Model for quality assurance in design, development, production, installation and servicing.
- ISO 9002: 1994, Quality systems - Model for quality assurance in production, installation and servicing

IEEE EMC Symposion 2005

Slide 24

484

Pre-requisites for Accreditation

ISO/IEC 17025:1999 – Management requirements

4.1   Organization

4.2   Quality System

4.3   Document Control

4.4   Review of Requests, Tenders and Contracts

4.5   Sub-Contracting of Tests

4.6   Purchasing Services and Supplies

4.7   Service to the Client

IEEE EMC Symposion 2005

Slide 25

Pre-requisites for Accreditation

ISO/IEC 17025:1999 – Management requirements

4.8   Complaints

4.9   Control of Nonconforming Testing Work

4.10 Corrective Action

4.11 Preventive Action

4.12 Control of Records

4.13 Internal Audits

4.14 Management Reviews

IEEE EMC Symposion 2005

Slide 26

Pre-requisites for Accreditation

ISO/IEC 17025:1999 – Technical requirements

5.1   General

5.2   Personnel

5.3   Accommodation/Environmental Conditions

5.4   Test Methods and Method Validation

5.5   Equipment

IEEE EMC Symposion 2005

Slide 27

Pre-requisites for Accreditation

ISO/IEC 17025:1999 – Technical requirements

5.6   Measurement Traceability

5.7   Sampling

5.8   Handling of Test Items (Samples)

5.9   Assuring the Quality of Test Results

5.10 Reporting the Results

IEEE EMC Symposion 2005

Slide 28

Pre-requisites for Accreditation

Quality system documentation requirements

- Documentation of quality system only to the extent necessary to ensure quality and consistent implementation

- Procedures can be included in quality system by reference (e.g., use of document control procedure of ISO 9000-2000 quality system)

- Whenever ISO 17025 refers to "policies and procedures", a written procedure is to be included in the quality system (shaded areas in A2LA ISO 17025 checklist)

- Whenever "records" are required per ISO 17025, objective evidence is to be provided (usually in writing), that a certain action took place

---

Pre-requisites for Accreditation

Requirements for policies and/or procedures, per ISO 17025 (Part 1)

- Clause 4.1.5.c: procedures to ensure the protection of its clients' confidential information and proprietary rights

- Clause 4.1.5.d: policies and procedures to avoid involvement in any activities that would diminish confidence in its competence, impartiality, judgment or operational integrity

- Clause 4.3.1: the laboratory shall establish and maintain procedures to control all documents that form part of its quality system

- Clause 4.3.2.1: a master list or an equivalent document control procedure identifying the current revision status and distribution of documents in the quality system shall be established

- Clause 4.3.3.3: if the laboratory's documentation control system allows for the amendment of documents by hand pending the re-issue of the documents, the procedures and authorities for such amendments shall be defined

---

Pre-requisites for Accreditation

Requirements for policies and/or procedures, per ISO 17025 (Part 2)

- Clause 4.3.4: procedures shall be established to describe how changes in documents maintained in computerized systems are made and controlled

- Clause 4.4.1: the laboratory shall establish and maintain procedures for the review of requests, tenders and contracts

- Clause 4.6.1: the laboratory shall have a policy and procedure for the selection and purchasing of services and supplies it uses that affect the quality of the tests

- Clause 4.8: the laboratory shall have a policy and procedure for the resolution of complaints received from clients or other parties

- Clause 4.9.1: the laboratory shall have a policy and procedures that shall be implemented when any aspect of its testing and/or calibration work, or the results of this work, do not conform to its own procedures or the agreed requirements of the client.

Pre-requisites for Accreditation

Requirements for policies and/or procedures, per ISO 17025 (Part 3)

- Clause 4.10.1: the laboratory shall establish a policy and procedure and shall designate appropriate authorities for implementing corrective action when nonconforming work or departures from the policies and procedures in the quality system or technical operations have been identified

- Clause 4.11.2: procedures for preventive actions shall include the initiation of such actions and application of controls to ensure that they are effective

- Clause 4.12.1.1: the laboratory shall establish and maintain procedures for identification, collection, indexing, access, filing, storage, maintenance and disposal of quality and technical records

- Clause 4.12.1.4: the laboratory shall have procedures to protect and back-up records stored electronically and to prevent unauthorized access to or amendment of these records

Slide 33 (bottom-left)

Pre-requisites for Accreditation

Requirements for policies and/or procedures, per ISO 17025 (Part 4)

- Clause 4.13.1: the laboratory shall periodically, and in accordance with a predetermined schedule and procedure, conduct internal audits of its activities
- Clause 4.14.1: in accordance with a predetermined schedule and procedure, the laboratory's executive management shall periodically conduct a review of the laboratory's quality system and testing and/or calibration activities
- Clause 5.2.2: the laboratory shall have a policy and procedures for identifying training needs and providing training of personnel
- Clause 5.3.5: Measures shall be taken to ensure good housekeeping in the laboratory. Special procedures shall be prepared where necessary

Slide 33

Slide 34 (top-left)

Pre-requisites for Accreditation

Requirements for policies and/or procedures, per ISO 17025 (Part 5)

- Clause 5.4.1: The laboratory shall use appropriate methods and procedures for all tests and/or calibrations within its scope. These include sampling, handling, transport, storage and preparation of items to be tested and/or calibrated, and, where appropriate, an estimation of the measurement uncertainty as well as statistical techniques for analysis of test and/or calibration data
- Clause 5.4.5.2: the laboratory shall record the results obtained, the procedure used for the validation, and a statement as to whether the method is fit for the intended use
- Clause 5.4.6.1: A calibration laboratory, **or a testing laboratory performing its own calibrations**, shall have and shall apply a procedure to estimate the uncertainty of measurement for all calibrations and types of calibrations

Slide 34

Slide 35 (bottom-right)

Pre-requisites for Accreditation

Requirements for policies and/or procedures, per ISO 17025 (Part 6)

- Clause 5.4.6.2: testing laboratories shall have and shall apply procedures for estimating uncertainty of measurement
- Clause 5.4.7.2.b: procedures are established and implemented for protecting the data
- Clause 5.5.6: the laboratory shall have procedures for safe handling, transport, storage, use and planned maintenance of measuring equipment to ensure proper functioning and in order to prevent contamination or deterioration
- Clause 5.5.10: when intermediate checks are needed to maintain confidence in the calibration status of the equipment, these checks shall be carried out according to a defined procedure
- Clause 5.5.11: where calibrations give rise to a set of correction factors, the laboratory shall have procedures to ensure that copies (e.g. in computer software) are correctly updated

Slide 35

Slide 36 (top-right)

Pre-requisites for Accreditation

Requirements for policies and/or procedures, per ISO 17025 (Part 6)

- Clause 5.6.1: the laboratory shall have an established program and procedure for the calibration of its equipment
- Clause 5.6.3.1: the laboratory shall have a program and procedure for the calibration of its reference standards **(only if internal calibration activities are performed)**
- Clause 5.6.3.3: checks needed to maintain confidence in the calibration status of reference, primary, transfer or working standards and reference materials shall be carried out according to defined procedures and schedules **(only if internal calibration activities are performed)**
- Clause 5.6.3.4: The laboratory shall have procedures for safe handling, transport, storage and use of reference standards and reference materials in order to prevent contamination or deterioration and in order to protect their integrity **(only if internal calibration activities are performed)**

Slide 36

Pre-requisites for Accreditation

Cisco.com

Requirements for policies and/or procedures, per ISO 17025 (Part 7)

√ Clause 5.7.1: the laboratory shall have a sampling plan and procedures for sampling when it carries out sampling of substances, materials or products for subsequent testing **(only if sampling is performed)**

√ Clause 5.7.3: the laboratory shall have procedures for recording relevant data and operations relating to sampling that forms part of the testing or calibration that is undertaken **(only if sampling is performed)**

√ Clause 5.8.1: the laboratory shall have procedures for the transportation, receipt, handling, protection, storage, retention and/or disposal of test and/or calibration items, including all provisions necessary to protect the integrity of the test or calibration item, and to protect the interests of the laboratory and the client

IEEE EMC Symposion 2005

Slide 37

Pre-requisites for Accreditation

Cisco.com

Requirements for policies and/or procedures, per ISO 17025 (Part 8)

√ Clause 5.8.4: the laboratory shall have procedures and appropriate facilities for avoiding deterioration, loss or damage to the test or calibration item during storage, handling and preparation

√ Clause 5.9: the laboratory shall have quality control procedures for monitoring the validity of tests and calibrations undertaken

N/A A2LA Advertising Policy, clause 1.1: the laboratory shall have a policy and procedure for controlling the use of the term "A2LA" and the "A2LA Accredited" logo

√ A2LA Traceability Policy, clause T.9.a: the in-house laboratory shall maintain documented procedures for the in-house calibrations and the in-house calibrations shall be evidenced by a calibration report, certificate, or sticker, or other suitable method, and calibration records shall be retained for an appropriate, prescribed time

IEEE EMC Symposion 2005

Slide 38

Pre-requisites for Accreditation

Cisco.com

Requirements for policies and/or procedures, per ISO 17025 (Part 9)

• A2LA Traceability Policy, clause T.9.d: the in-house laboratory shall have and apply procedures for evaluating measurement uncertainty. Measurement uncertainty shall be taken into account when statements of compliance with specifications are made

√ A2LA Traceability Policy, clause T.9.e: Reference standards shall be recalibrated at appropriate intervals to ensure that the reference value is reliable. Policy and procedures for establishing and changing calibration intervals shall be based on the historical behavior of the reference standard

• **This means:**
   30 procedures are applicable in general, for each laboratory
   7 procedures are applicable if the laboratory performs its own calibrations
   2 procedures are applicable if the laboratory performs product sampling

IEEE EMC Symposion 2005

Slide 39

Pre-requisites for Accreditation

Cisco.com

Requirements for records, per ISO 17025 (Part 1)

N/A Clause 4.4.2: contract review records

√ Clause 4.6.2: records of review of services and supplies

√ Clause 4.6.4: evaluation records of suppliers of services and supplies which are critical to performing testing

Clause 4.8: complaints records

√ Clause 5.2.5: personnel records

√ Clause 5.5.5: equipment records

√ Clause 5.7.3: sampling records **(only if sampling is performed)**

IEEE EMC Symposion 2005

Slide 40

Pre-requisites for Accreditation

Requirements for records, per ISO 17025 (Part 2)

- A2LA Traceability Policy, clause T.9.a: internal calibration records **(only if calibration activities are performed internally)**

- A2LA Traceability Policy, clause T.9.b: training records for internal calibration personnel **(only if calibration activities are performed internally)**

- The minimum content of some records (like equipment records) is specified in ISO 17025. If no further specification is provided, the laboratory must define the content of the records such that compliance with the requirements can be demonstrated

- Record keeping itself is defined in ISO 17025, clause 4.12

IEEE EMC Symposion 2005

Slide 41

Pre-requisites for Accreditation

Cisco.com

Applicable additional A2LA requirements

- A2LA Traceability Policy: it specifies requirements for calibration services to be used, how measurement uncertainty is to be determined and documented and specifies requirements for internal calibration activities

- A2LA Advertising Policy: it specifies guidelines for the use of the A2LA logo for endorsements of test reports, the use of the logo and accreditation status for marketing purposes and duplication of the logo

- A2LA Proficiency Testing Policy: it specifies an overall time frame in which all major test methods have to be enveloped in a proficiency testing program (if available), per ISO 17025, clause 5.9. The goal is to perform activities which demonstrate that the test results are of a certain quality over time

- A2LA Measurement Uncertainty Policy: defines requirements for the calculation of measurement uncertainty for test laboratories

IEEE EMC Symposion 2005

Slide 42

Pre-requisites for Accreditation

Cisco.com

ISO 17025 flow chart (1)

Accept work (clause 4.4)   ⇧   Identify Work (clause 5.8.2)

⇩   Record condition (clause 5.8.3)

⇩   Store samples (clause 5.8.4)

Test methods (clause 5.4)   ⇩   Prepare sample (clause 5.4.1)

Personnel (clause 5.2)   ⇨

Equipment (clause 5.5)   ⇨

Calibration (clause 5.6)   ⇨

Supplies (clause 4.6)   ⇨

IEEE EMC Symposion 2005

Slide 43

Pre-requisites for Accreditation

Cisco.com

ISO 17025 flow chart (2)

Subcontracting (clause 4.5)   ⇦   Ensure data quality (clause 5.9)

⇨   Provide report (clause 5.10)

⇨   Dispose samples (clause 5.8.1)

Each step in the generic work flow of a test laboratory is addressed by ISO 17025. This includes interaction with customers, subcontractors and suppliers of services and consumables.

IEEE EMC Symposion 2005

Slide 44

Pre-requisites for Accreditation

Scope of accreditation

- It states the competency of the laboratory and is based on test methods. These test methods can be called out in published standards or can be internally developed. In the latter case the test methods must be validated for suitability and accuracy

- Test methods on scopes can be dated (e.g., ANSI C63.4-2003). It is assumed that test laboratories comply with the latest version of a standard within <u>one</u> <u>year</u> after it went into effect

- If test methods are not dated on scopes it is implied that the laboratory has implemented the latest version of the cited standards

- Only the scope of accreditation, not the accreditation certificate, does document the technical capabilities of a laboratory

- The scopes of all accredited laboratories are kept in a data base and can be retrieved and viewed on the A2LA web page (http://www.a2la2.net)

IEEE EMC Symposion 2005

Slide 45

Pre-requisites for Accreditation

Cisco.com

SCOPE OF ACCREDITATION TO ISO/IEC 17025-1999

CISCO SYSTEMS, INC.

170 West Tasman Drive

San Jose, CA 95134-1706

Mr. Werner Schaefer   Phone: 408 853 8550

ELECTRICAL

Valid to: November 30, 2004   Certificate Number: 1178-01

In recognition of the successful completion of the A2LA evaluation process, accreditation is granted to this laboratory to perform the following product safety, telecommunications, environmental simulation, and electromagnetic compatibility (EMC/EMI) tests:

Test Technology	Test Method(s)
EMI/EMC	GR 1089, Issue 2 (1999): Sections 2 to 4 (excluding section 4.5.11-16, 4.6)
	GR 1089, Issue 3 (2002): Sections 2 to 4 (excluding section 4.6.7.1, 4.6.10-17, 4.8)
	CISPR 22
	EN 55022
	CNS 13438

IEEE EMC Symposion 2005

Slide 46

A2LA Accreditation Process

Cisco.com

Application – generic steps

- Specific information on the laboratory (e.g., contact information)

- Selection of Field(s) of Testing (e.g., EMC, Telecom, etc)

- Technical staff matrix (listing of authorized personnel vs. test methods on scope of accreditation)

- Application date
  - Attests to when laboratory is ready for assessment
  - Earliest date deficiencies can be written

- Send in the accreditation fee

- Assignment of assessor (laboratory can decide about acceptability)

IEEE EMC Symposion 2005

Slide 47

A2LA Accreditation Process

Cisco.com

Application – generic steps (1)

- Decide that accreditation is desirable for your laboratory; request an application package in those field(s) of testing or calibration of interest; purchase a copy of ISO/IEC 17025; identify who is to be responsible for meeting accreditation requirements and make the relevant resources available.

- For each field, list the methods or techniques used and, as applicable. For calibration parameters, calculate measurement uncertainty.

- Review the A2LA *General Requirements for Accreditation* and any applicable specific program requirements documents; evaluate how the criteria apply to the laboratory; identify clauses that do not apply or apply only to a limited extent, and identify the reasons for their non-applicability.

IEEE EMC Symposion 2005

Slide 48

490

A2LA Accreditation Process

Application – generic steps (2)

4. Identify the person in charge of the quality system (e.g., the quality manager). A quality system that functions well cannot come about without top management support and commitment (a requirement laid down in the criteria). In a large laboratory, the coordination of these activities may be too large a task for the top manager; it is for him or her to decide on how to handle this important subsidiary function. He or she may have to be assisted by someone who would be responsible for the development and maintenance of the documented quality system.

5. Discuss the relevant paragraphs of the criteria thoroughly with those directly involved in the subjects discussed. Identify the laboratory's weak points and the practices and procedures that must be revised.

IEEE EMC Symposion 2005

Slide 49

A2LA Accreditation Process

Cisco.com

Application – generic steps (3)

6. Examine whether organizational arrangements, practices and procedures meet the requirements laid down in the criteria and make improvements on the basis of this examination. This stage may be time-consuming but necessary in order to obtain accreditation. The investment of time is often justified by the resulting improvement in management: developing better procedures and improving reliability and accuracy of testing.

7. Document the policies, organizational arrangements and procedures in a quality manual and related documentation. Ensure that this fulfills the requirements of ISO/IEC 17025 and that the personnel concerned know and accept the content

IEEE EMC Symposion 2005

Slide 50

A2LA Accreditation Process

Cisco.com

Application – generic steps (4)

8. As a general rehearsal for the accreditation assessment, verify through internal audits and management reviews whether the arrangements and procedures described in the quality manual do in fact work, and whether they meet ISO/IEC 17025 requirements

9. Return your completed application to A2LA to initiate an assessment of your laboratory. A2LA will notify you of the names and provide brief curricula vitae of the assessor(s). If you have justifiable objections, changes in the assignment(s) can be made.

10. Application forms can be downloaded from the A2LA web page.

IEEE EMC Symposion 2005

Slide 51

A2LA Accreditation Process

Cisco.com

Application – required documentation

- Proposed scope of testing or calibration in terms of field(s) of testing or calibration, testing technologies, methods and relevant standards, and measurement uncertainty budgets if applicable
- Required forms (check A2LA web page for application package)
- Quality manual
- Organization structure
- Proficiency test plan and testing results
- Personnel competency matrix

All documentation must be provided in English and the assessment conducted in English.

IEEE EMC Symposion 2005

Slide 52

A2LA Accreditation Process

Accreditation process summary (1)

- The applicant laboratory obtains all necessary A2LA application forms, A2LA requirements and policy documents from the web site or directly from A2LA.

- The laboratory obtains an official copy of ISO/IEC 17025.

- The laboratory provides A2LA with faxed confirmation (see page 9 of the application) that a valid copy of ISO/IEC 17025 has been obtained. A2LA then provides the ISO/IEC 17025 Assessor Checklist to the laboratory.

- The applicant laboratory completes and returns the application for accreditation, all required supporting documentation, and payment.

- A2LA reviews the application documents and an appropriate assessor(s) is assigned, with laboratory concurrence.

Slide 53

A2LA Accreditation Process

Accreditation process summary (2)

6. The assessor contacts the laboratory to discuss the scheduling of the on-site assessment and request the quality documentation. Once documentation is reviewed for completeness, the assessment can be scheduled with the assessor(s).

7. The assessment or the pre-assessment is performed and includes: entry briefing; review of quality documentation, records, sample handling; interviews with technicians; demonstrations of tests/calibrations; examination of equipment and calibration records; written report of assessor's findings; and exit briefing.

8. The laboratory responds to any deficiencies with a written corrective action response.

Slide 54

A2LA Accreditation Process

Accreditation process summary (3)

9. The corrective action is reviewed by the A2LA staff and once complete, is forwarded to the Accreditation Council for a vote.

10. Accreditation is granted when affirmative votes are received, all concerns are resolved, and all fees are paid in full.

11. Surveillance audit is performed only in the first year after the initial assessment

12. Full re-assessment is performed every two years thereafter

13. Accreditation is valid for two years

Slide 55

A2LA Accreditation Process

On-site assessment (1)

- Once the application information is completed and the appropriate fees are paid, A2LA headquarters staff identifies and tentatively assigns one or more assessors to conduct an assessment at the laboratory's site.

- Assessors are selected on the basis of their testing or calibration expertise so as to be better able to provide guidance to the laboratories.

- They do not represent their employers (if so affiliated) while conducting assessments for A2LA. The laboratory has the right to ask for another assessor if it objects to the original assignment.

- Assessors work under contract to A2LA. Assessments may last from one to several days depending on the extent of the desired scope and the size of laboratory. More than one assessor may be required.

Slide 56

A2LA Accreditation Process

Cisco.com

On-site assessment (2)

- Assessors are given an assessor guide and checklists to follow in performing an assessment. These documents are intended to ensure that assessments are conducted as uniformly and completely as possible among the assessors and from laboratory to laboratory.

- Before the assessment is conducted, the assessor team requests copies of quality documentation and representative technical SOPs in order to prepare for the assessment.

- The quality manual and related documentation must be reviewed by the assessor team before the assessment can begin. This review is done ideally before the assessment is scheduled. Upon review of submitted documentation, the assessor(s) will provide the document review results to the laboratory in writing, and may ask the laboratory to implement corrective action to fill any documentation gaps required by ISO/IEC 17025 before scheduling the assessment.

IEEE EMC Symposion 2005

Slide 57

A2LA Accreditation Process

Cisco.com

On-site assessment (3)

- A pre-assessment visit may be requested by the laboratory or suggested by the assessor as an option at this point to enhance the success of the full assessment.

- Prior to scheduling the full assessment, the assessor reviews the draft scope(s) to determine the tests to possibly witness and checks on the availability of the technical personnel who perform the tests.

- An assessment agenda is provided by the assessor.

IEEE EMC Symposion 2005

Slide 58

A2LA Accreditation Process

Cisco.com

On-site assessment (4)

The full assessment generally involves:

- An entry briefing with laboratory management
- Interviews with technical staff
- Demonstration of selected tests or calibrations including, as applicable, tests or calibrations at representative field locations
- Examination of equipment and calibration records
- Audit of the quality system to verify that it is fully operational and that it conforms to all sections of ISO/IEC 17025, including documentation
- A written report of assessor findings
- An exit briefing including the specific written identification of any deficiencies.

IEEE EMC Symposion 2005

Slide 59

A2LA Accreditation Process

Cisco.com

On-site assessment (5)

- During the full assessment, the assessor has the authority to stop the process at any time and consult with A2LA staff and the laboratory's management to determine if the assessment should proceed

- In cases where the number of significant nonconformances affects the ability to successfully complete a full assessment, the visit may be converted to a pre-assessment. The full assessment is then rescheduled when the laboratory and assessor feel it is appropriate to proceed

- The objective of an assessment is to establish whether or not a laboratory complies with the A2LA requirements for accreditation and can competently perform the types of tests or calibrations for which accreditation is sought

IEEE EMC Symposion 2005

Slide 60

A2LA Accreditation Process

On-site assessment (6)

- However, when accreditation is required to demonstrate compliance with additional criteria which may be imposed by program requirements, such as in the case of CTIA or AEMCLRP, the A2LA assessment will include such additional criteria.

- Assessors may also provide advice, based on observations or in response to questions, in order to help the laboratory improve its performance

- However, the ultimate decision about implementation of corrective actions is to be made by the laboratory. Furthermore, no consulting activities are to be provided by the assessor nor should they be expected by the laboratory

- Assessments are often performed in accordance with published standards. Any ambiguity in these standards which are perceived as inadequate by the laboratory are to be brought to the attention of the standards committee. The assessor is not responsible for the content of the applied standards!

Slide 61

A2LA Accreditation Process

On-site assessment (7)

During the assessment, assessors may observe deficiencies. A deficiency is any nonconformity to accreditation requirements including:

- a laboratory's inability to perform a test, type of test, or calibration for which it seeks accreditation

- a laboratory's quality system does not conform to a clause or section of ISO/IEC 17025, is not adequately documented, or is not completely implemented in accordance with that documentation; or

- a laboratory does not conform to any additional requirements of A2LA or specific fields of testing or programs necessary to meet particular needs

Assessors will discuss deficiencies at the time they are discovered. The laboratory can implement corrective actions during the on-site assessment to address deficiencies.

Slide 62

A2LA Accreditation Process

On-site assessment (7)

- It is entirely possible that the laboratory will disagree with the findings that one or more items are deficiencies. In that case, the laboratory is requested to explain in its response why it disagrees with the assessor.

- If a new applicant laboratory fails to respond in writing within four months after the date of the exit briefing, it may be required to submit a new application and be subject to new fees and reassessment should it wish to pursue accreditation after that time.

- A new applicant laboratory that fails to resolve all its deficiencies within six months of being assessed shall be subject to being reassessed at its expense.

- Renewal laboratories must respond in writing within 30 days of the exit briefing, and resolve all deficiencies within 60 days of the exit briefing. Failure to meet these deadlines may result in adverse accreditation action

Slide 63

Specific Topics of Interest

Calibration service requirements (1)

- The traceability policy includes states the requirement for A2LA-accredited laboratories to obtain accredited calibration reports from their calibration providers or to obtain calibrations directly from a National Metrology Institute (NMI).

- During the laboratory's on-site assessment, the Assessor will review the laboratory's calibration records and determine during the assessment if:

  a) the lab can demonstrate that they have obtained calibration service from our national metrology institute, NIST, or another NMI; or

  b) the lab can demonstrate that the calibration was performed by an A2LA-accredited calibration lab or by a calibration lab that has been accredited by one of the mutual recognition arrangement (MRA) partners. Assessors must see a calibration certificate with the accreditation body logo included, or which otherwise makes reference to accredited status.

Slide 64

Specific Topics of Interest

Cisco.com

Calibration service requirements (2)

- A2LA has mandated that assessors must cite a deficiency in all cases if the conditions noted above are not met.
- To address the deficiency, laboratories must either:
  a) demonstrate in their corrective action response that they will use an acceptable source of calibration for the next calibration cycle; or
  b) request that A2LA consider providing an exception to the Traceability Policy
- To ensure uniformity of the decisions to grant these case by case exceptions, the request must be submitted to A2LA (not to the assessors) in writing within 30 days after the conclusion of the on-site assessment and must provide full justification for why the laboratory would like to continue using the current calibration service

---

Specific Topics of Interest

Cisco.com

Calibration service requirements (3)

A2LA considers the following to be minimally sufficient evidence of an "unsuccessful search" for an appropriate accredited calibration provider:

1) Equipment name and model
2) Parameter and range of calibration needed
3) Key words used in any website search for an accredited calibration provider
4) List of all sources investigated (e.g., specific accreditation body websites, hardcopy directories, state metrology labs, etc.)
5) Objective evidence that the measurement being provided by the present calibration vendor is traceable to SI units.

Specific Topics of Interest

Cisco.com

Calibration service requirements (4)

- Exceptions are valid until the next on-site assessment. Note that as more calibration services become accredited by A2LA and the MRA partners, fewer exceptions are being granted
- An exception to the traceability policy will not be granted based on cost considerations (e.g., the calibration service is being used is the cheapest service available)
- It is mandatory for the testing laboratory to ask for the correct calibration service. A complete calibration, under the calibration laboratory's scope of accreditation, is to be requested!
- Upon arrival of the test equipment from the calibration facility, the test laboratory must verify that the requested calibration service was indeed provided (review certificates to identify reference to accreditation or inclusion of logo, measurement uncertainty statements, etc.)

Specific Topics of Interest

Cisco.com

Measurement uncertainty requirements (1)

- Requirements for the determination of measurement uncertainty are called out in ISO 17025, clauses 5.4.6.2 and 5.4.6.3.
- A2LA acknowledged the difficulty for many laboratories in the field of EMC testing to determine measurement uncertainty estimates
- An annex to "A2LA's Interim Policy on Measurement Uncertainty for Testing Laboratories" categorizes various tests in the EMC field. It was decided by A2LA's EMAC committee to classify all EMC tests as category II, unless the standard specifically calls out the requirement to determine measurement uncertainty. In this case the test method would be classified as category V
- The assessor will have to indicate the measurement uncertainty category on the test method matrix

Specific Topics of Interest

Measurement uncertainty requirements (2)

The uncertainty categories available are:

I: Qualitative or semi-quantitative tests for which measurement uncertainty budgets will not be required.

II: Well-recognized test methods that specify limits to the values of the major sources of uncertainty of measurement and specify the form of presentation of calculated results. In such cases, the laboratory is considered to have satisfied this clause by following the test method and reporting instructions.

III: Chemical, environmental, or biological test methods based on published regulatory or consensus methods

IV: Test methods that need identification of the major components of uncertainty and a reasonable estimate of measurement uncertainty.

V: Test methods that need identification of all components of uncertainty and detailed measurement uncertainty budgets calculated in accordance with published methods that are consist with those described in the ISO *"Guide to the Expression of Uncertainty in Measurement"*

Specific Topics of Interest

Test equipment and environment suitability (1)

1) Suitability of test sites for measurement test site above 1 GHz

* Currently only 47 CFR Part 15 requires measurements above 1 GHz for digital devices (up to 40 GHz) as well as CISPR 11 for Group 2 equipment

* The following standards are called out as applicable test methods:
ANSI C63.4-2003 for 47 CFR Part 15
CISPR 16-2-3 for CISPR 11

* ANSI C63.4-2003 states in clause 5.5 that "facilities suitable for measurements in the frequency range 30 MHz to 1000 MHz are considered suitable for the frequency range 1 GHz to 40 GHz, including the presence of the ground plane". This means, that a test site that meets the NSA criterion in the frequency range 30 MHz to 1 GHz can be used to perform measurements above 1 GHz

---

Specific Topics of Interest

Test equipment and environment suitability (2)

1) Suitability of test sites for measurement test site above 1 GHz

* If a test site does not meet the NSA requirement below 1 GHz, a correlation measurement must be performed, which demonstrates the suitability of the site. It is not acceptable to simply state that "there is currently no test site validation requirements above 1 GHz" and not provide any indication about the suitability of the test site. This approach is also shared by the FCC.

* CISPR 11 calls out in clause 8.3 that measurements above 1 GHz have to be performed in free-space conditions, meaning, reflections from the ground plane shall not influence the measurement. CISPR 16-2-3 provides guidance in clause 7.4.1 (for substitution testing) as far as a verification procedure above 1 GHz is concerned. This proposal includes an acceptance criterion to establish the suitability of the test site for measurements above 1 GHz.

Specific Topics of Interest

Test equipment and environment suitability (3)

2) Suitability of spectrum analyzers for compliance measurements

* FCC Part 15 and Part 18 do allow the use of spectrum analyzers for compliance measurements. This is clearly called out in ANSI C63.4-2003, clause 4.1.1.2. Measurements in accordance with standards based on CISPR standards (e.g., EN 55011 or EN 55022) require the use of equipment which is in compliance with all requirements stated in CISPR 16-1-1.

* Spectrum analyzers without preselection commonly do not meet the impulse response requirements when measuring low frequency pulses (10 Hz or lower) using quasi-peak detection and the defined bandwidths. This means, spectrum analyzers cannot be used for compliance testing, due to lack of compliance with CISPR 16-1-1. It is entirely possible that very similar test results can be obtained with both a compliant EMI receiver and a spectrum analyzer. Nevertheless, the use of a spectrum analyzer is not permitted.

Specific Topics of Interest

Test equipment and environment suitability (3)

2) Suitability of spectrum analyzers for compliance measurements

* A system test can be performed using input signals as defined in CISPR 16-1-1 to evaluate the spectrum analyzer performance when measuring impulses with the quasi-peak detector. This "system test" will unambiguously determine if a spectrum analyzer meets the requirements in CISPR 16-1-1.

* These potential limitations for spectrum analyzers only exist in the frequency range below 1 GHz. Above 1 GHz the use of spectrum analyzers is permissible, as long as they meet all requirements called out in CISPR 16-1-1 clause 8.2. The important requirements to watch out for are the 1 MHz impulse bandwidth and the bandwidth accuracy of ± 10 % (per clause 8.2.a)

Summary

- Accreditation establishes trust and confidence in test data, with internal and external customers

- It determines a minimum level of technical proficiency as well as the proper implementation of and adherence to a quality system in accordance with ISO 17025

- Assessments are usually based on sampling. This means that not all test methods can usually be reviewed and testing observed in detail. Over time, all test methods are to be evaluated, but this may take a considerable amount of time (depending on the number of test methods on the scope of accreditation)

- Accreditation does not guarantee the accuracy of test results, nor does it guaranteed that no erroneous test results are provided

- Accreditation is, to a certain degree, ambiguous. ISO 17025 allows room for interpretation and so do technical standards! Overall, however, it allows easier comparison of test data, nationally and internationally

---

Summary

- Accreditation is often used to implement testing programs that are specific to a certain industry. That way technical proficiency and standardized test approaches can be implemented to meet specific needs

- Successful operation of an accredited laboratory requires support from senior management. Adequate resources are to be provided, along with the willingness for on-going training and continuous improvement of the quality system

- A clear determination of applicability of requirements will help to streamline quality and technical procedures. A2LA policies may contain requirements which also have to be met (i.e., traceability policy or proficiency policy)

- Despite the effort and resources that have to be spent to maintain an accreditation, the continuous improvement will help to gain competitive advantages. Quality, effectiveness and competence will set a accredited laboratory aside from its competitors!

WORKSHOP: EMC ISSUES AFFECTING AUDIO SYSTEMS FOR PROFESSIONAL, BROADCAST, AND CONSUMER USE (FR-PM-WS-19)

Jim Brown
Audio Systems Group

Topics include:

The new AES48 Standard that addresses "the pin 1 problem"—the improper termination of cable shields within equipment

Shield current induced noise and capacitance imbalance in cables as contributors to RFI

Inadequate low-pass filtering of audio inputs and outputs

What parts of the frequency spectrum tend to be most significant with respect to susceptibility, and why?

The use of ferrites to suppress RFI from 500 kHz through 1 GHz

Grounding techniques—isolated star vs. mesh—when is each most suitable, and why?

Troubleshooting techniques

Synchronous noise vs. random noise

The workshop is led by Jim Brown, Principal Consultant at Audio Systems Group, Inc. Jim has worked in the professional audio and broadcast industry since 1971, and has done independent research on EMC issues in audio and broadcast applications. He is a Fellow of the Audio Engineering Society (AES), and a member of the Society of Motion Picture and Television Engineers (SMPTE), the Acoustical Society of America (ASA), the National Academy of Recording Arts and Sciences (NARAS), the US Institute of Theater Technology (USITT), the Society of Broadcast Engineers (SBE), and the Jazz Institute of Chicago.

NOTES

EMC in Audio Systems

Jim Brown
Audio Systems Group, Inc.
Chicago
jim@audiosystemsgroup.com

The Basis of this Presentation

- Field testing of equipment
  - AM Broadcast fields
  - VHF/UHF Broadcast fields
- Lab testing of equipment
  - Cell phone
  - VHF/UHF talkie 150/450 MHz
  - Pin 1 testing of equipment
  - Differential mode excitation using SCIN
- Shield-current-induced noise tests of cable
- Additional work by other researchers

Field tests near WGN-AM (50 kW, 720 kHz)

The Basis of this Presentation

- Basic research on ferrites
  - Measurements of many materials
  - A better equivalent circuit
- Understanding ferrites for suppression
  - It's about choking current
  - Ferrites are inherently resonant
  - Both inductive and capacitive reactance
  - Resistance is good
  - Reactance can be bad – can resonate with the cable it is attempting to choke

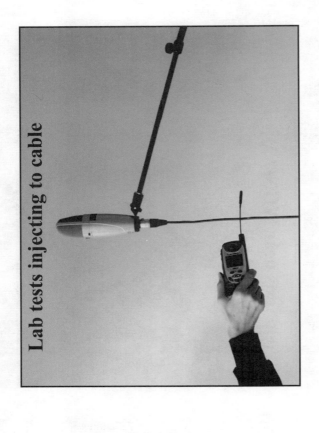

Lab tests injecting to cable

Audio System Characteristics

- Very wide dynamic range
  - 100 dB typical
- Sources and Electronics widely separated
  - 100 m cable runs at mic level (-130 dBV noise floor) are common
  - Vulnerable to LF, MF, and HF EMI
- Analog distribution at mic level is the rule
  - No digital mics
  - Latency and operational issues generally preclude digital distribution in live systems

Bench testing of equipment and cable

Audio System Architecture

- Source locations often widely separated
- Strong EMI sources in audio spectrum
  - Power and power harmonics
  - Switching transients
  - Clock signals
- Magnetic coupling to equipment and wiring
  - Common impedance coupling on shields of unbalanced wiring

Audio System Architecture

- Many sources (mics) often combined to a single output
  - EMI often coherent and in phase, thus adds by 6 dB for each doubling of number of sources receiving interference at equal level
  - Signals not coherent, so 3 dB/doubling
  - Signal/noise degrades by 3 dB/doubling
  - A signal buried in the noise on a single channel can be 10 dB above the noise if present in many inputs of a multi-mic mix

Audio System Architecture

- In performance systems, each microphone often feeds three preamps in parallel, each at a different location
  - Audience sound mix
  - Performer (stage monitor) sound mix
  - Recording/broadcast sound mix
- Splitting methods usually passive
  - Three-winding transformer w/Faraday shields
  - Hard-wired Y (no transformer)

Audio System Architecture

- Why Not Preamplify and then split?
- Preamps can't accommodate wide dynamic range of live performance, so gains may need to change during the show
  - That requires an additional operator, just to "babysit" the preamps! Out of the question for most installations.
  - The preamp/DA is expensive too!

Audio System Architecture

- System interconnection issues dominate
- Must be robust with respect to
  - Magnetic fields
  - Common mode voltages and currents
  - MF and HF RF on long cable runs
  - Differences in earth potentials of interconnected equipment
- Must be practical (and economical) for widely distributed system elements

Audio System Architecture

- Star-connected isolated-ground power systems are the rule for all but large video studios
- Mesh grounding can work in video facilities
  - Far fewer mics in use
  - Hundreds of coax shields to carry ground current
- Balanced signal interconnections
- Transformer inputs with Faraday shields important when high common mode voltages are present

Audio System Architecture

- Digital distribution, including fiber, works for interconnections between buildings and rooms, but is impractical for most "live" systems
  - Latency
  - Cost (related to scale)
  - Distributed sources
- Analog audio at mic level drives the design

Audio System Architecture

- Steel conduit provides magnetic shielding
  - Thin wall (EMT) provides about 17 dB at power frequencies
  - Rigid steel provides about 32 dB (ANSI/IEEE 518)
- Cable shields provide almost none (Ott)

How Are Consumer Audio Systems Different?

Primary Interference Mechanisms

- Pin 1 problems
  - Improper shield termination within equipment
- Shield-current-induced noise (SCIN)
  - Cable imbalance couples shield noise current to signal pair as a differential signal
  - Inadequate low-pass filtering lets it in the box
- Capacitance imbalance of cable degrades CMRR (4% - 6% typical of "good" cables)
  - No shield connection at receive end helps
    (Whitlock, JAES, June, 1995)

Audio System Architecture

- In some systems, wiring must be exposed (not in conduit)
  - Not practical (or expensive to install)
  - Renovations
- Must be routed away from strong fields
- Both cable and equipment must have good RF rejection

How are Consumer Audio Systems Different?

- All equipment is unbalanced (shameful!)
- Peak signal level is 1 volt sine wave (clip)
- Still have 100 dB dynamic range
  - Noise floor 10 μV
  - 100 μV clearly audible
- Still have noise on equipment grounds
- Shield current causes IR (and IZ) drops

Why isn't the shell the shield contact?

The Pin 1 Problem

- Pin 1 is the shield contact of XL connectors (AES14-1992)
- No connection should be made to the shell of cable-mounted connectors

---

Why isn't the shell the shield contact?

- **To minimize noise current on the shield!**
  - Interconnect wiring often terminates to XL's on steel panels grounded to the conduit system
  - High noise voltages between widely separated "grounds"
- No need to <u>connect</u> the shield to wiring panels
  - No active electronics to detect RF
  - Audio cable is lossy at RF
- Shield is carried <u>through</u> panel

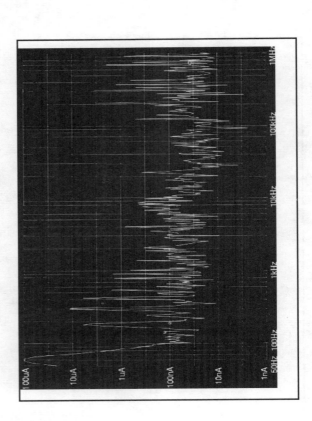

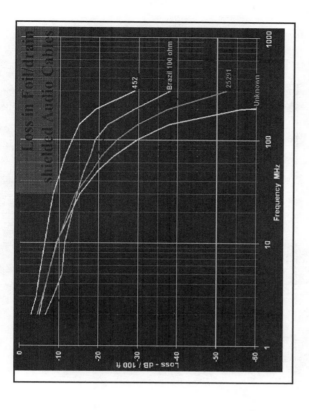

Consumer Audio Systems

- All equipment is unbalanced (shameful!)
- Peak signal level is 1 volt sine wave (clip)
- 100 dB dynamic range
  - Noise floor 10 µV
  - 100 µV clearly audible
- Noise on equipment grounds
- Shield current causes IR (and IZ) drops

Why isn't the shell the shield contact? (After all, it's concentric!)

- Audio cable is lossy at RF
  - VHF/UHF coupling to cable is important only very close to active electronics
- Minimizing noise current on the shield is far more important than slightly better UHF E-field shielding!

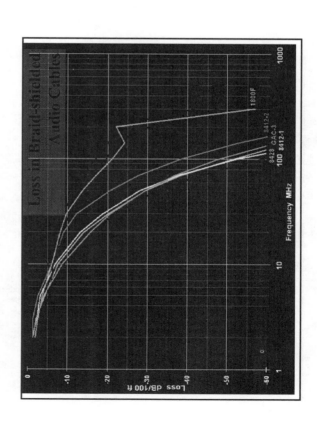

505

Other Sources of Shield Current

- AM Broadcast
- FM Broadcast
- Television Broadcast
- Cell Phones
- Ham Transmitters
- Digital Wireless Mics
- Radiated Noise from Lighting, etc.

A classic pin 1 problem at RF

- Black wire goes to enclosure (good)
- Far too LONG - Inductance makes it high impedance
  - 7.5 Ω @ 100 MHz, 60 Ω at 850 MHz
- Orange wire is circuit board common
- Common impedance couples RF to circuit board

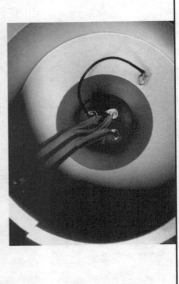

Sources of Noise on "Ground"

- Leakage currents to ground
  - Transformer stray capacitances
- Intentional currents to ground
  - Line filter capacitors
- Power wiring faults
- Shunt mode surge suppressors
- Magnetic coupling from mains power
  - Harmonic current in neutral

The Pin 1 Problem

- Pin 1 is the shield contact of XL connectors
- Cable shields must go to the shielding enclosure (and ONLY to the shielding enclosure)
- If shields go inside the box first (to the circuit board, for example), common impedances couple shield current at random points along the circuit board!
- Noise is added to the signal

- When the signal reference is connected at pin 1
  - the drop across Z_{SE} (RF noise) is coupled onto the signal reference bus
  - C_{STRAY} completes the path

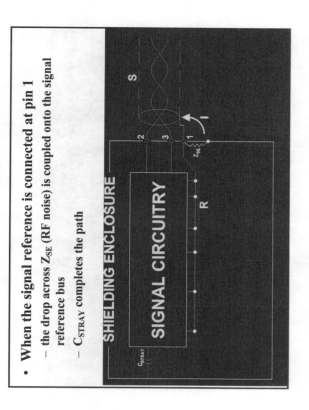

SHIELDING ENCLOSURE

SIGNAL CIRCUITRY

A pin 1 problem at RF
- Shield goes through connector retaining screw
  - 4 Ω @ 100 MHz, 30 Ω at 850 MHz
- Black wire is circuit board common
- Common impedance couples RF to circuit board
- This mic has RF problems

What Happens Inside the Box When There is a Pin 1 Problem?

- There is common impedance coupling along the reference bus too!
  - Shield current flow through the Z_1 impedances creates multiple voltage drops along the signal reference bus (RF noise)

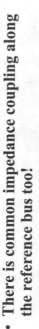
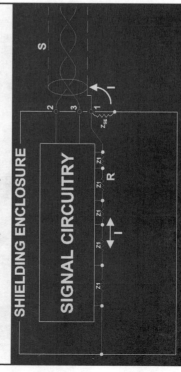

SHIELDING ENCLOSURE

SIGNAL CIRCUITRY

Another pin 1 problem at RF

- The spring is a poor connection
- Inductance of the loop
- Common impedance to circuit board

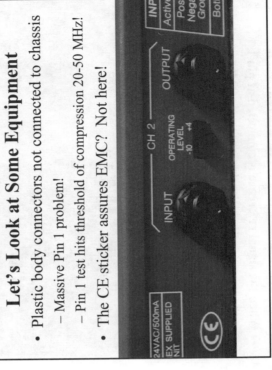

Let's Look at Some Equipment

- Plastic body connectors not connected to chassis
  - Massive Pin 1 problem!
  - Pin 1 test hits threshold of compression 20-50 MHz!
- The CE sticker assures EMC? Not here!

Another pin 1 problem at RF

- The screw gets loose
- Inductance of the wire, screw tab
- Common impedance to circuit board (wire + screw)
  - 4 Ω @ 100 MHz, 30 Ω at 850 MHz

A better connection for pin 1

- Broad, short copper, pressure fit to enclosure
- Less inductance
- Still some common impedance to circuit board
- 100 pf capacitors, common mode choke
- Much better RF performance, still not perfect

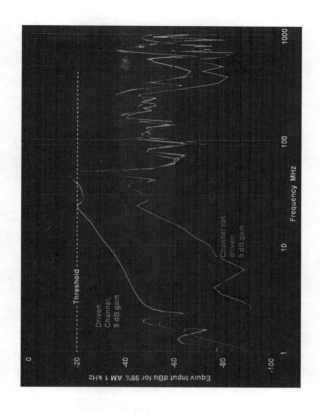

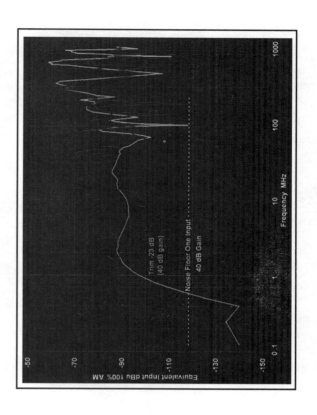

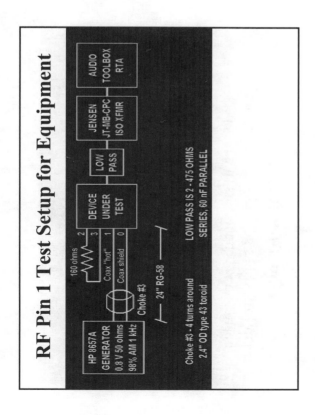

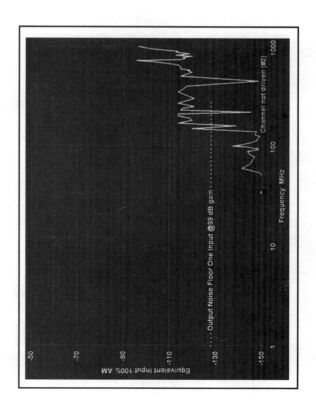

How Does It Happen?

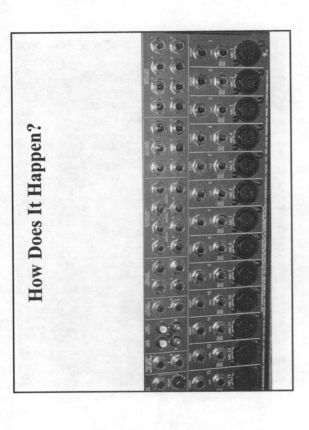

How Does It Happen?

The G terminal goes to the enclosure, right?

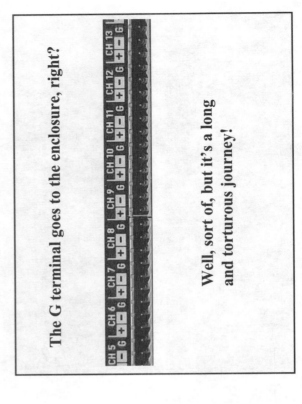

Well, sort of, but it's a long and torturous journey!

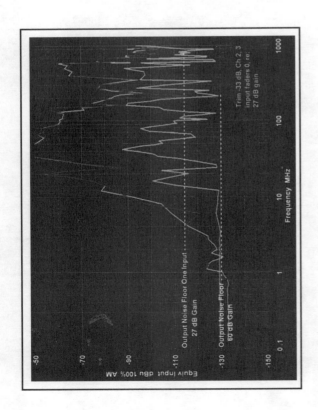

How Does It Happen?

- Pin 1 of XLR's go to chassis via circuit board and ¼" connectors (it's cheaper)
- XLR shell not connected to anything!
- RCA connectors not connected to chassis

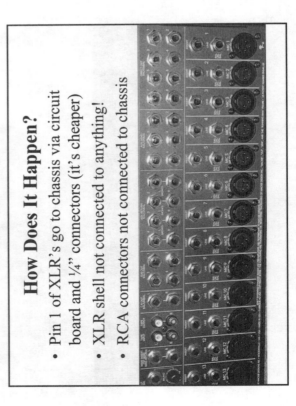

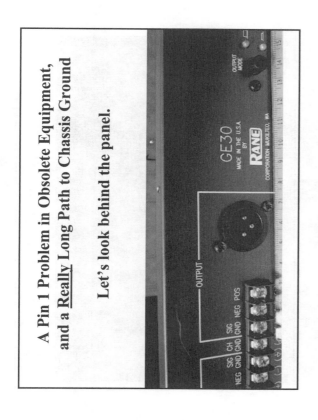

A Pin 1 Problem in Obsolete Equipment, and a <u>Really</u> Long Path to Chassis Ground

Let's look behind the panel.

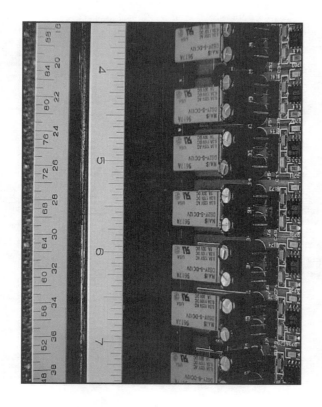

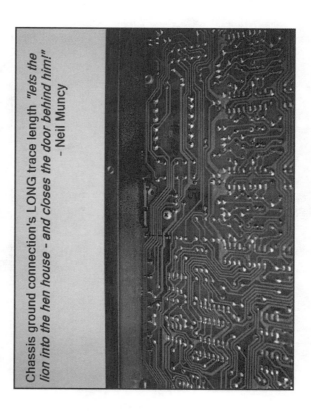

Chassis ground connection's LONG trace length *"lets the lion into the hen house - and closes the door behind him!"*
- Neil Muncy

Foil/Drain Shield

Braid/Drain Shield

Braid/Foil Shield

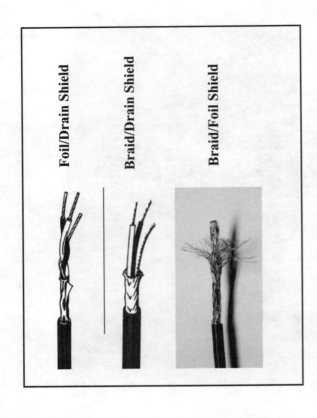

SCIN Measurement Setup

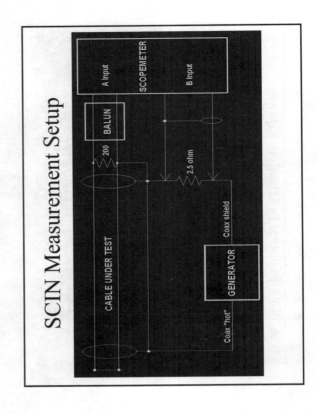

Cable shield construction can be part of the problem!

The drain wire is coupled more closely to the white conductor

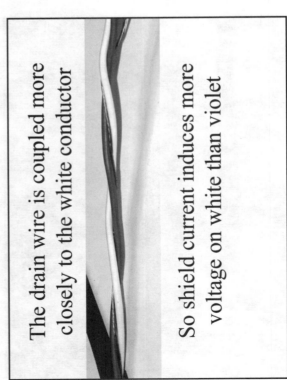

So shield current induces more voltage on white than violet

SCIN Measurements

- Spot frequency measurements (not swept)
- Measure in increments of 1 octave
  - 10 kHz - 4 MHz
- Not a fixed current
  - Need to maximize current at low frequencies
  - Measure it with the scopemeter
- Normalize data to 100 mA

Test Equipment

- Hewlett Packard 8657A RF Generator
  - 100 kHz - 1 GHz
- Hewlett Packard 200 CD Oscillator
  - 10 Hz - 600 kHz
- Fluke 199 200 MHz Scopemeter

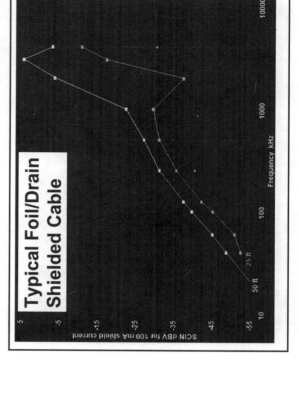

Typical Foil/Drain Shielded Cable

Resonances and Wavelength

- Measure 4 cable lengths
- 125 ft (38 m)
  - Greatest sensitivity at lower frequencies
  - Resonances and wavelength effects > 250 kHz
- Must measure short cables for good HF data
  - 50 ft (15.24 m) good to at least 500 kHz
  - 25 ft (7.6 m) good to at least 1 MHz
  - 10 ft (3 m) good to at least 2 MHz

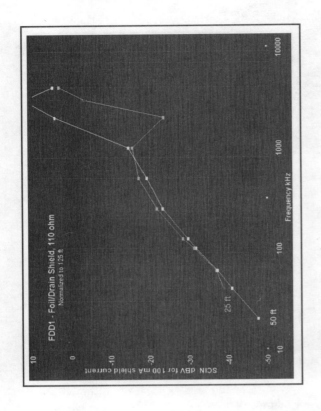

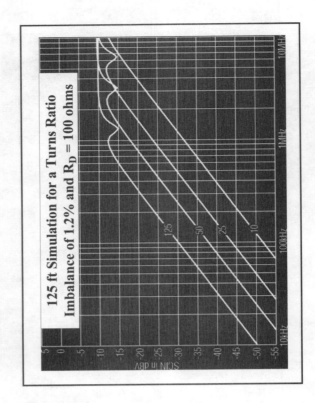

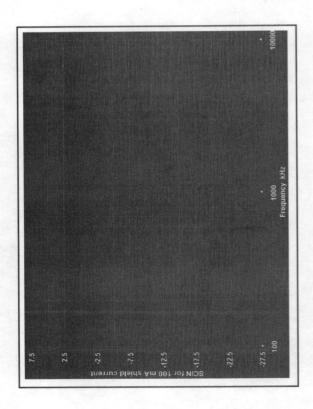

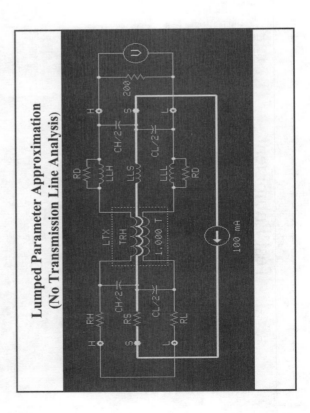

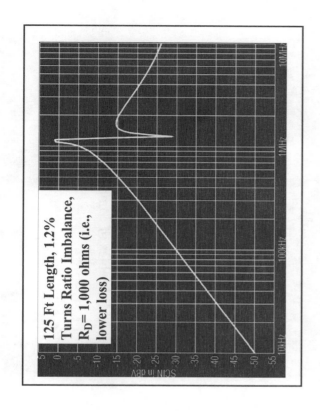

125 Ft Length, 1.2% Turns Ratio Imbalance, $R_D = 1,000$ ohms (i.e., lower loss)

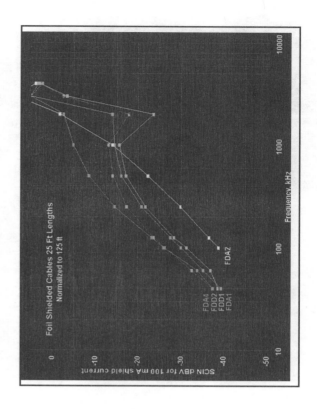

Foil Shielded Cables 25 Ft Lengths
Normalized to 125 ft

SCIN dBV for 100 mA shield current

FDA4
FDD2
FDD1
FDA1

FDA2

Frequency, kHz

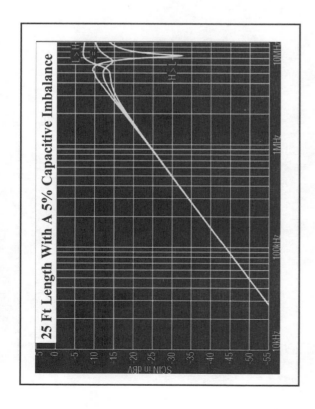

25 Ft Length With A 5% Capacitive Imbalance

SCIN in dBV

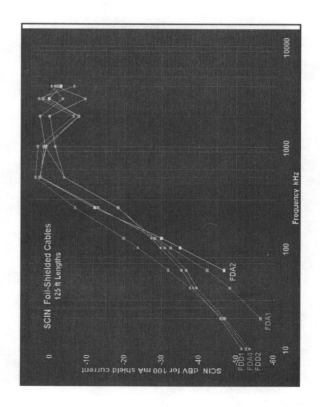

SCIN Foil-Shielded Cables
125 ft Lengths

SCIN dBV for 100 mA shield current

FDD1
FDA4
FDD2

FDA1

FDA2

Frequency, kHz

515

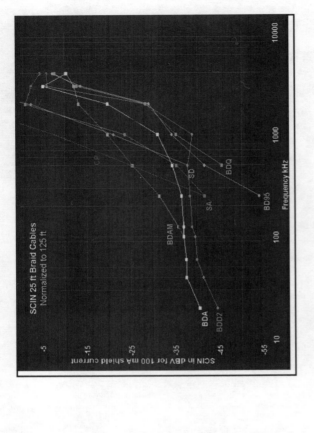

SCIN 25 ft Braid Cables
Normalized to 125 ft

Contribution of a Drain Wire

- SCIN is proportional to the fraction of the total shield current that flows in a drain wire
  - (Total shield resistance)/(Drain resistance)
  - Smaller drain wire => less SCIN
- SCIN in foil/drain-shielded cables is generally 20-30 dB greater than in braid-shielded cables of comparable construction

Braid Shielded Cables. 125 ft

Conclusions

- SCIN increases linearly with frequency in most cables well into the VHF spectrum
- Wavelength and reactive terms become increasingly dominant for cable > $\lambda/10$

Braid-Shielded Cables

- Algebraically additive terms
  - Imbalances in length of signal conductors
  - Imbalances in inductance of signal conductors
  - Imbalances in capacitance between signal conductors and the shield
  - Inductive reactance of the shield
- Reactive terms generally insignificant for cables $< \lambda/10$

Braid-Shielded Cables

- The presence of a drain wire in braid-shielded cables tends to degrade SCIN performance by about 10 dB at radio frequencies, and to a significantly greater degree between 10 kHz and 100 kHz.

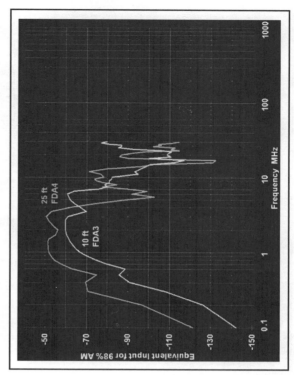

Test Setup for Equipment

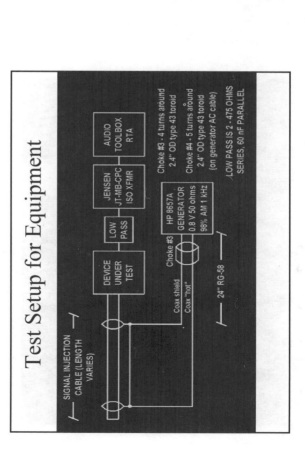

517

Don't Overlook Outputs

- RFI on loudspeaker lines is <u>very</u> common
- RF can enter equipment at the loudspeaker terminals when equipment is poorly filtered
- Parallel wire loudspeaker cables have poor RF rejection
- **Use twisted pairs for loudspeaker wiring!**
- Shielded loudspeaker wiring is almost never necessary (and rarely does much good)

Prototype EMC Connector

- Concentric capacitor connects shield to shell
  - Low inductance -- better connection
  - More continuous shielding
- Ferrite bead on pin 1
- Spring improves connection of shell to mating connector

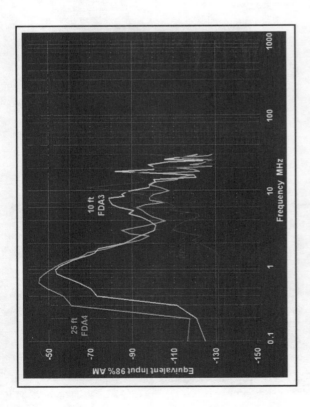

For Unbalanced interconnections, shield <u>resistance</u> can be important!

- **Shield current (noise) creates IR (and IZ) drops that add to the signal**
- $E_{NOISE} = 20 \log (I_{SHIELD} * Z_{SHIELD})$
- Coaxial cables differ widely
  - Heavy copper braid (8241F) 2.6 Ω /1000 ft
  - Double copper braid (8281) 1.1 Ω /1000 ft
  - Foil/drain shield #22 gauge 16 Ω /1000 ft
- Audio dynamic range 100 dB
  - For 1 volt signal, 10 μV noise floor

Prototype EMC Connector

- Concentric capacitor connects shield to shell
  - Low inductance -- better connection
  - More continuous shielding
  - Ferrite bead on pin 1
- Spring improves connection of shell to mating connector
  - Can "band-aid" a pin 1 problem
- **Reduces common mode voltage on signal pair**
- **Compatible with both "star" and "mesh" grounding**

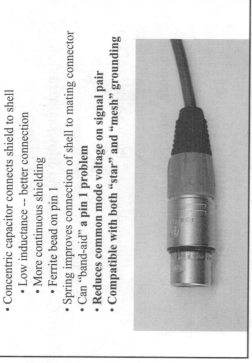

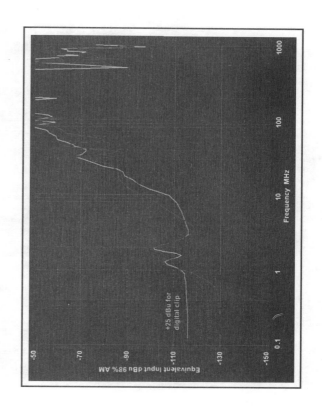

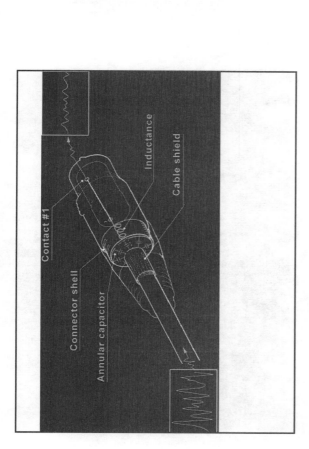

So the EMC connector can't help!

System Grounding Issues

- Don't confuse "grounding" and "shielding"
- Cable shields do <u>not</u> need to be "grounded"
- Cable shields <u>do</u> need to be connected to the equipment enclosure at the frequency of the interfering signal
- "Grounding" is a <u>safety</u> issue
- Connecting the shield allows current flow
  - Changes behavior as an antenna
  - Enables SCIN
  - Enables pin 1 problems

Benefits of the EMC Connector

- Better VHF/UHF Shield connection to enclosure
  - Reduces common mode voltage on pins 2 and 3
- "Fixes" VHF/UHF pin 1 problems
  - Removes shield connection from Pin 1 at VHF/UHF
  - Connects the shield to enclosure
- **No Benefit if XL Shells Not Connected to Enclosure inside Equipment**

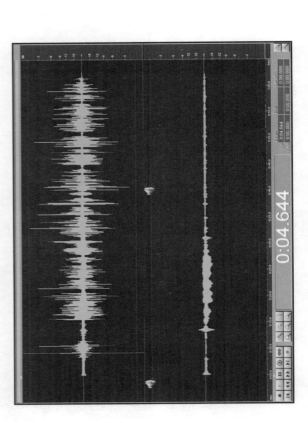

Almost no interference with no earth connection

System Grounding Issues

- An earth connection can make matters worse if it makes the cable a more efficient antenna
  - Excites Pin 1 problems
  - Excites SCIN

Severe interference when earth connection was added

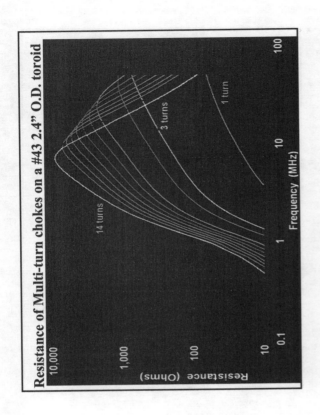

Resistance of Multi-turn chokes on a #43 2.4" O.D. toroid

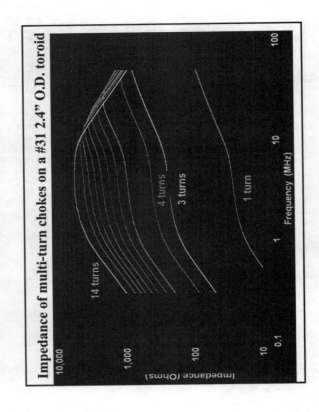

Impedance of multi-turn chokes on a #31 2.4" O.D. toroid

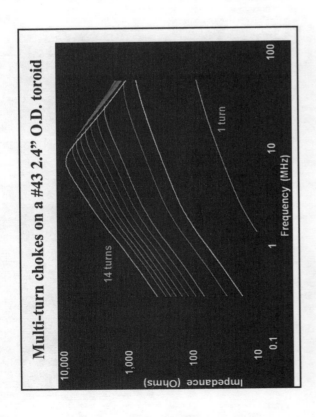

Multi-turn chokes on a #43 2.4" O.D. toroid

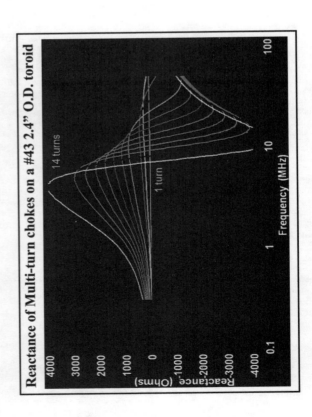

Reactance of Multi-turn chokes on a #43 2.4" O.D. toroid

522

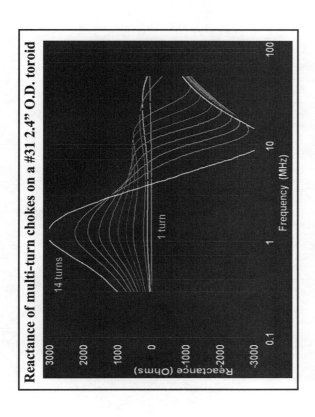

Resistance of multi-turn chokes on a #31 2.4" O.D. toroid

Resistance (Ohms)

14 turns

4 turns

3 turns

Frequency (MHz)

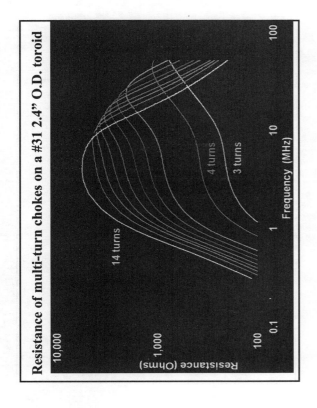

Reactance of multi-turn chokes on a #31 2.4" O.D. toroid

Reactance (Ohms)

14 turns

1 turn

Frequency (MHz)

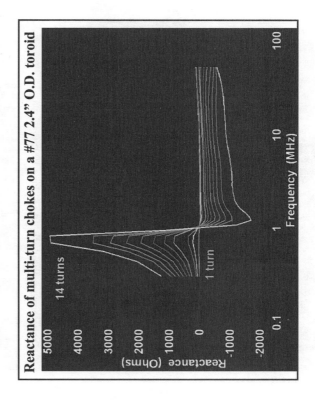

Impedance of multi-turn chokes on a #77 2.4" O.D. toroid

Impedance (Ohms)

14 turns

3 turns

1 turn

Frequency (MHz)

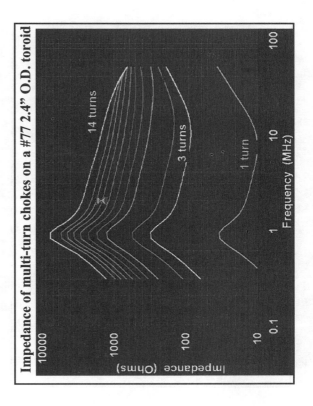

Reactance of multi-turn chokes on a #77 2.4" O.D. toroid

Reactance (Ohms)

14 turns

1 turn

Frequency (MHz)

AES Papers on EMC (www.aes.org)

- *Radio Frequency Susceptibility of Capacitor Microphones,* Brown/Josephson (AES Preprint 5720)
- *Common Mode to Differential Mode Conversion in Shielded Twisted Pair Cables (Shield Current Induced Noise),* Brown/Whitlock (AES Preprint 5747)
- *Testing for Radio Frequency Common Impedance Coupling in Microphones and Other Audio Equipment,* Brown (AES Preprint 5897)
- *A Novel Method of Testing for Susceptibility of Audio Equipment to Interference from Medium and High Frequency Broadcast Transmitters,* Brown (AES Preprint 5898)
- *Noise Susceptibility in Analog and Digital Signal Processing Systems,* Muncy, JAES, June 1995
- *Balanced Lines in Audio Systems: Fact, Fiction, and Transformers,* Whitlock, JAES, June 1995

EMC in Audio Systems

Jim Brown

Audio Systems Group, Inc.

http://audiosystemsgroup.com

Variable Speed Motors

- A Very Trashy (PWM) Source
  - Square Waves, Arcs
- Dumps Large CM Currents on Power
- Large Current Loop (Power Line to "Ground")
- Isolation Transformer Needed at Source, Secondary Bonded
- Couples into Wiring
- Couples into Microphones
- Couples into Equipment

Acknowledgements

- Bill Whitlock
- Ron Steinberg
- Markus Natter
- Bruce Olson
- John Schmidt (ABC)

- Neil Muncy
- David Josephson
- Werner Bachmann
- John Woodgate
- Fair Rite Products

Author Index